D1580240

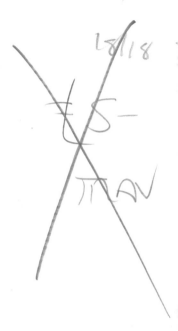

18/18

ES-
TITAN

Praise for

MUSIC
of
THE SPINNING WHEEL

Many people are influenced by the lives and actions of individuals who have devoted their lives to great and just causes. This book details the life and achievements of one of twentieth century's greatest figures, Mahatma Gandhi. Sudheendra Kulkarni has succeeded, in a deeply intellectual and fascinating way, in linking a wide range of related events, actions, and people together. In so doing, Kulkarni has created an intricate story of the way Gandhi's attitude has spread far and wide throughout the world, so giving us hope for a better future for our children.

—Dr Harold Kroto

Winner of the 1996 Nobel Prize in Chemistry, along with two other scientists, for the discovery of C_{60} Buckminsterfullerene, a new form of carbon; a pioneer in nanotechnology; the Francis Eppes Professor of Chemistry at the Florida State University, USA

This is a fascinating book and very relevant for the worldwide debate on the future of the Internet, and of digital technologies in general. My own study of several decades, as documented in my books, has shown that machine intelligence will surpass unenhanced human intelligence in the foreseeable future, (however, we will have the opportunity to enhance our intelligence, so we will be able to keep up). These new technologies have the potential to overcome major challenges such as poverty, disease, and harm to the environment. They will also introduce new challenges as all technologies since fire have been double-edged swords. Ancient philosophies from both the East and West can help guide us to use these new powers in optimistic and reassuring ways. Sudheendra Kulkarni provides us great insight into the wisdom of Mahatma Gandhi that can help us to reap the promise of the future while avoiding the peril.

—Ray Kurzweil

Inventor, a futurist in technology and its impact on society, author of the bestselling books The Age of Spiritual Machines *and* The Singularity is Near: When Humans Transcend Biology

Sudheendra Kulkarni's magnum opus is a welcome addition to Gandhian literature. The Mahatma was one of twentieth century's most skilled users of the media. He taught himself type-writing and encouraged others to learn the same; he once owned and operated a printing press. Without his weekly newspapers, the type-writer and the printing press, it would have been impossible for him to communicate his ideas. Kulkarni's argument that he would have embraced the Internet as readily as he had embraced the typewriter and the printing press is very persuasive indeed. Gandhi would also have a word of caution for the Internet age: don't let the medium dilute or destroy the message.

Gandhi incorporated into his philosophical framework modern ideas such as civil rights, equality of women, freedom of conscience and religion, and national unity based on civic nationalism. It is my hope and prayer that young Indian political thinkers really study Gandhi – and finally get over their morbid colonial fascination for Marx and Mao – and base their policies for India on Gandhi's political philosophy. This book will certainly help in this important mission.

—ANTHONY J. PAREL
Professor Emeritus of Political Science at the University of Calgary, Canada. Author of Gandhi: Hind Swaraj and Other Writings Centenary Edition; Gandhi's Philosophy and the Quest for Harmony, *and other books*

Mahatma Gandhi's life is often confused with his lifestyle. His personal abstinence was not a denial of mass production, nor his charkha the antithesis of modern machinery. He chose the first symbol of industry, the wheel, as his economic metaphor. His humanism put man at the centre of progress; his astute mind separated greed from wealth.

This intriguing and brilliant book challenges conventional thinking and offers a tremendously exhilarating perspective on the outstanding genius of the twentieth century.

—M.J. AKBAR
Editorial Director of India Today; *author of* Nehru: The Making of India; Tinderbox: The Past and Future of Pakistan, *and several other books*

This priceless offering provides a fascinating new meaning to the life and work of this timeless legend, Mahatma Gandhi. First, this book answers the question of the relevance of the Mahatma's teachings in today's global debates on subjects ranging from democracy to disarmament and from sexual ethics to sustainable development. The myth that the Mahatma was opposed to modern science and technology is broken with convincing evidence and insightful analysis. In fact, the Mahatma emerges as a romantic scientist. As we peruse the book, the spinning wheel with ageless ideals easily morphs into a computer disk and then we see the unique argumentation unfold that the Internet will harmonise the khadi spirit with globalisation and promote Gandhian economics. Scholarly articulation is provided to show that the Internet will lead us to envision Gandhiji's dream of a new non-violent, cooperative, sustainable and a morally guided world order. Critical thinking, creative interpretation, fresh insights and convincing argumentation based on deep and scholarly research are the highlights of this book. Reading this book was indeed a once-in-a-lifetime spiritual experience.

—DR R.A. MASHELKAR

National Research Professor & President, Global Research Alliance (GRA), National Chemical Laboratory; former director general of Council of Scientific and Industrial Research (CSIR); and a trustee of the Gandhi National Memorial Society, Pune

This book attempts to dispel popular misconceptions about Gandhiji's attitude towards modernisation. It shows how promising current developments in information technology could be, in the discovery of solutions that address the many political, economic and social issues that the Mahatma sought to resolve. Many of these problems affect us at a global level today. Sudheendra Kulkarni makes a compelling – and an optimistic – case for a future, where khadi and the spinning wheel continue to preserve their conceptual relevance, even in cyberspace. He has drawn a deft parallel between the universality of Gandhiji's teachings and the democratising power, and promise of the Internet and other IC Technologies.

A must read.

—S. RAMADORAI

Vice Chairman, Tata Consultancy Services (TCS), Advisor to the Prime Minister in the Prime Minister's National Skill Development Council

This is a deeply optimistic book, inspired by Mahatma Gandhi's thought and the possibilities of the Internet. It convincingly challenges the widely held view, for which there is only a superficial warrant, that Gandhiji was anti-science. He was not. He saw science as a tool and not as a worldview. Because it was that, science could be incorporated into a worldview, which had ethics, nonviolence, a concern for the environment and the well-being of ordinary people, at its center.

Whether the Internet justifies the optimism of this book depends on whether we can take up the inspired and urgent challenge that this book puts forward.

—PROF. UDAY S. MEHTA

Distinguished Professor of Political Science, City University of New York, and the author of a forthcoming book on Mahatma Gandhi

Spinning wheel and the Internet: seemingly, two vastly dissimilar tools. One represents the primitive end of the spectrum of technological evolution, the other its most advanced apex. Yet, in this thought-provoking book, the sharp intellect of Sudheendra Kulkarni shows how Mahatma Gandhi's conception of sustainable development and a non-violent world creates a kinship between the two. Clearly a labour of love, the author uses the spinning wheel and the Net to weave a web which provides fascinating insights and new perspectives on many contemporary issues, and shows the great relevance of Gandhian philosophy for the Internet Age. As someone closely associated with the world of Information Technology, I keenly welcome a debate on the unconventional ideas put forward in this book.

—KIRAN KARNIK
Former President of National Association of Software and Services Companies (NASSCOM), and author of The Coalition of Competitors: The Story of Nasscom and the IT Industry

Mahatma Gandhi didn't belong only to India; he was a world citizen. All of us can learn from his lifelong mission of truth and nonviolence and beneficially apply his teachings to the many grave challenges that humanity faces in the twenty-first century. In this context, Sudheendra Kulkarni's book offers an amazingly new perspective on Gandhi's views on science, technology and sustainable development. By co-relating his moral philosophy with the evolution of the Internet, this book contributes to the hope that the breathtaking advances in digital technologies can indeed help mankind achieve what I call 'breakthrough self-reinvention', and thereby evolve to an altogether higher level of harmony and positive capabilities.

—PROF. SHOJI SHIBA
Professor Emeritus, University of Tsukuba, Japan; pioneer of 'Breakthrough Management'; and Chief Advisor to the 'Visionary Leaders for Manufacturing' programme launched jointly by the Governments of Japan and India

Most complicated things in this world have very simple solutions. Mahatma Gandhi's novel concept of nonviolence proved to be stronger than the might of the British Empire...There is nothing like a new idea if one understands quantum physics. Ideas are always there in the universal consciousness which could be tapped by people with prepared minds.... I admire Sudheendra Kulkarni's ability to beautifully blend Mahatma's philosophy into the computer age.

—DR B.M. HEGDE
Eminent cardiologist; former Vice Chancellor, Manipal University; and author of many books on the philosophy of health and practice of medicine

Sudheendhra Kulkarni has written a well-researched book. What surprises me is his depth of knowledge on Gandhi – especially as he is not known to belong to the 'Gandhian' circles I had interacted with for over four decades! I am also very pleasantly surprised by his emphasis on the spiritual side of Gandhi – a very important part of Gandhi's philosophy which sadly has been neglected all along.

—T.S. ANANTHU

Trustee of Navadarshanam, who gave up a career in systems engineering to join the Gandhi Peace Foundation in 1977

Congratulations on writing a book which ties Mahatma Gandhi's teachings into an age sorely in need of self-reliance and simplicity. On behalf of the Abundance Foundation, I will say that we are also fans of Gandhi. Our nonprofit is the fiscal sponsor of a local North Carolina currency called the PLENTY, which is an acronym for "Piedmont Local EcoNomy Tender." (See Chapter 28) The motto inscribed on our currency is 'In Each Other We Trust', which echoes Gandhi's own teaching. We feel that use of the PLENTY ensures that dollars stay in our economy permanently. In Pittsboro, some companies pay their staff with PLENTYs, which can be exchanged at Capital Bank for U.S. dollars, so there is no threat of getting stuck with more local currency than you can spend.

The Abundance Foundation was formed to educate the public on sustainability topics, specifically, local food, renewable energy, water quality, conservation and as we all know, you can't do anything if you don't have community! We are happy that your book seeks to promote this Gandhian mission for India and the world.

—CAMILLE ARMANTROUT

An activist at the Abundance Foundation, Pittsboro, NC (USA), one of the thousands of voluntary organisations around the world that are advocating, and practicing, a decentralised and sustainable model of development using their own local currencies

Photo: Margaret Bourke-White
Courtesy: Getty Images/Time & Life Pictures/GandhiServe

MUSIC
of
THE SPINNING WHEEL

Mahatma Gandhi's Manifesto for the Internet Age

Sudheendra Kulkarni

AMARYLLIS

AMARYLLIS

The author has pledged to donate all royalty earnings from this book to
voluntary organisations that are trying to promote
Mahatma Gandhi's ideals.

This edition first published 2012

AMARYLLIS

An imprint of Manjul Publishing House Pvt. Ltd.

Editorial Office:
J-39, Ground Floor, Jor Bagh Lane,
New Delhi 110 003, India
Tel: 011-24642447/24652447 Fax: 011-24622448
Email: amaryllis@amaryllis.co.in
Website: www.amaryllis.co.in

Registered Office:
10, Nishat Colony, Bhopal 462 003, M.P., India

ISBN: 978-93-81506-16-5

Printed and bound in India by
Thomson Press (India) Limited

To
Atal Bihari Vajpayee

India's poet–prime minister who strove to implement his 'connectivity' vision:

Physical connectivity: through an unprecedented programme of construction of highways and rural roads;
Digital connectivity: through bold reforms that boosted the telecom and IT revolution;
Emotional connectivity: through a sincere effort, against severe odds, to promote heart-union among India's diverse communities;
Political connectivity: through a determined mission, braving several failures, to build national consensus and to promote coalition dharma;
Diaspora connectivity: through a pioneering initiative to strengthen the bonds between Mother India and her children living abroad; and
Neighbourhood connectivity: through an unrelenting endeavour, despite many thorns along the path, to normalise India's relations with Pakistan and China, and to strengthen her traditional relations with other neighbours.

As a grateful tribute for the trust Atalji reposed in me, for the affection he showed me, and for the precious opportunity he gave me to assist him in the promotion of the above vision.

CONTENTS

PART THREE
HARMONY SEEKER

PART FOUR
A BEACON FOR THE PRESENT AND THE FUTURE

PART FIVE
PROMISE OF THE INTERNET

EPILOGUE

ANNEXURES

Introduction

WHY ANOTHER BOOK ON MAHATMA GANDHI?

MAHATMA GANDHI REMAINS A DEEPLY ENIGMATIC FIGURE IN INDIA and the world. Easy to admire, difficult to understand in his totality, and almost impossible to follow, even in parts. There is very little about his outward personality – his attire, his extremely frugal food habits, his observance of a day of silence once a week, and his unconventional views on sex – that can conceivably endear him to the modern man living in the most consumerist and hedonistic era in human history. Yet, Gandhi has become the most popular and venerated Indian around the globe. There is something about the inner truth of his life, the glow of which remains undiminished with the passage of time. We may call it Gandhi's Truth since his lifelong extraordinary description. It not only sheds light on the failures and falsities, injustices and inadequacies, of the world we live in, but also shows the way forward.

At a time when India has been witnessing rapid erosion in ethics in politics, economics and public life in general, Gandhi is admired for practising the moral principles that he preached. As India and much of the rest of the world continue to grapple with the challenge of religious disharmony, his lifelong mission of trying to create harmony across various social barriers continues to evoke widespread adoration for him. Indeed, his mission culminated in his martyrdom for the cause of amity between Hindus and Muslims, and also between India and

Pakistan. Ironically, it was a Hindu extremist, Nathuram Godse, who assassinated the greatest Hindu in modern times. This fact of history makes his message especially relevant, both for India and the world, considering that the cause for which he sacrificed his life is as salient today as it was in his own lifetime.

Above all, admiration for him stems from his uncompromising advocacy of nonviolence, which was the defining element of Gandhi's Truth. It is not that most people who admire him for this reason truly believe that the ideal of a nonviolent world is ever realisable. Nevertheless, they see in him the source of their own hope in a just and peaceful tomorrow. It is a hope men cannot live without. He nurtures that hope both at local and global levels. For example, the United Nations (UN), which is the closest the international community has come to establishing something akin to a world government, may not have made much headway in de-militarising international relations and creating a new world order based on peace, justice and universal brotherhood. Yet, when it declared, in 2005, that Gandhi's birthday on 2 October would be observed each year as the Day of Nonviolence, it acknowledged him as a modern-day prophet of peace.

What is curious about Gandhi's Truth is that it is neither easy to grasp, nor easy to reject. His admirers appreciate some aspects of his life and message, but find it difficult to comprehend or agree with other aspects. Similarly, his critics may scoff at some of his actions and teachings, but usually, they too express varying degrees of appreciation for what he set out to achieve and, especially, for the sincerity and single-minded focus he brought to bear to his mission. Thus, it is easy to find critics among his admirers, and admirers among his critics.

The one aspect of Gandhi's Truth that is most enigmatic is his outlook – or *perceived* outlook – towards science and technology. By and large, both his admirers and critics contend that he was opposed to science, technology, machinery and modernity. We are currently in the most technologically advanced era in history. Science and technology have transformed the world in unimaginable ways. They are also the principal factors behind the unprecedented material prosperity that some sections of the global community have been enjoying and others are eagerly hoping to be a part of. This has persuaded many people in India and the world to believe that Gandhi, with his insistence on khadi, village industries and maximum local self-sufficiency, sought to stop the onrush of development aided by modern science and technology. Therefore, on the yardstick of technology-driven progress, many of Gandhi's admirers and critics alike consider him irrelevant to our times.

According to historian B.R. Nanda, who was one of the greatest interpreters of Gandhian philosophy: 'Gandhi's views on industrialisation did not commend themselves to the Indian intelligentsia, and even to many of his colleagues in the Congress leadership. To many of his eminent contemporaries – scientists, economists, industrialists, radicals, socialists, communists – Gandhian economics seemed a throwback to primitiveness; to a utopian pre-industrial position which was untenable in the modern world'.[1]

Gandhi himself was aware of the widespread skepticism about his advocacy of khadi and the charkha. 'Many people think', he wrote in an important booklet titled *Constructive Programme: Its Meaning and Place,* on 13 December 1941, 'that in advocating "Khadi" I am sailing against a headwind and am sure to sink the ship of Swaraj and that I am taking the country to the dark ages'.[2] Even as late as in September 1944, he gave vent to the divergence between his views and those of many senior Congress leaders on the issue. Speaking at a meeting of the All India Spinners' Association (AISA) at the Sevagram Ashram near Wardha in Maharashtra, he said: 'The Congress did accept the charkha. But did it do so willingly? No, it tolerates the charkha simply for my sake.'[3]

But was Gandhi really opposed to industrialisation and to modern science and technology? Did he, with his unusual ideas on development, seek to take India back in time – to the 'dark medieval age', as some of his critics claim? Or was he a visionary who not only foretold moral degradation and the looming crisis in sustainable development that both India and the world are currently experiencing, but also showed an alternative path of development that is pro-people, protective of the environment and also promotive of human evolution to a higher level? Was he utopian in his insistence that science, economics and ethics must go together, or was his insistence a warning that the world has ignored at its peril? Would he have shunned the Internet, arguably the greatest technological invention of mankind, or embraced it? What would he have said about nanotechnology, artificial intelligence and other breathtaking promises of science and technology in the twenty-first century?

Ever since my interest in Gandhi developed from the superficial to the serious, the question that began to agitate me with the force of an intellectual storm was this: How can Gandhi be relevant to our times in terms of his spirited advocacy and scrupulous practice of nonviolence and universal brotherhood, and yet be irrelevant on a parameter – the impact of science and technology – that uniquely defines the modern world? After all, Gandhi's Truth cannot be considered holistic enough, or even true enough, if it really was disdainful of the truth represented by modern scientific knowledge and its myriad beneficial applications. Therefore, I felt it necessary to resolve this contradiction by delving deep into Gandhi's ideas on science and technology.

The more I dug into this subject, the more convinced I became that Gandhi was far from being an opponent of modern science and technology. On the contrary, by redefining development, the Gandhian vision seeks to relocate the place of science and its practical uses in the overall terrain of human affairs where it can promote mankind's holistic progress, and not be used for exploitation and violence.

My curiosity to explore this subject was initially whetted when eminent scientist Dr R.A. Mashelkar, whose ardent advocacy for people-centric development of science and technology I greatly admire, delivered, at my invitation, a talk at the Observer Research Foundation (ORF) in Mumbai in April 2010 on 'Gandhian Engineering: More from Less for More'. If everything about the title of the talk was tantalising, its content would have made Gandhi truly happy. However, the first response from many of the puzzled invitees was: Do 'Gandhi' and 'engineering' go together? Engineering, they said, is all about machines and industries, whereas Gandhi was 'opposed to industrial development and production by machines'. When Dr Mashelkar informed me that he and renowned management guru Dr C.K. Prahalad (who sadly passed away just a couple of days before the talk) had collaborated to popularise the concept of 'Gandhian Engineering' globally, I felt even more eager to delve into an aspect of the Mahatma's life and legacy that remains widely misunderstood and inadequately explored even today.

The purpose of this book is not merely to dynamite the mountain of misconception on this score that survives even six decades after Gandhi's death. It is not merely to demonstrate that the moral symbolism of khadi and the charkha (spinning wheel) has an abiding relevance for the twenty-first century. Rather, it is also to postulate that the Internet – and all other digital-era technologies supported by it – have the potential to realise the kernel of what Gandhi had been envisioning to achieve through the spinning wheel: a new, nonviolent, inter-dependent, cooperative, sustainable and morally guided world order.

Internet as an Avatar of the Spinning Wheel

In the course of my study, I discovered to my own amazement that the future world shaped by digital technologies could well validate and actualise the fundamental philosophy of the spinning wheel. This possibility has arisen because the socio-economic and political conditions that gave rise to the use of science and technology in the pre-Internet era for the domination and disempowerment of large masses of people, are speedily changing in the age of the Internet. A new networked global community is emerging in which the Internet and digital technologies are providing intellectual and practical tools to the common people to change social, political and economic structures.

Indeed, as far as the transformative power of the digital-age technologies is concerned, mankind has so far seen only the proverbial tip of the iceberg. The twenty-first century will bring a tsunami of changes that will transform the material aspects of our world beyond recognition at all levels – global, national and local. Some of these far-reaching changes could become visible as early as by the middle of this century, as forecast, for example, by Ray Kurzweil, a celebrated techno-futurist whom I interviewed for this book *(see Annexure I)*. In his landmark book *The Singularity is Near: When Humans Transcend Biology* (2005), Kurzweil writes: 'I set the date for the Singularity – representing a profound and disruptive transformation in human capability – as 2045. The non-biological intelligence created in that year will be one billion times more powerful than all human intelligence today'.

These technology-driven changes, my book argues, will prove Gandhi right. For they will mean transition from globalisation to glocalisation; from centralisation to decentralisation; from power and prosperity in the hands of a few to many; from prosperity defined purely in material terms to that which gives primacy to the richness of culture and ethical values; from unhealthy competition to healthy cooperation; from an exploitative attitude towards nature and its resources to an attitude of harmonious co-living. The disconnect between economics and ethics, which the world has experienced for the past several centuries with the onset of colonialism and the mad race to conquer distant markets, will be substantially reduced. Old technologies gave birth to this exploitative order. New technologies, if used wisely, will dig its grave. Several forms of large-scale violence, such as wars between nation-states, will become a thing of the past. Isn't this what khadi and the spinning wheel of Gandhi's conception stood for?

This discovery and its comprehensive exposition, I modestly claim, are this book's distinctive contribution to the study of Mahatma Gandhi. All the eleven chapters in the last part of this book are devoted to this theme. Among other things, I have attempted to show how Gandhian ideals have been echoed by many pioneering thinkers and innovators in the world of digital technologies – Norbert Wiener, Alan Turing, Vannever Bush, J.C.R. Licklider, Jon Postel, Doug Engelbart, Tim Berners-Lee, Richard Stallman, K. Eric Drexler, Lawrence Lessig, Bill Joy, Jaron Lanier, Michio Kaku, and others. Another legendary and universally admired name from the digital world – Apple cofounder Steve Jobs – is also included in this list. His famous biographer Walter

Isaacson tells us how Gandhi was one of Jobs's personal heroes who inspired him to Think Different.

All Big Ideas in history have two aspects: that which is true for a particular time and space in history, and that which is timeless. Some of what Gandhi sought to achieve through the spinning wheel had temporary relevance, which was circumscribed by the historical context and the specific needs of India's freedom movement. It is no longer germane to our times. However, much of the Gandhian agenda is also of abiding relevance for India and the world. Indeed, this latter aspect of the message of khadi and the charkha has in many ways become more relevant in the twenty-first century than when Gandhi was alive. The Internet, as we shall explore in this book, has the capability and an opportunity to actualise the ageless ideals of the spinning wheel.

The principal learning from Gandhi's charkha movement is that technology must empower the common man and that it should be a binding force for society to pursue a lofty goal. Both of these are true for the Internet. Anyone can connect to it freely (although this freedom needs to be actively safeguarded). Anyone can benefit from, and contribute to, the ocean of information and knowledge contained in it. In the process, the Internet has also become a new uniting power on a planetary scale by bringing individuals, groups, countries and cultures together in virtual as well as real spaces. Indeed, it is midwifing the birth of altogether new communities cutting across physical, racial, religious, economic and cultural barriers. Thus, it has become more than a technology of empowerment; it has become an ally and a catalyst in human evolution.

I have illustrated this point by giving many examples in this book. Consider how the Internet is rapidly expanding the terrain of global intelligence and wisdom. Until now, intelligence and wisdom were accessible to small communities (universities, research labs and organisations, monasteries, establishments of knowledge workers and spiritual seekers, etc.) and through mediums with limited reach (books, specialised journals, etc.). In contrast, the Internet, especially the special-focus social networking sites on it, are helping the seekers of information, knowledge and wisdom overcome the limits of number (of participants) and distance (between them). As Jean-François Noubel, a visionary who has founded one such website, TheTransitioner.org, says, 'We are currently witnessing the evolution from localised collective intelligence to global collective intelligence.'

This can have a profound impact on the nature of economic, social, political and governance organisations in the future. Today's large organisations, which are the products of the industrial revolution, colonialism, capitalism, communism and variants of these, work mostly on the predatory instincts of self-survival, control, conquest or elimination of the adversary, disrespect for the environment and lip service to human dignity. Violence in some form or the other is hard-wired into the functioning of many of these organisations. In contrast, the Internet has been slowly spawning new kinds of collectivities which promote Gandhian values such as cooperation, mutual trust and caring, sharing of resources and collective growth. For example, referring to the ideas of Noubel and other New Age thinkers, I have tried to explain how the Internet has been changing the nature of money itself. Noubel, a passionate advocate of a new international monetary system based on free (local) currencies, says:

> Money as we know it has a built-in architecture that attracts scarcity, centralisation, concentration, secrecy, proprietarisation. Our current monetary system is a product of the ideology of the Victorian society. Its structure no longer fits the systemic needs of today's world (harmonising local and global needs, sustainability, gift economy, wisdom...). Money is about to go into a fundamental evolution toward free currencies. Each community will be able to create its own currencies. In the same manner that there are today millions of discussion groups, blogs, media platforms and social networks, there will be millions of currencies made for wealth to circulate within these networks. This will become the most important evolution for humanity in the future.[4]

Don't we find strong echoes of Gandhian economics in this Internet-enabled evolution of money and socially owned wealth?

Lest I be misunderstood, I should hasten to introduce a necessary caveat here. I affirm that the Internet has the *potential* to realise the ideals that Gandhi associated with the charkha. However, whether its potential is substantially realised in the coming decades or not depends on the wisdom content of a number of other socio-political factors, which too have been identified in the book.

Gandhi was passionately wedded to the scientific spirit. He gave pride of place to science both in his vision of an ideal society and also in his practical experiments aimed at creating a new paradigm of village-centric economic development that gave the first priority to the last man in society – the philosophy of Antyodaya[5]. Moreover, although the spinning wheel was at the centre of his economic and social campaign, he was by no means dogmatic about it remaining the sole instrument of his economic philosophy forever and everywhere. He repeatedly urged both his followers and his critics to understand what khadi and the charkha *stood for*, what they *connoted*, and what he sought to achieve through them in a specific historical situation in India. During India's liberation struggle, his leadership had achieved the impossible with khadi – it became a mass movement with a nationwide sweep for the first time in its history. In the words of the celebrated French writer André Malraux, Gandhi made the entire nation wear 'a humble plebian garment (like) the uniform of freedom'. Jawaharlal Nehru, India's first prime minister, poetically described that khadi had become 'the *livery* of India's freedom'. Gandhi himself repeatedly affirmed that khadi was not merely a *vastra* (cloth) but a *vichaar* (an idea and an ideal).

However, Gandhi also made it clear that the charkha was not to be a fixed feature of India's economic development forever. He had contemplated a 'better substitute' for the charkha in a changed socio-economic situation. He was willing to accept a different set of machines and industries capable of promoting the ideals he associated with khadi and the spinning wheel – namely, a nonviolent, non-exploitative and harmony-promoting economic development.

Indeed, towards the end of his life, Gandhi was anticipating the birth of a new technological device, a nonviolent machine that '*helps every individual*' in the world. A primary objective of this book is to posit that the Internet fulfills the expectations of the machine that Gandhi had been visualising. Obviously, he could not have pictured in his mind the Internet or the birth of the digital era. Nevertheless, it is one of the little-recognised facets of Gandhi's greatness that he was anticipating, and hoping for, the arrival of a new scientific tool that would promote his vision of a just and holistic development of the entire human race.

His choice of the spinning wheel as a symbol to proclaim his vision was, after all, dictated by his socio-political mission – primarily, but not limited to, India's liberation from the British colonial rule. The choice was deliberate: he opted for the simplest and the least technologically developed tool to symbolise his mission only to underscore the fact that the Western economic system had misused modern science and technology for colonial exploitation and for promoting a soulless materialistic 'civilisation', both of which necessitated wars and violence on a massive scale. However, Gandhi had a strong historical sense to affirm that the European domination of the world was a 'nine-day wonder', and that the future would summon a just, new global order if backed by a sufficiently powerful, determined, wisdom-directed human effort. He was acutely aware that new tools of science and technology would be needed in the future to realise what the spinning wheel stood for. He was also convinced that man's inventive genius would give birth to such revolutionary new technological tools. For example, this is what he wrote in his journal *Young India* on 5 February 1925:

Many things are impossible and yet are the only things right. A reformer's business is to make the impossible possible by giving an ocular demonstration of the possibility in his own conduct. Whoever thought it possible before Edison to speak to people hundreds of miles away from us? Marconi went a step further and made wireless communication possible. *We are daily witnessing the phenomenon of the impossible of yesterday becoming the possible of today. As in physical science so in psychological. (Emphasis added)*

The claim of this book is that the new tools of science and technology that Gandhi had envisioned, and which can fulfill the promise of the spinning wheel, are represented by digital technologies anchored in the Internet.

A good deal of new research over the future of the Internet substantiates this book's main thesis. For example, in *World Wide Mind: The Coming Integration of Humanity, Machines and the Internet,* author Michael Chorost posits that the coming together of the human mind and the machine mind can make all of us more human and not less. In *Program or Be Programmed: Ten Commands for a Digital Age,* media theorist Douglas Rushkoff writes: 'We are creating a blueprint together – a design for our collective future. The possibilities for social, economic, practical, artistic and even spiritual progress are tremendous. Just as words gave people the ability to pass on knowledge for what we now call civilisation, networked activity could soon offer us access to shared thinking – an extension of consciousness still inconceivable to most of us today'.[6]

Similarly, Neil Gershenfeld, director of the Center for Bits and Atoms at the Massachussetts Institute of Technology (MIT), and author of *FAB: The Coming Revolution on Your Desktop: From Personal Computers to Personal Fabrication,* expresses the hope that the progress of digital technologies can bring joy and 'spiritual liberation'. Gandhi would have been pleased by the pioneering work that scientists like Gershenfeld have been doing at the grassroots to use digital technologies for rural development across the world, including in India. Discussion on the future of the Internet forms a significant part of this book.

Actualisation of the enormous potential of the Internet to promote nonviolent and sustainable development depends on the morally self-restrained conduct of individuals and institutions. Hence, this book also contains my philosophical speculation about the future of information technology, based on some prescient thoughts of Gandhi himself on satyagraha and swaraj. In Gandhian conception, Satya (Truth) also defines the moral and ontological dimension of life, and is not merely the true–false matrix that drives scientific research in the material world. Similarly, swaraj means a lot more than political 'freedom' for a nation. It essentially means enlightened and ethically guided self-governance, in which the 'self' stands as much for the individual as for the other concentric social institutions in what Gandhi describes as the Oceanic Circle. This Oceanic Circle is circumscribed by the infinite Cosmic Self – God Himself, who, according to Gandhi, is a synonym for Truth. In Vedantic terms, it represents a non-hierarchical order starting from identifying the self with the individual being at the lowest end to the Universal Being at the highest. In other words, an individual or a nation can be said to have attained swaraj only if their conduct is in alignment with the canons of truth. Similarly, satyagraha (insistence for truth or truth force) of the Mahatma's conception was not merely a tactic or a method of protest, as it has unfortunately been reduced to today. Clinging to truth had to be a way of life in every human activity in every era of history.

'Prediction is very difficult, especially about the future,' said Niels Bohr (1885–1962), the Nobel laureate quantum physicist. Nevertheless, the fundamental prediction this book makes is that the marriage of modern technologies with swaraj and satyagraha will shape tomorrow's nonviolent world. This optimism is based on the fact that the latest developments in information technology and other futuristic technologies (genetics, nanotechnology, robotics, etc.) tell the fascinating story of science's journey from man's outer reality to his inner reality.

Rediscovering the Relevance of Gandhi's *Hind Swaraj*

The context for this book was the centenary of the publication of Gandhi's seminal work *Hind Swaraj* (Indian Home Rule), which was published in Gujarati in 1909 and in English in 1910. The nationwide debate on *Hind Swaraj*, which was catalysed by the centenary, is certain to continue in the years to come – with greater intensity than ever before. This is because *Hind Swaraj*, in which Gandhi first announced his life mission, is nearly as important for understanding his mind as is his autobiography, *My Experiments with Truth*. Reading this little book of just over 30,000 words, which Gandhi wrote in just four days[7] during his voyage from England to South Africa in the form of a fictional dialogue between a critical reader and a principled but persuasive editor, was a mind-expanding experience for me. He wrote it as if he was under a spell. 'The writing went on at such a furious pace that when the right hand got tired, Gandhi continued with the left: forty of the 275 pages were written by the left hand. In the entire manuscript, only sixteen lines have been scratched out and only a few words changed here and there'.[8]

Sermon on the Sea – an allusion to the Sermon on the Mount by Jesus Christ – is how John Haynes Holmes (1879–1964), an influential Christian minister and pacifist in the US, who was inspired by Gandhi, titled an edition of *Hind Swaraj*[9] that he published in 1923. Holmes wrote in his introduction: 'With him [Gandhi] there moves the tidal sweep of the oriental genius, the magic mysticism of the Indian soul. At a time when the West is sinking into the choas of its own mad making, is there any greater or better hope than this sublime endeavour of the East to find a new basis for political and social life? Is it too much to say that upon the success of Gandhi, in his divine adventure, there hangs the destiny not merely of India but of our race?'

Clearly, *Hind Swaraj* is original, inspirational and paradigm-shifting writing at its best. No other book in the world, during the era of colonialism, critiqued the West's materialistic civilisation with greater ferocity. Similarly, no other book served as a comprehensive ideological preparation for its author to lead an anti-colonial struggle in his native country. Erik Erikson, an American psychoanalyst who won the Pulitzer Prize for his book *Gandhi's Truth: The Origins of Militant Nonviolence* (1969), calls *Hind Swaraj* 'a rather incendiary manifesto'. Not surprisingly, it was banned by the British as seditious literature.

It continues to be incendiary even today because it challenges the Western paradigm of development at the most fundamental level, a paradigm that, alas, has been uncritically adopted by much of the rest of the world, including India, in the post-Gandhi era.

Precisely for this reason, a superficial reading of *Hind Swaraj* can make readers misjudge the book and reinforce their misconceptions and prejudices about Gandhi's views on science, technology and modernisation. In the excellent centenary edition of *Gandhi: Hind Swaraj and Other Writings*, Anthony J. Parel, who edited it, writes: 'No other question treated in *Hind Swaraj* has provoked so much controversy as has the question of machinery – in the current idiom, technology'. As mentioned earlier, many people continue to think that Gandhi's thoughts in *Hind Swaraj* on technology and industrialisation are antiquated. This explains the tepid response of the Indian government and Indian political parties, including the Congress, to the centenary of the publication of this book. I was surprised to find even Rajmohan Gandhi, the Mahatma's scholarly grandson and author of many superb books, declare that *Hind Swaraj* 'is a text for its times, not a text for all time'.[10]

I beg to differ. Gandhi himself never disowned any of the seminal thoughts expressed in this book, although he later revised the formulation of his views on a few specific points. I believe that the main theme of *Hind Swaraj* continues to be relevant to the pressing issues being debated today in India and the world. Parel is absolutely right in saying that *Hind Swaraj* is the 'seed from which the tree of Gandhian thought has grown to its full stature'. If it is accepted that no debate on the future of human civilisation is complete without reference to Gandhi, then it stands to reason that no discussion on him is complete without reference to *Hind Swaraj*.

In a brief but necessary diversion, I must mention here an important, and less known, fact about the person who served as the catalyst for Gandhi to write *Hind Swaraj* – his dear friend and benefactor Dr Pranjivan Mehta. Gandhi himself has recorded that 'All the argument in the book is reproduced almost as it took place with him' during the one month that he stayed with Dr Mehta in a hotel room in London in 1909. I recently met Dr Pranjivan Mehta's great-grandnephew, Arun Mehta, a Mumbai-based publisher. He showed me some rare historical documents portraying the fascinating relationship between Dr Mehta and Gandhi. In a letter to Gopalkrishna Gokhale dated 28 August 1912 (that is, three years *before* Gandhi returned from South Africa), Dr Mehta prophetically described Gandhi as 'one of those rare men who are occasionally born to elevate humanity in the land of their birth'. He also wrote: 'As far as I can see, it seems to me that India had not produced an equally far-seeing political prophet like him during the last five or six centuries. If he was born in the 18th century, India would have been a far different land to what it is now and history would have been altogether differently written'.

In an earlier letter to Gokhale dated 8 November 1909, Dr Mehta described Gandhi as 'a great Mahatma'[11] – that is, long before Rabindranath Tagore did so. I am truly grateful to Arun Mehta – a man of spiritual orientation – for making me aware of Dr Mehta's clairvoyant assessment of his friend. And I look forward to the publication of the much-needed biography of this remarkable comrade of Gandhi, whose life substantiates the claim that those who are fortunate to have a close relationship with a saint also have saintly qualities.

Gandhi's Prophesies about the Science of Nonviolence

This book is not exclusively focussed on *Hind Swaraj*. My reflections scan a much wider terrain of Gandhian literature, including what others have written about him. Nevertheless, it is my humble contribution to the debate on those themes in *Hind Swaraj* which pertain to science, technology, protection of the environment and sustainable development. There are other important themes in *Hind Swaraj*, such as Hindu-Muslim relations and the path to be followed for India's national liberation, which are beyond the palette of this book.

I have also attempted to explore a highly important insight that Gandhi brought to bear on his advocacy of nonviolence – what he himself called the 'science of nonviolence'. Mankind is all too familiar with the Science of Violence. The close relationship that science forged with violence in the twentieth century contributed to the catastrophes that rained death and destruction on Earth in the form of the two World Wars and several other wars. Gandhi had prophesied the outbreak of massive wars in Europe as far back as in 1908. ('Europe will be a veritable hell on earth.'[12]) His lifelong campaign for nonviolence was not merely on moral or simplistically pacifist grounds. It was premised on a scientific understanding, rooted in his concept of satyagraha. As we shall see, he audaciously prophesied that science itself would, in future, advance the cause of nonviolence. 'We are constantly being astonished at the amazing discoveries in the field of violence,' he observed, and then predicted: 'But I maintain that far more undreamt of and seemingly impossible discoveries will be made in the field of nonviolence.'[13] Further, he said, 'Science has yet much to learn. It has so far touched only the hem of the garment.'[14]

Gandhi's faith in the regenerative potential of science and technology echoes a similar reassuring thought penned by the German poet Friedrich Hölderlin:

> But where danger is, grows
> The saving power also.[15]

I believe that the 'saving power' of science in our age is the Internet, if it is guided by satyagraha (truth force) and swaraj (the ethic of enlightened self-governance).

Our discussion in this book also focusses on another prophesy by Gandhi: 'If nonviolence is the law of our being, the future is with woman'.[16] We examine it from the point of view of evolutionary biology and affirm that the future of mankind will be governed by the principle of 'survival of the kindest', rather than 'survival of the fittest'. And since women are superior to men in terms of possessing life-protecting qualities such as kindness, cooperation, love, self-sacrifice and faith, their all-round empowerment is a pre-requisite for creating tomorrow's nonviolent world.

Our discussion on Gandhi's advocacy of nonviolence would have been woefully incomplete if it had skirted the issue of nuclear weapons, including India's own decision to possess them. Reminding the readers about what Gandhi had said about the 'sinful use of science' is a necessary and useful effort in mobilising a powerful worldwide public opinion for the complete elimination of all weapons of mass destruction from the face of our sacred planet. Gandhi was horrified when the atomic age announced its birth by causing a holocaust in Hiroshima and Nagasaki during the Second World War (1939-45). His philosophy of Nonviolence will surely contribute to the death of this age as far as nuclear weaponry is concerned. The use of nuclear science for peaceful and developmental purposes, which he had endorsed, should of course continue.

Exploration, discovery and application of truth in all its manifestations are the raison d'être of science. These were also at the core of the Mahatma's mission and vision. This begets some beguiling questions: Is the 'truth' that Gandhi experimented with, different from 'scientific truth'? How did he harmonise rational truths produced by a scientific approach and spiritual truths based on faith? How did he find in his humble spinning wheel the various attributes of Truth – nonviolence, love, justice and beauty? How did he discover in it the power of God realisation? In examining these questions, I have sought to persuade the reader to get a glimpse of a principle that Gandhi passionately affirmed – Truth is God. It appears in a profound conversation that he had with Romain Rolland, a Nobel laureate writer and India-loving peace activist, in 1931. I regard this affirmation to be Gandhi's greatest contribution to philosophy, the mother of all sciences, arts and socio-political reforms and revolutions.

A Note on the Title of This Book

Gandhi's quest for truth and nonviolence was also a quest for harmony. And the most universal language of harmony is music. He frequently uses the term 'music of the spinning wheel' in his writings on the charkha and khadi. When I first came across this term in my reading of Gandhian literature, I was intrigued by what it meant. After all, I had read that Gandhi wanted the charkha to become so efficient as to be made noiseless. Was he then referring to its music of silence? What *is* the music of silence? Was Gandhi a mystic? Like the Japanese Zen garden, whose infinite beauty is hidden in its emptiness and stillness, was music of the cosmos stored in the silence of the Mahatma's charkha?

Fritjof Capra, an American physicist and author of several bestselling books, describes who a mystic is in *The Tao of Physics: An Exploration of the Parallels Between Modern Physics and Eastern Mysticism.* 'A mystic is a person who is deeply aware of the powerful presence of the divine Spirit: someone who seeks, above all, the knowledge and love of God, and who experiences to an extraordinary degree the profoundly personal encounter with the energy of divine life. Mystics often perceive the presence of God throughout the world of nature and in all that is alive, leading to a transfiguration of the ordinary all around them. However, the touch of God is most strongly felt deep within their own hearts'.[17]

How perfectly this describes Gandhi! He was always attentive to the silent touch of God, understood as truth, in everything he set out to do. 'Silence,' he said, 'is a great help to a seeker after Truth like myself.'[18] In spite of being the leader of a national movement that was fighting the mightiest empire in the world, and one who was constantly engaged in mass activities, he used to observe a weekly day of *maun* (silence) each Monday. If spinning took at least an hour of his time on other days, he spun much longer on Mondays. It was a conscious decision to learn to remain inward-focussed. 'The Divine Radio', he wrote, 'is always singing if we could only make ourselves ready to listen to it, but is impossible to listen without silence'.[19]

My desire to do a serious study of the philosophy of the charkha was first kindled by the ring of mysticism surrounding the term 'music of the spinning wheel'. The study, which took several years, has culminated in this book. Hence, its title reflects the origin of the initial inspiration. I have attempted a detailed decoding of its meaning in Chapter 14. Hidden in the 'music of the spinning wheel' is also the 'message of the spinning wheel'. Now, if the Internet is the modern-day incarnation of the charkha, as I have posited in this study, all of us netizens around the world have to ask ourselves: How can we experience the music of harmony within ourselves when we work on the Internet? And how can we spread, and actualise, the message of harmony through our work? These questions, too, form a line of inquiry in this book, and are sought to be answered in the affirmation that forms its subtitle: 'Mahatma Gandhi's Manifesto for the Internet Age'.

Incidentally, the meeting between Gandhi and Rolland, which took place at the latter's picturesque villa in the Alps near Geneva, provided the context for me to explore the mystical connection between the 'music of the spinning wheel' and the 'music of Beethoven'. This connection was personified by Gandhi's devoted British-born associate and adopted daughter, Mirabehn (formerly Madeleine Slade). Her fascinating, and poignant, life begins and ends with the transformational influence of Beethoven's music. Rolland, one of the finest exponents of Western art and culture, regarded Beethoven to be a 'European Mahatma'. He was also instrumental in sending Mirabehn to serve the Indian Mahatma. As such, I think that this mystical connection between India and Europe is not only relevant to our discussion, but is also worthy of a separate study on the cross-continental confluence of art, science, faith, service of humanity and spiritual love. This mystical link is partly explored in *Mira & the Mahatma*, a highly readable novel by noted psychoanalyst Sudhir Kakar.

My exploration of Gandhi's brahmacharya (sexual self-restraint being a partial meaning of it) forms the longest chapter in this book. It turned out to be so without my having anticipated it, but now I realise why. Brahmacharya, as Gandhi explains in his autobiography, was so important for him that it prepared him for the path of satyagraha, both having appeared, significantly, in the same year (1906) in his life. Thereafter, truth, nonviolence and brahmacharya become inseparable in his personal mission till the end of his life. Indeed, the more I studied their interconnectedness, the stronger became my conviction that it is impossible to adequately understand Gandhi's life or mission without understanding his approach to sex.

Along with this conviction came a few important learnings. Firstly, his brahmacharya practice was highly scientific and goal-oriented, and not the outcome of some irrational and prejudiced understanding of a man-woman relationship. Secondly, there was an incredible degree of honesty and transparency in the way he examined his own sexuality. Thirdly, as in every other activity of his, he was highly innovative, even at the risk of placing himself at the centre of a controversy, in his brahmacharya experiments. Fourthly, his emphasis was not only on the virtue of sexual self-restraint but also – rather, more so – on the control of all the senses in emotion, thought, word and deed. He repeatedly stressed that control of the mind is more difficult than control of the wind, a thought that is central to the science of yoga.

Fifthly – and this is an important line of exploration in this book – a perfect brahmachari acquires superhuman powers, which he or she can harness for achieving a positive social goal. Gandhi's brahmacharya experiments, which were an integral part of his Experiments with Truth, had an ambitious goal: to so strengthen the power of his nonviolent socio-political mission that it could not only bring India freedom from the British rule in a bloodless way, but also become a believable model for ushering in justice through peaceful means elsewhere in the world. In the final tragic years of his life, when India was partitioned in an orgy of communal bloodshed, Gandhi made extraordinary efforts to perfect his brahmacharya in order to be able to extinguish the flames of hatred and fratricidal violence. That he was himself finally consumed by these flames does not negate either the sacredness or the scientific soundness of his mission, untried by any other world leader in modern times. Rather, the very fact that someone in our epoch valiantly endeavoured to divinise his sexual energy to promote nonviolence on a societal scale – and also achieved amazing successes along the way – carries immense insights and promises for the future evolution of human sexuality. I have explored this issue by posing, and answering, the question: 'Is Gandhi's Brahmacharya relevant today?' In doing so, I have also indicated where I find his views on sex unconvincing.

Studying the philosophy of brahmacharya and Gandhi's practice of it has been a highly introspective and educative experience for me. It has reinforced my belief that our world, which is intoxicated with superficial images, understandings and practices of sex, has as much to learn from Gandhi in this department of life as in others such as economy, ecology, disarmament, women's empowerment, inter-faith harmony and social justice.

That Gandhi was deeply religious in his outlook and practice is well known. But what is little known is that he was also extremely scientific in all matters where science has a place. 'My life is largely governed by reason and when it fails, it is governed by a superior force that is faith,'[20] he said. His own writings on this subject are astonishingly copious. Therefore, it is baffling that many educated Indians continue to have misconceptions on this score. The reason for this is, partly, our compartmentalised understanding of science, made worse by the dogmatic belief that science and faith are two mutually exclusive and contradictory categories. The lack of comprehension of his scientific approach is due to the fact that Gandhi, contrary to the current paradigm of science, took a holistic view of the relationship between the triad of Man, Nature and God – and hence between science, economics and ethics. His view was well articulated by his trusted lieutenant J.C. Kumarappa: 'In the traditional archives of knowledge, religion, sociology and economy have all been reserved in their separate and exclusive spheres. Man has been divided into various watertight compartments. The left hand is not to know what the right hand does. Nature does not recognise such divisions. She deals with all life as a whole'.[21]

Gandhi's passion to deal with 'life as a whole' is also evident from his profound meditations on art and beauty. They not only shed further light on the meaning of 'music of the spinning wheel', but have also revealed to me a striking internal harmony between Gandhi's economic, social, scientific, spiritual and artistic philosophies. The title of this chapter, 'Mahatma, a true artist whose mission was to make Gods out of men of clay', is derived from a tribute that Nandalal Bose, one of the greatest Indian artists of the last century, paid to him.

'The wholest of men, and one of the most miraculously energetic' is how Erikson has described Gandhi in his book. It's not my claim that I have attempted to capture the 'wholeness' of Gandhi's life in this book. Nevertheless, I have humbly set out to portray his integral, non-compartmentalised, scientific and ethics-inspired worldview. I have also sought to introduce the readers, especially young readers who are curious but insufficiently familiar with his life and philosophy, to many hard-to-believe facets of his personality – how the Mahatma was also an educationist, spinner, scavenger, cobbler, cook, nurse, nature-cure specialist, dietician, bee-keeper, carpenter, an avid user of the microscope and the telescope, a champion of technological innovation and an experimentalist par excellence. Seeing this multifaceted portrait of Gandhi is necessary for a better understanding of his *weltanschauung*. Such a portrait will show that, far from being anti-science, his worldview elevates science to a higher level of human pursuit and imparts to it a nobler purpose that is consistent with both mankind's needs and the Divine Law. It is my firm belief that only a holistic Gandhian worldview – and reform of individual and institutional conduct based on such a worldview – can help India, and the rest of the world, overcome the gigantic challenges they are facing.

I would like to emphasise one more thing: This book is not the work of idle academic curiosity about an iconic figure of yesteryears. It is a call to action and service, based on my reflections on what Gandhi means to India and the world, today and tomorrow. Our country, in particular, needs to rediscover the relevance of his teachings if it is not to commit the follies of its own past and, also, if it is not to repeat the follies of the West. In his teachings, we find the right guidance to reunite our divided society and also our fractured subcontinent. In his teachings, we find the right principles to reform our economic and political systems, both of which are today mired in deepening corruption. In his teachings, we find that a new and harmonious Man-Nature relationship, which is now badly ruptured to the detriment of both, can indeed be created with the right use of modern technologies. Finally, his teachings are also a call, as described in this book, for human beings to become 'more than human' by ascending the Godward evolutionary path.

I have summed up my appeal for action in the epilogue by saying, 'It's time we all became Internet Satyagrahis'. A new age is dawning. This is not the hour to be caught asleep.

The autobiographical beginning to this book ('My Journey from Mahatma to Marx, and Back'), I must confess, was a necessity because Gandhi has been the biggest influence in my own choice of a life of public service. I am reminded here of what eminent historian and writer Ramachandra Guha has said in the opening sentence of his book *An Anthropologist Among the Marxists and Other Essays* (2001) – 'Inside every thinking Indian there is a Gandhian and a Marxist struggling for supremacy'. Guha is right. In the philosophical and political struggles in my own life, the Gandhian in me decisively prevailed over the Marxist in me. Therefore, I couldn't have written this book without sharing with the reader *what the Mahatma has meant to me.*

An explanatory note on why the book is replete with quotes, many of them fairly long ones, from the Mahatma. Two reasons: firstly, anyone familiar with his writings will readily agree with the observation made by Joseph Lelyveld, author of *Great Soul: Mahatma Gandhi and His Struggle With India* (2011), that Gandhi is 'infinitely quotable'. One can read and re-read the works of great thinkers without ever feeling a loss of freshness. Even repetitions of thought have a novelty of their own. Secondly, this book is about Mahatma Gandhi and nobody can tell the incredible story of his life, a stormy voyage of ideas and actions, better than in his own words. The book, therefore, has made the Mahatma do a good bit of the talking. At the same time, it has been my humble attempt to weave a new commentary that is aimed at reminding ourselves why he, despite having been once disparagingly described by Winston Churchill as 'a half-naked fakir', remains a prophetic figure in the Internet age.

I do hope I have succeeded, at least partly, in assembling the many disparate bits and pieces of available information accessed from diverse sources to create a coherent, living and speaking portrait of Mahatma Gandhi, the rarest of rare practitioner of a superior science whose relevance for self-realisation, social transformation and human evolution is indeed timeless.

PART ONE

PATHWAYS
TO
SATYAGRAHA

Where he sat became a temple...

1

MY JOURNEY FROM
MAHATMA TO MARX, AND BACK

⤞⚬⬦⬦⬦⬦⚬⬥⤝

Both capitalism as well as communism have failed to take account of
the Integral Man. One considers him a mere selfish being hankering
after money, whereas the other has viewed him as a feeble lifeless cog
in the whole scheme of things. Both result in dehumanisation of man.
Man, the highest creation of God, is losing his own identity. We must
re-establish him in his rightful position, bring him the realisation of his
greatness, reawaken his abilities and encourage him to exert for attaining
the divine heights of his latent personality. This is possible only through
a decentralised economy.

— Pandit Deendayal Upadhyaya, ideological guru of the
Bharatiya Janata Party, in *Integral Humanism.*

THE ENCOUNTER OF MANY INDIAN INTELLECTUALS AND
political activists with Mahatma Gandhi has never been smooth,
and I am no exception. My understanding of the Mahatma
has undergone a sea change over the years, as the following brief
autobiographical detour would show.

The year was 1969, Gandhi's birth centenary. I was in the seventh
standard. In my hometown Athani, a small place in northern Karnataka
where I had a part of my school and college education, the government
had organised a *taluka*-level elocution competition for students on

what Gandhi meant to them. I told my aunt, who was helping me prepare for the event that I would speak on Gandhi as a scientist. She was utterly surprised. 'He was a great man, but how can you call him a scientist?' she asked. With a twelve-year-old's rudimentary understanding of a big concept like science, I replied in my mother tongue, Kannada: 'Scientists search for truth. So did Gandhiji. Scientists conduct experiments. So did Gandhiji, as the title of his autobiography tells us. Scientific experiments influence society. Gandhiji's experiments with truth also influenced India and the world.'

I won the second prize.

Thirty years later. I was working in the Prime Minister's Office (PMO) as an aide to Atal Bihari Vajpayee. Computers and Information Technology (IT) had become buzzwords in the 1990s and India's IT industry, though still in its infancy, had begun to show tremendous promise. I had persuaded Atalji to give high priority to the promotion of IT in our government's vision of development. Atalji, a poet-turned-politician, had never used a computer in his life. (*'Arre bhai, mujhe to computer chalaana bhi nahin aata,'* – I don't even know how to use a computer – is what he had said in his typical jocular and self-mocking style, when I first made the suggestion.) Nevertheless, he supported India's IT and telecom agenda with great enthusiasm and conviction. In one of his speeches, he even described IT as India's Tomorrow.

My own faith in the power of IT gave me an idea for the 2001 Republic Day Parade, the annual celebration in which states and ministries of the Central Government showcase their messages and achievements on tableaux that drive along the Raj Path in the national capital. To discuss the idea, I called my friend, the late Dewang Mehta, who, as the head of the National Association of Software and Service Companies (popularly known as NASSCOM), was widely praised as a young and charismatic icon for India's IT industry. I had been working closely with him in the Prime Minister's Task Force on IT and Telecom.[1] 'Why don't we create a tableau this year to convey a quintessentially Indian vision of IT-led development?' I asked him, explaining the concept and its visual representation that I had in mind. The float would have a large replica of Gandhi's charkha, in which the hub-

and-spokes wheel would morph into a spinning computer CD with an appropriately coined slogan. 'A creative team of designers would be able to communicate this idea to the nationwide television audience in an appealing manner,' I said.

'Wow, this is unique!' exclaimed Dewang. 'Let's do it. But the float should also in some way present the message of the Internet, which has a big potential to benefit India's khadi and traditional village industries. It can enable our weavers, artisans and craftsmen to have access to the best designs from different parts of India and the world. They can display and sell their products online for buyers around the globe. The Internet can also train the younger people in artisan communities. This is important because India's heritage of arts and crafts is fast vanishing.' He added that he had started a small effort in this direction for the craftswomen in Gujarat, his home state. 'Gandhiji would have been happy seeing the village folk talk about computers in his own mother tongue.'

Dewang and I rushed to meet the officer in the Defence Ministry in charge of preparations for the Republic Day Parade. 'An interesting concept,' he said, 'but you are several weeks too late. Our arrangements for this year's parade are already over. You may try it next year.' Sadly, Dewang passed away after a few months, and I never again pursued the idea.

The idea of the spinning wheel morphing into a computer disk was the outcome of a long, and by no means smooth, metamorphosis of my own thoughts about Mahatma Gandhi. It took an arduous ideological journey in my life to resolve the tension in favour of an understanding that khadi and the computer were, after all, not antagonistic.

There was a time, after I had joined the Indian Institute of Technology (IIT) Bombay, when I had moved away from the Mahatma to Marx. My reflections on the stark inequalities and exploitation in the Indian society, and my encounters with heart-wrenching poverty in both the villages of Karnataka and the slums of Bombay, made me believe that a communist revolution was the only answer to these ills. At an intellectual level, I came to believe, as so many Indian students and professionals still do, that Gandhi's views on science and technology were wrong and his model of development was medieval. How can anybody agree with him, I wondered, when he says that 'the revival of hand-spinning and hand weaving will make the largest contribution to the economic and the moral regeneration of India'?[2] Wasn't he being irrational, I thought, in his denunciation of big cities as breeders of vice and violence, and in his insistence that 'you have to be rural-minded before you can be nonviolent, and to be rural-minded you have to have faith in the spinning wheel'?[4]

Students in Indian universities and technology institutions can hardly be faulted for harbouring the view that Gandhi was anti-science, anti-machines and anti-modernity. Several generations of scientists, science-popularisers, policy-makers and men of arts and letters, both in India and abroad, have held this notion. Albert Einstein, in an interview in 1935, said, 'I admire Gandhi greatly but...Gandhi is mistaken in trying to eliminate or minimise machine production in modern civilisation. It is here to stay and must be accepted.'[5] Robert Payne, author of the widely read biography *The Life and Death of Mahatma Gandhi*, writes: 'Gandhi was against science'.[6] Charlie Chaplin had confessed that he was confused about 'Gandhi's abhorrence of machinery', even though he sympathised with his struggle for India's freedom. Philosopher Bertrand Russell, whose books are read by every serious student interested in the world of ideas, described Gandhi as 'unquestionably a great man, both in personal force and in political effect'. Nevertheless, he believed that the Mahatma had no place in the modern era. 'While his memory deserves to be revered,' Russell wrote, 'it would be a mistake to hope that India will continue to have the outlook that to him seemed best. India, like other nations, has to find her place in the modern world, not in the dreams of a bygone age. His work is done and if India is to prosper, it must be along other roads than his'.[7]

A far more dismissive view of Gandhi's khadi campaign as anti-science had come from Aldous Huxley[8], a renowned British writer who is a favourite among book-loving students: 'Tolstoyans and Gandhiites tell us that we must "return to nature"; in other words, abandon science altogether and live like primitives, or, at best, in the style of our medieval ancestors. The trouble with this advice is that it cannot be followed – or rather, it can be followed if we are prepared to sacrifice at least 800-900 million human lives. Science, in the form of modern industrialisation and agricultural technology, has allowed the world's population to double itself in about three generations'.

This view was shared by many a policy maker in India, including Meghnad Saha, a brilliant astrophysicist who influenced Free India's model of planning and building heavy industries. In a conversation with Russian scientists, Saha told them that he and other Indian scientists had 'as little regard' for Gandhi's thoughts on economic and social development as 'you Russians have for Tolstoy'. Saha also asserted: 'We do not for a moment believe that better and happier conditions could be created by discarding modern scientific technique and reverting to the spinning wheel, the loin cloth and the bullock cart'.[9]

Speaking for myself, the strong influence of Marxist ideology on me those days, combined with several years of activism in the communist movement, had further alienated me from the Mahatma. To the ears of an atheist, which I then was, his words – 'I see God in every thread that I draw on the spinning wheel' – meant mere mumbo jumbo. So, too, was his affirmation that 'the spinning wheel represents to me the hope of the masses. The masses lost their freedom with the loss of the Charkha'.[10]

Then, of course, there was Karl Marx's own disparaging analysis about the 'deeply reactionary character of that (India's) village system and the indispensable necessity of its destruction if mankind is to advance'. Calling village life in India 'undignified and vegetative', he had written: 'We must not forget that these idyllic village-communiities, inoffensive though they may appear, had always been the solid foundation of Oriental despotism, that they restrained the human mind within the smallest possible compass, making it the unresisting tool of superstition, enslaving it beneath traditional rules, depriving it of all grandeur and historical energies'.[11] Having been, thus, brainwashed into believing that India's village system was the fount of Oriental Despotism and that this system needed to be destroyed 'if mankind is to advance', most Indian students influenced by communism developed a deep prejudice towards Gandhi. Their prejudice grew into intense hostility as a result of his uncompromising stand on ahimsa (nonviolence) and his religion-inspired worldview[12].

In spite of his fundamental differences with Marxists, Gandhi had high regard for Karl Marx. Here is a report of his discussion with political workers in Midnapore, Bengal, in 1946 as published in *Amrita Bazar Patrika*: 'Gandhi was asked about Karl Marx. He got the opportunity and privilege of reading *Das Capital*, he told them, whilst he was in detention. He entertained high regard for his industry and acumen. But he could not believe in his conclusions. He had no faith in violence being able to usher in nonviolence. World thought was moving and was outdating Karl Marx. That, however, did not detract from the merit of the great man's labours'.[13]

However, my subsequent disillusionment with the ideology and reality of communism – which started before the collapse of communism in the erstwhile Soviet Union and the disintegration of the Soviet Union itself – pulled me back from Marx to Mahatma. Indeed, my study of Gandhi's life and literature threw light not only on what was wrong with communism, but also on what was right with his thoughts on science, technology, development and, to mention a commonplace term which glows with profound meaning when Gandhi uses it, CIVILISATION.

The turning point came with the realisation that everything Gandhi said and did originated from a deep and lifelong quest for the answer to the central question: How to re-enshrine morality and righteousness (dharma, a word very dear to his heart) in every activity and every institution of human life? Neither capitalism nor communism had bothered itself with this quest. Indeed, morality in thought and conduct were irrelevant in these two contending ideological-political systems, both of which were engendered by Western civilisation. The false claims of capitalism and communism, their focus solely on the satisfaction of man's material needs (even their partial successes in this regard having been scarred by inequity, injustice and violence),

Karl Marx (1818-83): *The twentieth century witnessed both the rise and fall of the communist movements around the world. Gandhi had high regard for Marx's acumen, even though he had fundamental differences with Marxists. He had predicted that historical developments would render Marx's theory outdated.*

and the serious deficiencies in their institutions of governance were apparent even in Gandhi's times. They became even starker in the decades after his departure.

In response to a reporter's question in London in 1931 – 'Mr. Gandhi, what do you think of Western Civilisation?' – his famous reply was: 'I think it would be a good idea!'[14] Why did he show such disbelief and disapproval? In hindsight, we can find the answer in the sheer scale of harm that the West wrought on mankind – the bloody history of the West's colonial domination of the rest of the world; Europe's glittering prosperity blackened by its rapacious exploitation of its colonies in Asia, Africa and Latin America; the two horrific World Wars that the West inflicted upon both itself and the rest of the globe, killing millions of people; the Cold War that divided the world into two rival blocs; the communist dictatorships in the Soviet Union, and other countries that suppressed freedom, denied human dignity and also caused enormous violence on citizens by the state apparatus; the military dictatorships in Latin America and Africa propped up by the US; and the wars of aggression in Korea, Vietnam, Iraq and Afghanistan. If the enormity of the West's culpability is acknowledged, we can better appreciate why Gandhi was seeking a civilisational alternative in his critique of European industrialism and imperialism.

For me, the main point of departure back from Marx to the Mahatma was the question of violence as a tool in political activities as well as a principal element in state policy. Most Marxists justify, directly or indirectly, violence as an agent of change in politics and society. They do so by referring to the entrenched institutionalised violence against the poor in capitalist societies. After all, it was Karl Marx himself who had famously said: 'Violence is the midwife of every old society pregnant with a new one.' What Marx did not foresee, and also seemed to belittle, is that communist revolutions midwifed by violence produced regimes that themselves became perpetrators of violence on a monstrous scale. The principal reason for this degeneration was the irreligious and anti-spiritual nature of the ideology and practice of communism, which, in contrast to one of Gandhi's key principles, arrogantly claimed that ends justified the means. What history has proved, however, is that some of the noble ideals of communism were defiled by the violent, oppressive and grossly unethical means adopted by communist dictatorships.

Gandhi's approach to socio-political change was fundamentally different because it was genuinely spiritual and guided by the universal human values of everlasting relevance. Castigating both capitalism and communism for the horrific crimes committed by them, he asked: 'What difference does it make to the dead, the orphans and the homeless whether the mad destruction is wrought under the name of totalitarianism or the holy name of liberty and democracy? I assert in all humility but with all the strength at my command, that liberty and democracy become unholy when their hands are dyed red with innocent blood.'[15]

'The past two wars of our generation,' he said, 'have proved the utter bankruptcy of such economic orders (capitalism and communism). Incidentally, the wars seem to me to have proved the bankruptcy of war, meaning in forcible and naked language of violence, which is not less because it is organised by States reputed to be civilised. Whether nonviolence will effectively replace violence for keeping the peace of the world remains to be seen. Certain it is that mankind, if it continues along its mad career of exploitation of the weak by the strong, must rush to annihilation foretold by all religions.'[16]

As Europe became a theatre of butchery during the Second World War, on a scale never witnessed before in human history, Gandhi expressed his anguish as well as his unshakable faith in ahimsa. 'I know mine is a voice in wilderness. But it will someday ring true. If liberty and democracy are to be saved, they will only be by nonviolent resistance no less brave, no less glorious, than violent resistance. And it will be infinitely braver, and more glorious because it will give life without taking any'.[17]

My return to the path of the Mahatma was complete. He helped me understand that the ideology of communism as propounded and practiced by its votaries is alien to the soil of India's own progressive social, intellectual and spiritual traditions. In him, I saw an heroic attempt to evolve, as he himself had claimed, 'a truer socialism and truer communism than the world has yet dreamt of'.[18]

'Prayer is to the soul what food is to the body': *Gandhi after an evening prayer meeting at Juhu Beach, Bombay, in May 1944. The English pacifist writer Laurence Housman, who once chaired a meeting in Gandhi's honour at the Friends House in London in 1931, said to him: 'Mr. Gandhi, you are a strange man. You are so simple that you puzzle people; you are so honest that men doubt you.'*

2

'I AM NOT A SERVANT OF INDIA, I AM A SERVANT OF TRUTH.'

❖

What was his great power over the mind and heart of man due to? Ages to come will judge and we are too near him to assess the many facets and his extraordinarily rich personality. But even we realise that his dominating passion was truth. That truth led him to proclaim without ceasing that good ends can never be attained by evil methods, that the end itself is distorted if the method pursued is bad. That truth led him to confess publicly whenever he thought he made a mistake – Himalayan errors, he called some of his own mistakes. That truth led him to fight evil and untruth wherever he found them regardless of the consequences... His physical body has left us and we shall never see him again or hear his gentle voice or run to him for counsel. But his imperishable memory and immortal message remain with us.

— Jawaharlal Nehru, in a homage to Mahatma Gandhi
two weeks after his assassination on 30 January 1948.

THE MORE ONE READS GANDHI, AND ALSO READS ABOUT HIM, the stronger one realises that he was not an ordinary mortal. Of course, he was not perfect. But there has been no other leader in modern world history who tried to rise above his own imperfections as earnestly and transparently as he did. Nor is there another leader who attached as much importance to self-purification for the pursuit of the goal of social transformation. For Gandhi, the Self and Society were two mutually extensive arenas where the battle for Truth had to be fought. His concept of society was not restricted by narrow nationalism. Even though his love for India was limitless, he was at heart an internationalist who cared as much for the welfare of the rest of the world as he did for India's. Which is why he had the inner courage to say, without being misunderstood by his countless followers: 'I am not a servant of India, I am a servant of Truth'.

Gandhi had begun his efforts to spiritualise politics and economics fairly early in his life. This is evident from the goal he set for himself long before he returned to India from South Africa, where he spent twenty self-transformative years of his life – from April 1893 to July 1914, with a brief interlude of a few months that he spent in India. The goal was not merely India's political independence from British rule. If that were his only objective, history would have recorded him not as a Mahatma but merely as yet another leader of a national liberation struggle. His quest really was for India's civilisational rebirth, which he hoped would then contribute to a civilisational renewal worldwide. It made him adopt an ethical and dharma-guided approach to all aspects of social life, national reconstruction and world affairs. It was his unshakable conviction that India could attain swaraj in the true sense of the term only by learning from India's own ancient civilisation. Swaraj for him meant not only self-rule but, more importantly, rule over self. 'Swaraj,' he explained, 'really means self-control. Only he is capable of self-control who observes the rules of morality, does not cheat or give up truth, and does his duty to his parents, wife and children, servants and neighbours. Such a man is in enjoyment of swaraj, no matter where he lives. A state enjoys swaraj if it can boast of a large number of such good citizens'.[1]

G.D.H. Cole (1889-1959), a famous English historian and Fabian socialist, once remarked that Gandhi 'is as near as a man can be to Swaraj in a purely personal sense'. More than six decades after India attained political freedom, is our country anywhere close to having swaraj of Gandhi's conception?

Gandhi further contended that, where the Indian civilisation had still survived, the credit went not to the mansions of the city-dwelling rich but to the huts of the village poor. His critics, not only Marxists but also followers of Dr B.R. Ambedkar, a great social reformer who was a trenchant critic of the Mahatma, deride him even today for 'romanticising' poverty and rural India. The charge is misplaced. Gandhi was deeply anguished by the grinding poverty in India, and by the decay and deformities in our once-proud village communities, both of which were an outcome of the British pillage of our country.[2] He wanted this poverty and backwardness to end. But unlike either traditionalist or radical leaders of his time, he had recognised wealth of a different kind amongst the Indian poor: the lofty moral and ethical ideals of India's civilisation, which had been preserved by many of its unlettered villagers through all the vicissitudes of history. He attributed this to their having been relatively untouched by the 'industrial civilisation'. He did not want this intangible wealth to disappear with the welcome arrival of material prosperity in Free India.

History is witness to the fact that India's freedom struggle became a mass movement only because of Gandhi's astonishing success in reaching out to the rural populace. Before his arrival on the political scene, the Indian National Congress (INC) was just a patriotic platform of the urban educated elite. The real reason for Gandhi's success is not generally understood. His outward appearance as a semi-naked saint no doubt had an impact on the common people. But the Indian society, which has witnessed countless saints and *sanyasis* of the purest kind throughout its long history, also instinctively realised that Gandhi's outer appearance was indeed a manifestation of his inner saintly character.

Here was a national leader who lived, and dressed, like the poorest of the poor in India. He had brought about drastic changes in his own lifestyle, 'which were partly a response to his inner urge for austerity, but they also satisfied another urge in him: to identify himself with the "least, lowliest and the lost". He used a stone instead of soap for his bath...and ate his frugal meal with a wooden spoon from a prisoner's bowl'.[3] But here also was a leader who was seeking to mobilise the common people of India by talking to them not in the language of the lowest common denominator of power politics, as many politicians today do, but in the language of the highest common denominator of morality and dharma. He made it clear to them, and to the whole world that his intent was not to secure the strength of numbers for forcing the British to quit India.

Gandhi repeatedly expressed the fear that mere transfer of power from British hands to Indian hands might result in a foreign exploiter being replaced by native exploiters. He wanted swaraj not for a minority, but for the suffering multitudes. And even for the multitudes, he did not want only the freedom of the bread. In explaining 'the secret of Swaraj' to his rural audiences, he had the audacity to tell them: 'We are engaged in a spiritual war'. In this 'war', he said, his weapon would be the 'sword of ethics'.[4] Being a servant of God (a term that was, for him, synonymous with Truth), he identified himself in this 'war' with the poor humanity because he saw Living God (*Daridranarayan*) in them. And they in turn identified with him because they saw in him a saint-warrior, worthy of the kind of reverence they, and all their preceding generations, had always reserved for saintly men and women. Therefore, it is necessary to remember that Gandhi didn't become a Mahatma because Rabindranath Tagore or someone else gave him that honourable title. It was because millions of ordinary Indians accepted him as a Mahatma in their hearts.

A man of utmost humility, and also amazing wit, he never liked to be treated as a human being of a special or superior kind. He wrote: 'If I would admit that I am a Mahatma, a great soul, I would also have to admit that others are small souls. But *small soul* is a self-contradiction'. He did not like to be called a saint. 'I am not a *saint who has strayed into politics,*' he famously said, 'I am a politician who is trying to become a *saint*'.[5] *(Emphasis added)*

English pacifist writer Laurence Housman [1865-1959], who once chaired a meeting in Gandhi's honour at the Friends' House in London in 1931, said to him: 'Mr. Gandhi, you are a strange man. You are so simple that you puzzle people; you are so honest that men doubt you.'

As befits a true saint, praise or worldly rewards and awards meant nothing to him. In 1934, an editorial in *Christian Century*, an influential US magazine, suggested his name for the Nobel Peace Prize. His reaction to this suggestion, as recorded by Agatha Harrison, an English follower of the Mahatma, is revealing. She was accompanying Gandhi and Rajendra Prasad (a freedom fighter who later became independent India's first president) during their tour of the earthquake-hit areas of Bihar when the editorial appeared. Harrison, who was apparently excited by the suggestion, showed it to Gandhi. It was a Monday, his weekly day of silence. 'The expression on his face was a study as he read it through carefully. Then, selecting a very small scrap of paper, he wrote: "Do you know of a dreamer who won attention by adventitious aid?" With a broad smile he handed this to me and went on with the work I had interrupted'.[6]

Renowned historian Ramachandra Guha says: 'It is a matter of shame that Gandhi was never awarded the Nobel Peace Prize; the shame is also felt by those who decide on the prize in Oslo, who have since made amends by awarding it to (several) "Gandhians".' Among them are Martin Luther King, Nelson Mandela, Archbishop Desmond Tutu, the Dalai Lama, Aung San Suu Kyi and Tawakkul Karman.

Understanding this moral and spiritual quest of Gandhi is critical to our understanding of so many other aspects of his vision and work:

- *Why he rejected both capitalism and communism:* Gandhi cautioned the rich businessmen in India against thinking that they could 'gain American wealth but avoid its methods'.[7] Such an attempt, if it were made, 'is foredoomed to failure', he said. He did not believe that 'an Indian Rockefeller would be better than the American Rockefeller'.[8] Rather, he held that 'it will be hard for an India made rich through immorality to regain its freedom'.[9] Even though he was less harsh in his criticism of communism, he was forthright in stating: 'I can no more tolerate the yoke of Bolshevism than of capitalism'.[10]
- *Why he vehemently disapproved of the West's materialistic civilisation:* Gandhi firmly believed that India was engaged in a struggle between

the Kingdom of Satan, as symbolised by British imperialism, and the Kingdom of God represented by India's ancient civilisation. Echoing the view of Edward Carpenter, an influential British socialist philosopher and poet, he said that Western civilisation 'is a malady which needs a cure. The growth of big cities is only a symptom of that malady'.[11] 'It is our dharma to reject Western civilisation. The supremacy of brute force, worshipping money as God, spending most of one's time in seeking worldly happiness, breath-taking risks in the pursuit of worldly enjoyments of all kinds, the expenditure of limitless mental energy on efforts to multiply the power of machinery, the expenditure of crores on the invention of means of destruction, the moral righteousness which looks down upon people outside Europe – this civilisation, in my view, deserves to be altogether rejected'.[12] He characterised the European civilisation as 'a nine days' wonder, yet another of those 'ephemeral civilisations that have come and gone'. 'We pray that India may never be reduced to the same state as Europe'.[13]

- *Why he opposed the Western model of education:* Gandhi called it 'rotten' because it placed money-making above morality. He was especially fierce in his censure of lawyers and doctors who, 'like so many leeches, suck the blood of the poor people...to indulge in luxuries'.[14]
- *Why he was critical of the Western model of industrialisation:* Gandhi discovered in the charkha the source of hope for a new kind of moral machinery, a new kind of economic development, a new kind of relationship between the people engaged in an economic activity, a new kind of relationship between Man and Nature – indeed, a new nonviolent and dharmic paradigm for the future development of the Indian and global civilisation.

Gopal Krishna Gokhale (1866-1915) was one of the foremost leaders of India's national movement before Gandhi's arrival on the scene. He had recognised Gandhi's potential long before the latter's return to India, based purely on press reports of the satyagraha movement in South Africa. In his speech at the Lahore session of the Congress in 1909, Gokhale said: '...a purer, nobler, a braver and a more exalted spirit has never moved on this earth. Mr Gandhi is one of those men who, living an austerely simple life themselves and devoted to all the highest principles of love to their fellow-citizens and to truth and justice, touch the eyes of their weaker brethren as with magic and give them a new vision... in him Indian humanity at the present time has really reached its high watermark.'

Gokhale visited South Africa in 1912 at Gandhi's invitation to study the satyagraha movement by the people of Indian origin. Upon his return, he again paid rich tributes to Gandhi, saying: '... only those who have come into personal contact with Mr Gandhi as he is now can realise the wonderful personality of the man. He is without doubt made of the stuff which heroes and martyrs are made. Nay more. He has in him the marvellous spiritual power to turn ordinary men around him into heroes and martyrs.'

Remarkably, the most decisive life-transforming events that set Gandhi on a path of spiritually guided politics took place not in India but in distant South Africa. We shall therefore now move there to see the sources and signposts of this transformation.

Lawyer Gandhi in South Africa.

Gandhi's teachers: *(Clockwise) Socrates, John Ruskin,
Leo Tolstoy and Srimad Rajchandraji.*

3

SOUTH AFRICA:
WHERE GANDHI BECAME A MAHATMA

--※◇◈◇※--

Riz Khan: *How much do you think that Mahatma Gandhi's philosophy of nonviolence still lives on?*

Nelson Mandela: *Mahatma Gandhi has had an enormous influence on the approach of leaders of thought to specific problems throughout the world. Peace as the most powerful weapon to resolve a mutual problem, is a lesson that is deeply entrenched throughout the world. And Gandhi has played a key role in that respect.*

— 'Gurus of Peace', a series of interviews with Nobel Peace Prize winners influenced by Mahatma Gandhi. The series was conceived and directed by filmmakers Bharatbala and Kanika.

MYSTERIOUS ARE THE DIRECTIONS AND DESTINATIONS OF HUMAN life. We are each born somewhere, our pathways take us to disparate places, and life becomes a series of externally driven events, which, in the case of most people, seem to reveal no pattern or purpose. This is not so in the case of extraordinary men and women through whom destiny chooses to advance its own hidden agenda. Their life journeys seem to have an underlying objective and also a predetermined roadmap to guide their movement towards that destination. When judged on the scale of cosmic time, geological time, and the evolutionary time of life on our planet, the lives of ordinary men and women appear to have no significance at all. However, this is not so in the case of men and women of destiny, whose lives, though as finite in time as others', glow with meaning. And that meaning, a closer examination reveals, is linked to the very birth, existence and the ultimate goal of the universe.

Gandhi was one such man of destiny.

How else can one explain his journey to South Africa? Though trained as a lawyer in England, he had miserably failed in his profession upon his return to India. It is this failure, and all the financial hardships that it entailed, which prompted him to take up the offer of a wealthy Muslim trader from Gujarat, Seth Dada Abdullah, to assist him in a legal case in South Africa. When his ship left the shores of Bombay for Durban in April 1893, the contract he was carrying with him stipulated that he would stay there for only one year. But destiny willed otherwise. He went on to spend more than a third of his working life in that country. Gandhi's distinctively dharmic approach to transforming one's self, society and the world – to bring them in harmony with Truth, the Law of God, and with all that He has created – acquired its essential characteristics in South Africa, before developing to its fullness in India.

It is a transformation best described in the words of Nelson Mandela, who was much influenced by Gandhi's life and teachings: 'You gave us Mohandas Gandhi; we returned him to you as Mahatma Gandhi'. A similar observation is made by Hassim Seedat, the great South African student of Gandhi's life and literature: 'I am proud of the fact that the world's biggest diamond was found in our mines, but what we returned to you as Mahatma Gandhi was an incomparably more precious and polished diamond'.[1]

Fatima Meer, Mandela's close associate in the anti-apartheid movement and a renowned Gandhian scholar-activist, has this to say about what South Africa did to Mohandas Karamchand Gandhi, in her book *Apprenticeship of a Mahatma: A Biography of M.K. Gandhi (1869-1914)*:

> On the 18th of July, 1914, twenty-one years after his arrival, Mohan accompanied by his family, left South Africa. He had come to the country as a young man of twenty-three, a semi-

Englishman. His host, on meeting him, had wondered how he could afford to keep such an expensive-looking dandy. His tastes had continued to be expensive for a while, but they had changed through the intermingling of thoughts and experiences. Now he left the country bearing all the signs of a man who would soon be recognised as a saint. As Christ became the Saviour, Muhammed the Prophet, Gautama the Buddha, the little boy frightened of the dark became the Mahatma and paid the price of all Mahatmas.[2]

The transformation of Gandhi into a Mahatma in remote South Africa is, by any reckoning, one of the most extraordinary events in modern human history. The decisive change agent in this transformation was the maturing of his views on dharma, loosely translated into English as religion. He had absorbed the universal message of the Hindu scriptures during his childhood in Gujarat, having been introduced to the *Ramayana, Mahabharata, Bhagavat Purana* and other holy scriptures by his mother. His interest in religion developed further during his training in law in England. However, it was in South Africa that he made the most intense study of all the religions of the world and came to the conclusion that dharma or religion is but one tree with many branches, and it is based on truth, nonviolence and justice. Truth became his God, and nonviolence the means of realising Him.

He discovered that all the great religions of the world inculcate the equality and brotherhood of mankind and extol the virtue of tolerance. He also realised that all religions, in their essence, stand on a foundation of certain common moral values, which do not privilege the strong against the weak but, rather, impose a greater obligation on the strong to protect the weak. There are also specific unacceptable aspects in all religions that need to be discarded when they militate against justice and human conscience. Which is why, Europe's oppression of Asia, Africa and other parts of the world, and its misuse of Christianity for this purpose, made him declare: 'That religion and that nation will be blotted out of the face of earth which pins its faith on injustice, untruth or violence'.[3]

Moreover, it was in South Africa that Gandhi's understanding of, and belief in, Hinduism got greatly strengthened – no doubt after an arduous process of self-questioning – leading him to affirm that 'it was through the Hindu religion that I learnt to respect Christianity and Islam'. About the *Bhagavad Gita's* profound influence on him, he writes in his autobiography: 'Just as I turned to the English dictionary for the meanings of English words that I did not understand, I turned to this dictionary of conduct for a ready solution of all my troubles and trials'. The *Gita* also taught him that Hinduism is not an exclusive religion. 'In it there is room for the worship of all the prophets in the world'.[4]

It is this conviction in the power of religion which made Gandhi use it as the main idea and idiom in all his social and political campaigns, first in South Africa and later, on a grander scale, in India.

Since his religious faith was anchored in universal moral values, and not in rituals and geographical loyalties, he freely and enthusiastically absorbed the noblest thoughts from foreign minds – Socrates, Plato, Ruskin, Tolstoy, Wallace, Thoreau, Carlyle, Emerson and others. In this sense, he personified the Rig Vedic maxim *Aano bhadrah krtavo yantu vishwatah* – 'Let noble thoughts come to me from all directions'. South Africa made Gandhi an uncompromising internationalist.

All the three philosophers who had a major transformative impact on his thinking, entered his life in South Africa. Two were foreigners: John Ruskin and Leo Tolstoy. The third was Srimad Rajchandraji (1867-1901), a Jain merchant-cum-monk in Bombay. Gandhi has written this about Rajchandraji's influence on him: 'I have since met many a religious leader or teacher…and I must say that no one else has ever made on me the impression that he did. …Srimadji was an embodiment of non-attachment and renunciation. His words went straight home to me. His intellect compelled as great a regard from me as his moral earnestness…The thing that cast its spell over me … was his wide knowledge of the scriptures, his spotless character, and his burning passion for self-realisation. I saw later that this last was the only thing for which he lived'.[5]

My scholar-friend Chandrika has written a well-researched monograph *Gandhi's Guru: An insight into the life and teachings of the Jain saint, Srimad Rajchandraji.* Though a monk, circumstances had made him run his jewellery business at a shop in Bombay's Zaveri Bazaar. However, he had laid down for himself a code of business, based on complete honesty and truthfulness, from which he never deviated. Chandrika narrates two anecdotes that illustrate his moral character, which helped shape Gandhi's satyagraha philosophy in South Africa.

Once an Arab trader sold Rajchandraji some pearls. However, the trader returned the next day saying that he had been scolded by his brother for selling the gems at a low price. Rajchandraji immediately took the packet he had purchased and returned it to the Arab trader, saying: 'For a deal to be successful both parties should be happy.'

On another occasion, a contract had been signed between Rajchandraji and another businessman requiring the latter to supply some gems for an agreed price. However, just before the contract could be executed, the price of gems rose sharply. The businessman was at his wit's end, knowing that he would have to incur a huge loss, but also knowing that the contract was binding. When Rajchandraji went over to meet him, the worried businessman promised to honour his commitment, but begged for time. Upon knowing the reason for the delay in the supply of gems, Rajchandraji took out the contract and tore it up. 'If this piece of paper is the cause of your loss of peace, it is not worth the ink it is written with. The supreme duty of human beings is to help each other in times of trouble.' When the businessman, both amazed and relieved, thanked him with tears in his eyes, Rajchandraji simply said: 'I drink milk, I do not draw blood.'

Gandhi had interacted with Rajchandraji when he was a jobless lawyer in Bombay. He had just returned from England after completing his studies in 1891. 'There was no business or other selfish tie that bound him to me, and yet I enjoyed the closest association with him', Gandhi writes. 'I was but a briefless barrister then, and yet whenever I saw him he would engage me in conversation of a seriously religious nature. Though I was then groping and could not be said to have any serious interest in religious discussion, still I found his talk of absorbing interest… deep down in me was the conviction that he would never willingly lead me astray and would always confide to me his innermost thoughts. In my moments of spiritual crisis, therefore, he was my refuge'.

When Gandhi's inner quest intensified in South Africa, where he initially experienced a spiritual crisis on several occasions, he again found guidance from his correspondence with Rajchandraji. Once he put no less than twenty-seven searching questions in a letter to his spiritual mentor, whose comprehensive answers helped mould his views on religion, especially on Hinduism. We reproduce here only two such questions and answers from that correspondence, as they represent a fine combination of reason and faith.

Gandhi: When it is said that dharma or religion is the highest thing, then is there any harm in asking reasons for its superiority and validity?

Srimad Rajchandraji: To declare the superiority and validity of the teachings of dharma without considering the reasons thereof is undoubtedly very harmful. For it will give rise to propagation of all sorts of things good or bad, meritorious and not so meritorious. The validity or non-validity, superiority or otherwise of a thing can only be established by cogent and potent reasons. I think only those teachings of dharma are best which prove themselves to be strong and sound in destroying the cycle of births and deaths; and in realising this pure and peaceful state of life.

Gandhi: What do you think about the final fate of the universe?

Srimad Rajchandraji: It is unbelievable to me that one day the universe will be empty of souls and the drama of life will come to an end due to their liberation. To me the universe is a running concern. It is a system of double traffic of birth and death, of integration and disintegration. It will continue to be what it is today. Change is its law. The old order is being replaced by the new. If it grows in one part, it decays in the other. If we make a close study of this problem we would come to the conclusion that total destruction or '*pralaya*' of this universe is impossible. The universe, of course, does not mean this earth alone.

Gandhi's tribute to his spiritual guide would be incomplete without these lines: 'I have drunk to my heart's content the nectar of religion that was offered to me by Srimadji. He hated the spread of irreligion in the name of religion and he condemned lies, hypocrisy and such other vices, which were getting a free hand in his time. He considered the whole world as his relative and his sympathy extended to all living beings of all ages'.[6]

What Gandhi had learnt from Rajchandraji was subsequently reinforced by Ruskin's influence on him. *Unto This Last* by Ruskin (1819–1900), Gandhi tells us in his autobiography, had 'a magic spell' on him. Reading it, during a train journey from Johannesburg to Durban, made him 'determined to change my life in accordance with the ideals of the book'. In 1908, Gandhi paraphrased this book into Gujarati, entitling it *Sarvodaya* – 'The good of the individual is contained in the good of all'. The concept of *sarvodaya,* which is completely antithetical to the capitalist principle of 'each one for himself', thus became one of Gandhi's many unique contributions to the lexicon of progressive politics.

His conviction that real swaraj could not be attained either through violence or by adopting the Western model of industrialisation first appeared in *Sarvodaya,* which was a curtain-raiser for *Hind Swaraj.* 'We in India are very much given nowadays to an imitation of the West', Gandhi writes in this book. 'It is necessary to imitate the virtues of the West, but there is no doubt that Western standards are often bad, and every one will agree that we should shun all evil things...The exclusive search for physical and economic well-being prosecuted in disregard of morality is contrary to divine law'.

In his paraphrase of *Unto This Last,* Gandhi is quite blunt in warning Indians that although 'British rule in India is an evil, let us not run away with the idea that all will be well when the British quit India... India was once a golden land, because Indians then had hearts of gold. The land is still the same but it is a desert because we are corrupt'. If we look at the state of politics, governance, business and other professions in India today, we realise that Gandhi's warning had a prophetic ring to it. Along with the warning came the sage advice: 'India can become a land of gold again only if the base metal of our present national character is transmuted into gold. The philosopher's stone which can effect this transformation is a little word of two syllables – *Satya* (Truth)'.[7]

It is a marker of Gandhi's catholicity that even though he denounced the materialistic civilisation of the West, he was at his transparent best in proclaiming his love for the Western people and his admiration for the positive influences from alien lands and cultures. When his critics misinterpreted his message in *Hind Swaraj* as a tirade against the British people, he declared:

> By the rejection of Western civilisation I never meant, nor do I mean today, shunning everything English or hating the British. I revere the *Bible*. Christ's Sermon on the Mount fills me with bliss even today. Its sweet verses have even today the power to quench my agony of the soul. I can still read with love some of the writings of Carlyle and Ruskin. Even now the tunes and the verses of many English hymns are like *amrit* (nectar) to me.[8]

While in South Africa, Gandhi was also influenced by the pacifist philosophy of Leo Tolstoy (1828–1910), the great Russian writer. Indeed, 'Tolstoy Farm' was the name he gave to the second commune he established in South Africa (near Johannesburg) in 1910. The correspondence between the two – one already a legend in the world of literature and nearing the end of his life, and the other a still-unknown Indian at the beginning of his experiments with Truth in an alien land – is a telling proof of how great minds in history have transcended the limitations of geography and nationality to enter into a dialogue in service of humanity. Gandhi himself translated Tolstoy's famous *Letter to a Hindoo* into Gujarati and published it in his newspaper *Indian Opinion,* which he had founded in South Africa in 1903 as a platform to awaken the dispirited community of Indian immigrants, most of whom were indentured workers. Tolstoy's book *The Kingdom of God is Within You* 'overwhelmed' him, prompting him to write: 'At that time, I was skeptical about many things and sometimes entertained atheistic ideas. When I went to England, I was a votary of violence, I had faith in it and none in nonviolence. After I read this book, that lack of faith in nonviolence vanished'. The book strengthened his conviction that the 'law of love', with its superiority over the habit of hatred, can bring about heart-transformation in the perpetrators of violence and oppression. It also enabled Gandhi to understand the essential nature of Christianity, and to realise how it resonated with his understanding of Hinduism.

Another common feature in Hinduism and Christianity, which he discovered through his reading of Tolstoy, is the principle of 'Bread Labour' – 'the divine law that man must earn his bread by laboring with his own hands'. Gandhi's creative integration of this principle, which is also stated in the *Bhagavad Gita*, into his economic philosophy provides a highly useful guidance for poverty-alleviation strategies in our times.

Upon receiving a copy of *Hind Swaraj*, which Gandhi had sent him, Tolstoy wrote in his diary on 20 April 1910: 'In the evening read Gandhi about civilisation; wonderful'. The next day he wrote again: 'Read book about Gandhi. Very important. I should write to him'.[9] Then, in a letter on 8 May 1910, he said: 'Dear friend, I read your book with great interest because I think the question you treat in it: the passive resistance – is a question of the greatest importance, not only for India but for the whole humanity'.[10] This was one of the last letters that the ailing and tormented writer wrote before he died in November 1910.

In a tribute Gandhi later paid to Tolstoy, he called him his teacher. 'Russia gave me in Tolstoy, a teacher who furnished a reasoned basis for my nonviolence. He blessed my movement in South Africa when it was still in its infancy and of whose wonderful possibilities I had yet to learn. It was he who had prophesied in his letter to me that I was leading a movement which was destined to bring a message of hope to the downtrodden people of the earth'.[11]

Socrates was another of Gandhi's heroes. Before *Sarvodaya* was written, Gandhi had published in 1906 a summary of Plato's *The Apology of Socrates* in his newspaper *Indian Opinion*. (*The year 1906 is highly significant in Gandhi's life, as we shall see in Chapter 24.*) From this greatest of Greek philosophers, he learnt fearlessness and readiness to sacrifice one's life for one's ideals and convictions. Like Socrates, he came to believe that the best way to live was to pursue one's own self-development rather than seek fame and material wealth. Socrates, who famously said: 'I know that I know nothing', had influenced Gandhi's own humility, which was to so impress the world in later years. 'Socrates in Plato's *Apology* gives us some idea of our duty as men', he wrote. 'And he was as good as his word. I feel that Ruskin's *Unto This Last* is an expansion of Socrates' ideas'.

What a radiant constellation of stars in the sky of human thought had destiny configured for the South African Gandhi to illumine the path as well as the true meaning of India's swaraj!

Destiny had also willed South Africa to be the arena for a battle for justice, in which Gandhi would discover an altogether new type of weapon – a nonviolent weapon which he called satyagraha. The modern world had seen nothing like it before. It would see him wield that weapon in many an epic battle when he returned to India. The next two chapters will elucidate the meaning of satyagraha, how it was discovered, and also why both its meaning and its discovery are significant for today's world.

'Phoenix Never Dies!'

Before we leave the South African Gandhi behind, I must recall my own unforgettable visit to this beautiful country as a member of Prime Minister Atal Bihari Vajpayee's delegation to the Commonwealth Summit in 1999. I took the first opportunity to go to the Phoenix Settlement, near Durban, which Gandhi had set up in 1904. It was a deeply distressing experience. Nothing was left there of what was the first of the four ashrams that Gandhi established in his lifetime. Everything was in ruins. The home in which Gandhi lived had disappeared, except the plinth. The building that published *Indian Opinion*, the first of the many journals he founded, had been reduced to bare walls. What is worse, the entire place had become a haven for petty criminals. My guide too advised me not to stay on for long. I wondered: Why shouldn't the governments of India and South Africa collaborate to suitably preserve the Phoenix Settlement, and also the Tolstoy Farm near Johannesburg, as memorials depicting the two transformational decades in Gandhi's life?

In a letter to Maganlal Gandhi, his nephew, on 24 November 1909, Gandhi had explained why he had named his first ashram 'Phoenix

Settlement': 'Its significance, as the legend goes, is that the bird phoenix comes back to life again and again from its own ashes, ie., it never dies. ...We believe that the aims of Phoenix will not vanish even when we are turned to dust'. Happily, the one hundred acre Phoenix Settlement, located about twenty-five kilometres from Durban, has now been rebuilt as a Gandhi memorial. It was reopened on 27 February 2000 by Thabo Mbeki, then president of South Africa.

My visit to Durban was made unforgettable by the opportunity I had to meet two great South African personalities. One is Andrew Verster, a noted white artist, a deeply sensitive human being, and a great devotee of Gandhi. He was instrumental in organising a major exhibition called AfriKhadi, both in South Africa and in India, a few years ago. Andrew took me to meet the legendary Fatima Meer (1928-2010), a stalwart of the anti-apartheid struggle, a close comrade of Nelson Mandela and also the author of his acclaimed biography *Higher than Hope*. Her father, Moosa Meer, a migrant from Gujarat, was a trusted associate of both Gandhi and Mandela.

Fatima Meer, who was jailed several times by the apartheid government, began her political career at the age of seventeen when she was a high school student. The white racist regime had enacted a segregation law which restricted the Indian community's economic and residential rights to specific areas in the country. The community resisted by organising satyagraha, the first since Gandhi left South Africa. She made tireless efforts to research, and popularise, Gandhi's life and message. Her book *Apprenticeship of a Mahatma,* which I have referred to earlier, was banned twice by the apartheid regime. She was closely involved in the activities of the Phoenix Settlement. She established a school and a crafts training centre at the ashram. Both were closed by the apartheid government. She played a prominent role in promoting understanding between Hindu, Muslim, and Christian communities, and also between the native African and Indian communities.

The precious gift that Fatima Meer presented to me at her home in Durban – *South African Gandhi (1893-1914),* a 1200-page book edited by her – has preserved for me my memories of this courageous and gentle-faced fighter for human freedom and dignity.

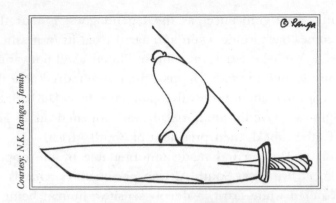

'One step at a time is enough for me': *I know the path. It is straight and narrow. It is like the edge of a sword. I rejoice to walk on it. I weep when I slip. God's word is: "He who strives never perishes". Though from my weakness I fail a thousand times, I will not lose faith, but hope that I shall see the Light when the flesh has been brought under perfect subjection, as some day it must'.*

4

SATYAGRAHA
A Unified Theory of Truth Linking
Science, Religion and Social Change

—◦❖◇❖❖◇❖◦—

We who follow Gandhi Maharaj's lead
*   have one thing in common among us:*
We never fill our purses with spoils from the poor
*   nor bend our knees to the rich.*
When they come bullying us
*   with raised fist and menacing stick,*
We smile to them, and say:
*   your reddening stare may startle babies out of sleep*
*   but how frighten those who refuse to fear?*

— Rabindranath Tagore (1861-1941)
This poem, 'Gandhi Maharaj', was written in February 1940.

SATYAGRAHA WAS SOUTH AFRICA'S GIFT TO INDIA AND THE world. For it was here that Gandhi coined the term that became synonymous with his philosophy and praxis. It was also here that he conducted his early experiments in satyagraha, before applying its bold colours on the vaster canvas of India's freedom struggle.

What is remarkable about Gandhi – and this can be regarded as one of his unique achievements when his life is compared with that of other great personalities in the modern era – is that his philosophy of satyagraha synthesised the concept of truth in three seemingly disparate areas of human life: science, religion and social change. Understanding this is crucial to knowing why Gandhi represents the hope for a new global civilisation that will integrate the power of technology with the wisdom of progressive traditions in world history.

Modern civilisation has habituated us into thinking that science and religion are two separate, independent and even mutually conflicting, human endeavours. Albert Einstein says:

> Science and religion, which have so much in common, often seem to be at 'war' with one another these days. For many science has become their religion while others try to conform science to their religion. Both 'heartless science' and 'mindless religion' miss truths about the nature of our existence in the universe. Naturally each side is quick to point out the 'errors and flaws' that are 'obvious' in the other's position.

Similarly, the relationship between religion and social change has also followed a bumpy road. Those committed to progressive social change have often found in organised religion not an ally but, indeed, an obstacle. In extreme cases, some proponents of social change have rejected religion altogether and embraced atheism. As Gandhi confesses in his autobiography, he too at one point in his life in England was tempted by the idea of atheism. Even those who do not discard religion entirely argue that religion should be kept out of social transformative activities, especially politics.

The third side of the triangle – the relationship between science and social change – has also remained weak and tenuous. The spectacular advances in science have not contributed to a concomitant improvement in the quality of life the world over. The principal reason for this is the fact that, although science has enormous potential to promote human welfare, it has become a handmaiden of an economic and governance system in which private profit takes precedence over public welfare, and short-term goals push long-term good of the society and ecology to the back seat. Even policies and schemes with lofty objectives stumble in the area of implementation because of the lack of political will to remove the inertia and inefficiency in the delivery mechanism.

A simple and stark example would suffice to drive home this point. Breathtaking advances have taken place in the science of ophthalmology, India itself having emerged as a nation capable of providing hi-tech eye care. Yet, as many as fifteen million Indians suffer from blindness. Most of them could have been prevented from turning blind if only the National Blindness Control Programme, launched as far back as in 1976, had been implemented effectively on a war-footing with the backing of the requisite political will.

One of the little understood achievements of Gandhi is how he became relevant to all three sides of the triangle of science, religion and social change. His success lay in the fact that he drew all three sides with the same ink of Truth. Through satyagraha, he developed what may be called a unified theory and praxis of Truth. After all, the very title of his life story is his 'Experiments with Truth'. Nothing was excluded from these experiments – be it his struggle against the British colonial rule or the evil of untouchability in Hindu society; be it his advocacy of women's empowerment or of scientific research into sanitation, public health, education and village industries for holistic human development; be it his campaign for animal care or his campaign against wars and nuclear weapons. Truth was his guiding force even in his mission to promote inter-faith harmony and in his passion to demonstrate the power of love to foster universal brotherhood.

In other words, Truth was indivisible and all-encompassing for him. And he repeatedly drove home this message to his followers:

> Generally speaking, observation of the law of Truth is understood merely to mean that we must speak the truth. But we in the Ashram should understand the word *Satya* or Truth in a much wider sense. There should be Truth in thought, Truth in speech, and Truth in action. To the man who has realised this Truth in its fullness, nothing else remains to be known, because all knowledge is necessarily included in it. What is not included in it is not Truth, and so not true knowledge; and there can

be no inward peace without true knowledge. If we once learn how to apply this never-failing test of Truth, we will at once be able to find out what is worth doing.[1]

In the field of religion, Gandhi emphasised that God, a concept that for him was inter-changeable with Truth, did not discriminate among His children. 'It is impossible that God, who is the God of Justice, could have made the distinctions that men observe today in the name of religion'.[2] It is a 'travesty', he said, 'of true religion to consider one's own religion as superior and other's as inferior'.[3] 'God, who is the embodiment of Truth and Right and Justice, can never have sanctioned a religion or practice which regards one-fifth of our vast population as untouchables'.[4]

Since science, by definition, must accept truth wherever it is found, Gandhi brought to bear a similar scientific approach upon his religious quest. 'My religion enables me, obliges me to imbibe all that is good in all the great religions of the earth'.[5] Since there is no finality or perfection in science, the search for truth being a never-ending process, he underscored that no religion could claim to be perfect. 'Religion of our conception, thus imperfect, is always subject to a process of evolution and re-interpretation'.[6]

Just as no scientist and no branch of science can claim to have found the final truth, no prophet and no faith, according to Gandhi, can be regarded as the knower of the complete truth about God. 'For me', he wrote, 'truth is the sovereign principle, which included numerous other principles. This truth is not only truthfulness in word, but truthfulness in thought also, and not only the relative truth of our conception, but the Absolute Truth, the Eternal Principle, that is God. There are innumerable definitions of God, because His manifestations are innumerable. They overwhelm me with wonder and awe and for a moment stun me. But I worship God as Truth only. I have not yet found Him, but I am seeking after Him. I am prepared to sacrifice the things dearest to me in pursuit of this quest. Even if the sacrifice demanded be my very life, I hope I may be prepared to give it. But as long as I have not realised this Absolute Truth, so long must I hold by the relative truth as I have conceived it'.[7]

From this concept of men being capable of knowing only relative truths followed another important component of Gandhian philosophy: his belief that multiplicity of religions is both natural and inevitable. 'Does not God himself appear to different individuals in different aspects?' he asked. 'Yet we know that He is one. But Truth is the right designation of God. Hence there is nothing wrong in every man following Truth according to his lights. Indeed it is his duty to do so. Then if there is a mistake on the part of any one so following Truth, it will be automatically set right'. We can see here how Gandhi applies the self-corrective principle of science to the quest for God. 'In selfless search for Truth nobody can lose his bearings for long. Directly he takes to the wrong path he stumbles, and is thus redirected to the right path'.[8]

Belief in the relativity of truth instilled in Gandhi respect for, and tolerance of, diverse viewpoints, including those that were critical of him. His exposition of this principle is masterly. 'It has been my experience that I am always true from my point of view, and am often wrong from the point of view of my honest critics. I know that we are both right from our respective points of view. And this knowledge saves me from attributing motives to my opponents or critics. The seven blind men who gave seven different descriptions of the elephant were all right from their respective points of view, and wrong from the point of view of one another, and right and wrong from the point of view of the man who knew the elephant. I very much like this doctrine of the manyness of reality. It is this doctrine that has taught me to judge a Musalman from his standpoint and a Christian from his. Formerly I used to resent the ignorance of my opponents. Today I can love them because I am gifted with the eye to see myself as others see me and vice versa. I want to take the whole world in the embrace of my love'.[9]

Scientific truth is not the monopoly of any person, community or country. Similarly, Gandhi believed that persons embodying moral greatness and ideal conduct were not the monopoly of any particular faith. They belong to all faiths and all are equally worthy of veneration and emulation. For him, this was a cardinal truth of religion. 'In this connection', he wrote, 'it would be well to ponder over the lives and examples of Harishchandra, Prahlad, Ramachandra, Imam Hasan and Imam Husain, the Christian saints, etc.'[10]

Gandhi's advocacy of nonviolence in matters of religion also contained a scientific logic. Arguments and counter-arguments within or between different faiths, he wrote, 'should exclude the use of violence because man is not capable of knowing the absolute truth and, therefore, not competent to punish'.[11]

One of the most popular Gandhian resources on the Internet is an audio record of his thoughts on God. During Gandhi's stay in England in 1931, the Columbia Gramophone Company requested him to make a record for them. He said that he could not speak on politics but, if they wanted, they could record his thoughts on spiritual matters. The six-minute audio-clip on YouTube presents Gandhi at his self-reflective best.[12]

There is an indefinable mysterious power that pervades everything. I feel it though I do not see it. It is this unseen power which makes itself felt and yet defies all proof, because it is so unlike all that I perceive through my senses. It transcends the senses. But it is possible to reason out the existence of God to a limited extent. Even in ordinary affairs we know that people do not know who rules or why and how He rules and yet they know that there is a power that certainly rules.

In my tour last year in Mysore I met many poor villagers and I found upon inquiry that they did not know who ruled Mysore. They simply said some God ruled it. If the knowledge of these poor people was so limited about their ruler, I, who am infinitely lesser in respect to God than they to their ruler, need not be surprised if I do not realise the presence of God – the King of Kings. Nevertheless, I do feel, as the poor villagers felt about Mysore, that there is orderliness in the universe, there is an unalterable law governing everything and every being that exists or lives. It is not a blind law, for no blind law can govern the conduct of living beings and thanks to the marvelous researches of Sir J.C. Bose it can now be proved that even matter is life.

Thoughts on God: *Gandhi at the studio of the Columbia Broadcasting Service (CBS) in London where he recorded, on 13 September 1931, his only radio message to the people of USA.*

That law then which governs all life is God. Law and the law-giver are one. I may not deny the law or the law-giver because I know so little about it or Him. Just as my denial or ignorance of the existence of an earthly power will avail me nothing even so my denial of God and His law will not liberate me from its operation, whereas humble and mute acceptance of divine authority makes life's journey easier even as the acceptance of earthly rule makes life under it easier. I do dimly perceive that whilst everything around me is ever changing, ever dying there is underlying all that change a living power that is changeless, that holds all together, that creates, dissolves and recreates. That informing power of spirit is God, and since nothing else that I see merely through the senses can or will persist, He alone is.

And is this power benevolent or malevolent? I see It as purely benevolent, for I can see that in the midst of death life persists, in the midst of untruth truth persists, in the midst of darkness light persists. Hence I gather that God is life, truth, light. He is love. He is the supreme Good.

But He is no God who merely satisfies the intellect, if He ever does. God to be God must rule the heart and transform it. He must express himself in every smallest act of His votary. This can only be done through a definite realisation, more real than the five senses can ever produce. Sense perceptions can be and often are false and deceptive, however real they may appear to us. Where there is realisation outside the senses it is infallible. It is proved not by extraneous evidence but in the transformed conduct and character of those who have felt the real presence of God within. Such testimony is to be found in the experiences of an unbroken line of prophets and sages in all countries and climes. To reject this evidence is to deny oneself. This realisation is preceded by an immovable faith. He who would in his own person test the fact of God's presence can do so by a living faith and since faith itself cannot be proved by extraneous evidence the safest course is to believe in the moral government of the world and therefore in the supremacy of the moral law, the law of truth and love. Exercise of faith will be the safest where there is a clear determination summarily to reject all that is contrary to truth and love. I confess that I have no argument to convince through reason. Faith transcends reason. All that I can advise is not to attempt the impossible.

Gandhi's thoughts on God were never metaphysical in nature, unconcerned about the realities in society and unrelated to the imperative need to change them for the better. God's law meant to him, above all, justice and equality. Therefore, in the field of social change, he brought to bear the zeal of a religious reformer, determined to put into practice the truth of human equality. He declared a war on untouchability and made it an integral part of his social, as well as political, campaign. In 1932, he founded the Harijan Sevak Sangh, a voluntary organisation committed to the eradication of untouchability in Hindu society. Within a few years its branches were established in almost every town in India, and they attracted tens of thousands of volunteers. It popularised a new identity for 'untouchables' – as Harijan or Children of God. Being Children of God, those belonging, due to certain historical circumstances, to the lowest strata of society could not be inferior to those born in the so-called upper castes. He further affirmed that this unjust stratification was an aberration of history, and not sanctioned by the basic tenets of Hinduism.

In 1933, he founded a new journal named *Harijan*. It became the vehicle for popularising his bold reformist agenda. There are scores of instances of his support to the efforts of Hindu social reformers in their struggle for equal rights and status for 'untouchables'. In the historic temple town of Madurai in Tamil Nadu, for example, he wholeheartedly backed the entry of untouchables into Hindu temples, which was opposed by some upper-caste people. When the Congress party assumed power in 1936 in Madras province under the leadership of C. Rajagopalachari, who was a devout Gandhian, the Mahatma applauded Rajaji (as Rajagopalachari was popularly known) for issuing an ordinance permitting Harijans into all temples. Earlier in 1923, he had travelled to neighbouring Kerala to make common cause with Narayana Guru, a revered saint who was born into a 'lower caste', in the latter's crusade against caste inequality. In Gujarat, his comrade-in-arms was Thakkar Bapa, a widely respected social worker, who strove for the upliftment of tribal people.

Mention must be made here of the serious differences between Gandhi and Dr B.R. Ambedkar on the issue of how to ensure a life of dignity, equality and justice to the depressed classes – untouchables – in the Hindu society. Gandhi favoured a reformist approach. Though radical in its sweep, it was essentially centred on bringing about reforms within the Hindu society. Ambedkar adopted the path of social rebellion, which ultimately saw him renounce Hinduism and embrace Buddhism. The dispute between the two great men came to a head when Ambedkar raised the demand for separate electorates for the untouchables. The demand was supported by the British, whose 'Communal Award' sought to incorporate this provision into the constitution of colonial India. Gandhi strongly opposed Ambedkar's demand on the ground that it would lead to national disintegration and splintering of the Hindu society. He had seen through the 'divide-and-rule' stratagem of the colonial government. He began an indefinite fast at Yerawada Jail in Poona in September 1932, which lasted six days. The outcome of this fast was the Poona Pact[13], which provided for reserved seats for untouchables out of the general or mixed electorates. Incidentally, the same concept of reserved seats was later unanimously carried forward in independent India's Constitution, of which Ambedkar himself was the chief architect.

On 8 May 1933, Gandhi began a fast lasting twenty-one days for self-purification and for making upper-caste Hindus aware of their moral and social responsibility to eradicate untouchability and accept Harijans as their equals.

Two points merit special emphasis here. Firstly, despite his differences with Ambedkar, Gandhi admired him for his spirited espousal of the cause of untouchables, noting that only a person born into the family of untouchables could know the real pain and indignity of this social evil in the Hindu society. The Gandhi-Ambedkar debate is highly instructive for anyone interested in knowing not only the merits of their respective approaches, but also their differing personalities. Secondly, it was Gandhi who suggested to the Congress leaders to induct Ambedkar into the Constituent Assembly and utilise his talent in drafting the constitution of free India. It was also Gandhi who prevailed upon Prime Minister Jawaharlal Nehru to induct Ambedkar into his Cabinet as India's first law minister.

If broadmindedness, total absence of rancour, and genuine sensitivity towards the opponent's viewpoint are the hallmark of a great leader, then Gandhi truly emerges as a Mahatma in his debate with Ambedkar.

Similarly, although Gandhi had some differences with the Rashtriya Swayamsevak Sangh (RSS), a Hindu nationalist organisation which did not agree with his approach to India's independence, he appreciated the RSS for not recognising untouchability or caste hierarchy in its ranks.

Gandhi's belief in the truth of human equality found equally strong articulation and advocacy in another important area of social change: women's empowerment. It was his conviction that God had made women in a superior mould, and assigned to them a nobler mandate. The world would become a better place, he frequently affirmed, if women would only realise their dignity and innate nature, and made full use of their qualities for the progress of humankind. For them to perform this role, the main pre-requisite was to refuse to be slaves of men. In a remarkably candid letter written to Rajkumari Amrit Kaur, one of the many courageous women who dedicated their lives to the Gandhian cause, he wrote: 'Man has delighted in enslaving you and you have proved willing slaves till the slaves and the slave-holders have become one in the crime of degrading humanity. My special function from childhood, you might say, has been to make woman realise her dignity. I was once a slave-holder myself but Ba proved an unwilling slave and thus opened my eyes to my mission'.[14]

Here we see how Gandhi recognised the relevance of satyagraha even in the domain of family relationships. He gives credit to his wife Kasturba for defying his unjust and unreasonable diktats and thereby teaching him a lesson in domestic satyagraha. He soon realised that since women were the most ardent lovers of peace and nonviolence, they were better suited than men to become torch-bearers of truth. 'Women strengthen my belief in swadeshi and satyagraha', he wrote. 'If I could inspire in men devotion as pure as I find in the women, within a year, India would be raised to a height impossible to imagine'.[15]

Apart from truthfulness and commitment to nonviolence, fearlessness was a quality that Gandhi valued the most among fellow satyagrahis. Fearlessness everywhere and in every circumstance in life – *sarvatra bhayavarjana*, is how a daily prayer in his ashram extolled this virtue. He had very high expectations from satyagrahis, as can be seen from the following exhortation.[16]

He (a Satyagrahi) should be able to stand guard at a single spot day and night; he must not fall ill even if he has to bear cold and heat and rain; he must have the strength to go to places of peril, to rush to scenes of fire, and the courage to wander about alone in desolate jungles and haunts of death; he will bear, without a grumble, severe beatings, starvation and worse, and will keep to his post of duty without flinching; he will have the resourcefulness and capacity to plunge into a seemingly impenetrable scene of rioting; he will have the longing and capacity to run with the name of God on his lips to the rescue of men on the top storeys of buildings enveloped in flames; he will have the fearlessness to plunge into a flood in order to rescue people being carried off by it or to jump down a well to save a drowning person.... The substance of it all is that we should cultivate the capacity to run to the people in danger and distress, and to suffer cheerfully any amount of hardship that may be inflicted upon us.

He who understands this fundamental principle will easily be able to frame rules of physical training for satyagrahis. I have a firm belief that the very foundation of this training is faith in God. If that is absent, all the training one may have received is likely to fail at the critical moment.

What was Gandhi's method of training satyagrahis in fearlessness? Good health, physical fitness and capacity to bear hardships were of course essential. However, 'the only weapon of the satyagrahi is God', he wrote, 'by whatsoever name one knows Him. Without Him the satyagrahi is devoid of strength before an opponent armed with monstrous weapons. Most people lie prostrate before physical might. But he who accepts God as the only Protector will remain unbent before the mightiest earthly power'. There is no room, he said, for the satyagrahi to be trained in the use of lethal weapons like the sword or the spear. 'Far more terrible weapons than we have seen are in existence today, and newer ones are being invented every day. Of what fear will a sword rid him who has to cultivate the capacity to overcome all fear – real or imaginary? I have not yet heard of a man having shed all fear by learning sword play. Mahavir and others who imbibed ahimsa did not do so because they knew the use of weapons, but because in spite of the knowledge of their use they shed all fear'.

All religions of the world have extolled the virtue of fearlessness rooted in faith in God. Fear God, and none else need you fear – this is the teaching of all religions. Hence, 'God-fearing' has become synonymous with 'pious'. Gandhi's philosophy and practice of satyagraha elevates the same teaching from the personal to the public sphere. Work in public life entails enormous risks and challenges, and often brings many hardships. A true revolutionary can face these with equanimity if he makes truth, nonviolence and unselfishness – in short, God – his shield. Gandhi, himself an embodiment of fearlessness, inspired and guided thousands of such revolutionaries during India's freedom struggle.

Gandhi's stay in South Africa says something remarkable about his initial spiritual evolution and holds important lessons for inter-faith engagement in our own times.

He was born into a deeply religious Hindu family. In his native Gujarat, the beliefs and customs of Hindus and Jains are so intricately interwoven that Jainism naturally had a deep impact on his personality. The centrality of ahimsa or nonviolence in his philosophy and life's mission can certainly be traced to the influence of Jainism on him. Since Buddhism is an integral part of the Indian ethos, it too reinforced his belief in nonviolence. Paying tribute to the founder of Sikhism, he said, 'Guru Nanak made no distinction between Hindus and Muslims. For him the whole world was one'.[17]

Gandhi's discovery of the greatness of two other faiths that are an integral part of the Indian civilisation, Islam and Christianity, took place in South Africa. His study of the *Bible*, and his intense interactions with Christian priests, convinced him of the virtue of social service as the central theme of religious practice. He saw it as a form of active love of humanity, something which was given less importance in the religious practice of Hindus. Nonviolence in the Hindu way of life was mostly passive love; it meant not inflicting harm on anybody. From Christianity, he internalised the spirit of serving the needy, and institutionalised it in the working of his ashrams, first in South Africa and later in India.

Gandhi accepted every source of illumination and inspiration with an open and unprejudiced mind, always emphasising the common core of all religions. He writes in his autobiography: 'My young mind tried to unify the teaching of the *Gita*, the Light of Asia (Buddha) and the Sermon on the Mount. That renunciation was the highest form of religion appealed to me greatly'.[18]

From Islam, he internalised another important truth, and incorporated it in his practice of satyagraha, as we shall see in the next chapter.

11 September 1906: *Birth of Gandhi's satyagraha movement in South Africa, inspired, partly, by the Islamic concept of 'Greater jihad'.*

11 September 2001: *Islamist terrorists, misusing the message of jihad, attacked the Twin Towers in New York and other targets in USA.*

5

HOW ISLAM INFLUENCED SATYAGRAHA
Two 9/11s; two different jihads

⇥⚬❖❖❖⚬⇤

Gandhi's uniqueness lies in the fact that he proposes a spiritual solution to the material crisis in which humanity finds itself. He seeks to heal through Truth (Satya) which he identifies as God. Where the social and political scientists focus exclusively on the empirical, the here and now, Gandhi sees the here and hereafter as a continuum...Human relations, he proposes, are based on love and not on the law of supply and demand. Liberal and Marxist economic theory, he states, separate the spiritual from the material and are therefore bound to result in conflict, war and failure. He offers a holistic, healing approach to human communion.

— Fatima Meer, in *The South African Gandhi* (1893-1914), which she edited. She was a renowned South African scholar and anti-apartheid crusader.

I**T IS WELL KNOWN THAT GANDHI'S RESPECT FOR ISLAM WAS AN** important dimension of his universalism. After all, he made Hindu-Muslim unity the mission of his life. What is less well known is that Islam played a pivotal role in the genesis of Gandhi's concept of satyagraha.

I first learnt about this when I visited the office of the Natal Indian Congress in Durban, and the mosque located in front of it. Gandhi had established the Natal Indian Congress in 1894 to fight discrimination against Indians by the white rulers in South Africa. Many of its members were Muslim traders from Gujarat, one of whom was in fact instrumental in bringing lawyer Gandhi to South Africa. The imam of the mosque told me, 'Gandhi used to come to this mosque often to discuss his idea of satyagraha with his Muslim followers.' More startlingly, the imam said, 'Gandhi understood that there is much in common between satyagraha and the Islamic concept of jihad.'

Gandhi has devoted an entire chapter in his book *Satyagraha in South Africa* (first published in 1928) to describe this new nonviolent method of protest, and also the role that Islam played in its advent. The concept came to him like a bolt from the blue during a meeting of the Natal Indian Congress on 11 September 1906. (The date 9/11 is significant for our subsequent discussion on jihad.) The Indian community was agitating against an unjust and discriminatory ordinance promulgated by South Africa's racist government. Every Indian – man, woman and child of eight years and over – had to register and carry a pass, to be produced on demand to a white police officer. Those who failed to do so, were liable to be fined, imprisoned or deported to India. A resolution drafted by Gandhi committed Indians not to submit to the ordinance in the event of its becoming law and be ready to suffer all the penalties flowing from such non-submission. 'I must confess,' Gandhi writes, 'that even I myself had not then understood all the implications of the resolution; nor had I gauged all the possible conclusions to which they might lead'.

Here is how Fatima Meer, in her book *Apprenticeship of a Mahatma*, describes his speech at this historic meeting, held in a cinema hall in Johannesburg that was overflowing with over 3,000 angry delegates, many of whom were urging violent resistance to the ordinance: 'He took the platform and began to speak. He cast a slow, quiet spell and as he did so, bound Hindus, Muslims and Christians as one within its web. He told them that their goal was not to conquer and dominate, but to realise the universal dignity and God-given equality of men. He told them that they would fight, not with their bodies but with their souls, for soul-force was stronger than any gun and more enduring than any cannon'.

But it is best to listen to Gandhi's own words to know what happened:

Inspired by Mahatma Gandhi: *Nelson Mandela and Fatima Meer, who wrote his widely acclaimed biography* Higher Than Hope.

I fully explained this resolution to the meeting and received a patient hearing. …The resolution was duly proposed, seconded and supported by several speakers, one of whom was Sheth Haji Habib. He was a very old and experienced resident of South Africa and made an impassioned speech. He was deeply moved and went so far as to say that we must pass this resolution with God as witness and must never yield a cowardly submission to such degrading legislation. He then went on solemnly to declare in the name of God that he would never submit to that law, and advised all present to do likewise… I was at once startled and put on my guard. Only then did I fully realise my own responsibility and the responsibility of the community.[1]

What was unique about this resolution? After all, the Indian community had passed many such resolutions before and also amended some of them in the light of further reflection or fresh experience. Quite a few resolutions, though passed unanimously, had not been observed by all concerned. Gandhi explained that amendments in resolutions and failure to observe resolutions on the part of persons who are party to their adoption, are ordinary experiences of public life all the world over. 'But' – and this is where the 9/11 resolution differed fundamentally from the previous ones – 'no one ever imports the name of God into such resolutions'. Gandhi developed this thought further by saying:

> In the abstract there should not be any distinction between a resolution and an oath taken in the name of God. When an intelligent man makes a resolution deliberately he never swerves from it by a hair's breadth. With him his resolution carries as much weight as a declaration made with God as witness does. But the world takes no note of abstract principles and imagines an ordinary resolution and an oath in the name of God to be poles asunder. A man who makes an ordinary resolution is not ashamed of himself when he deviates from it, but a man who violates an oath administered to him in the name of God is not only ashamed of himself, but is also looked upon by society as [a] sinner.

Gandhi was taken aback by Sheth Haji Habib's suggestion of an oath with God as witness. He thought out its possible consequences. His perplexity gave place to enthusiasm because the invocation of the name of God had suddenly triggered a profound and unutterable inner realisation. However, he felt that the people attending the meeting should be told of all the consequences of taking a pledge. He therefore sought the presiding officer's permission to explain to the gathering the implications of Sheth Haji Habib's suggestion. The permission was granted and he rose to address the meeting.

> I wish to explain to this meeting that there is a vast difference between this resolution and every other resolution we have passed up to date and that there is a wide divergence also in the manner of making it. It is a very grave resolution we are making, as our existence in South Africa depends upon our fully observing it. The manner of making the resolution suggested by our friend is as much of a novelty as of a solemnity. I did not come to the meeting with a view to getting the resolution passed in that manner, which redounds to the credit of Sheth Haji Habib as well as it lays a burden of responsibility upon

him. I tender my congratulations to him. I deeply appreciate his suggestion, but if you adopt it you too will share his responsibility. You must understand what is this responsibility, and as an adviser and servant of the community, it is my duty fully to explain it to you.

We all believe in one and the same God, the difference of nomenclature in Hinduism and Islam notwithstanding. To pledge ourselves or to take an oath in the name of that God or with Him as witness is not something to be trifled with. If having taken such an oath we violate our pledge we are guilty before God and man. Personally I hold that a man, who deliberately and intelligently takes a pledge and then breaks it, forfeits his manhood. And just as a copper coin treated with mercury not only becomes valueless when detected but also makes its owner liable to punishment, in the same way a man who lightly pledges his word and then breaks it, becomes a man of straw and fits himself for punishment here as well as hereafter. Sheth Haji Habib is proposing to administer an oath of a very serious character. There is no one in this meeting who can be classed as an infant or as wanting in understanding. You are all well advanced in age and have seen the world; many of you are delegates and have discharged responsibilities in a greater or lesser measure. No one present, therefore, can ever hope to excuse himself by saying that he did not know what he was about when he took the oath.

I know that pledges and vows are, and should be, taken on rare occasions. A man who takes a vow every now and then is sure to stumble...But every one of us must think out for himself if he has the will and the ability to pledge himself. Resolutions of this nature cannot be passed by a majority vote. Only those who take a pledge can be bound by it. This pledge must not be taken with a view to produce an effect on outsiders. ...Everyone must only search his own heart, and if the inner voice assures him that he has the requisite strength to carry him through, then only should he pledge himself and then only will his pledge bear fruit.

Never one to give an advice to others that he did not follow himself, Gandhi then turned to his own personal responsibility in adhering to the pledge.

> If I am warning you of the risks attendant upon the pledge, I am fully conscious of my responsibility in the matter. It is possible that a majority of those present here may take the pledge in a fit of enthusiasm or indignation but may weaken under the ordeal, and only a handful may be left to face the final test. Even then there is only one course open to someone like me, to die but not to submit to the law. It is quite unlikely but even if every one else flinched leaving me alone to face the music, I am confident that I would never violate my pledge...[2]

I have given this long excerpt here because it clearly explains how Gandhi found a new spiritual basis for his social and political activity. If God is accepted as the supreme witness and judge of one's actions, then there is no scope for deviation from an oath taken in God's name. The seed of this thought had been planted in him in his early childhood. His mother had familiarised him with Sant Tulsidas' *Ramcharitmanas*[3], in which a widely popular line proclaims: *Raghukul reet sada chali aayi, pran jaye par vachan na jaayi.* (A promise once given cannot be broken even if it entails sacrificing one's life. Such was the code of life in the clan of Lord Rama, and it has continued to guide society ever since.)

Gandhi further narrates in the book *Satyagraha in South Africa* that he struggled a lot to search for one word that would embody the truth that he had discovered and best describe its meaning to the common people. Maganlal Gandhi, his close confidante, suggested the word *sadagraha*, which means 'good conduct'. *Sat* in Sanskrit means not only 'good' but also 'truth'. Gandhi, who regarded truth to be a wider and more demanding concept than 'goodness', therefore coined the word 'satyagraha'.

Satyagraha literally means 'insistence for truth'. In the light of the above excerpt, it can also be translated as 'clinging to truth'. Since truth and God were synonymous for Gandhi ('Nothing so completely describes my God as Truth'), satyagraha means following a way of life that holds steadfastly to God. A true satyagrahi, therefore, is one who dedicates his life to God.

Gandhi's genius lies in the fact that satyagraha respects atheism and appeals even to atheists. 'Denial of God we have known,' he writes. 'Denial of Truth we have not known. The most ignorant among mankind have some Truth in them. We are all sparks of Truth. The sum-total of these sparks is indescribable, as yet unknown Truth, which is God. I am being daily led nearer to It by constant prayer'.[4] Thus, by postulating that Truth is God, Gandhi accomplished something remarkable – he desectarianised God. This is why people of all faiths, and also atheists, began to respect him.

A devout Muslim's invoking of God as witness in a struggle against injustice prompted Gandhi to unveil his concept of satyagraha. But is there a convergence between satyagraha and jihad? There is. In his preface to *Satyagraha in South Africa,* Gandhi himself describes satyagraha as 'dharma-yuddha', the pure translation of which is not 'religious war' but 'war for righteousness'. Satyagraha is a 'war' in which there is no killing or violence; rather, the individual battles within himself for self-purification, so that there is no trace of selfishness, cunning, untruth, evil or fear in him. 'A *dharma-yuddha*', writes Gandhi, 'can be waged only in the name of God, and it is only when the Satyagrahi feels quite helpless, is apparently on his last legs and finds utter darkness all around him, that God comes to his rescue'.

In Islam, jihad means 'dharma-yuddha'. It is of two types: 'Greater jihad' (*jihad-e-akbar*) and the 'Lesser jihad' (*jihad-e-asghar*). 'Greater jihad' means nearly the same as satyagraha, for it calls for a fight against one's own inner impurities like selfishness, greed and egoism. 'Lesser jihad' means to fight with the sword, which the *Quran* sanctions in the rarest of rare cases. All moderate interpreters of Islam underscore that 'jihad' is misused by fundamentalists and terrorists to kill innocent people.

And herein lies the contrast between the two 9/11s. Most people in the world associate September 11 with the horrific terrorist attack at four different targets in the United States on that fateful day in 2001. Nearly 3,000 innocent people perished in those attacks, which were carried out by men motivated by a perversely distorted interpretation of jihad.

However, there was another, earlier, 9/11, in 1906, when nearly 3,000 people of Indian origin congregated in the old Empire Theater in Johannesburg. They were protesting against an unjust law sought to be introduced by the racist government in South Africa. As we have described above, it was at this meeting that Gandhi, a young lawyer-leader of the Indian community, had his first encounter with positive jihad, which he later developed into a philosophy and strategy of satyagraha.

We thus see that diverse influences from around the world acted upon Gandhi in South Africa and transformed him into a Mahatma. By the time he returned to his motherland in January 1915, he had fully armed himself with the revolutionary thought of satya and ahimsa for India's, and Indians', swaraj. In scientific terminology, it can be said that he had found all the basic concepts of his science in South Africa, and also successfully conducted 'proof-of-concept' experiments in the laboratory of life and struggle in that country. Now the time had come for application of these concepts on a vaster scale for a far more ambitious goal – securing swaraj for his motherland. Shortly after his arrival in India, his science found for itself a revolutionary tool of application in the form of the spinning wheel.

PART TWO

ROMANCE
WITH
SCIENCE

Mahatma, the Innovator: *In response to Gandhi's appeal for technological innovation, this improved version of the spinning wheel was built at Kirloskarwadi, Maharashtra, by charkha specialist Ganesh Bhaskar Kale (right) and placed at the Sevagram Ashram.*

The Poet, the Saint and their illuminating debate on technology: *Both Rabindranath Tagore and Gandhi were world-citizens, stars in a night sky that showed the troubled humanity the path to a better future.*

6

A 'THOUGHT REVOLUTION'
Technology for a New Civilisation

⤛⋆◈⋆⤜

We need some quite new concept of reality, some revolutionary upheaval in past habits of thought...this is the concept made increasingly explicit by new methods and tools of scientific research, of the entirely inescapable physical interconnectedness of the planet which the human race must share if it is to survive...We have forgotten to be good guests, how to walk lightly on the earth as its other creatures do.

— Barbara Ward, (1914-81), a British economist and an early advocate of sustainable development. She is the author of *Spaceship Earth* and is credited with having coined the term. She also co-authored (with Rene Dubos) *Only One Earth* for the landmark 1972 UN Conference on the Human Environment in Stockholm.

WHY DID GANDHI ZERO IN ON CHARKHA AS HIS TOOL FOR India's swaraj when he returned from South Africa? The choice was dictated by two factors, one objective and the other subjective. The objective factor was the wrenching poverty in most of the 7,50,000 villages of British India. The subjective factor was Gandhi's own genius of symbolism, the art of iconifying the essential message of a mass movement. Soon after his return from South Africa, Gandhi – not yet a leader with mass popularity and still wearing the traditional Kathiawadi attire of long dhoti, round-necked tunic and turban, as against the shirtless half-dhoti that he switched to in 1921 – undertook a nationwide tour to get a first-hand feel of India. He was shocked to see the extent of pauperisation of India's villages and hamlets by colonial exploitation. What he saw convinced him that the road to India's freedom had also to be the road to the rural population's freedom from poverty and unemployment. Furthermore, it had to be a road on which millions of people belonging to different castes and communities in India's diverse and divided society could find the motivation to travel together. Additionally, it also had to be a road whose destination was not merely freedom, but swaraj in the sense in which he had propounded it in *Hind Swaraj* – not just political independence from British rule but India's civilisational renaissance, with each individual's moral elevation.

The tool or the machine that Gandhi was looking for had to satisfy all these three criteria, and more. It had to be inexpensive enough to be within the reach of the multitudes, simple enough to be used by one and all, and familiar enough to be revived from the collective memory of a past when its universal use was woven into India's prosperity, social structure and heritage of arts and aesthetics. Above all, the machine had to convey the Mahatma's message of nonviolence. It had to be the 'weapon' that unarmed Indians could use to defeat the then mightiest power on earth, and thus broadcast to the whole world that nonviolence was stronger than violence. In this sense, the machine and its product had to have a moral message for the entire world and not just for India.

The charkha and its product, khadi, fulfilled all these criteria.

The word 'charkha' is derived from the Sanskrit word 'chakra', which has myriad meanings – mathematical (circle), physical (disc or wheel), metaphorical (Lord Krishna's *Sudarshan Chakra*, which is a protector of good from evil), and mystical (centres of subtle energy in the human body which are correlated to the energy of constellations in the universe). Gandhi's charkha carried all these meanings, even though, it was, outwardly, nothing more than an ultra-simple machine.

In the Gandhian vision, a judgment on machinery cannot be separated from the consequences that machinery produces – the means are inextricably linked to the end. Many scientists, technology creators, businessmen and academicians of our time would stoutly counter this proposition. They would argue, instead, that technology is value-neutral and consequence-neutral. Their premise contains a strange paradox. On the one hand, they take great pride in pointing out that the distinctive hallmark of the twenty-first century is the emergence of a technology-driven civilisation with an ever-widening global footprint. However, on the other hand, they contend that technology and technology creators should be kept out of any normative evaluation of this civilisation!

In contrast, Gandhi found it unthinkable to accept any machine or its product without reference to how it would promote nonviolence, world peace, global brotherhood, human welfare, and man's knowledge about his place and purpose in the universe. Consider how he defines the 'khadi spirit'. 'It means fellow-feeling with every human being on earth. It means a complete renunciation of everything that is likely to harm our fellow creatures'.[1] He repeatedly exhorted both his followers and critics that they would err in understanding his charkha campaign if they ignored what the charkha 'stands for', 'connotes' and 'implies'. For him, the charkha was an outward symbol of satya and and ahimsa. In other words, khadi did not refer merely to another type of cloth that he lobbied for because it was swadeshi or indigenous. Rather, khadi was an advertisement for a new national and world order anchored in human values, and the charkha was a symbol of those technologies that could help usher in the new nonviolent global order.

Let us briefly examine the message of khadi and charkha for India and the world, as the Mahatma propagated it. With tireless repetitiveness, he underscored the charkha's three-pronged – economic, cultural and spiritual – message[2] for India.

The charkha's 'economic message' was that it gave poor villagers a cheap, honest and self-reliant 'supplementary industry' to agriculture to earn a livelihood, thus addressing the problem of unemployment and extreme want. 'Let us realise that the British rule is imposed upon us because British commerce is forced upon us,' he told his countrymen. Therefore, the economic basis of colonialism had to be defeated with such a nonviolent 'weapon' that even the poorest of the poor could wield it in this battle. That 'weapon' was the charkha. 'Lanchashire cloth is a symbol of our helpless exploitation, whereas

Khadi is the symbol of self-help, self-reliance and freedom, not merely of individuals but of the whole nation'.[3] He advised his critics not to scoff at the economic importance of a villager, especially a poor village woman, earning a daily income of '3-6 *annas*' (sixteen annas was one rupee) because even this meagre earning would be a 'veritable boon' to their family in times of distress. Moreover, he reminded them about a major benefit of decentralised production: the spinners would be working at home, and at hours of their choice. Thus, for crores of 'semi-starved' people in India, whose traditional home-spinning and home-weaving industry had been destroyed by the mills of Manchester, the charkha represented at least a small degree of freedom, self-respect and self-sufficiency.

The 'cultural message' of the charkha lay in his appeal to the rich also to take to it, since this act of 'sacrifice' on their part would make the 'spinning wheel a symbol of their identification with the poorest of the soil'. It would re-establish the Indian city-dwellers' emotional bond of caring and cooperation towards villagers. For, without mincing words – and these words have acquired far greater relevance today – he reminded the urban rich that 'the villagers of India have been reduced to pauperism' and 'ground down to dust, not merely under the foreigners' heels but under your heels, under my heels'.[4] Therefore, he told them that mere lip service to the cause of India's freedom would not do. He wanted urban Indians to wear khadi as that would provide a market for the cloth spun by their rural compatriots. More importantly, he wanted the rich to feel that, 'if they (the poor) toiled for us, we spin for their sakes'.[5]

Gandhi also saw a multivalent cultural role for the charkha in strengthening India's national movement. Thus, he hoped that its universal adoption across the country would help in bridging the caste divide, eradicating untouchability, strengthening communal harmony between Hindus and Muslims, and, through all these attendant outcomes, promoting national unity and national pride. Many Muslim followers of the Mahatma took to spinning and wearing khadi. Prominent among them were Khan Abdul Ghaffar Khan, who was also called Frontier Gandhi; Abul Kalam Azad, a leader of nationalist Muslims who later became independent India's first education minister; Rafi Ahmed Kidwai, a Congress Socialist leader who became India's first minister for communications; and Allah Bux Soomro, a powerful Congress leader in Sindh who was murdered for his advocacy of Hindu-Muslim unity. 'In recommending spinning wheel', Gandhi wrote, 'my sole idea has been to place before the country a programme, which would easily appeal to the common mind and also be a unifying force'.[6]

Talking about national pride, this was his advice to the students and researchers at the prestigious Indian Institute of Science (IISc) in Bangalore, which he visited in 1927. 'Don't be afraid of wearing the cloth the poor women make for you, don't be afraid of your employers showing you the door if you wear khadi. I would like you to be men, and stand up before the world firm in your convictions. Let your zeal for the dumb millions be not stifled in the search for wealth'.[7]

The 'spiritual message' of the charkha flowed from Gandhi's belief in the inseparable nexus between economics and religion. He expressed this belief with the precision of a scientific formula in an article titled 'Spinning a Supremely Spiritual Message', in Young India on 15 September 1927: 'Religion to be worth anything must be capable of being reduced to the terms of economics' and 'economics to be worth anything must also be capable of being reduced to the terms of religion or spirituality'. To drive home his point, he added: 'It is because the message of the spinning wheel is supremely spiritual for this land that it has got tremendous economic consequences as also political consequences'.

What a huge contrast there is between Gandhi's religious (dharmic) approach to politics and the widely practiced political approach to religion these days!

Gandhi would repeat the spiritual message of the spinning wheel with a saintly zeal, emphasising that the charkha inculcated in its practitioners the virtue of nonviolence and self-realisation. 'The charkha stands for simple life and high thinking. It is a standing rebuke against the modern mad rush for adding material comfort upon comfort and making life so complicated as to make one doubly unfit for knowing oneself and one's God'.[8]

The spinning wheel also reaffirmed a fundamental principle of all religions: bread labour. Gandhi was much influenced by the teaching of the *Bible* – 'Earn thy bread by the sweat of the brow'. He found the corresponding teaching in Hinduism in the concept of *sharir yajna* – offering body labour as a sacrifice to God and thereby earning the right to enjoy its fruits. He considered it a 'law of God' that the body must be fully worked and utilised. According to Gandhi, eating food without working for it is tantamount to stealing the fruits of others' labour. Hence, full employment for every able-bodied individual in society is the cornerstone of Gandhian economics. How to ensure mass employment to the rural poor, whose livelihoods had been destroyed courtesy colonial exploitation by the British, in a self-reliant, dignified and spiritually satisfying manner? This was the question that Gandhi grappled with when he joined India's freedom struggle. He found the answer in the spinning wheel, which, he proclaimed, 'is the auspicious symbol of *Sharir Yajna*'.[9]

Gandhi's resounding articulation of the 'triple message of khadi' came when he launched the Non-Cooperation Movement in 1920. It was his first major nationwide campaign after his return from South Africa. It quickly established him not only as a mass leader, but also as a mass leader of the kind that the world had never seen. Boycott of foreign cloth was an important operational plank of this campaign. Several others in India's national movement had made similar appeals earlier. However, what distinguished Gandhi from previous campaigners against foreign goods were two uniquely creative and strategic thoughts. Firstly, he supplemented the negative call for boycott of foreign cloth with a positive appeal for the adoption of indigenously produced khadi. This created an economic, political, emotional and moral bond between the classes and the masses, thus imparting to India's freedom movement the much-needed national and mass character, which was missing before Gandhi assumed its leadership.

Secondly, in campaigning for khadi, Gandhi underscored that its significance was not only national but also global. He did so by weaving the message of a new nonviolent and non-exploitative world order. This is what he wrote in *Young India* in 1921:

It is my claim that as soon as we have completed the boycott of foreign cloth we shall have evolved so far that we shall necessarily give up the present absurdities and remodel national life in keeping with the ideal of simplicity and domesticity implanted in the bosom of the masses. We will not then be dragged into an imperialism which is built upon exploitation of the weaker races of the earth, and the acceptance of a giddy materialistic civilisation protected by naval and air forces that have made peaceful living almost impossible. On the contrary we shall then refine that imperialism into a commonwealth of nations which will combine, if they do, for the purpose of giving their best to the world and of protecting, not by brute force but by self-suffering, the weaker nations or races of the earth. *Non-cooperation aims at nothing less than this revolution in the thought world.* Such a transformation can come only after the complete success of the spinning wheel. India can become fit for delivering such a message, when she has become proof against temptation and therefore attacks from outside, by becoming self-contained regarding two of her chief needs – food and clothing.[10] *(Emphasis added)*

Gandhi's civilisational distinction between the West and the Rest is clear – one a 'giddy materialistic civilisation' built upon the 'exploitation of the weaker races of the earth' and another that seeks to peacefully transform the world into a 'commonwealth' of cooperative nations. The distinction is also clear in his adoption of satyagraha, a unique nonviolent method of protest. His nonviolence was not a weapon of the weak and the coward; rather, it transformed an enslaved people into morally brave and steadfast warriors for freedom. Gandhian nonviolence was not non-resistance, it was nonviolent resistance.[11] It aimed at the inner transformation of both those who wielded this 'weapon' and also those against whom the 'weapon' was used. Indeed, Gandhi described satyagraha as the 'moral equivalent' of war[12], an idea that we shall discuss in greater detail later. *(See Chapter 8.)*

What a mighty 'thought revolution' it was!

One can see Gandhi returning to this world-changing thought again and again in his advocacy of the charkha and khadi. 'The charkha,' he writes, 'is a symbol not of commercial war but of commercial peace. It bears not a message of ill-will towards the nations of the earth but of goodwill and self-help. It will not need the protection of a navy threatening a world's peace and exploiting its resources, but it needs the religious determination of millions to spin their yarn in their own homes as today they cook their food in their own homes. *I may deserve the curse of posterity for many mistakes of omission and commission, but I am confident of earning its blessings for suggesting a revival of the Charkha. I stake my all on it. For every revolution of the wheel spins peace, goodwill and love.* And with all that, inasmuch as the loss of it brought about India's slavery, its voluntary revival with all its implications must mean India's freedom'.[13] *(Emphasis added)*

Is there any other leader in modern world history who made a mere machine, and the rough home-spun cloth produced by that mundane machine, such mighty symbols for his call for a civilisational transformation?

Satyagraha was the Message, Khadi its Propagator

News about Gandhi's unique method of nonviolent protest action against racial discrimination in a far-off land, which he called satyagraha, had begun to travel to India long before he bade an emotional goodbye to his fellow satyagrahis and left the shores of South Africa for the last time. In spite of the fact that newspapers, with limited circulation, were the only form of mass media that existed those days, the paltry news that trickled in from South Africa filled educated Indians associated with the anti-British movement with admiration, pride and curiosity. When Gandhi introduced satyagraha in the context of India's freedom movement – his first satyagraha struggle in India was in Champaran (Bihar) in 1917, when he took up the cause of poor indigo farmers – it immediately electrified the nation, capturing the imagination of the rich and poor, educated and illiterate alike. He expected every active participant in the satyagraha movement to be a moral exemplar to society – and not the typical rabble-rouser political activist we see today – ready to sacrifice his or her all for the nation's freedom but in a manner that morally elevated both the satyagrahis and the common people they sought to mobilise. However, he knew that it was unrealistic to expect every Indian to adhere to the same high moral standards as a well-trained satyagrahi in his ashram. He wanted millions of people to participate in the freedom movement and slowly imbibe the ideals of satyagraha. How could this be achieved?

Gandhi found the right answer to this question in the charkha and khadi. Once both the masses and the elite took to wearing the garment of freedom, and also to spinning the yarn of freedom, he believed that they would inevitably come under the influence of the higher values of life in which he sought to anchor India's freedom struggle. Here are a few moving episodes that illustrate the magic power of khadi in bringing the best out of ordinary Indians.

During the Second World War, a wealthy woman satyagrahi was arrested by the police when she gave an anti-British speech in front of the Lamington Road police station in Bombay. Usually, the police allowed such protesters to visit their homes and bring their clothes and other essential things before being produced before the court and then sent to jail. However, denying the lady satyagrahi this minimum courtesy, the police informed her that she would be taken to the court directly and then to prison. Hearing this, she took off all the jewellery she was wearing – diamond earrings, gold bangles and a pearl necklace – wrapped the ornaments in her handkerchief and handed them over to a khadi-clad person among the spectators. She also gave him her residential address and said: 'May I request you to give these ornaments to my folks at home?' The man, in a state of utter disbelief, asked her: 'I am a total stranger. Don't you suspect that I might run away with these precious ornaments?' The lady satyagrahi replied: 'Brother, you have on your body Gandhi's khadi. You won't commit the sin of running away with the ornaments which I have handed over to you in good faith.' The man complied with her request.[14]

The above episode shows how khadi became ingrained in our national character and became the embodiment and silent messenger of moral values – *vishwas* (trust), *tyag* (sacrifice), *aparigraha* (non-acquisitiveness or non-greed) and *asteya* (non-stealing). Its wearers earned new respect and dignity in society. However, they knew that wearing khadi was not a casual act. It placed upon the wearers a new responsibility for virtuous behaviour. 'Khadi furnishes the acid test of public honesty,'[15] Gandhi said. 'A real khadi wearer,' he wrote, 'will not utter an untruth. A real khadi wearer will labour no violence, no deceit, and no impurity.'[16] Never after his death has India seen such a silent but fairly fruitful attempt at the moral regeneration of society.

Now the other tale. It proves not only how the poor were magnetically attracted to the Mahatma, but also how he valued the meagre contributions from the poor for his khadi campaign much more than big sums donated by the rich. Once, during a tour of rural Orissa, a poor old woman who listened to his speech wanted to meet him. She was bent with age and her clothes were in tatters. The volunteers tried to stop her, but she fought her way to the place where Gandhi was sitting. She touched his feet, took out a copper coin worth one paisa from the folds of her sari, and placed it in front of him. Gandhi thanked her respectfully and kept the copper coin with him. Jamnalal Bajaj, a well-known businessman, benefactor and follower of Gandhi, who also was treasurer of the Charkha Sangh (spinners' association), happened to be travelling with him. He asked Gandhi for the coin but Gandhi refused. 'I keep cheques worth thousands of rupees for the Charkha Sangh,' Bajaj said laughingly, 'yet you won't trust me with a copper coin.' Gandhi's reply: 'This copper coin is worth much more than those thousands. If a man has several lakhs and he gives away a thousand or two, it doesn't mean much. But this coin was perhaps all that the poor woman possessed. She gave me all she had. That was very generous of her. What a great sacrifice she made! That is why I value this copper coin more than a crore of rupees.'[17]

Sudhir Kakar, noted psychoanalyst and author, narrates a similar episode in his book *Mira & the Mahatma*. In 1929, Gandhi asked Mirabehn to accompany him on his tour of villages in North India.

'Her job was to help in the collection of money after Bapu finished his speech. Armed with a cloth bag she, along with other members of the party, moved amidst the tightly-packed crowds squatting on the ground, collecting copper and nickel coins from poor peasants eager to contribute to Gandhi's cause. Once, Bapu made a stirring appeal to the audience in a women's meeting to donate their ornaments to the cause of combating untouchability. Mira was moved to tears at the way the poor village women began pulling off their rings, earrings, bracelets and anklets, vying with each other to be among the first to put what was possibly the only wealth they possessed into the collection bags. One young woman caught hold of her hand and pointed to her sole ornament, a heavy silver anklet gleaming softly against her dark skin. It was so thick that she needed help to pull it off. Mira pulled at it one way and the woman the other, till the anklet was removed from her leg. Her face was beaming with pride when she handed the anklet to Mira. "For Mahatmaji," she said simply.'[18]

Such was the man. And such were the people he inspired.

Tagore Gandhi Debate on the Spinning Wheel: How the Mahatma Conquered his Critic

Even when Gandhi was alive, there was no dearth of critics who questioned his advocacy of khadi and charkha. Many of his admirers, too, had misgivings on this score. Rabindranath Tagore, India's greatest poet in modern times, was one of them. In his two articles 'The Call of Truth' (*The Modern Review*, October 1921) and 'The Cult of the Charkha' (*The Modern Review*, September 1925) the poet criticised Gandhi for making spinning a form of 'ritual'. He wrote:

> ... if man (can) be stunted by big machines, the danger of his being stunted by small machines must not be lost sight of...The performance of petty routine duties ... imparts skills to the limbs of the man who is a bondsman, whose labour is drudgery; but it

kills the mind of a man who is a doer, whose work is creation …
The depths of my mind have not been moved by the Charkha
agitation … (and) there are others who are in the same plight
as myself – though it is difficult to find them all out. For even
where hands are reluctant to work the spindle, mouths are all
the more busy spinning its praises … I am afraid of a blind faith
on a very large scale in the Charkha in the country which is so
liable to succumb to the lure of short-cuts when pointed out
by a personality about whose moral earnestness they can have
no doubt… By doing the same thing day after day, mechanical
skill may be acquired; but the mind, like a mill-turning bullock,
will be kept going round and round a narrow range of habit…
The Charkha is doing harm because of the undue prominence
which it has thus usurped.

Gandhi's self-defence in the face of criticism coming from a person
as great as Tagore ('The world today does not possess his equal as a
Poet,' is how he had described Tagore) was typically Gandhian, free
of even a hint of hurt but full of both love for the critic and also
courage of conviction to stand by his own thoughts. He welcomed the
criticism by endorsing the virtue of free and frank exchange of views
in a meaningful debate. 'Why should mere disagreement with my views
displease (me)?' he asked.

If every disagreement were to displease, since no two men agree
exactly on all points, life would be a bundle of unpleasant
sensations and therefore a perfect nuisance. On the contrary,
the frank criticism pleases me. For our friendship becomes the
richer for our disagreements. Friends to be friends are not called
upon to agree even on most points. Only disagreement must
have no sharpness, much less bitterness, about them. And I
gratefully admit that there is none about the Poet's criticism.

Thus conceding that others had a right to protest when they believed
that he was in error, Gandhi further remarked: 'My profound regard
for him (Tagore) would make me listen to him more readily than to
any other critic… A reformer who is enraged because his message

is not accepted must retire to the forest to learn how to watch, wait and pray.'

However, when it came to responding to the crux of Tagore's criticism, Gandhi was unwavering in self-defence. He denied any widespread blind obedience in India to his advocacy of the charkha. He conceded that educated people in urban India might not have understood the message of the charkha, but he hoped that at least the poet would go deeper and realise its relevance.

I do indeed ask the Poet and the Sage to spin the wheel as a sacrament.... It is my conviction that India is a house on fire because its manhood is being daily scorched; it is dying of hunger because it has no work to buy food with ... Our cities are not India. India lives in her seven and a half lakhs of villages, and the cities live upon the villages... The city people are brokers and commission agents for the big houses of Europe, America and Japan. To a people famishing and idle, the only acceptable form in which God can dare appear is work and promise of food as wages. God created man to work for his food, and said that those who ate without work were thieves... Is it any wonder if India has become one vast prison? Hunger is the argument that is driving India to the spinning wheel ... 'Why should I who have no need to work for food spin?' may be the question asked. Because I am eating what does not belong to me ... Trace the course of every *paisa* that finds its way into your pocket, and you will realise the truth of what I write .... A plea for the spinning wheel is a plea for recognising the dignity of labour ... It was our love of foreign cloth that ousted the wheel from its position of dignity. Therefore I consider it a sin to wear foreign cloth...it is sinful for me to wear the latest finery of Regent Street, when I know that if I had but the things woven by the neighbouring spinners and weavers, that would have clothed me, and fed and clothed them ... I must consign the foreign garments to the flames and thus purify myself, and thenceforth rest content with the rough Khadi made by my neighbours.

Gandhi also wrote: '...the Poet lives for the morrow and would have us do likewise .... But I have had the pain of watching birds who, for want of strength, could not be coaxed even into a flutter of their wings .... I found it impossible to soothe suffering patients with a song of Kabir. The hungry millions ask for one poem – invigorating food. They cannot be *given* it. They must *earn* it. And they can earn it only by the sweat of their brow'.

Tagore's respect for the Mahatma grew with the passage of time. In his speech on Gandhi's birthday in 1937, delivered to the students of Santiniketan, he said: '... many wondered if India could ever rise again by the genius of her own people, – until there came on the scene a truly great soul, a great leader of men, in line with the traditions of the great sages of old...Mahatma Gandhi. Today no one need despair of the future of this country, for the unconquerable spirit that creates has already been released.'

Tagore continued: '... though Christ declared that the meek shall inherit the earth, Christians now aver that victory is to the strong, the aggressive ... It needed another prophet to vindicate the truth of this paradox and interpret "meekness" as the positive force of love and righteousness, as *satyagraha* ... Gandhi has made of this "meekness" or *ahimsa*, the highest form of bravery, a perpetual challenge to the insolence of the strong.'

In 1938, Tagore showered more praise on the Mahatma in an article 'Gandhi the Man', which was published by Visva-Bharati after Gandhi's death in a special commemorative volume. The language of his praise glows with the highest level of beauty and sincerity.

An ascetic himself, he does not frown on the joy of others, but works for the enlivening of their existence day and night. He exalts poverty in his own life, but no man in India has striven more assiduously than he for the material welfare of his people. A reformer with the zeal of a revolutionary, he imposes severe restraints on the very passions he provokes. Something of an idolater and also an iconoclast, he leaves the old gods in their dusty niches of sanctity and simply lures the old worship to better and more humane purposes. ...He condemns sexual life as inconsistent with the moral progress of man, and has a horror of sex as great as that of the author of *The Kreutzer Sonata*, but unlike Tolstoy, he betrays no abhorrence of the sex that tempts his kind. In fact, his tenderness for woman is one of the noblest and most consistent traits of his character, and he counts among the women of his country some of his best and truest comrades in the great movement he is leading. He advises his followers to hate evil without hating the evil-doer...

Great as he is as a politician, as an organiser, as a leader of men, as a moral reformer, he is greater than all these as a man, because none of these aspects and activities limits his humanity ... an incorrigible idealist and given to referring all conduct to certain pet formulae of his own, he is essentially a lover of men and not of mere ideas ... If he proposes an experiment for society, he must first subject himself to its ordeal. If he calls for a sacrifice, he must first pay its price himself ... none of the reforms with which his name is associated was originally his in conception. They have almost all been proposed and preached by his predecessors or contemporaries .... Nevertheless, it remains true, that they have never had the same energising power in them as when he took them up; for now they are quickened by the great life-force of the complete man who is absolutely one with his ideas, whose visions perfectly blend with his whole being .... Perhaps he will not succeed. Perhaps he will fail as the Buddha failed and as Christ failed to wean men from their iniquities but he will always be remembered as one who made his life a lesson for all yet to come.[19]

The Gandhi-Tagore symphony casts the spotlight on the best aspects of national awakening during India's freedom struggle. They were both world-citizens, stars in a night sky that showed the troubled humanity the path to a better future.

Forever on the move: *Gandhi revised his earlier views on machinery and machine-assisted travel. 'Under my scheme,' he said, 'men in charge of machinery will think not of themselves or even of the nation to which they belong but of the whole human race.'*

7

WAS GANDHI OPPOSED TO SCIENCE AND TECHNOLOGY? A CARICATURE!

As a man who has devoted his whole life to the most clear-headed science, to the study of matter, I can tell you as the result of my research about the atoms, this much: There is no matter as such! All matter originates and exists only by virtue of a force which brings the particles of an atom to vibration and holds this most minute solar system of the atom together... We must assume behind this force the existence of a conscious and intelligent Mind. This Mind is the matrix of all matter.

— Max Planck (1858-1947), founder of Quantum Theory.
The famous Planck's Constant has been named after him.

WE NOW RETURN TO THE QUESTION WHICH WE ASKED AT the beginning of this book. Was Gandhi really opposed to science and technology (S&T)? Misunderstanding in this regard is largely due to a superficial reading of his literature, as indeed I had done during my own student days. As in the case of all great religious scriptures, his writings demand attentive study. Superficiality breeds stupidity.

It is true that Gandhi himself states his case with such messianic conviction that it is sometimes susceptible to be mistaken for obstinacy or even fanaticism. For example, anyone would be flabbergasted by reading this line which appears in *Hind Swaraj* – 'Machinery is the chief symbol of modern civilisation; it represents a great sin'. Or, in *Hind Swaraj* again, this comment against a mode of mass transport that he himself would regularly use in his later years to criss-cross all of India: 'Railways have impoverished the country ...and they propagate evil'.[1] *(As we shall see in Chapter 12, Gandhi later changed his views about railways, and also about machinery in general.)*

However, a closer reading of *Hind Swaraj* would reveal that his searing comments on modern machinery were on account of its incontrovertible contribution to the pauperisation of India and to the enrichment of Britain. He repeatedly told Europeans that their greed-driven industrial growth had led to the moral downfall of their societies, making them blind even to the teachings of their own religion. He urged them to heed the words of Alfred Russell Wallace (1823–1913), the celebrated British biologist and anthropologist, who had written that the advance of science had not reduced hatred and injustice, and added 'not an inch to the moral stature of Europe'.[2]

In 1931, when the imperialist powers in Europe were pushing the world towards another major war, he wrote: 'What is the cause of the present chaos? It is exploitation, I will not say, of the weaker nations by the stronger, but of sister nations by sister nations. And my fundamental objection to machinery rests on the fact that it is machinery that has enabled these nations to exploit others'.[3]

It is true that Gandhi in his South African years termed material progress, achieved with the help of modern machinery, as evil and satanic. Nevertheless, in later years he revised and calibrated his views on modern science and machinery in the light of his own subsequent experiments with truth. He did so without changing his basic conviction that S&T must promote the all-round progress of the entire humanity, and also that material progress should be regarded not as an end in itself but as a means to achieve cultural and spiritual ascent.

Gandhi's approach to science was predicated on the belief that life must be viewed in its wholeness, and not as unrelated parts. He also believed that science's inquiry into any and every aspect of life should be informed by love for all human beings. Indeed, for science to be truly meaningful and useful, its love must extend to the entire cosmic web of creation. That he envisaged the possibility, desirability, and inevitability of a different type of nonviolent and humanising S&T is conclusively evident from a study of the totality of what he said, wrote and did in his life. Let me cite some instructive examples.

The idea of pursuit of scientific truth, without the motive of personal benefit and even at the risk of personal wellbeing, had gripped Gandhi's mind right from his South Africa days. In the pages of *Indian Opinion*, the newspaper he started around the same time that he established his first ashram, Phoenix Settlement near Durban, he extolled scientists whose courage and spirit of inquiry was worthy of emulation. He gave the example of an Italian scientist named Metusi, who bravely collected data from Mount Vesuvius while the volcano (its eruption in 1906 killed over one hundred people) was still active. 'In the vicinity of the volcano, there is a meteorological station where Professor Metusi lives. The station is in great danger of being destroyed any moment by the lava from the volcano. However, Professor Metusi has not abandoned his post and keeps sending information to Naples about the volcano. It is a matter of no ordinary courage thus to stay amidst danger. No one has forced him to stay at the danger spot. Nothing can be said in his reproach if, like thousands of other men, he leaves the place to save his life. Yet he has refused to leave. When many Indians too of this calibre are born in India or South Africa, we shall cease to suffer as at present.'[4]

In 1919, ten years after the publication of the book that led some people in India and the West to see it as proof that Gandhi wanted to turn the clock back on scientific and technological development, he wrote: 'Opposition to mills or machinery is not the point. What suits our country is the point. I am not opposed to the movement of manufacturing machines in the country, nor to improvements in machinery. I am only concerned with what these machines are made for. I may ask, in the words of Ruskin, whether these machines will be such as would blow off a million men in a minute or they will be such as would turn waste lands into arable and fertile lands'.[5]

In 1927, writing in *Young India*, Gandhi said that his 'sacred spinning wheel' – note his use of the word *'sacred'* – 'is itself an exquisite piece of machinery'.[6] One of the main purposes of the Satyagraha ashram that he established in Ahmedabad in 1915 was to train 'satyagrahi scientists'. Their task was to strengthen the khadi movement with new innovations and improvements in the charkha and the allied machines used in the cooperatively run cottage industries so that the poor could earn more from their labour. Once during his interaction with Congress workers in Bengal, he was asked a question: 'What do you mean by the science of spinning? What things are included in it?' Gandhi replied:

> I have often said that I can do without food but not without sacrificial spinning. I have also claimed that no one in India has perhaps done his spinning with such unfailing regularity and conscientious diligence as I. And yet I will say that all that by itself cannot take the place of scientific knowledge. Scientific knowledge requires constant probing into the why and wherefore of every little process that you perform. Mere affirmation that in charkha there is swaraj and peace is not enough. A scientific mind will not be satisfied with having things scientific just on faith. Faith becomes lame when it ventures into matters pertaining to reason. Its field begins where reason's ends. Conclusions based on faith are unshakable whereas those based on reason are liable to be unstable and vulnerable to superior logic. To state the limitation of science is not to belittle it. We cannot do without either science or faith – each in its own place.[7]

'The spinning wheel,' he repeatedly said, 'will not become a power for the liberation of India in our hands unless we have made a deep study of the various sciences related to it.' The 'science of khadi,' he wrote, 'requires technical and mechanical skill of a high order and demands as much concentration as is given by Sir J.C. Bose to the tiny leaves of plants in his laboratory before he wrests from them the secrets of nature'.[8] On another occasion, he wrote that 'the rediscovery of the "cunning of the hands", which had earlier brought fame to Indian

Gandhi's admiration for scientists and entrepreneurs

(L to R, first row) Maganlal Gandhi, Nobel laureate Sir C.V. Raman, Sir J.C. Bose, (second row) Ardeshir Godrej, Jamsetji Tata, Sir Ratan Tata, (third row) Acharya P.C. Ray, Jamnalal Bajaj and G.D. Birla.

textiles but had been lost later, would require the same kind of scientific attention that Bose and (C.V.) Raman gave to their work'.[9]

Gandhi had immense regard for two brilliant contemporary Indian scientists – Sir J.C. Bose (1858–1937) and Acharya P.C. Ray (1861-1942). He advised students to follow their example. 'Their researches have been devoted in order to enable us to come nearer to our Maker…. I feel that we are placed on this earth to adore our Maker, to know ourselves, in other words, to realise ourselves and therefore to realise our destiny.'[10] Sir J.C. Bose had won international fame as an outstanding Indian botanist. About him, Gandhi wrote: 'Thanks to the marvellous researches of Sir J.C. Bose it can now be proved that even matter is life'.[11]

In Acharya Ray, a well-known professor of chemistry at Calcutta University and a pioneer in the pharmaceutical industry (he founded Bengal Chemicals), Gandhi saw an example of plain living and high thinking. 'It is difficult to believe', he wrote, 'that the man in simple Indian dress wearing simple manners could possibly be the great scientist and professor'. The admiration was mutual. Ray, who was instrumental in inviting the South Africa-based Barrister Gandhi to attend the Calcutta session of the Congress in 1901, later wrote: 'The frequent conversations which I used to have with Mr. Gandhi made a deep and lasting impression on me. He was earning as a barrister several thousand rupees a month but he was utterly regardless of worldliness – "I always make it a point to travel third class in my railway journeys, so that I might be in close personal touch with the masses – my own countrymen – and get to know their sorrows and sufferings." Even after the lapse of thirty years, these words still ring in my ears. Truth lived is a far greater force than truth merely spoken'.[12]

An aside: when asked why he always travelled third-class, the Mahatma quipped: 'Because there is no fourth-class in railways!'

Mention of Ray in this context is appropriate for another reason. He was one of those numerous scientists who had earlier disagreed with Gandhi when the latter made the charkha the symbol of India's freedom movement. In his memoirs, *Autobiography of a Bengali Chemist*, he writes: 'Being an industrialist on a humble scale, I, at first, scoffed at the very idea of this primitive, uncouth instrument competing with machinery'. However, Ray changed his opinion after seeing acute rural poverty during his active involvement in the relief work for the victims of the devastating famine in East Bengal (1921) and flood in North Bengal (1922). 'I could not fail to notice what an immense boon the Charkha would have proved to the starving people if it had not been abandoned nearly a century before...I need not be understood as saying all big scale industries should be smashed. ... But you will agree with me that if the same result can be brought about by means much less harmful, surely that is preferable.'

Gandhi was a strong votary of electrification of every village in India. 'I would prize every invention of science made for the benefit of all,' he said.[13] Sadly, the goal of total electrification has still not been achieved – nearly one lakh out of the six lakh villages in our country have no electricity, a deprivation whose true severity can be gauged from the additional fact that fifty-six percent of rural households in the remaining five lakh villages that are supposed to be 'electrified', have no electricity.

Innovation is the buzz word these days. However, as far back as in 1921, Gandhi instituted a prize of ₹5,000 (equivalent to about ₹2,00,000 in 2012) in order to attract inventors from all over the world to improve the efficiency of khadi production. Eight years later, he increased it to rupees one lakh! He was obsessed with the idea of technological innovations that could improve the quality of life in rural India. 'In one thing I do not mind being a beggar', he wrote with characteristic humility in one of his numerous letters to inventors near and far. 'I would beg of you your scientific talent. You can ask your engineers and agricultural experts to place their services at our disposal. They must not come to us as our lords and masters but as voluntary workers. A Mysore engineer who is a Pole (Maurice Frydman) has sent me a box of hand-made tools made to suit village requirements. Supposing an engineer of that character comes and studies the tools and cottage machines, he would be of great service'.[14]

Khadi production was by no means the only sphere in which he sought the assistance of S&T. He wanted every facet of India's economic and social life, especially in rural areas, to be appropriately modernised by S&T. In 1934, at Gandhi's urging, the INC established the All India Village Industries Association (AIVIA) near Wardha with Dr J.C. Kumarappa as its secretary. The AIVIA had on its advisory board three of the towering names in Indian science – Sir C.V. Raman, who had won Nobel Prize for Physics in 1930, Sir J.C. Bose and Acharya P.C. Ray. Kumarappa himself was a distinguished economist who had studied at Columbia University in USA.

Sir C.V. Raman, India's first Nobel laureate scientist, had great regard for Gandhi. He and his wife Lokasundari had visited Gandhi and Kasturba at Sevagram Ashram in 1936. 'Gandhi's teachings,' he remarked, 'stressed the supreme virtue of the human spirit, utterly indestructible and unconquerable. India can never hope to find a place in the sun, unless it upholds the value of the human spirit.'[15] On 7 February 1948, Sir C.V. Raman paid homage to Gandhi with an address on All India Radio, in which he said: 'I was not an active participant in the struggle for India's political emancipation. Neither did I seek to contact the leaders engaged in it. But the Mahatma was obviously so different from anyone that I had ever known that each of the many occasions on which I saw, met or heard him, remained vividly impressed on my memory.' He likened Gandhi to the 'great humanitarians in the past that Asia has produced' whose 'life has left behind a permanent impress on the minds and lives of humanity.'[16] In honour of the Mahatma, he instituted the annual Gandhi Memorial Lecture at the Raman Research Institute in Bengaluru. Till his death in 1970, Raman never failed to deliver this lecture.

In 1938 Gandhi established Magan Sangrahalaya, India's first exhibition centre for khadi and rural technologies, at AIVIA. He named it after Maganlal Gandhi, one of his closest associates from his days in South Africa. Maganlal was not only a brilliant innovator, but also a model satyagrahi who had internalised Gandhi's 'living faith' in khadi. His book *Vanat Shastra* (*Charkha Shastra*, in English) was regarded as a classic on khadi science. Praising another satyagrahi, Jhaverbhai Patel, for studying the *ghani* (traditional oil making contraption) 'with the zeal and precision of a scientist', Gandhi called upon his colleagues at AIVIA to be 'men of science' to improve other cottage industries.

Gandhi himself wrote extensively in his journals on rural economic activities such as handmade paper, *gur* (jaggery) and *khandsari* (another type of jaggery), compost manure, hand-pounding of rice, village *chakkis* (flour grinder), dairy, tannery, bee-keeping, etc. 'Not Denmark but India should be model State for the finest experiments in dairy,'[17] he said. He wanted *goshalas* (cow farms) to become ideal dairies and tanneries that can 'provide decent employment for thousands of people, including educated people, since both dairy and tannery work require expert scientific knowledge.'[18] Once he sent a questionnaire to several well-known doctors and chemists, asking them 'to enlighten me on the chemical analysis and different food values of polished and unpolished rice, jaggery, sugar and so on'.[19] The response disappointed him. 'Is it not a tragedy that no scientist should be able to give me the chemical analysis of such a simple article as *gur*? The reason is that we have not thought of the villager'.[20]

To those of his critics who said that he was relying on 'primitive methods' for the uplift of Indian villages, he responded by saying that he had 'no partiality' for return to the so-called 'primitive methods' for the sake of them. 'I suggest the return, because there is no other way of giving employment to the millions of villagers who are living in idleness. In my opinion, village uplift is impossible, unless we solve the pressing economic distress. Therefore, to induce the villagers to utilise their idle hours is in itself solid uplift work'.[21] He demonstrated with concrete examples how khadi and charkha created and nurtured a sustainable, symbiotic and employment-intensive ecosystem in the villages. 'Every ten hand-spinners mean an addition of one whole-time weaver, one whole-time carder, not to mention more work for *dhobis* (washermen), tailors, carpenters, blacksmiths, dyers, printers, etc.'[22]

Gandhi was by no means blind to the need for India to build its own indigenous assets in crucial heavy industries. As early as in his South Africa years, when he was yet to become famous in India as the Mahatma, he had enthusiastically supported the development of India's native shipping industry. His study of how the British rulers had systematically de-industrialised India led him to conclude that 'Indian shipping had to perish so that British shipping might flourish'.[23] He had come to know that V.O. Chidambaram Pillai (1872-1936), a great patriotic entrepreneur and a staunch Congressman from Tamil Nadu, had started the Swadeshi Steam Navigation Company to break the monopoly of British shipping in the coastal trade with Ceylon (now Sri Lanka). VOC, as Pillai was popularly called, had received assistance in this enterprise from Lokamanya Bal Gangadhar Tilak and Aurobindo Ghosh, two of the foremost leaders of India's freedom movement in the first two decades of the last century. Gandhi's exchange of letters with VOC shows that he commended the latter's shipping initiative and even collected funds for him in South Africa. Similarly, he also publicly supported the initiative of two other swadeshi entrepreneurs, Narottam Morarjee and Walchand Hirachand, to start the indigenous Scindia Steam Navigation Company in Bombay in 1919.

While in South Africa, Gandhi inspired the birth and growth of another great Indian industrial enterprise – the House of Godrej. It was founded in 1897 by Ardeshir Godrej, to whom Gandhi was both a friend and a mentor. Godrej was a great inventor, a quality that immensely impressed Gandhi who motivated him to produce locks and steel cupboards of international standards 'in the interest of the country' as a step towards making India self-reliant. Both Ardeshir and his brother Pirojsha Godrej were generous supporters of India's freedom movement and ardent practitioners of Gandhi's swadeshi philosophy. Today, Godrej is one of India's leading manufacturing conglomerates and produces one of the most trusted range of goods.

It is not widely known that the ties between Gandhi and Tata, India's most admired and diversified group of companies, were intimate. Gandhi had high regard for Jamsetji Nasserwanji Tata (1839-1904), founder of the Tata Group and a great philanthropist. When Tata passed away, Gandhi paid a glowing tribute to him in *Indian Opinion* (20 May 1905): 'He (Jamsetji Tata) was a man of deep compassion. Tears came to his eyes at the thought of the sufferings of the poor. Though he possessed unlimited wealth, he spent nothing from it on his own pleasures. His simplicity was remarkable. May India produce many Tatas'!

In August 1925, he visited the Tata Steel plant at Jamshedpur. He was a guest of R.D. Tata, a first cousin of Jamsetji Tata and father of the legendary J.R.D. Tata. Interestingly, the purpose of the visit was to resolve certain labour issues. Marvelling at this showpiece of swadeshi industry, he said, 'I wish this great Indian firm all the prosperity that it deserves and to this great enterprise every success.' Addressing the workers of Tata Steel in the presence of his host, he hoped that 'the relations between this great house and labourers who work here under their care will be of the friendliest character.' He reiterated that 'capital and labour should supplement and help each other.' Elaborating his ideal, he said: 'They should be a great family living in unity and harmony, capital not only looking into the material welfare of the labourers but their moral welfare also; capitalists being trustees of the welfare of the labouring classes under them.' His message to the workers: 'May God grant that, in serving the Tatas, you will also serve India and will realise that you are here for a much higher mission than merely working for an industrial enterprise'.[24]

Gandhi had been looking forward to his visit to Jamshedpur for a long time: 'It was my ambition to see one of the greatest, if not the greatest, Indian enterprise in India'. This is because his cordial relations with the House of Tatas went back to the years of his struggle in South Africa. He admired Jamsetji Tata for his patriotism and indomitable swadeshi entrepreneurship. The first cotton mill that Tata had established in Nagpur in 1877 was called Empress Mills, to mark the proclamation of Queen Victoria as the empress of India. However, eighteen years later, he established the Swadeshi Mills in Bombay to mark the beginning of the Swadeshi movement in India. Sir Ratan Tata, Jamsetji's second son, had been a great supporter of Gandhi's satyagraha movement in South Africa. 'Parsis are known the world over for their generous gifts', Gandhi wrote in grateful acknowledgement of this support to him. 'Mr Tata has been true to that spirit of generosity. We have had many generous donations from him'.[25] Tata's donations helped Gandhi's newspaper in South Africa *Indian Opinion* survive. 'The paper would have been in dire straits if Mr Tata's generous help had not been drawn upon to meet its needs'.

Gandhi gratefully recalled this in his speech in Jamshedpur by saying, 'In South Africa when I was struggling along with the Indians in the attempt to retain our self-respect and to vindicate our status, it was Sir Ratan Tata who first came forward with assistance.'[26]

Indian communist leaders of the time, who fanatically held the theory of Marxism and its practice in the now extinct Soviet Union as the model for the entire world, sought to malign Gandhi for sharing the dais with a capitalist like Tata. Gandhi stoutly defended himself by saying, 'Well, I am not ashamed of the honour. Mr. Tata appeared to me to be a humane and considerate employer. He readily granted all the prayers of employees and I heard later that the agreement was being honourably kept...Let there be no misunderstanding. I am not opposed to organisation of labour, but as in everything else, I want its organisation along Indian lines, or if you will, my lines.'[27]

It is worth noting here that the birth of the Federation of Indian Chambers of Commerce and Industry (FICCI) in New Delhi in 1927 was due to the advice and blessings of Gandhi. Acting upon this advice, Ghanshyamdas Birla, his close associate in the Indian business fraternity, founded FICCI as an apex organisation to further the interests of India's patriotic business community. Similarly, he inspired the Bombay-based Indian Merchants Chamber (IMC), an organisation representing trade, commerce and industry, to pursue the goal of making India's economy self-reliant and become a part of the country's freedom movement. Impressed by the IMC's dedication, he accepted to become its honorary patron.

Although Gandhi never hesitated to describe himself as 'a friend of the capitalists', he drew a clear distinction between 'my *friendship* with capital' and 'my *identification* with labour'. In his address to the workers of Tata Steel, he said: 'As you know, I am a labourer myself. I pride myself on calling myself a scavenger, a weaver, spinner, farmer and what not.' No wonder, he felt more at home staying at Bhangi Colony (scavengers' quarters) than at Birla House in New Delhi.[28]

That Gandhi was completely non-dogmatic and non-xenophobic on the question of machinery is clear again from an interview he gave to *Manchester Guardian* during his visit to London in 1931. He would welcome any machinery that met the needs of the common people, he said. He even mentioned that he himself used machinery for making soap in village industries and, further, that he imported it from England. 'It is only the devoted few who can live the simple life without machinery. The masses will never do without it...Civilisation, a cultured life with a place in it for literature and the arts, is possible without the artificial wants the machinery has created. But I don't deceive myself. I know that the masses will not lead such a life. It is for the few.'

In an interaction with Harold Laski, Kingsley Martin and others in London, he said, 'Steel industry does not lend itself to hand labour. It is either the irresponsible critic or the enemy that spreads the rumour that I am opposed to machinery. I should have the most delicate machinery to make fine surgical instruments.'[29] On another occasion, he candidly admitted that 'India is not, and will not be for a long time to come, entirely self-contained in all her wants.'[30] He mentioned that India would need to import such hardware as could not be indigenously manufactured.

In 1936, a Japanese correspondent asked Gandhi whether he was against the machine age. He replied, 'To say that is to caricature my views. I am not against machinery as such, but I am totally opposed to it when it masters us...' The correspondent asked further, 'You would not industrialise India?' Gandhi's answer, 'I would indeed, in *my* sense of the term.'[31]

In 1940, when his devout young follower Dr Rammanohar Lohia (who later became a fiery leader of the socialist movement) asked him to clarify his views on industrialisation, Gandhi stated, 'I do visualise electricity, ship-building, ironworks, machine-making and the like existing side by side with village handicrafts.'[32]

Despite Gandhi's repeated clarifications, many of his critics, especially leftists, continued to propagate that he was opposed to modern science and machinery. One such critic was V.K. Krishna Menon, a firebrand British-educated political activist who later became India's defence minister. He expressed his misgivings to his mentor Jawaharlal Nehru. The latter showed the letter to Gandhi, whose reply to Menon, dated 8 August 1945, is an example of both his humility and his pro-poor convictions. 'I am not frightened of the word "machine". Therefore, if a life-giving machine can be made in India and will do the work of the spinning wheel more quickly and better, I would have it and pay a tempting prize to the inventor. I may add by way of information that we have increased the speed of the spinning wheel from one to five... You will be wrong if you suspect that I discourage you. I simply share with you my opinion based on extensive experience. For, if anybody can produce a machine analogous to the Singer Sewing Machine (invented by Isaac Merritt Singer), I should dance with joy. It is said that his love for his wife was so great that he would spare her the drudgery of working her needle with the hands. He presented her with a humane machine. I would welcome another such Singer, only not for one woman but for the starving millions of India'.[33]

Although Gandhi devoted his entire public life in India to the advocacy of khadi and the spinning wheel, he neither adopted nor favoured coercive methods to achieve his mission. 'Promotion of khadi does not mean,' he said in his address to the trustees of the All India Spinners' Association, held at Sevagram Ashram on 1 December 1944, 'that we want to close down the textile factories by legislation. We want to achieve our purpose by revolutionalising the psychology of the people.'[34]

Gandhi had recognised the importance of bright Indian students having world-class education in cutting-edge S&T, even if it meant their studying in reputed foreign universities. This was, indeed, a part of his swadeshi concept. For example, we learn from the admirable research on 'Mahatma Gandhi and MIT', done by Prof. Ross Bassett of the University of North Carolina that Gandhi encouraged many of his followers to send their meritorious children to study at the prestigious Massachussetts Institute of Technology (MIT) in the United States of America. One of them was Bal Kalelkar, son of his trusted comrade Kaka Kalelkar, who helped him establish Gujarat Vidyapeeth in Ahmedabad. Bal Kalelkar had grown up in Sabarmati Ashram and, at the age of eighteen, was the youngest among the seventy-eight satyagrahis selected by the Mahatma to participate in the historic Salt March to Dandi in 1930. When he decided to earn a Master's degree in Mechanical Engineering from MIT in 1941, Gandhi wrote a letter of recommendation that read: 'This is to introduce young Kalelkar to all my friends in America. He was brought up under my hands. He is one of the most promising among the boys brought up in Satyagraha Ashram. Any help rendered him will be appreciated'.

Prof. Bassett's research reveals that families associated with Gandhi sent as many as nine sons to MIT during India's freedom movement. One of them was Nathu Pandya, who returned to India to become a distinguished technocrat and educationist. After India gained independence, he served as an important member of the Sarkar Committee that recommended the setting up of the IITs, on the pattern of MIT. Says Prof. Bassett: 'Gandhi's approach to science, technology and India's industrialisation was more complex than common mythology suggests. He was both idealistic and pragmatic. He did not object to hi-tech when their benefits for people were evident on a holistic consideration.'

Eve Curie, daughter of the Nobel laureate French scientist Marie Curie, and a well-known journalist with the *Herald Tribune Syndicate*, New York, interviewed Gandhi in Delhi in 1942. After the interview, she presented to him a biography of her mother authored by herself. Gandhi read that book with great interest and conveyed his appreciation of the celebrated scientist to his colleague Dr Sushila Nayyar: 'She was a true ascetic. I feel like going to Paris to just see her house. None of our scientists have suffered such hardships as she. Thanks to the British, we all learnt to work according to the systems they created. We created white elephants like "research departments"...but how much work is actually happening there?"' Sushila Nayyar writes that he 'became a big fan of the book' and asked her 'to do a good translation of it into Hindi'.[35]

Gandhi's views on the subject of S&T were understood in the right perspective by his renowned admirer in Europe, Romain Rolland. In a letter to Stefan Zweig (1881–1942), the famous Austrian novelist and playwright who had misgivings about Gandhi's stand on science and modernisation, Rolland writes: 'As to what you write about his attitude to machinery, well, it's a most strange error, fostered by the

German press which has never taken the trouble to make a close study of Gandhi's thought and action because at heart it has no sympathy for him. Gandhi – today's Gandhi – in no way condemns machinery or industrial techniques, insofar as they bring help and relief to humanity; his quarrel is merely with the murderous excess and the morbid myth of overproduction. When you look at India, you find a very special situation...Since English domination has undermined village crafts which added to the insufficient profits they drew from land, millions of men have been reduced to poverty and malnutrition. The most urgent problem is to bring back craftsmanship, of which the simplest form, accessible to all and bringing in sure returns, is the spinning wheel'.[36]

In articulating his views on the kind of industrialisation he favoured – or disfavoured – Gandhi did not skirt the crucial issue of the conflict between labour and capital. Here his views were distinctly socialist and internationalist. In a conversation with a reader, who confronted him on his thoughts on modern civilisation, he explained: 'Organisation of machinery for the purpose of concentrating wealth and power in the hands of a few and for the exploitation of many I hold to be altogether wrong. Much of the organisation of machinery of the present age is of that type. The movement of the spinning wheel is an organised attempt to displace machinery from that state of exclusiveness and exploitation and to place it in its proper state. *Under my scheme, therefore, men in charge of machinery will think not of themselves or even of the nation to which they belong but of the whole human race.* Thus, Lancashire men will cease to use their machinery for exploiting India and other countries but on the contrary they will devise means of enabling India to convert in her own villages her cotton into cloth. Nor will Americans under my scheme seek to enrich themselves by exploiting the other races of the earth through their inventive skill.'[37] (*Emphasis added*)

Gandhi showered high praise on Euclid (Greek mathematician from the third century BC), Isaac Merritt Singer (inventor of the Singer sewing machine) and Marie Curie (the Polish scientist who won two Nobel prizes in physics and chemistry).

Mathematics is regarded as the mother of all sciences. It is also at the heart of every machinery and technology. Therefore, those who think that Gandhi was opposed to S&T would do well to know what he thought of this most abstract of all the branches of knowledge.

Gandhi was deeply interested in mathematics, an interest that was ignited by his study of Euclid's theorems in school. He regarded the language of mathematics as a manifestation of the language of truth. He often referred to Euclid to explain his social and philosophical thoughts. The following conversation that R.R. Keithahn, an American missionary had with him in 1937 is quite instructive. Keithahn was not quite sure what Gandhi had in mind when he said that all religions were not only true but equal. Scientifically, he felt, it was hardly correct to say that all religions are equal. People would make comparisons between animists and theists. 'I would say,' said Keithahn(K), 'it is no use comparing religions. They are different ways. Do you think we can explain the thing in different terms?'

Gandhi (G): You are right when you say that it is impossible to compare them. But the deduction from it is that they are equal. All men are born free and equal, but one is much stronger or weaker than another physically and mentally. Therefore, superficially, there is no equality between the two. But there is an essential equality: in our nakedness. God is not going to think of me as Gandhi and you as Keithahn. And what are we in this mighty universe? We are less than atoms, and as between atoms there is no use asking which is smaller and which is bigger. Inherently we are equal. The differences of race and skin and of mind and body and of climate and nation are transitory. In the same way, essentially, all religions are equal. If you read the *Quran*, you must read it with the eye of Muslim; if you read the *Bible*, you must read it with the eye of Christian; if you read the *Gita*, you must read it with the eye of a Hindu. Where is the use of scanning details and then holding up a religion to ridicule? Take the very first chapter of *Genesis* or of *Matthew*. We read a long pedigree and then at the end we are told that Jesus was born of a virgin. You come up against a blind wall. But I must read it all with the eye of a Christian.

K: Then even in our *Bible*, there is the question of Moses and Jesus. We must hold them to be equal.

G: Yes. All prophets are equal. It is a horizontal plane.

K: If we think in terms of Einstein's relativity all are equal. But I cannot happily express that equality.

G: This is why I say they are equally true and equally imperfect. The finer the line you draw, the nearer it approaches Euclid's true straight line, but it never is a true straight line. The tree of religion is the same, there is not that physical equality between the branches. They are all growing, and the person who belongs to the growing branch must not gloat over it and say, 'Mine is the superior one'. None is superior, none is inferior, to the other.[38]

Gandhi's Self-Image: A Scientist More than a Saint!

Gandhi's views on S&T evolved over time, and this evolution was not devoid of dilemmas in his mind. What is remarkable and instructive is the honesty and transparency that marked the way he grappled with the tension between the ideal and the possible. A good example is the inner struggle he had to wage in coming to terms with the most visible symbols of modern civilisation – the railway and the motor car. As he has explained in *Hind Swaraj*, his criticism of railways was based on how the British used this infrastructure to consolidate their colonial rule. However, there was another reason. Gandhi was also critical of the modern man's craze for fast and unnecessary mobility, which he believed made man pay less attention to his inner self. 'Speed is not the end of life. Man sees more and lives more truly by walking to his duty', he wrote in *Harijan* of 30 September 1939, in an article titled 'On the Train to Simla.' The article provoked an erstwhile admirer of Gandhi – referred to, simply, as 'R' – to write to him: 'I am surprised that, with all the fund of humour you possess, you could not see how the words "On the train to Simla" pointed the finger of ridicule to the statement "Man sees more and lives more truly by walking to his duty"'.

Never one to evade uncomfortable questions, Gandhi replied: 'I was in my senses when I wrote the note referred to. I might easily have avoided the exact place where it was penned. But I wanted to add point to my remark and to discover to the reader the vast gulf that separates me from my ideal. Let the waverers take heart from the fact that though my note containing the flat contradiction of the ideal has provided my friend with mirth, I have got the credit for trying my best to live up to the ideals I may profess. If I am to make an ever-increasing approach to my ideal, I must let the world see my weaknesses and failures so that I may be saved from hypocrisy and so that, even for very shame I would try my utmost to realise the ideal. The contradiction pointed out by the friend also shows that between the ideal and practice there always must be an unbridgeable gulf. The ideal will cease to be one if it becomes possible to realise it. The pleasure lies in making the effort, not in its fulfilment. For, in our progress towards the goal we ever see more and more enchanting scenery'.[39]

Gandhi then referred to *Hind Swaraj* and said: 'The key to understand that incredibly simple (so simple as to be regarded foolish) booklet is to realise that it is not an attempt to go back to the so-called ignorant, dark ages. But it is an attempt to see beauty in voluntary simplicity, poverty and slowness. I have pictured that as my ideal. I shall never reach it myself and hence cannot expect the nation to do so. But the modern rage for variety, for flying through the air, for multiplicity of wants, etc., have no fascination for me. They deaden the inner being in us. The giddy heights which man's ingenuity is attempting, take us away from our Maker who is nearer to us than the nails are to the flesh which they cover'.[40]

While Gandhi aspired to this ideal, he was also aware of the gap between his aspiration and achievement. In his conversation with 'R', the aforementioned reader of his journal, he says: 'Ideally, I would rule out all machinery, even as I seek the absolute liberation of the soul. But machines will remain because, like the body, they are inevitable. The body itself is the purest piece of mechanism; but if it is a hindrance to the highest flights of the soul, it has to be rejected'.[41] *(More about Gandhi's remarkable conversation with 'R' in Chapter 10.)*

Although Gandhi ceaselessly tried to experience the 'flights of the soul', he did not opt for the life of a monk living in the Himalayas. 'The Himalayas of my penance are where there is misery to be alleviated, oppression to be relieved. There can be no rest for me so long as there is a single person in India...lacking the necessaries of life, by which I mean a sense of security, a lifestyle worthy of human beings – that is, clothing, education, food and shelter of a decent standard'.[42] He remained a man of action in the din of politics and the drama of life until his last breath. 'My Himalayas are here,'[43] he affirmed again on 29 January 1948, the penultimate day of his life, as he tried heroically to douse the fires of communal violence in Delhi, Punjab, Bihar and Bengal. In his autobiography, *The Story of My Experiments With Truth*, Gandhi writes: 'To see the universal and all-pervading Spirit of Truth face to face we must be able to love the meanest of creation as oneself. And a man who aspires after that cannot afford to keep out of any field of life.... If I found myself entirely absorbed in the service of the community, the reason behind it was my desire for self-realisation'.

It is appropriate to mention here that Gandhi's own self-image was that of a scientist! 'It (saint) is too sacred a word to be lightly applied to anybody, much less to one like myself who claims only to be a humble searcher after Truth, knows his limitations, makes mistakes, never hesitates to admit them when he makes them, and frankly confesses that he, like a scientist, is making experiments about some of "the eternal verities" of life'.[44]

As behoves a man of scientific temper, Gandhi never claimed finality for his ideas. He didn't even claim that he had all the answers. He once described satyagraha as 'a science in the making'.[45] This self-image as a scientist – rather, as a seeker after Truth who is willing to revise his own views in the light of new facts and fresh reflection, even at the risk of appearing inconsistent – is presented even more assertively in the following words of incomparable beauty.

> I would like to say to the diligent reader of my writings and to others who are interested in them that I am not at all concerned with appearing to be consistent. In my search after Truth I have discarded many ideas and learnt many new things. Old as I am in age, I have no feeling that I have ceased to grow inwardly or that my growth will stop at the dissolution of the flesh. What I am concerned with is my readiness to obey the call of Truth, my God, from moment to moment, and therefore, when anybody finds any inconsistency between any two writings of mine, if he has still faith in my sanity, he would do well to choose the later of the two on the same subject.

M.K. Gandhi
Harijan, 29 April 1933

Incidentally, this quotation from Gandhi appears at the beginning of all his books published by Navajivan Trust, Ahmedabad.

After reading such honest, candid and wise words, what can we say about this man? We can only think of him as someone who belonged to that superior evolutionary phase of man (*Satya Yug*) which existed in the distant past and which will surely return in the distant future.

Gandhi's four ashrams: *(clockwise) Phoenix Settlement in Durban (1904 – picture shows the printing press where Gandhi published his newspaper* Indian Opinion*); Tolstoy Farm near Johannesburg (1910); Sabarmati Ashram in Ahmedabad (1915); and Sevagram Ashram near Wardha, Maharashtra (1936).*

Illustrations: Rathin Mitra; AICC Publication (1985)

Courtesy: Gandhi Smriti

Paramahansa Yogananda (left) having a meal with Gandhi when he visited the Sevagram Ashram in 1935. He later wrote: 'On the side of his plate was a large lump of very bitter neem leaves, a notable blood cleanser. Gandhi bit by bit was eating the neem paste with as much relish as if it had been a delicious sweetmeat. In this trifling incident I noted the Mahatma's ability to detach his mind from the senses at will.'

8

THE ASHRAM AS AN R&D CENTRE
Gandhi's Amazing Experiments in Dietetics

⇢⟶⟁⬧⬥⬧⟁⟵⟢

The ideology of progress and the role of advertising are two of the basic reasons that our society is obsessed with materialism... As with other excesses, promotion of gluttony – a form of overconsumption that directly affects the body – is a product of consumer society. Food manufacturers compete fiercely to win market share by engineering foods that appeal to the palate. The result is that most of the foods offered today are laced with fat, sugar and salt. This fierce competition does not simply persuade consumers to change from one product to another: it also means that consumers eat more....Both the pharmaceutical and the food industries profit from obesity and, once again, the medical profession and drug companies play a crucial role in diverting us from asking what it is about our society that gives rise to these pathologies.

– Clive Hamilton, an Australian scholar-activist who has written
several bestselling books such as *Growth Fetish (2003),*
Affluenza (2005), and *Requiem for a Species.*

THERE IS NO SPHERE OF HUMAN DEVELOPMENT, AND ALSO NO ASPECT of what has now come to be recognised as 'social infrastructure' (education, healthcare, drinking water and sanitation, creation of sustainable livelihoods, women's empowerment, care of the vulnerable and marginalised sections of society, animal care, etc.) which escaped Gandhi's scientific attention. His two ashrams in South Africa and two in India – Phoenix Settlement near Durban (1904) and Tolstoy Farm near Johannesburg (1910), Sabarmati Ashram in Ahmedabad (1915) and Sevagram Ashram near Wardha in Maharashtra (1936) – were the laboratories in which he conducted a wide range of experiments in applied sciences. He used to tell visitors that his ashram itself was a 'scientific and prayerful experiment'.

Gandhi personally conducted amazing research into dietetics and healthcare, bringing an eager scientific mind to bear on the two inter-related subjects. The starting point of research was his belief that 'a man becomes what he eats' – the grosser the food, the grosser the body. This explains why he became a strong votary of vegetarianism. He favoured the virtue of frugalism in eating. 'One should take just enough food for the requirements of the body and no more. The body was never meant to be treated as a refuse bin holding the foods that the palate demands.' For him, food was not something that just satiated hunger; rather, it was an integral part of shaping the human consciousness[1]. He said: 'When food submerses in the body, and through the body in the soul, its relish disappears, and then alone does it begin to function in the way nature intended it to.'

His personal spiritual growth was not the sole purpose of his research into dietetics. For him, food security of the poor people – maximum nutrition at minimum cost – was also a priority. Here again, we see Gandhi's ingenuity in the application of his khadi philosophy to the fulfilment of people's food needs. Just as he advocated local production of cloth using a locally grown raw material for local consumption, the 'Gandhi-diet' focussed on low-cost nutritious food articles that could be locally produced or sourced and that did not travel far. Being a 'practiced cook', he wrote about cooking practices that did not diminish the nutritive value of foods used by the poor. He cautioned that factory-milled wheat and rice were inferior to hand-ground cereals. He stressed the medicinal qualities of cheaply available food items such as tamarind and sour lime.

Bharatan Kumarappa, editor of a remarkable volume of Gandhi's writings on *Diet and Diet Reform* (Navajivan Publishing House, Ahmedabad), has noted that Gandhi never relied on mere theory or second-hand knowledge but 'incessantly' carried on experiments in diet, both on himself and on his fellow ashramites. Kumarappa writes: 'He experimented with ovens, vessels for cooking, quantity of water to be used, steaming, boiling, baking, determining what ingredients are to be used or avoided in cooking, various ways of making bread, manufacture of jams and *murabbas* out of fruits and orange-skins which might otherwise be wasted or thrown away, use of green leaves as salads, preparing dishes out of oilcake and soya beans, combining various articles to constitute a balanced diet, and making up of suitable diets for invalids and convalescents. He had the weights of his *ashramites* recorded regularly and carefully observed the effects of changes introduced in their diet. He took nothing for granted. His experiments were conducted with a view to finding out the most wholesome food and the wisest ways of preparing it, all the time keeping in mind the poverty of our people and their slender resources'.

Here was a scientist at work! And all these experiments were conducted by a man whose own meals were a study in frugality: 'I take generally: 8 *tolas* of germinating wheat, 8 *tolas* of sweet almonds reduced to a paste, 8 *tolas* of green leaves pounded, 6 sour lemons, and 2 ounces of honey.'[2] (One *tola* was 11.66 grams.) He would often change his diet, alternating germinating wheat with germinating gram, almond paste with coconut milk, etc. He would also consume one litre of goat's milk, which he preferred over cow's milk because the former, he discovered, has greater amounts of vitamin A and minerals, and is good for the heart and arteries. Once he remained a fruitarian for five years. At another time he experimented with eating mainly uncooked food. (The only thing touched by fire that he consumed was hot water with lime and honey.) In a letter to Richard Gregg (1885-1974), the American pacifist philosopher who was much influenced by the Mahatma, he said that living on sun-baked fruits and nuts without using fire would bring animal passions under conscious control.[3]

Gandhi knew that his dietetic practices were the subject of ridicule in some circles, but he remained undeterred. 'I have been known as a crank, faddist, mad man. Evidently the reputation is well deserved', he wrote in *Young India* (13 June 1929). He recounts an interesting story of how his dietetic experiments on himself, which he had begun as a twenty-year-old student in London, led him to become a proponent of uncooked food under the influence of one Sundaram Gopalrao, a naturopath in Rajahmundry, now in Andhra Pradesh. Let us hear it in Gandhi's own words:

> **Gandhi (G):** Would you advise me to adopt entirely raw food?
> **Sundaram Gopalrao (S.G.):** Certainly, why not? I have cured many cases of chronic dyspepsia in old men and women through a balanced diet containing germinating seeds.
> **G:** (*gently remonstrating*) But surely there should be a transitional stage.
> **S.G.:** No such stage is necessary. Uncooked food, including uncooked starch and protein are any day more digestible than cooked food. Try it and you will feel all the better for it.
> **G:** Do you take the risk? If the cremation ceremony takes place in Andhra, the people will cremate your body with mine.
> **S.G:** I take the risk!
> **G:** Then send me your soaked wheat. I commence from today.
> Poor Gopalrao sent the soaked wheat. Kasturba, not knowing that it could possibly be meant for me, gave it to the volunteers who finished it. So I had to commence the experiment the following day. It is therefore now a month when I am writing these notes. I am none the worse for the experiment. Though I have lost five pounds in weight, my vitality is unimpaired....

Besides revealing his sense of humour, this excerpt also shows how a research-based healthy diet and rigorous self-discipline helped Gandhi (height: 5 ft 3 inches; weight: a mere 100 pounds; Body Mass Index: 17.7) 'to keep fit and wage a war that required all his energy and determination'.[4] Even in the last year of his life, when he was seventy-eight, he worked eighteen hours a day. Sometimes his working hours extended to twenty-one.

Talking about Gandhi's sense of humour, he had it in abundance. Once when he landed in France, the French were shocked to see him in a loin-cloth. He told them with a smile: 'You in your country wear plus-fours, but I prefer minus-fours.' Some still kept wondering whether he was going to meet the King of England or to move about in a cold country and among well-dressed people in his scanty dress. Gandhi assured them with a twinkle in his eyes: 'The king has enough for both of us.' An American lady once asked him: 'Mr. Gandhi, when will you be visiting America, people are eager to see you'. His reply: 'Yes, I have heard about that. They have kept the zoo and cage ready so that everyone can see this strange creature.' Those who saw him, of course, never missed his unusually gentle face and sparkling eyes, highlighted by the wire-thin frame of his spectacles.

Gandhi's asceticism, was transparent. In 1931, on his way to London, the customs officials asked him to declare his possessions. His reply: 'I am a poor mendicant. My earthly possessions consist of six spinning wheels, prison dishes, a can of goat's milk, six home-spun loin cloths, and my reputation which cannot be worth much.'[5]

Gandhi had physical fitness in abundance. The best description of how incredibly fit he was can be found in the many letters that Romain Rolland wrote to his European friends after the five days that the Mahatma spent in Rolland's villa near Geneva in 1931. 'The frail appearance of the little man is the only thing about him that is deceptive. (It) gives a false idea of the unshakable solidity of his body and his will. He's as hard as nails. When he walks on his skinny heron-like legs, he doesn't walk; he runs like a hare, and there's no one who can follow him...Even the best walkers have difficulty in following him. On the Monte Mario he left a trail of panting journalists behind him... And he could talk to the crowds for twenty-four hours at a stretch without a crack in his voice or in his train of thought... He is a tiger-tamer... (As to the European cold in December), for the five days and nights he spent here, when the weather was rainy and freezing, he always had all the windows open, day and night; bare legs and bare head, too, in all weathers. If no one kills him, he hasn't reached the end of his battles. We would do well to draw inspiration from his recipes for mental and dietary hygiene'.[6]

Self-Suffering as the 'Moral Equivalent of War'

Mention must be made here that Gandhi experimented not only in eating but also in fasting. His research into the subject, which began by observing his family tradition of observing fasts on special days of the Hindu calendar, had convinced him that regular fasting detoxifies the body and tempers the baser instincts of man – 'a genuine fast crucifies the flesh and to that extent sets the soul free...Buddha, Jesus and Mohammed fasted so as to see God face to face'. He also said that fasting helped him empathise with the poor. Additionally, he routinely resorted to fasting for penance, which became an integral part of his unique method of political agitation. He explained: 'My religion teaches me that whenever there is distress which one cannot remove, one must fast and pray...(Fasting and prayer) are the earnest cry of a soul in anguish. It cannot but influence the whole world and cannot but make itself heard in the divine court'.[7] He fasted seventeen times for India's freedom, for twenty-one days on two occasions, once even in his seventies!

Sometimes his British critics flayed him for resorting to fasting as a way of coercing the colonial government, and said coercion could not be nonviolent. To this, Gandhi's reply, in characteristic humility, was: his fasting was 'the same kind of coercion which Jesus exercised upon you from the cross'.[8] Suffering is the inevitable outcome of fasting as an act of protest against injustice. However, Gandhi audaciously describes such suffering as the Moral Equivalent of War. He explains it convincingly by stating that, up to the year 1906, he simply relied on appeal to reason whenever there was a case of injustice against the Indian community in South Africa. He was a good draftsman who always had a close grip of facts, which was the necessary result of his meticulous regard for truth. But he found that reason failed to produce an impression on South Africa's white racist rulers. His followers were angry and many of them talked of wreaking vengeance. 'I had then to choose between allying myself to violence or finding out some other method of meeting the crisis and stopping the rot and it came to me that we should refuse to obey legislation that was degrading and let them put us in jail if they liked. Thus came into being the moral equivalent of war'.[9]

After he returned to India, his many encounters with the unjust and callous British authorities further convinced him that people cannot secure justice by reason alone but have to suffer for it. 'Suffering is the law of human beings; war is the law of the jungle. But suffering is infinitely more powerful than the law of the jungle for converting the opponent and opening his ears, which are otherwise shut, to the voice of reason. Nobody has probably drawn up more petitions or espoused more forlorn causes than I and I have come to this fundamental conclusion that if you want something really important to be done you must not merely satisfy the reason, you must move the heart also. The appeal of reason is more to the head but the penetration of the heart comes from suffering. It opens up the inner understanding in man. Suffering is the badge of the human race, not the sword'.[10]

Gandhi's ideas and experiments in food and fasting are indicative of the kinship between head and heart or, in other words, between science and faith. According to Hindu scriptures, food (*annam*) is an immanent form of *Brahman* (the eternal, infinite and transcendent power that has created life) – *annam parabrahma swaroopam.* Upanishads say that Brahma, the God of Creation, is both reason (the realm of science) and spirit (the realm of faith). They describe food as representing an eternal Truth. Therefore, suffering caused by denial of food as an act of protest against cruelty and injustice, sends an appeal to the Creator. And the same Creator subsequently causes a change of heart in the perpetrator of violence, because He is the common father of both the victim and the doer of wrong. This makes both – the victim waging the 'moral equivalent of war' and also the wrongdoer who responds to it nonviolently by undergoing a change of heart – rise higher in the esteem of the Creator.

This nonviolent method of effecting positive change in society through heart-transformation of the people has not yet become an accepted way of conflict-resolution. Nevertheless, its superiority over all other ways of resolving conflicts is evident, more so because the change so effected is durable.

Relevance of Gandhi's Experiments in Dietetics

Are Gandhi's experiments in dietetics still relevant for our world in the twenty-first century? The answer is strongly in the affirmative for several reasons. Firstly, even though excess consumption on an unprecedented scale, coupled with access to a globalised variety of food, characterise the eating habits of the well-to-do in almost every country in the world, persistence of acute hunger on a large scale continues to mark the other side of the shameful reality. According to the UN Food and Agriculture Organisation (FAO), there were 925 million hungry people in the world in 2010. As many as forty million more people were pushed into hunger in 2008 alone due to the global financial crisis that was accompanied by the world food price crisis. Shockingly, FAO's studies show that less than ten percent of the world's undernourished people are hungry because of famine. In other words, chronic hunger is not so much due to lack of food as because of the fact that the poor lack opportunity to earn enough income to buy available food. In India, which is all set to become a two trillion dollar economy and where the urban rich can taste international cuisine at international prices, nearly half of our children age five or younger are malnourished. This is certainly not because India is suffering from an acute shortage of food.

Clearly, the prevailing world economic order and the dominant model of economic growth are incapable of removing poverty and hunger. The world will have to adopt a new model of growth guided by Gandhian ideals. This new model has to give priority to providing full, productive and sustainable employment to all able-bodied persons and also to making locally grown nutritious food available to local populations. This will enable individuals and communities to abide by the principle of Bread Labour, so essential to live one's life with dignity.

Dignity must also be restored to farmers, who, in spite of labouring to feed an ever-growing global population, remain deprived of both prosperity and societal recognition. Empowering local farming communities is necessary for another reason – hunger in the world cannot be removed by relying on large-scale, volatile and speculation-driven trade and transportation of food items across continents. This also means that the rich bio-diversity in agriculture, which is sought to be destroyed by the commercial interests of giant food multinationals, must be preserved. People in every agro-climatic zone should be able to have, and relish, natural and local food that is suitable to that zone.

Secondly, we must realise that the prevailing economic system, which needs for its very survival excessive consumerism among the rich and excessive deprivation among the poor, does not satisfactorily answer the basic question which self-reflective people have asked since time immemorial: Do human beings eat to live, or live to eat? Our ancient traditions sought to teach people the ethic of eating and fasting by combining it with the ethic of virtuous living. Today, eating – and consuming other goodies offered by the marketplace – is delinked from all that adds real value and virtue to life. Indeed, in an instance of perverse etymological subversion, 'good life' and 'fine dining' have come to mean thoughtless and limitless consumption of a never-ending variety of goods, the more expensive and exclusively branded the better. Frugality of the kind that Gandhi advocated, so that man can come closer to his Maker, is being regarded as a foe of economic growth. Measured in abstract gross domestic product (GDP) terms, and stripped of all cultural and spiritual parameters, economic growth has become the be all and end all of human existence.

There is a third reason why Gandhi's experiments in dietetics are still relevant. Even though the general population cannot be expected to emulate his extremely frugal food habits, nobody can ignore the inseparable connection between food and health. What we eat, how we eat, and how much we eat significantly impact our physical, mental, emotional and spiritual health. Gandhian philosophy understands health in a holistic sense. Gandhi, the radical and relentless researcher, conducted a series of serious experiments in holistic health and nature cure, to which we now turn in the next chapter.

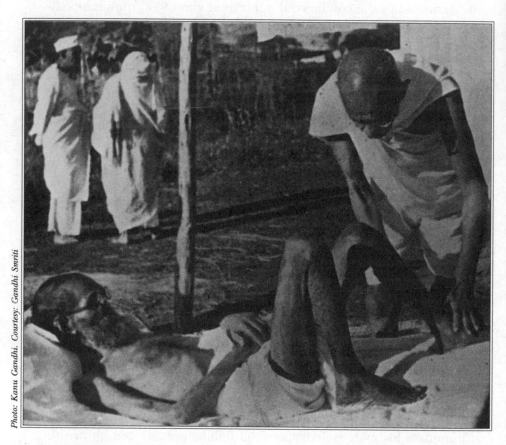

'Leprosy is not a stigma': *Gandhi personally treated a leper patient, an eminent Sanskrit scholar and freedom fighter named Parchure Shastri, at his Sevagram Ashram in 1940. Shastri recovered after some years of affectionate care and treatment. 'Nature cure,' Gandhi said, 'does mean a change for the better in one's outlook on life itself.'*

9

A CHAMPION OF NATURE CURE AND HEALTHCARE RESEARCH

→>%◇-⊗⊗◇-३←←

Doctors are like chandeliers, beautiful and exquisite, but expensive and inaccessible...I am like a little lamp, inexpensive and simple. And I can transfer light from one lamp to another, lighting the lamp of better health easily, unlike the chandeliers. Health workers like me can light another and another and thus encircle the whole earth. This is Health for All.

— Muktabai Pol, a village health worker from Jamkhed (Maharashtra) at a conference in Washington, D.C. May 1988. The Comprehensive Rural Health Project, Jamkhed (CRHP), founded by Dr Raj Arole and Dr Mabelle Arole, is inspired by Gandhian philosophy.

G ANDHI'S PASSION FOR NATURE CURE AND HOLISTIC HEALTHCARE was an extension of his deep interest in dietetics. He had an unwavering confidence in the ability of the body and the mind to heal themselves given the right opportunity and a conducive environment. Here too, as in the case of his approach to clothing and food, we see the application of the khadi philosophy of self-reliance. 'In nature cure,' he said, 'everybody can be his or her own doctor, not so in various other systems of medicine.' Disease, according to him, is due to a breach of Nature's laws. 'Nature has provided within the human body itself the means of cleansing it, so that when illness occurs, we should realise that there exists impure matter in the body and that she has commenced her cleansing process.'[1]

His experiments in treating diseases with natural curative agents only, without the use of modern drugs, had helped him gain considerable expertise during his long stay in South Africa. 'When I practised as a barrister,' he reminisced, 'cordial relations were established with my clients so that we looked upon one another almost as members of the same family. The clients therefore made me a partner in their joys and sorrows. Some of them sought my advice being familiar with my experiments in nature-cure... I made many such experiments on the (Tolstoy Farm), and I do not remember to have failed in even a single case.'[2] Among his regular patients were many Europeans, for some of whom he became the family physician. Since he had no formal education in medicine, and because his method of treatment was against the established rules of medical science, he earned the reputation in South Africa of being the first 'coolie quack' who was also, of course, the first 'coolie barrister'!

Gandhi continued his nature cure practice in both Sabarmati and Sevagram ashrams after his return to India. Sevagram, in particular, was a symbol of extreme self-denial for him and his colleagues. It was located in one of the hottest regions of the country, with no roads, no post office, no shops and no electricity. He wanted it that way, because most people in rural India lived in such conditions of deprivation. 'Whatever it may be to others, Sevagram is to me an inexhaustible source of joy', he wrote.[3] 'I am going to become a villager', he, who started living in a thatched hut, wrote on 6 July 1936 to Henry Polak, his friend and fellow-ashramite in South Africa. He wanted his close followers and also the national leaders, who came to see him, to understand the problems of those who lived in India's villages. For example, the very first monsoon brought malaria, typhoid or dysentery to the surrounding villages and also to the inmates of the ashram. Gandhi himself had an attack of malaria, so strong that the local physician, who treated him, panicked and urged him to move to the civil hospital at Wardha, the nearby town. He reluctantly agreed, but quickly regretted his decision. He felt that he had no right to go to a hospital, a facility beyond the reach of the villagers of Segaon (where the ashram was located). His illness made him think seriously about the health problems of rural India. He wrote: 'My malaria has quickened my resolve to study the problem of making Segaon malaria-proof. If I am to make my approach to village life, I must persevere in my resolve not to desert it in the hour of danger to life and limb'.[4]

Curing the social disease of untouchability in the villages around Sevagram became a major priority for Gandhi. He made a Harijan inmate in his ashram cook for him. Caste prejudices of 'high' and 'low' were deeply entrenched even among the untouchable castes themselves. Therefore, he refused to have his hair cut by the village barber so long he denied his services to other Harijans. By urging every ashramite to become his or her own scavenger, himself included, he sought to remove the social stigma attached to the scavenging profession. In his journal writings and also discourses during the prayer meetings, he made the people aware of the health benefits of good sanitary practices.

Nursing the sick using naturopathy methods was his passion. 'A man of truth must also be a man of care' was a lesson that he had learnt early in life from reading the Upanishads. He sponged the patients, gave enema and baths and applied mud-poultices, which was his unique nature cure practice. He had proved for himself, and also successfully tested in hundreds of cases that the simple and cheap method of mud-therapy cured headaches, ordinary boils and acted as a pain-killer. He had no fear of any infection when he treated patients.

His caring and healing instincts would become especially stronger when he encountered patients who had been shunned by society because of the stigma attached to their ailments. Thus, he had special concern for leprosy patients, whose wounds he would personally wash and dress. One of Gandhi's more famous photographs shows him giving a massage to a leper patient, an eminent Sanskrit scholar and freedom fighter named Parchure Shastri, at Sevagram Ashram in 1940. The two were together in Yeravada Jail in Poona in 1922. Gandhi treated his leprous wounds everyday, a routine that was not abandoned even when he had momentous political matters to attend to. He even determined the patient's diet. Shastri recovered after some years, thanks to the affectionate care and treatment he received from Gandhi and other ashramites.

It pained him greatly that India was 'a home of lepers next only to Central Africa'. Worse still, 'leper is a word of bad odour'.[5] 'Why,' he asked, 'should there be a stigma attached to leprosy any more than any other disease? Leprosy work is not merely medical relief; it is transforming frustration of life into joy of dedication, personal ambition into selfless service,' thus, urging his followers to work for the reintegration of leprosy patients into the mainstream of society. Since there was no specific cure for leprosy those days, he fervently hoped that 'medical science would find one soon so that this accursed disease could be forever eradicated'.[6]

In 1945, a year after Gandhi's wife Kasturba passed away, his followers set up a trust in her name to address the needs of women and children. He blessed the initiative and gave many constructive social programmes to be carried out by the Kasturba Gandhi National Memorial Trust. Leprosy eradication was one of its prime tasks.

It is worth mentioning here that Baba Amte (1914–2008), a worthy follower of Mahatma Gandhi, and his wife Sadhanatai, dedicated their lives for the rehabilitation and empowerment of people suffering from leprosy and other disabilities. Their two sons, Vikas and Prakash, and two daughters-in-law, Bharati and Mandakini – all doctors – have continued this godly work at the three ashrams that Baba Amte established in the tribal district of Gadchiroli in Maharashtra.

Another devoted doctor couple that is following Gandhi's footsteps by serving the poorest and the most neglected are Abhay Bang and his wife Rani Bang. Their work in Gadchiroli district, under the banner of their own organisation Society for Education, Action and Research in Community Health (SEARCH), has won national and international acclaim. Dr Abhay Bang's parents, Thakurdas and Suman Bang, were prominent leaders of the Sarvodaya movement. He spent his childhood in Gandhi's Sevagram Ashram. Significantly, he and his wife have named their ashram Shodhgram, which is dedicated to applying medical research for better healthcare in rural areas. (*'Shodh'* in Sanskrit means search and research.) Dr Abhay Bang's book *Sevagram to Shodhgram* gives an inspiring account of how traditional knowledge and modern scientific knowledge can be combined with a Gandhian approach to empower common people to live healthy and dignified lives.[7]

Gandhi knew the smallest detail of each sick person in his ashram and made it a point to visit every patient, usually on his way back from his daily walks. He gave detailed instructions to inmates managing the kitchen on how to prepare a special diet for the sick. The common joke in his ashram was: 'If you want Bapu to be near you, fall ill.'

Gandhi frequently extolled the virtues of nature cure in his speeches. When he visited Ashtanga Ayurveda Vidyalaya in Calcutta in 1925, he said: '...I belong to that noble, growing, but the still small, school of thought which believes more in prevention than in cure, which believes in Nature doing things for herself even for suffering humanity if we would but let Nature take her course. I believe that the less interference there is on the part of doctors, on the part of physicians and surgeons, the better it is for humanity and its morals.'[8]

He penned a remarkable book on nature cure titled *Key to Health* while he was imprisoned in Aga Khan Palace in Poona during 1942-44. 'Anyone who observes the rules of health mentioned in this book', he wrote, 'will find that he has got in it a real key to unlock the gates leading him to health. He will not need to knock at the doors of doctors or *vaidyas* from day to day'. In this book, he propounded his belief that 'the human body is the universe in miniature'. That which cannot be found in the body, he asserted, is not to be found in the infinite (*anant*) universe, referring to a famous Sanskrit adage *Yat Pinde Tat Brahmande.* 'The universe within reflects the universe without. It follows therefore that if our knowledge of our own body could be perfect, we would know the universe'.[9]

In *Key to Health,* Gandhi explains the healing powers of earth, air, water, sun, *akash* (sky), food and condiments. He also describes the health-destroying qualities of intoxicants, opium and tobacco. He devotes many pages of this book to elucidate his views on brahmacharya (narrowly understood as celibacy), which we shall discuss in detail in Chapter 24.

His thoughts on the therapeutic quality of the sky are highly original. 'The more we utilise this great element *akash*, the healthier we will be. The first lesson to be learnt is this that we should not put any partitions between ourselves and the inifinite sky which is very near and yet very far away. If our bodies could be in contact with the sky without the intervention of houses, roofs and even clothes, we are likely to enjoy the maximum amount of health. This is not possible for everyone. But all can and should accept the validity of the statement and adapt life accordingly. To the extent that we are able to approach the state in practice, we will enjoy contentment and peace of mind. This train of thought taken to the extreme leads us to a condition: when even the body becomes an obstacle separating man from the infinite. To understand this truth is to become indifferent to the dissolution of the body. For to lose oneself in the infinite is to find oneself. The body thus ceases to be a vehicle for self-indulgence...This must mean service of mankind, and through it finding God'.

Gandhi tells us that his 'desire to be in tune with the infinite' saved him 'from many complications in life'. How? 'It led not merely to simplicity of household and dress but all round simplicity in the mode of my life. In a nutshell, and in the language of the subject under discussion, I have gone on creating more and more contact with *akash*. With the increase in the contact came improvement in health. I had more contentment and peace of mind and the desire for belongings almost disappeared. He who will establish contact with the infinite possesses nothing and yet possesses everything. In the ultimate analysis, man owns that of which he can make legitimate use and which he can assimilate. If everybody followed this rule, there would be room enough for all and there would be neither want nor overcrowding.'

After this philosophical thought, he gives readers some practical advice. 'It follows that one should make it a point to sleep in the open. Sufficient covering should be used to protect oneself against the inclemencies of the weather against cold and dew...For the rest, the starlit blue canopy should form the roof so that whenever one opens one's eyes, he or she can feast them on the ever changing beautiful panorama of the heavens. He will never tire of the scene and it will not dazzle or hurt his eyes. On the contrary, it will have a soothing effect on him. To watch the different starry constellations floating in their majesty is a feast for the eyes. One who establishes contact with the stars as living witnesses to all his thoughts will never allow any evil or impurity to enter his mind and will enjoy peaceful, refreshing sleep'.

Gandhi then describes the healing qualities of the emptiness of akash within our bodies by referring to the virtue of regular fasting. 'We must not fill up the digestive tract with unnecessary foodstuffs. We should eat only as much as we need and no more. ...An occasional fast, say once a week or once a fortnight will enable one to keep the balance even. If one is unable to fast for the whole day, one should miss one or more meals during the day. Nature abhors a vacuum is only partially true. Nature constantly demands a vacuum. The vast space surrounding us is the standing testimony of the truth.'

We see here once again how Gandhi boldly challenges conventional wisdom, which holds that Nature avoids vacuum. He ingeniously explains that vacuum or the state of nothingness is also a natural reality and beneficial to human health and happiness in certain circumstances. This profound thought echoes Zen and other mystical philosophies around the world, all of which regard nothingness as sacred.

The crowning glory of Gandhi's commitment to naturopathy was the establishment, in 1946, of the renowned nature cure sanitorium in Uruli Kanchan, a village near Poona. He went into minute details of the working of the institution – accommodation, sanitation, book-keeping, signboards, etc. Even though India's freedom struggle had entered into its chaotic final phase by then, he still found time to spend eight days in this poverty-stricken village, populated mostly by Dalits. He personally treated hundreds of patients with the help of Dr Dinshaw Mehta and Manibhai Desai, who later established the Bharatiya Agro Industries Foundation (BAIF). He asked Desai to take up cattle development to ensure a good supply of milk, which could alleviate the poverty of the rural populace. When Desai protested that he knew nothing of veterinary science, Gandhi responded: 'Learn veterinary medicine scientifically by studying a book and practically by dismembering dead cows!' Desai, who was a Brahmin, did both. He dissected over 400 carcasses, and in the process became an authority on cattle physiology.[10]

Gandhi was a strong votary of ayurveda, yoga, unani, siddha and homeopathy systems of medicine, which have now come to be known by the acronym AYUSH. 'I am as anxious', he wrote, 'as the tallest among our Ayurvedic physicians can be to free ourselves from the tyranny of Western medicines which are ruinously expensive and the preparation of which takes no account of the higher humanities'. However, his dialogue with the practitioners of ayurveda was marked by candour and not without occasional criticism. 'I have no doubt that there is abundant wisdom in Sanskrit medical works. Our physicians appear to be too lazy to unearth that wisdom in the real sense of the term. They are satisfied with merely repeating the printed formula'. He appealed to ayurvedic physicians to shun the arrogant boast that there was no disease which they could not cure. He urged them, 'for the sake of this ancient science' to inculcate 'a spirit of genuine search', to constantly verify whether their own actual experience supports the textual prescriptions, and thereby further develop the science of ayurveda[11].

Once when he encountered criticism for saying that some ayurvedic practitioners were narrow-minded in their rejection of everything Western, Gandhi defended himself by saying, 'I do like everything that is ancient and noble, but I utterly dislike a parody of it. And I must respectfully refuse to believe that ancient books are the last word on the matters treated in them. As a wise heir to the ancients, I am desirous of adding to and enriching the legacy inherited by us.'[12]

In spite of his spirited advocacy of swadeshi, Gandhi was not a blind supporter of Indian knowledge or Indian products. Even in 1926, he unhesitatingly backed modern science developed abroad wherever he thought that it promoted human welfare. 'I have never considered the exclusion of everything foreign under every conceivable circumstance as part of Swadeshi...Swadeshi which excludes the use of everything foreign, because it is foreign, no matter how beneficial it may be, and irrespective of the fact that it impoverishes nobody, is a narrow interpretation of Swadeshi'.[13] Twenty years later, he wrote: 'My love of Nature Cure and of indigenous systems does not blind me to the advance that Western medicine has made'.[14]

Courtesy: Gandhi Smriti

'A man of truth must also be a man of care': *Nursing the sick using naturopathy methods was Gandhi's passion. At his ashrams, he used to sponge the patients, give enema and baths and apply mud-poultices. He had proved that mud-therapy cured headaches, ordinary boils and acted as a pain-killer. In this picture Gandhi can be seen with a mud-pack on his head.*

For example, he noted that he found nothing as effective as quinine for malaria or tincture iodine for simple pains, both developed by modern medicine. He was convinced about the great medicinal properties of honey and took a keen interest in bee keeping, but bemoaned the lack of standardisation in honey making which was insisted upon in the West. In a letter to the volunteers of the AIVIA, he wrote: 'I am told that in foreign countries such a careful analysis of honey is made that no sample which fails to satisfy a particular test is bottled for the market. In India we have got vast resources for the production of the finest honey, but we have not much expert knowledge in the matter'.[15]

He appealed to Indian medical professionals to conduct original research in many areas and not to become copycats. 'Has Indian medicine no fresh contribution to make to the medical science?' he asked them. 'Or must it always rely upon the patented nostrums that, together with other foreign goods, are dumped down upon this unfortunate soil? Why should the West have a monopoly of making researches?' His advice sounds as relevant today as it was when he gave it decades ago.

Gandhi was unhappy to see that modern medicine had 'given a cold shoulder' to naturopathy. He blamed both parties for this state of affairs. The practitioners of allopathic medicine, he said, 'have got into the habit of confining themselves to whatever is included in their own curriculum. They present an attitude of indifference, if not that of contempt, for anything that lies outside their groove.' On the other hand, while sympathising with the feeling of grievance that the nature curists nursed against modern medicos, he censured the tendency among the former to 'make tall claims' in spite of their 'very limited scientific knowledge' and their lack of the 'spirit of organisation'. He bemoaned that 'each one is self-satisfied and works by himself instead of all pooling their resources for the advancement of their system. No one tries to work out in a scientific spirit all the implications and possibilities of the system. No one tries to cultivate humility'.

How relevant these words are even today! Many enlightened medical practitioners in our country have been urging the government to reform the system of medical education by introducing a course in integrated system of medicine that combines AYUSH, naturopathy and allopathy. Their appeal has fallen on deaf ears so far. Allopathy rules the roost, whereas AYUSH and naturopathy suffer neglect and marginalisation in our healthcare policies and programmes.

No less damning is the fact that although Gandhi advocated a healthcare system in which the needs of the poor came first, independent India has promoted a system in which the healthcare needs of the poor receive the last priority. Primary and secondary healthcare services by government and municipal bodies have become a victim of inadequate funding, rampant corruption, gross inefficiency, bureaucratic control and apathy by most private practitioners. On the other hand, tertiary healthcare has been so excessively commercialised that it has become unaffordable for all but the super rich.

In spite of all the rhetoric in government policies, preventive and promotive measures of healthcare – which were the mainstay of Gandhi's experiments in dietetics and holistic health – have been consistently neglected in favour of hospital-based and capital-intensive curative care, which itself has become a purely business proposition for the private sector.

The worst victims in this system are the poor and the middle class, especially in rural areas, for whom a single instance of major illness in the family requiring hospitalisation and purchase of expensive drugs is a sure prescription for pauperisation and indebtedness.

Solutions to these problems certainly exist. Many of them can be found in a proper understanding of Gandhi's holistic philosophy of human health and in a serious, sustained and sincere effort at implementing that understanding for transforming our economy, politics, social relations and, most importantly, for transforming ourselves.

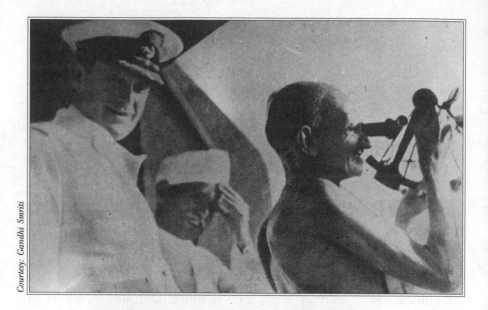

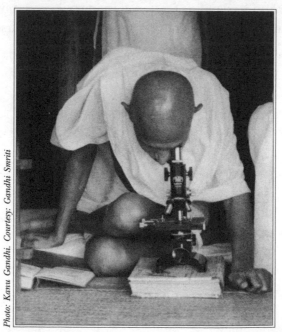

A romantic attraction for machines that served humanity: *(Above) Gandhi peering through a nautical telescope while on a voyage to London in 1931. (Below) Studying leprosy germs through a Jena microscope at the Sevagram Ashram in 1940. Gandhi had a fascination for astronomy and conjectured the possibility of humans landing on distant planets.*

10

'EVERYTHING CAN BE TURNED INTO A SCIENCE OR A ROMANCE...'

⇥⟡◇◆◇◇⟡⇤

Religion deals with the truths of the metaphysical world, just as chemistry and the other natural sciences deal with the truth of the physical world. The book one must read to learn chemistry is the book of (external) nature. The book from which to learn religion is your own mind and heart. The sage is often ignorant of physical science, because he reads the wrong book – the book within and the scientist is too often ignorant of religion, because he, too, reads the wrong book – the book without.

— Swami Vivekananda (1863–1902).

S CIENCE KNOWS NO NATIONAL BOUNDARIES. LONG BEFORE THE advent of globalisation, scientific knowledge and applications based on that knowledge have been known to have travelled far and wide across mountains and oceans. The 'zero' had its origin in India, but monks and traders took it to the Arabian peninsula in the west, from where it went to Europe, and then to China in the east, from where it went to Japan. Similarly, the science of silk and paper originated in China but spread to many places in Asia and beyond. Hakims, the multi-talented medicine-men and philosophers from Arabia, influenced the growth of chemistry and astronomy in Europe. Persian architecture had a big influence on the mosques and monuments built in India during the Mughul period, just as the glory of ancient India's temple architecture can still be found in Myanmar, Vietnam, Cambodia, Laos, Indonesia and Malaysia. We have earlier seen how Euclid, the Greek philosopher who is regarded as the 'Father of Geometry', kindled in Gandhi's mind a deep and lifelong interest in mathematics.

Internationalism is thus the true spirit of science. And Gandhi, an internationalist both in conviction and conduct, firmly believed that knowledge, irrespective of the place of its origin, belonged to the entire humanity. He would sing paeans to machines of foreign origin if he thought that they helped reduce human suffering or ease human drudgery. His principal point of departure from the West's scientific and technological traditions was that science must be used to promote human welfare and not as a tool of warfare and exploitation.

To illustrate this, let us see the following excerpt from an article ('A Morning with Gandhi') about his conversation with Mr R, whom we have encountered earlier in Chapter 7. It appeared in *Young India* of 13 November 1924.

> 'R' asked him: 'Are you against all machinery, Bapuji?'
>
> 'How can I be,' he answered, 'when I know that even this body is a most delicate piece of machinery? The spinning wheel itself is a machine. What I object to, is the craze for machinery, not machinery as such. The craze is for what they call labour-saving machinery. Men go on 'saving labour' till thousands are without work and thrown on the open streets to die of starvation. I want to save time and labour, not for a fraction of mankind, but for all. I want the concentration of wealth, not in the hands of a few to ride on the backs of millions. The impetus behind it all is not the philanthropy to save labour, but greed. It is against this constitution of things that I am fighting with all my might.'
>
> 'Then Bapuji', said 'R', 'you are fighting not against machinery as such, but against its abuses which are so much in evidence today.'
>
> 'I would unhesitatingly say "yes"; but I would add that scientific truths and discoveries should first of all cease to be mere instruments of greed. Then labourers will not be

overworked and machinery instead of becoming a hindrance will be a help. I am aiming not at eradication of all machinery but limitation...The supreme consideration is man.'

Gandhi then gives an interesting example of a foreign-made machine invented with man as the supreme consideration. He tells 'R':

'Take the case of the Singer Sewing Machine. It is one of the most useful things ever invented and there is a romance about the device itself. Singer saw his wife ... and simply out of love for her he devised the sewing machine, in order to save her from unnecessary labour. He, however, saved not only her labour but also the labour of everyone who could purchase a sewing machine.'

'But in that case', said 'R', 'there would have to be a factory for making these Singer Sewing Machines.'

'Yes,' said Bapu. 'But I am socialist enough to say that such factories should be nationalised, or State-controlled. They ought only to be working under the most attractive and ideal conditions, not for profit, but for benefit of humanity, love taking the place of greed as motive. It is an alteration in the conditions of labour that I want. This mad rush for wealth must cease, and the labourer must be assured, not only of a living wage, but a daily task that is not a mere drudgery. The machine will, under these conditions, be as much a help to man working it as to the state, or the man who owns it. Therefore, replace greed by love and everything will come right.'

Gandhi's use of the word 'romance' to describe the sewing machine is deliberate. In his long essay titled 'What is Khadi Science?', he writes: 'Everything can be turned into a science or a romance if there is a scientific or a romantic spirit behind it'. He mentions that 'the late Maganlal Gandhi had a living faith in the potency of khadi. It was for him a thrilling romance. And he wrote the elements of the science of khadi...A science to be science must afford fullest scope for satisfying the hunger of the body, mind and soul'.[1]

He was fascinated not only by the charkha, but also by an even more basic device for cotton-spinning called *takli*. It is spun like a top on a simple spindle, perhaps the simplest machine ever invented by man. Its attraction for Gandhi lay in the fact that it was cheaper than the charkha and hence more affordable to the poorest of the poor. Besides its contribution to poverty alleviation, he liked its meditative and calming effect. 'I have realised its power and romance,' he said in his inaugural speech at an educational conference in Wardha in 1937, attended, among others by Dr Zakir Husain, an eminent educationist who later became the president of India.[2] He wanted takli-spinning to be made an integral part of his Nayi Talim system of education at the primary level. He said he could teach village children all about the circle and other concepts in geometry using takli 'without even mentioning the name of Euclid'.

The remarkable thing about Gandhi was that he was capable of seeing 'romance' as much in the science of a simple takli as in the technology of a steel plant. We have earlier referred to Gandhi's visit to the Tata Steel plant in Jamshedpur in 1925. According to the notes kept by Mahadev Desai, his trusted secretary and soulmate, 'the noble enterprise and extraordinary industrial genius of the late Jamsetji Tata' possessed 'the character of a romance'. Gandhi, who had gone there as a 'friend of the Tatas', took keen interest in seeing the 'gigantic works' of the plant. He admired how 'within the space of twenty years a hamlet which was surrounded by scrub and jungle has been converted into a picturesque site with a town on it of 105,000 souls'. The well-planned development of the township with suitable houses and roads, the establishment of a technological institute, the sewage disposal plant, and the setting up of a hospital and dispensaries 'where not only the employees but also people from neighbouring villages are treated free of charge' – all these made a favourable impression on Gandhi.[3]

And talking about his romantic attraction for machines that served humanity, including those of foreign origin, how can we not recall here that moving photograph of the Mahatma studying leprosy germs through a microscope at Sevagram Ashram in 1940? The telescope too was dear to him. Always keen on learning something new, he began to study the stars during his prison term in Yeravada (Poona) when he was past sixty. He took his first lessons in astronomy from a co-prisoner, for which he borrowed two large-sized telescopes from a wealthy follower in Bombay and got the permission of prison authorities to install them in front of his cell. He also read numerous books on astronomy, among them *Magic of the Stars* by Maurice Maeterlinck; *Greek Astronomy* by Sir Thomas Heath; *Hindu Astronomy: Ancient Science of the Hindus* by G.R. Keay; and a book on the life of Galileo. 'Every free minute I get I devote myself to astronomy. It is a wonderful subject, and more than anything else impresses upon me the mystery of God and the majesty of the universe. To be lying on your back in the open air on a starry night and regarding universe after universe in the immeasurable expanse, you cannot help becoming a worshipper of God. My mind leaps with joy as I do so. Oh, it is marvellous'![4]

Gandhi's passion for astronomy had made him conjecture the possibility of humans landing on stars and planets. 'The stars address silent discourses to us. It is a holy companionship. It may perhaps be that upon being able to reach the planets and stars one will get the same experience of good and evil that one gets on earth. But truly divine is the peaceful influence of their beauty from this distance...All these thoughts have made me a keen watcher of the infinite skies'.[5]

If such was his ardour for scientific discoveries about the universe, at both the microscopic and cosmological dimensions, could he have opposed the twenty-first century advances in microscopy (fluorescence microscopy which helps in the study of DNA and genetic diseases) and in telescopy (Hubble Telescope, which has sent to us images of infinite beauty from the farthest reaches of the cosmos – galaxies forming when our universe, which was born about 13.7 billion years ago, was 700 million years old)?

It is perhaps not a coincidence that the father of the Indian space research programme, Dr Vikram Sarabhai, was born into a family in Ahmedabad which was deeply devoted to Mahatma Gandhi, and often played host to him.

Karel Hujer: An Astronomer Describes
his Days with 'Maharshi' Gandhi

This chapter on Gandhi's romance with science, especially his fascination for stars and the cosmos, would be incomplete if it made no reference to what a leading astronomer of the last century has said about him. Dr Karel Hujer (1902–88), a professor of astronomy and physics at the University of Tennessee at Chattanooga, USA, had come to India in 1935 to study Hindu astronomy at the Benares Sanskrit Library. Hujer, a Czechoslovakian, had left his country of birth before the Nazi occupation and settled in the United States. In India, he visited Santiniketan to meet Rabindranath Tagore. He gave lectures in many Indian universities during his travels in India.

But Hujer's most memorable experience came when Gandhi invited him to be his guest at Sevagram Ashram. He spent two weeks there lecturing in the evenings to the Mahatma and his inmates about the philosophical aspects of modern astronomy. At Gandhi's suggestion, the Congress party invited him to participate in and deliver two lectures during its sessions in Wardha in August 1935.

After Gandhi's assassination, Hujer wrote a moving tribute in November 1948 titled 'Mahatma Gandhi, My Host'. Here are some excerpts:

> The most inspiring moment of my life will ever be that first sight of the Mahatma of India. Squatted on the ground, close to his countless harijans, there was the retiring, spiritual giant in his radiant simplicity, disarming friendliness and childlike unselfishness. In the apparent physical frailness there was so little of him, yet one could but feel an overwhelming power of the streaming torrent of a morally disciplined man, a spiritually matured and free sanyasi, a seer of ages. That instant is unforgettable. It occurred to me that if nothing else were accomplished, my pilgrimage in India had reached its fulfillment. ... Of his first utterances in the meeting, I recall those in regard to the message I then conveyed to Bapuji from Romain Rolland whom I had visited in Villeneuve,

Switzerland, prior to my departure for India. Long before that time, Romain Rolland, a free citizen of Europe, as I might call him, recognized in Gandhi his spiritual kinship and thus was perhaps the first to write a remarkable biography of the guru of contemporary India. ...

During my first presence at the evening prayer with Mahatma, I believe the sky was the most wonderful, the heavens the most mysterious that could ever be revealed to me. I was pleased to learn that he knew and enjoyed some of the popular works of my first teacher of astronomy, Camille Flammarion of France, who had impressed him some years before.

At Wardha Ashram, each day brought new and revealing light on Bapuji's inexhaustible source of simple wisdom. I was most deeply grateful for every moment possible to be in the close company of Bapu, as during those inspiring walks, during the period of his spinning when he would interview an endless chain of callers...And what a blessing to have been able to sit at the feet of the master during his Monday period of silence!

Those daily brisk walks at the time of approaching evening meditations, the chanting from the *Bhagavad Gita* and the period of prayer in particular provided the most blessed communion which returns to my memory as a heavenly feast of the soul. There the redeemed seer converted them into very simple codes of guidance. Once when I was asked to give an astronomical talk on our wonderful universe, he said to me: 'Put it so every child could understand.' I think of this advice when occasionally I hear a handful of specialists in the field of atomic physics who become intoxicated by their language in which they estrange themselves from humanity.

It all appears as a dream in this age, in our civilisation of super-force and prospects of atomic frenzy. Yet that dream became a reality and I am grateful for this grace of God. Maharishi! A great seer has passed this way and something of him will ever remain with us. All tyrants, dictators, and politicians, no matter how glorious in this age, will fall into utter oblivion but the Mahatma's memory will grow with the lapse of time.

In Gandhiji's companionship I realised that boundless spiritual beauty which lifts the soul above this world. Mahatma represents a majestic example and a guiding light in this age of materialism, when once again the East must reassert its ancient position of spiritual guidance while the West is submerged in the endless battlefields of chronic, serial world wars.

Once, at the noon meal, while Mirabehn, barefooted, approached Bapuji's seat, I could not resist the mysterious overwhelming awareness of participation in a spiritual feast in Christ's companionship. For the path of the Great Soul of India is the path of a seer of ages. Above the bloodstained freedom in integrated selfishness, sometimes described as a nation, Mahatma's road leads toward something more than liberation, toward that ancient and ageless wisdom, the victory of the spirit over the body. In our age we have no choice, for as John Haynes Holmes has stated, it is Gandhi or the atomic bomb.

In November of 1949, Hujer came to India again to participate in the World Peace Conference in memory of Mahatma Gandhi. En route home, he delivered a message from Jawaharlal Nehru to Albert Einstein in Princeton. Einstein took a keen interest in knowing about the discussions at the conference.

'Romance' and 'science' are not words that figure in the popular imagination of an ascetic like Gandhi. But, then, he was a romantic scientist of a unique kind. His fascination for the microscope on the one hand and for the telescope on the other, flowed from his reading of his favourite Upanishad, *Kathopanishad,* which says: *Anor aniyam mahato mahiyan /Atmasya jantor nihito guhayam* (Smaller than the smallest atom, larger than the infinite vast, the Supreme Soul breathes in the secret heart of man). I am reminded here of what Carl Sagan, the famous astrophysicist, author of bestselling books such as *Cosmos* and *Broca's Brain: Reflections on the Romance of Science*, and an admirer of Gandhi[6], has said on the subject: 'There is something religious, in a broad sense, about scientific investigation because we are drawn to it by what appears to be its awesome beauty and intricacy... We feel a deep-seated union with the universe because we are indeed made of the same stuff.'

While the beauty of stars and galaxies mesmerised Gandhi, he found the same beauty in service to society in an area that is generally regarded as ugly, dirty and lowly – sanitation, which we shall read about in the following chapter.

'If we do not keep our backyards clean, our swaraj will have a foul stench':
Gandhi had started doing a scavenger's job, and conducting scientific experiments in sanitation, from his South Africa days. His campaign for sanitation had twin social objectives – eradication of untouchability and promotion of the dignity of labour.

11

A SANITARY SCIENTIST'S UNFULFILLED
DREAM OF 'TOILETS FOR ALL'

On his second trip to India from South Africa, Gandhi attended the Congress session in Calcutta (1901)... The sanitary condition of the Congress camp was horrible. Some delegates used the verandah in front of their rooms as latrines. Gandhi reacted immediately. When he spoke to the volunteers, they said: 'This is not our job, this is a sweeper's job.' Gandhi asked for the broom and cleaned the filth. He was then dressed in western style. The volunteers were astonished but none came forward to assist him. Years later, when Gandhi became the guiding star of the Indian National Congress, volunteers formed a bhangi (scavengers') squad in the Congress camps. Once Brahmins only were made to work as bhangis.

— *Bahuroopee Gandhi* (Multifaceted Gandhi) by Anu Bandopadhyaya (1964),
with a foreword by Jawaharlal Nehru.

SCIENCE AND TECHNOLOGY, TO BE TRUE TO THEIR CALLING, MUST serve society by focussing their problem-solving powers on the most pressing challenges facing the common people. No political leader anywhere in the world highlighted this progressive approach to S&T more forcefully, more holistically and more uniquely than Gandhi did. This is evident from his zealous activism on two issues that were dearest to his heart – environmental cleanliness and sanitation. He went to the extent of proclaiming: 'Sanitation is more important than political independence.'[1] A few months before India became independent, he exhorted: 'If we do not keep our backyards clean, our swaraj will have a foul stench'.[2]

He was deeply distressed by the stark contradiction between our religious precept – 'Cleanliness is next only to godliness' – and the ubiquitous lack of hygiene and sanitation in India. 'Our lavatories bring our civilisation into discredit,' he said in anguish. 'We like to have an enjoyable bath, but don't mind dirtying the wells, tanks and rivers, by whose side we perform ablutions. These practices should be considered as a great vice. They are responsible for the disgraceful state of our villages and the sacred bank of sacred rivers and for the diseases that spring due to the lack of sanitation.'[3]

One of Gandhi's earliest laments on this subject came when he went to participate in the Kumbh Mela[4] in Haridwar in 1915 – not with the sentiments of a pilgrim but as a volunteer to do sanitation work. For although he was overwhelmed by the piety of hundreds of thousands of devotees who had come to have a dip in the sacred Ganga, he was appalled by the people's unhygienic habits and even more by the insanitary conditions in Haridwar, one of the holiest of places for Hindus. 'I had gone there full of hope and reverence. But while I realised the grandeur of the holy Ganga and the holier Himalayas, I saw little to inspire me in what man was doing in this holy place. To my great grief I discovered insanitation, both moral and physical. ...There is defilement of the mighty stream even in the name of religion. Thoughtless ignorant men and women use for natural functions the sacred banks of the river where they are supposed to sit in quiet contemplation and find God. They violate religion, science and laws of sanitation'.[5]

He returns to this theme again and again, whether he is visiting a pilgrimage centre such as Gaya in Bihar or hill stations like Mahabaleshwar and Panchgani in Maharashtra. 'I have no desire to advertise the insanitation of Gaya, a prince among the holy places of Hinduism. It was because my Hindu soul rebelled against the stinking cesspools I saw in a principal street of Gaya that I was obliged to draw pointed attention to it in my reply to the address of the Gaya municipality...Every municipality should constitute a model school for teaching the science of sanitation. Of city sanitation we have not yet much knowledge. We do not mind what happens to our neighbours, so long as our own houses are in fair order'.[6]

In 1946 Gandhi visited Panchagani, an idyllic hill station south of Bombay, to open a *dharmashala* (charitable rest house for the poor). Here is what he wrote: 'Panchgani is a fine hill resort. The air itself is like medicine. But if the present insanitary conditions continue, Panchagani will cease to exist as a health resort. In a climate like theirs, there should never be any epidemic. Yet they had the plague only the year before and had to vacate the bazaar which was indescribably dirty'. He then proceeded to make some concrete suggestions. The first and foremost was night-soil disposal. Having become a *bhangi* (human excreta-picker) himself, he thought of it first. He had done a scavenger's job from his South Africa days. He knew how to do it without dirtying himself. The sight of a bhangi carrying the night-soil can on his head made him sick. Scavenging is a fine art, he said. Not only must the cleaning be perfect, but the manner of doing it, and the instruments used, must be clean and not revolting to one's sanitary sense. 'You have only to see the privy I use. It is spotlessly clean without a trace of smell. That is so because I clean it myself.'[7]

As in many other cases, this votary of swadeshi had no hesitation in telling his countrymen that they had much to learn from the West in matters of cleanliness. Read this exhortation in 1925:

> I learnt 35 years ago that a lavatory must be as clean as a drawing-room. I learnt this in the West. I believe that many rules about cleanliness in lavatories are observed more scrupulously in the West than in the East. There are some defects in their rules in this matter, which can be easily remedied. The cause of many of our diseases is the condition of our lavatories and our bad habit of disposing of excreta anywhere and everywhere. I, therefore, believe in the absolute necessity of a clean place for answering the call of nature and clean articles for use at the time.[8]

Gandhi abhorred the profession of manual scavenging, which the Indian society had forced 'untouchable' communities to perform. 'No one should clean and carry human excreta of others just to earn one's livelihood. There must be some scientific method of human waste disposal'. A leader who routinely cleaned the latrines in his own ashram, the Mahatma urged his fellow satyagrahis to 'master the art and science of sanitation... by dint of inexhaustible perseverance and patience that never looks back and knows no defeat'. His aim: eradication of the traditional system of scavenging so that the community of scavengers could be 'clothed with the dignity and respect due to them'. In his next birth, he said, 'I will like to be born into a family of scavengers, so that I may relieve them of the inhuman, unhealthy and hateful practice of carrying night soil.' Once, in his speech at a prayer meeting in New Delhi, he said: 'What is so distressing is that the living quarters of the menials and sweepers employed in the Viceroy's House are extremely dirty... I shall be satisfied only when the lodgings of the ministers' staff are as neat and tidy as their own.'[9]

Although Gandhi loathed manual scavenging and did everything he could to introduce scientific improvements in the practice of scavenging – his ashrams converted human waste into organic fertiliser and numerous experiments were conducted to invent toilets that required less water – he nevertheless took pains to highlight the dignity of labour associated even with this most stigmatised vocation. He exhorted upper-caste and upper-class people who regarded its practitioners as untouchables to know that a scavenger was indeed serving God by serving fellow human beings, and hence deserved to be treated with respect and gratitude. 'A scavenger who works in His service shares equal distinction with a king who uses his gift in his name and as a mere trustee', Gandhi wrote. 'I am not ashamed to call myself a *bhangi*, and I ask every *bhangi* not to be ashamed of his calling', he added. To drive home the point further, he told his countrymen: 'The ideal *bhangi* of my conception would be a Brahmin par excellence, possibly even excel him. My mother was certainly a scavenger inasmuch as she cleaned me when I was a child. Even so the *bhangi* protects and safeguards the health of the entire community by maintaining sanitation for it'.[10]

Indeed, in the last years of the British Raj, when hectic parleys were underway between British officials and leaders of the Congress party and Muslim League on the shape of independent India, Gandhi was living not in any opulent bungalow in Lutyen's New Delhi, but in the Bhangi Colony (scavengers' quarters) in Old Delhi, where he took the lead in its cleaning up operations and held his daily prayer meetings.

Sanitation and problems of rural development were recurring themes in Gandhi's correspondence with ordinary people, from whom he used to get hundreds of letters each day. He would take great pains to reply to them individually or respond to their questions and suggestions elaborately in his journals.[11] (Among the many ordinary Indians' letters displayed in the Gandhi Museum in New Delhi, there is one whose sender didn't know the address on which to send it to and simply wrote on the post card: Mahatma Gandhi *jahan ho wahan* – 'wherever he is'!)

In 1937, he received one such letter from 'a humble villager of Birbhum' near Santiniketan in Bengal, asking him: 'What is an ideal Indian village in your esteemed opinion...and which of the village problems should a (constructive) worker try to solve first of all?' Gandhi's answer: 'An ideal village will be so constructed as to lend itself to perfect sanitation...The very first problem the village worker will solve is its sanitation. It is the most neglected of all the problems that baffle workers and that undermine physical well-being and breed disease. If the worker became a voluntary scavenger, he would begin by collecting night soil and turning it into manure and sweeping village streets. He will tell people how and where they should perform daily functions and speak to them on the value of sanitation and the great injury caused by its neglect. The worker will continue to do the work whether the villagers listen to him or not'.[12]

'Clean Inside, Clean Outside'

I get moved each time I read Gandhi's exhortation about the neglect of sanitation, because India's apathy towards this basic human need, and right, continues unabated even now. We have legally abolished manual scavenging, but much of rural and urban India continues to be as insanitary as in his time, perhaps more so. Consider the shaming observation by a United Nations study in 2010 stating that there are 'more mobile phones than toilets' in India – as many as 665 million Indians, most of them in villages, defecate in the open. According to UNICEF, only thirty-one percent of India's population had access to improved sanitation facilities in 2008 – fifty-four percent in urban areas and twenty-one percent in rural areas. Open defecation is a common sight not only in villages but also in the slums in Indian cities.

In Mumbai, the country's commercial and financial capital where several billionaires live in opulent mansions alongside 55 percent of the city's population which ekes out a wretched existence in slums, as many as '20 percent of all slum dwellers defecate in the open'. Further, 'only 14 percent of the community toilets in slums have some water, and in its absence, the users are forced to carry their own pails...Women and children face difficulties in using poorly maintained toilets in the city'. These and other shocking facts are revealed in the Mumbai Human Development Report (2009), produced by the city's municipal corporation itself. Paucity of funds is certainly not the reason for this sorry state of affairs. After all, Mumbai's municipal corporation is the richest in the country. The real reason lies in not paying heed to the first principle of good civic governance enunciated by the Mahatma. When he visited the Mayavaram Municipality in Tamil Nadu in 1927, he told his audience: 'The first condition of any municipal life is decent sanitation and an unfailing supply of pure water.'

As far back as in 1925, Gandhi had written: 'During my wanderings nothing has been so painful to me as to observe our insanitation throughout the length and breadth of the land. I do not believe in the use of force for carrying out reforms, but when I think of the time that must elapse before the ingrained habits of millions of people can be changed, I almost reconcile myself to compulsion in this the most important matter of insanitation'.[13]

Has independent India heeded the Mahatma's warning? Every day 4,000 children across the world die due to diarrhoea, which is caused by poor sanitation and impure water. Fully one-fourth of this number are children born in India.

Poor sanitation continues to pollute the environment even in the holiest of holy pilgrimage centres in India. One only has to visit Varanasi to know that the situation has become worse in the last hundred years. The holy Ganga is so heavily polluted that, according to one estimate, nearly one million people living in the villages and towns along the banks of the river die each year due to various water-borne diseases. Not surprising, since nearly 300 million litres of sewage is discharged into the Ganga daily.

Poor sanitation has a direct effect on women's dignity, health, education and empowerment. It is well known that lack of toilets in schools is one of the primary factors behind the large-scale dropout of girl students in villages and in urban slums. Studies have also shown that lack of access to toilets for women in public places and work places – they are few, far between, poorly maintained and often unsafe – is one of the main reasons for high levels of urinary tract infections among working and frequently commuting women.

The United Nations' Millennium Development Goals (MDGs) mandate our country (and other developing countries in the world) to halve the proportion of people without access to water and sanitation by 2015. At the current rate of progress, India may not be able to reach the MDGs for water and sanitation even by 2050. Clearly, India is facing a mega-crisis in this most important index of human development. In Gandhi's time, at least some part of the blame could be legitimately placed on the British rulers for neglecting this problem. But whom can we blame now except our own governments and ourselves? Shouldn't we, at least now, appreciate why Gandhi accorded the highest priority to the much-neglected basic needs of the poor in India's economic development, including in the development of science and technology? It is indeed possible to achieve the goal of Nirmal Bharat (Clean India), both in rural and in dense urban areas, by evolving appropriate strategies that combine the requisite political will, people's active participation, reform of people's habits, useful inputs of science and technology, and, above all, adoption of Gandhi's broader concept of cleanliness to mean removal of both physical and moral insanitation in society. The mantra that will energise this transformation is 'Clean Inside, Clean Outside'.

'Education for life, education through life and education throughout life':
The basic premise of Gandhi's Nayi Talim was learning through doing, focussed on the all-round development of hand, head and heart. Education had to be rooted in the culture, life and needs of the people. To achieve this, he said, 'The vidyapeeth (university) must go to the village'.

12

NAYI TALIM
Gandhi's Answer to Why India Missed
its Own 'Industrial Revolution'

Many students, especially those who are poor, intuitively know what the schools do for them. They (policy makers) school them to confuse process and substance. Once these become blurred, a new logic is assumed: the more treatment there is, the better are the results; or, escalation leads to success. The pupil is thereby 'schooled' to confuse teaching with learning, grade advancement with education, a diploma with competence, and fluency with the ability to say something new. His imagination is 'schooled' to accept service in place of value. Medical treatment is mistaken for health care...police protection for safety...the rat race for productive work... Equal educational opportunity is, indeed, both a desirable and a feasible goal, but to equate this with schooling is to confuse salvation with the Church.

— Deschooling Society by Ivan Illich (1926–2002),
Austrian philosopher.

WE NOW COME TO A QUESTION THAT STUDENTS OF SCIENCE, history and economics in India often ask themselves: 'Why did India not have its own industrial revolution?' Gandhi did not skirt this question; rather, he answered it in his own creative and action-oriented manner. He was convinced that the decline and stagnation of India's native industrialisation was because of the divorce between the magic of the artisan's hand and the majesty of the scholar's mind. He believed that India had fallen into an unhappy state because 'we looked upon masons, shoe-makers, carpenters, blacksmiths and barbers as inferior to us, we had taken away all courtesy, learning, decency and culture from their trades and homes. We treated skilled work as low and exalted clerical work and thus invited slavery for ourselves'.[1]

There was a time, before the British conquest of India, when artisans and traditional providers of basic services were given proper respect in society. For example, the original word for *chamar* (shoe-maker) was *charmakar*, which, like *shilpakar* (builder or idol-maker) or *kalakar* (creator of arts), is quite honourable. Indeed, blacksmiths, carpenters, coppersmiths, goldsmiths, sculptors, etc., were called *viswakarma* (artisans with skills akin to those of the Creator of the Universe). There were different castes performing these traditional vocations, but there was symbiosis amongst all of them in the social and cultural ecology of the Indian village. The British rule not only pauperised rural India, but it also tore asunder this symbiotic relationship. This destructive process was accelerated by the spiritual corruption among Brahmins and other so-called 'upper castes', who promoted self-serving notions of 'high' and 'low' among vocation-based castes in society. The belittling of manual and artisan work was an outcome of this spiritual corruption. Unlike Japan, India failed to preserve the synergy and mutual respect between manual and intellectual work, and has paid a heavy price.

Gandhi repeatedly spoke and wrote about India's neglect of the village crafts due to the decoupling of education from manual training. 'Manual work has been regarded as something inferior, and owing to the wretched distortion of the *varna*, we came to regard spinners and weavers and carpenters and shoemakers as belonging to the inferior castes and the proletariat. We have had no Cromptons and Hargreaves[2] because of this vicious system of considering the crafts as something inferior divorced from the skilled. If they had been regarded as callings having an independent status of their own equal to the status that learning enjoyed, we should have had great inventors from among our craftsmen'.[3]

However, Gandhi held that the British rule was also responsible for the stagnation of India's industrial development. After all, before the British began its colonial pillage of India, our country was known for its vibrant achievements in industry, agriculture, arts and sciences. Until around 1750, India, together with China, was producing some seventy-three percent of the world's total industrial output. Even in 1830, what our two economies produced accounted for sixty percent of world industrial output. In technology, India manufactured steel that was superior to the steel then made in Britain. India was quite advanced in ship-building and seafaring. In textiles, India's capabilities were so refined that, in Gandhi's words, 'the lovely maidens of Assam weave poems on their looms'.[4] All this changed with Britain's deliberate policy of de-industrialisation of India. Among the methods England employed to destroy India's native village-based industrial base was the destruction of our traditional educational infrastructure.

In his long address at the Royal Institute of International Affairs, London, on 20 October 1931, Gandhi did not mince words in putting the historical record straight:

> I say without fear of my figures being challenged successfully, that today India is more illiterate than it was fifty or a hundred years ago, and so is Burma, because the British administrators, when they came to India, instead of taking hold of things as they were, began to root them out. They scratched the soil and began to look at the root, and left the root like that, *and the beautiful tree perished*. The village schools were not good enough for the British administrator. There are statistics left by a British administrator which show that, in places where they have carried out a survey, ancient schools have gone by the board, because there was no recognition for these schools, and the schools established after the European pattern were too expensive for the people. Our (future independent) state would revive the old village schoolmaster and dot every village with a school both for boys and girls[5].

Gandhi's greatness lies in the fact that he not only rejected colonial education, but he also put forward a radical alternative for an enlightened national system of education, which, he hoped, would be followed in independent India. He sought to create a practical remedy to this malady by launching a new paradigm of education that he called Nayi Talim (new education) or *Buniyadi Talim* (basic education). He formulated it at an All India Educational Conference, which he convened at his Sevagram Ashram in October 1937. His ashram became the laboratory to test this new system, which valued the innate capabilities of every section of India's diverse society and was guided by the integral vision of man, society and nature. With Sevagram becoming his permanent address in the last twelve years of his life (he stayed there for over seven years), he and his colleagues conducted various experiments in basic education in this place and, through this place, in many other parts of the country. Teachers and students from all over the country came to Sevagram for learning.

The basic premise of Nayi Talim was that education had to be rooted in the culture, life and needs of the people. It was defined as 'education *for* life, education *through* life and education *throughout* life'. As opposed to rote learning, it emphasised developing one's holistic personality through doing, thinking, caring and serving. The objectives of Nayi Talim were three-pronged. Firstly, it was people-centric. A child belonging even to the lowest stratum of society must receive basic education. Education had to be free and compulsory up to the age of fourteen years. Women must have equal right to education as men. To achieve this, Gandhi said, 'the *vidyapeeth* (university) must go to the village'.

Secondly, the new education system had to be character-centric. It must build the child's moral character right from the time of the primary school. He emphasised that 'literary training itself added not an inch to one's moral height or character-building'. Essentials of all religions should be taught to pupils for moral upbringing and also to promote communal harmony and universal brotherhood.

Thirdly, basic education had to be craft-centric. Learning would now be re-connected to doing. Education and work should not be separated. 'I hold that true education of the intellect can only come through a proper exercise and training of the bodily organs – hands, feet, eyes, ears, nose, etc. I would begin children's education by teaching them a useful handicraft and enabling them to produce from the moment they begin their training. I hold that the highest development of the mind and the soul is possible only under such a system of education. However, every handicraft has to be taught not merely mechanically as is done today, but scientifically – that is, the child should know the why and wherefore of every process. I am not writing this without some confidence, because it has the backing of experience. I have myself taught sandal-making and even spinning on these lines with good results'.[6]

'My plan to impart primary education through the medium of village industries,' he boldly declared, 'is the spearhead of a silent social revolution fraught with the most far-reaching consequences'.[7]

Making schools work-centric, Gandhi explained, had another benefit: each village school could become self-reliant with the help of productive economic activities such as gardening, agriculture, horticulture, dairy, spinning, weaving and other village crafts. He once poetically desired that he wanted not only 'thinking brains' but also 'thinking fingers'. He wanted 'work to vitalise learning, and learning to vitalise work'.[8]

Nayi Talim also emphasised the teaching of 'mathematics and the various sciences' that are useful for an intelligent and efficient exercise of a person's vocation. 'If to this is added music and literature by way of recreation', Gandhi wrote, 'it would give the student a perfect well-balanced, all-round education in which the intellect, the body and the spirit have all full play and develop together in a natural, harmonious whole. Man is neither mere intellect, nor the gross animal body, nor the heart or soul alone. A proper and harmonious combination of all three is required for the making of the whole man'.[9] Thus, his system of education focussed on all-round development of the three Hs: hand, head and heart.

Moreover, Gandhi was of the firm view that basic initial education must be imparted in the mother tongue. 'The foundation that Macaulay laid of education in India has enslaved us', Gandhi wrote in *Hind Swaraj*. According to him, initial education in the mother tongue facilitates the capacity for natural expression and stimulates creative development of the intellect and aesthetics. 'English education, in the manner it has been given, has emasculated the English-educated Indian, put a severe strain upon the nerves of our children, made them crammers and imitators, unfitted them for original work and thought, and disabled them for filtrating their learning to the family or the masses. The foreign medium has made our children practically foreigners in their own lands. It is the greatest tragedy of the existing system... Among the many evils of foreign rule, this blighting imposition of a foreign medium upon the youth of the country will be counted by history as one of the greatest. It has sapped the energy of the nation, it has estranged them from the masses, it has made education unnecessarily expensive. If this process is still persisted in, it bids fair to rob the nation of its soul. The sooner, therefore, educated India shakes itself free from the hypnotic spell of the foreign medium, the better it would be for them and the people... No country can become a nation by producing a race of imitators'.[10]

Gandhi's views on the language question are germane to the discussion on why English-educated India has still, by and large, remained a land of imitators and not innovators. The cognitive enslavement caused by English education – 'in the manner in which it has been given', as Gandhi helpfully emphasises – continues to this day. And so does the alienation of the educated from the masses. ('Those in whose name we speak we do not know, nor do they know us.' – *Hind Swaraj*) On the other hand, those who learn only in non-English languages continue to be deprived of the knowledge of modern scientific and technological knowledge. *(See Chapter 26 for a fuller discussion on the question of teaching of non-English languages in India's education system.)*

On the role and functioning of teachers, Nayi Talim departed radically from the convention. In line with the concept of lifelong or continuing education proposed by many progressive educational thinkers, it emphasised that a teacher must also be a keen learner. In a talk with the teachers and students of Khadi Vidyalaya in Sevagram,

Gandhi said: 'A teacher who establishes rapport with the taught, becomes one with them, learns more from them than he teaches them. He who learns nothing from his disciples is, in my opinion, worthless. Whenever I talk with someone I learn from him. I take from him more than I give him. In this way, a true teacher regards himself as a student of his students. If you will teach your pupils with this attitude, you will benefit much from them.' [11]

On another occasion, in a speech at the All-India Teachers' Training Camp in Sevagram on 19 November 1944, he expounded his educational philosophy comprehensively. We see in it how much it differs from the crass commercialisation of education in today's India. The following extract also shows how his mind chased one wise thought after another in a seamlessly artistic oratory covering both micro and macro issues.

> Your work will be that of pioneers... It is not an easy task that you have before you. This New Education will not help you get big jobs carrying high salaries and emoluments. But yours will be the privilege to go among and serve the villagers in their villages. Palatial buildings and costly equipment can, therefore, have no place in your scheme of work... True education can only be given under conditions of utmost simplicity.
>
> All the buildings here in the Talimi Sangh are built of local material and with the help of local artisans. We have thereby established a living link between ourselves and the people. That by itself is an education for the people and constitutes the foundation of our future educational work. If you thoroughly assimilate this ideal of simplicity and its importance in the New Education, you will have justified your training here. You will then appreciate your work.

Gandhi emphasised that cleanliness of the mind and body was the first step in education. 'Prayer does for the purification of the mind what the bucket and the broom do for the cleaning up of your physical surroundings.' The prayers had to be from all religious traditions. 'God has innumerable names, but the most beautiful and suitable in my opinion is Truth. Let Truth, therefore, rule every action of our life, be it ever so insignificant. Let every morsel of food that we eat be sanctified with His name and consecrated to His service. If we eat only to sustain the body as an instrument of His service not only will it make our bodies and minds healthy and clean, the inner cleanliness will be reflected in our surroundings also. We must learn to make our latrines as clean as our kitchens.'

Gandhi believed that what was true about the individuals was also true about society. The various functions in the human body, according to him, have their parallel in the corporate life of society. Therefore, what he said about the inner and outer cleanliness of the individual applied to the whole society. He then went on to extrapolate the seemingly simple-sounding principle of cleanliness to his big idea of how it would help create a nonviolent society.

> In the mighty world, man, considered as an animal, occupies but an insignificant place. Physically, he is a contemptible worm. But God has endowed him with intellect and the faculty of discrimination between good and evil. If we use this faculty to know God, we become a power for good. Abuse of that talent converts us into an instrument of evil, so that we become like a scourge and a plague and fill this earth with strife and bloodshed and unhappiness and misery.
>
> The struggle between the forces of good and evil is ceaseless and eternal. The former have Truth and Ahimsa as weapons against the latter's falsehood, violence and brute force. There is nothing more potent in the universe than God's name. If we enthrone Him in our hearts and keep Him there always, we shall know no fear and lay for ourselves rich treasure in life.[12]

Remarkably, Nayi Talim laid great emphasis on teachers and other grown-ups learning from children – especially the virtue of pure and spontaneous love. Gandhi discussed this aspect with Maria Montessori (1870-1952), the famous Italian educator for whose educational philosophy and practice he had very high regard, when he met her in London in 1931. He told her: 'I am impatient to realise the presence of my Maker, who to me embodies Truth, and in the early part of my career I discovered that if I was to realise Truth, I must obey, even at the cost of my life, the law of love. And having been blessed with children, I discovered that the law of love could be best understood and learned through little children.'[13]

It is possible to see from the above description of Nayi Talim that Gandhi's new educational philosophy had multivalent objectives, all rooted in his vision for the future independent India.

- It sought to catalyse India's own indigenous process of industrialisation without shutting the doors on the scientific and technological knowledge from the rest of the world.
- It aimed at creating livelihood opportunities to the rural populace using local resources and thus making Indian villages self-reliant. (We shall later see, in our discussion in Part V on the Internet-driven phenomenon of Glocalisation, how use of local resources is far more energy efficient than transporting resources, and, therefore, supportive of sustainable development. We shall also show that hi-tech can be a promoter of this Gandhian vision.)
- By emphasising craft-centric education and insisting on taking the school to village huts, it sought to support a silent, nonviolent social revolution in rural India. After all, most of the artisans, craftspeople and others engaged in menial services belonged to 'untouchable' communities. Thus, Gandhi's educational philosophy was an assault on untouchability, which he castigated as a 'crime against God and men'. (Let me add here that some extremist Ambedkarites' prejudiced diatribe against Gandhi as being 'anti-Dalit' is an assault on truth.)
- By envisioning that literacy and acquisition of knowledge and skills did not remain a monopoly of the 'upper castes', Nayi Talim attempted to promote social justice and economic opportunities for the 'lower castes'.

- By including the teaching of essential principles of all religions in the school curriculum, it underscored the importance of value education that is sorely lacking in the secular mainstream education system today.
- By re-enshrining the dignity of labour in the education system, Gandhi attempted to change the mindset of the elites in society. He advised the students from wealthy families 'not to feel puffed up, if they were made to sit on a chair, nor to feel ashamed, if asked to use a broom'.[14]
- Rather than recognising the narrowly utilitarian value of education, Nayi Talim elevated education as a peaceful method of establishing a new and progressive social order, one in which every member would be able to realise her or his full potential.

What is clear from the above discussion – the active promotion of various arts and crafts in his ashrams, Gandhi's own personal experiments in this field, and his initiative to establish organisations like the All India Spinners' Association, All India Village Industries Association, Harijan Sewak Sangh and the Leprosy Foundation – is that he firmly believed that India's native industrial revolution depended as much on *artisanisation* of Indian science and society, as on *intellectualisation* of artisans.

Sadly, the rulers of independent India chose not to be guided by the principles of Nayi Talim in formulating the educational policy and in building the educational infrastructure suitable to the needs of national reconstruction. Even though they continued paying ritualistic homage to the Mahatma, in reality, they concluded that his educational vision had become outdated. As a result, many of the ills of the colonial system of education that Gandhi had strongly criticised have not only continued but also become more deeply entrenched.

This is starkly evident in the curriculum and pedagogy in our rural schools where children of farmers and artisans enrol. The relevance of much of what is taught in these schools does not become apparent to rural children. Conversely, what is relevant to these communities is not taught to them. For example, isn't it astounding that agriculture is not even a subject in our village schools, although most students studying in these schools come from *kisan* families? Similarly, the school curriculum completely bypasses the native skills, traditionally acquired learnings, and the rich artistic-literary heritage of our various 'backward' castes and tribes in rural India.[15] Our school system demands rote learning, which impairs children's creativity. It attaches little importance to the amazingly deep local knowledge resources of India's diverse communities. It functions under the premise that education is only that which is rammed into the young minds by textbooks and guidebooks. By corollary, those who are out of the school system or have underperformed are deemed 'uneducated', even if they possess skilled hands, intelligent minds and untapped talent. All this has debilitating sociological and psychological consequences for them as well as for their families.

Moreover, the number of children deprived of a place even in the formal education system is not insignificant. As many as eight crore children who come out of primary schools in India find their path blocked to further schooling because there simply aren't enough secondary schools in rural areas – a reality that has prompted many educationists to comment that these children are not 'dropouts' but 'pushouts'. Even those who somehow complete their ten years of schooling perform poorly in the formal school system and end up swelling the ranks of the unemployed or poorly employed.

The Indian Parliament enacted a Right to Education (RTE) law in 2009, which conferred the right to free and compulsory education on children between six and fourteen years. However, as we have seen, Gandhi had envisioned many decades ago that what the children of India need is not just the right to education, but also the *right* education. Nayi Talim was the experimental shape of his vision. He did not get enough time to develop its concept and practice beyond school education to encompass higher and professional education. Nevertheless, the continued relevance of both his vision and the basic principles of his experiment has been affirmed by all innovative and pro-people educationists in India and abroad.

Sadly, India's prevailing school, college and university system has almost completely abandoned Gandhi's thoughts on education. What can be a more scathing commentary on the neglect of a work-oriented approach in our education system than the fact that as many as ninety percent of the basic graduates (in arts, science and commerce streams) and seventy-five percent of the engineering graduates produced by Indian colleges lack employable skills[16]? By ignoring Gandhi's thoughts on holistic education, our country is paying a heavy price in the form of pervasive poverty, unemployment, unbalanced development and wasted human resources in both rural and urban India.

Gandhi had also forewarned about other problems that are plaguing the system of education, especially higher education, in India. Fully a hundred years ago, his *Hind Swaraj* had described the colonial and capitalist model of education as 'rotten' because it placed money-making above morality. Has the situation changed much in today's India? He would certainly be more horrified by seeing the crass and ubiquitous commercialisation of education today, right from nursery to professional courses. If he had censured lawyers and doctors of his time for 'sucking the blood of the poor people' like 'so many leeches', and for 'indulging in luxuries', what would he have said about today's money-chasing merchants of education?

Clearly, India needs thorough-going educational reforms guided by Gandhi's noble and futuristic philosophy, which aims at creating a New Man, a New Society and a New Civilisation.

Gandhi and Montessori: Education as the Art of Approaching the 'Milky Way' of Children's Love

The force that can create a New Man, a New Society and a New Civilisation is love or nonviolence, the study and practice of which ought to be the chief aim of education. We have earlier in this chapter encountered Gandhi's conversation with the great educationist, Dr Maria

Montessori, in which he talked about the 'law of love' and how it can be best learnt through 'little children'. It is appropriate to conclude this chapter with what Dr Montessori wrote on this subject in an article titled 'Gandhi and the Child'. (This and many other contributions are included in a superb commemorative volume *Mahatma Gandhi: Essays & Reflections,* edited by Dr S. Radhakrishnan, which was brought out on the occasion of his seventieth birthday on 2 October 1939. It was published by Jaico Publishing House, Bombay.)

> ...His (Gandhi's) spirit is like a great energy that has the power of uniting men because it effects some inner sensitivity and draws them together. This mysterious and marvellous energy is called Love. Love is the only force that can bring about a real union between men. Without it, they are drawn into a superficial association by force of external circumstances and the pursuit of material interest. But this association without love is insecure and leads to dangers. Men should be united in both ways – by a spiritual force attracting the soul, and by material organisation.
>
> I felt this very deeply when Gandhi paid a short visit to Europe some years ago, and stayed a few days in Rome on his homeward voyage. I then felt that there emanated from Gandhi a mysterious power. During his stay in his honour, and while he sat on the floor and spun, children sat around him, serene and silent. And all the adults who attended this unforgettable reception were silent and still. It was enough to be together; there was no need of singing, dancing or speeches...
>
> We must think about this spiritual attraction; it is the force that can save humanity, for we must learn to feel this attraction to each other, instead of being merely bound by material interests.

Dr Montessori then poses a question – 'How can we learn this? – and answers it herself in a profound manner, echoing Gandhi's own thoughts about the Law of Love.

These spiritual forces always exist around us, just as cosmic rays exist in the universe, but they are concentrated by special instruments, through which we can detect them. These instruments are not so rare as might be thought: they are Children! If our soul is far from the child, then we only see his small body, just as we see the star in the sky as a little shining point where really there is an immense extension of heat and light. We must be nearby to feel the greatness of the mysterious energy radiating all around. The art of spiritually approaching the child, from whom we are too far, is a secret that can establish human brotherhood, it is a divine art that will lead to the peace of mankind. The children are so many, they are numberless, they are not one star, they are more like the Milky Way, that stream of stars that passes right across the heavens.

On his birthday, I ask Gandhi to give honour to the child in India and in the world.

The full import of what Gandhi told Dr Montessori in 1931 – '(i)f I was to realise Truth, I must obey, even at the cost of my life, the law of love' – and what she wrote about him eight years later can be better understood if we recall the historical context in which these two great souls affirmed their faith in the Power of the Child. The deaths and devastation caused by the First World War were fresh in the minds of the people of Europe and elsewhere. The foreboding about the worse horrors of the approaching Second World War had spread pessimism and helplessness everywhere. It is in such dark and depressing times that Gandhi, Montessori and other great contemporary thinkers of the world discovered a ray of hope in children's education, especially in the saving strength of the pure innocence of children.

The world wars are behind us. But we still face gigantic challenges that have jeopardised human welfare and happiness; some challenges even threaten our very survival on this beautiful, bountiful and supremely generous planet. Our search for peace and human brotherhood continues. This search will remain fruitless so long as men allow themselves to be 'drawn into a superficial association by force of external circumstances and the pursuit of material interest'. As Dr Montessori, who spent a lifetime learning from children and then devising a system for their education, reminds us, 'The art of spiritually approaching the child, from whom we are too far, is a secret that can establish human brotherhood, it is a divine art that will lead to the peace of mankind.'

Gandhi's Nayi Talim was also about spiritually approaching children – learning the law of pure love from them and then educating them, as they grow in years, in the practice of the same law to become the healers of our ailing world.

What is the important pedagogic lesson that can be drawn from the thoughts of Gandhi and Montessori? Simply this – if only teachers and policy makers in education can harvest this spiritual energy of children and help society to learn and practice the Law of Love, they would be laying the foundations of lasting peace and genuine social progress.

Is anyone listening?

A consummate all-rounder: *Jawaharlal Nehru, Sardar Vallabhbhai Patel and other members of the Congress Working Committee (CWC) had come to the Sevagram Ashram in August 1935 to seek Gandhi's advice on some important political matters. When they arrived, they found him giving instructions to ashram inmates in shoe-making. 'If you like, you may also watch how a good sandal is made,' he told the Congress leaders, to which Patel jokingly remarked: 'Mahatmaji, is there anything in which you will confess that you are not an expert?'*

Illustration: Sudhir Tailang

13

PREACHING WITH PRACTICE
A Mahatma who was also a Cobbler, Scavenger, Carpenter, Cook, Weaver, Farmer and Medicine-Man...

--❦--

'But this is absurd,' people usually say to you, 'for people of our sphere, with profound problems standing before us, – problems philosophical, scientific, artistic, ecclesiastical and social. It would be absurd for us ministers, senators, academicians, professors, artists, a quarter of an hour of whose time is so prized by people, to waste our time on anything of that sort, would it not? – on the cleaning of our boots, the washing of our shirts, in hoeing, in planting potatoes, or in feeding our chickens and our cows, and so on...?' But why should we do a hundred other things which serfs formerly did for us? Because we think that it is necessary so to do; that human dignity demands it; that it is the duty, the obligation, of man.

— Leo Tolstoy (1828-1910), *On Labour and Luxury.*

GANDHI NEVER PREACHED WHAT HE DIDN'T PRACTICE HIMSELF. The concept of Nayi Talim germinated in the soil of his self-cultivation of the knowledge of various crafts and professions. He was the best exemplar of his own precept about the need to dispense with the dichotomy between learning and doing. Here are a few unbelievable anecdotes[1] about him as a 'toiler', 'cook', 'teacher', 'doctor', 'scavenger', 'shoe-maker', 'farmer', etc.

D.G. Tendulkar, who wrote the widely acclaimed eight-volume biography *Mahatma: Life of Mohandas Karamchand Gandhi*, states: 'The creative hand that wrote inspiring editorials and letters, spun thread on a charkha, wove on a loom, cooked new dishes, used a needle skilfully and tended fruit trees and vegetables, was equally adept in tilling land, drawing water from a well, hewing wood and unloading heavy goods from a cart'. Once, after one of his several arrests,[2] the magistrate asked Gandhi what his occupation was. Gandhi said, 'I am a spinner, weaver and farmer.'[3] He was then sixty-four.

His study of the books on religion and his own spiritual search had convinced him that every person should do some manual labour each day. Mental work alone was not enough. When a hut was being built in his ashram, he was the first man to climb to the top of the structure to put the roof. He was a good carpenter who made his own bookshelf. Spinning, weaving, papermaking, tannery, leather work, oil-pressing, paddy-husking, pottery, soap-making, bee-keeping, carpentry, smithery, cultivation of orchards and medicinal plants ... there was hardly any cottage industry or farm-related activity that did not find a place in his ashrams. All the inmates in his ashrams, himself included, lent a hand to any work that lay before them. Hindus, Muslims and Christians, Parsis and Jews, Brahmins and Harijans, labourers and lawyers, Indians and foreigners, all lived as members of one big family, united by a common purpose and guided by a common leader. All of them ate in a common dining room, and their meals were prepared in a common kitchen.

He had set this example of commune life in his South African ashrams and continued it in his Indian ashrams. In South Africa, Barrister Gandhi ground wheat in a hand-mill, then dressed up and walked five miles to reach his office. He would keep awake a whole night nursing plague-stricken miners. He wrote articles for his newspaper *Indian Opinion*, typed them out himself, composed them in his own printing-press and, if necessary, lent a hand in working a hand-driven printing machine. He was good at binding books. Ten years of farm life in South Africa armed him with good knowledge of farming. He popularised the nonviolent and more scientific method of beekeeping that did not displace the honeycomb, or destroy the bees. Using his knowledge of botany, he explained how bee-keeping near a harvesting land or a garden of fruits and vegetables increased the yield from plants.

Gandhi had learnt shoe-making while serving a prison term in South Africa. On the day of his release, he gave a present to General Jan Smuts, who had jailed him. 'What is it, any bomb?' asked the white military officer, who was a much-hated figure among Indians. When he opened the packet, Smuts found a pair of leather sandals. Gandhi said: 'This is my parting gift for you. I have made them with my own hands.' More than three decades later, General Smuts, who went on to become the prime minister of South Africa, wrote on Gandhi's seventieth birthday: 'In jail he prepared for me a pair of sandals. I have worn them for many a summer, though I feel that I am not worthy to stand in the shoes of so great a man.' A perfect example of how Gandhi practiced his own dictum: 'Hate the sin, not the sinner'.

Tendulkar, Gandhi's marathon biographer, tells us about an interesting episode that took place in his Sevagram Ashram in August 1935. Nehru, Patel and other members of the Congress Working Committee, the party's highest decision-making body, had come to the ashram to seek Gandhi's advice on some important political matters. When they arrived, they found him giving instructions to ashram inmates in shoe-making. 'If you like, you may also watch how a good sandal is made,' he told Congress leaders, to which Sardar Vallabhbhai Patel jokingly remarked: 'Mahatmaji, is there anything in which you will confess that you are not an expert?'

But there was another surprise in store for the Working Committee members. The Sevagram Ashram, located in the countryside, often attracted snakes and scorpions. Gandhi had invited a local expert to teach him and other inmates how to treat snake and scorpion bites. One day, during the Congress leaders' stay at the ashram, 'they were alarmed to find Gandhi with a poisonous snake coiled round his neck attending to a man who claimed to teach the handling of snakes and the cure of snake bites. For the latter part of the demonstration someone had to be bitten and Gandhi volunteered. But this his companions would not endure and the experiment was given up'.[4]

Once when he was imprisoned in India, a prison-mate was bitten by a scorpion. Gandhi immediately became a healer; he washed the fellow-prisoner's wound, wiped it and sucked off the poison. The treatment worked.

Gandhi's philosophy and style of work were such that he did not discriminate between what is conventionally seen as more important and less important. Prof. Vinay Lal, in his essay *Gandhi and the Ecological Vision of Life,*[5] tells us that, even as he worked alongside all others in the ashram – peeling potatoes, sweeping the floor, etc. – he would conduct interviews and dictate his voluminous correspondence. 'According to Mirabehn, "Big people of all parties, and of many different nations would come to see Bapu, but he would give equal attention to the poorest peasant who might come with a genuine problem." In the midst of important political negotiations with senior British officials, he would take the time to tend to his goat. He remained supremely indifferent to considerations of power, popularity, prestige, and status in choosing his companions; similarly, he was as attentive to the minutest details as he was to matters of national importance. One of his associates has reported – and such stories are legion – that when news reached Gandhi of the illness of the daughter of a friend, he wrote to her a long letter in the midst of an intense political struggle in Rajkot, detailing the medicines that she was to take, the food that she was to avoid, and the precautions she was to exercise'.

Prof. Lal narrates two seemingly insignificant but highly insightful anecdotes from Gandhi's life. At an annual session of the INC in Bombay, Kaka Kalelkar, an associate of Gandhi found him frantically searching for something one evening. When his inquiry revealed that it was no more than a two-inch pencil, he offered Gandhi his own pencil and pleaded with him not to waste his time. But Gandhi insisted that he could not have any other pencil. 'You don't understand,' he said, 'I simply must not lose that little pencil! Do you know it was given to me in Madras by Natesan's little boy? He brought it for me with such love! I cannot bear to lose it.' Prof. Lal comments: 'If today we effortlessly substitute one pencil for another, what prevents us from substituting something else in its place tomorrow? What are the limits of substitutibility? If we recognised that we hold even a pencil in trust, would we not treat the earth more gently? And when this trust is betrayed, how do we calibrate the nature and extent of that betrayal?'

Lal recounts a second pencil story, as told by Jehangir Patel, another associate of Gandhi. One morning Patel found Gandhi examining the tiny stub of a pencil 'which had been put ready for his use'. Gandhi commented that whoever had sharpened the pencil was 'very angry', adding: 'See how roughly and irregularly the wood has been scoured and cut.' At breakfast, Gandhi looked around the table, and as soon as his eyes fell on young Manu, he asked her: 'Manu, you sharpened my pencil this morning, didn't you, and you were feeling angry when you did it?' 'Yes, I was,' she replied. 'Well,' said Gandhi, 'please don't sharpen my pencil while you are angry, it distresses me.'

In *Harijan*,[6] the journal that he founded in 1933 as an educational instrument in his socio-political campaign, he gave detailed instructions on how to make compost manure using the things that were near at hand, things that cost nothing – cow dung, night soil, urine, peelings of vegetables and water hyacinths. With labour and application, compost manure could be made without any capital. In his ashrams, night soil and urine were conserved in shallow pits. He had found through his experiments in sanitation in South Africa that the earth's crust, to the depth of one foot, is full of germs that turn filth into manure, whereas filth buried very deep produces foul gases and pollutes the air. Gandhi urged farmers to use organic manure, since use of chemicals might result in depletion of the soil in spite of their promise of dramatic results. How prophetic were his fears when we consider that half of the Western world today is against the use of chemical fertilisers.

A devout Hindu, Gandhi was deeply committed to the cause of cow protection. 'The cow is a poem of pity', he wrote in *Young India*. 'One reads pity in the gentle animal. Protection of the cow means protection of the whole dumb creation of God. The appeal of the lower order of creation is all the more forcible because it is speechless… Cow protection to me is not mere protection of the cow. It means protection of all that lives and is helpless and weak in the world'. He was distressed to see the pitiable condition of the cows. 'In no country on earth were the cow and its progeny so ill-treated as in India where the cow is held in veneration. Many *pinjrapoles* and *goshalas* are dens of torture'.[7]

Although he was opposed to the killing of the cow, he was all for making the 'wisest use of her hide, bone, flesh, entrails, etc.', after its death. He took a keen interest in village tanning, which was looked down upon by high-caste Hindus. He lamented that 'one of the most useful and indispensable industries has consigned probably a million people to hereditary untouchability. An evil day has dawned upon this unhappy country when labour began to be despised and, therefore, neglected. Millions of those who were the salt of the earth, on whose industry this country depended for its very existence, came to be regarded as low class and the microscopic leisured few became the privileged classes, with the tragic result that India suffered morally and materially'.[8]

His approach to reforming village tanning had twin objectives – social and technological. He castigated upper-caste Hindus for condemning village tanners to live a life of isolation in 'filth and degradation', and called for restoration of the latter's dignity as equal members of the village community. Secondly, he advocated technical innovation in tanning to bring prosperity to tanners and to make their profession hygienic. 'An army of chemists can find scope for their inventive talent in this great industry...Tanning chemists have to discover improved methods of tanning...Here is work for the cent percent Swadeshi lover and scope for the harnessing of technical skill to the solution of a great problem. The work fells three apples with one throw. It serves the Harijans, it serves the villagers, and it means honourable employment for the middle-class intelligentsia who are in search for employment. Add to this the fact that the intelligentsia have a proper opportunity of coming in direct touch with the villagers'.[9]

Although Gandhi was leading India's national liberation struggle against the mightiest empire then ruling large parts of the world, he, remarkably, spent more time on non-political activities than on the political campaign. 'Gandhi's preoccupation with these problems jarred on some of his colleagues', wrote the late B.R. Nanda.[10] 'They wondered why he should fritter away his energies on such apparent trivialities, when momentous political issues were crying for attention. Mahadev Desai tells us about a conversation Jawaharlal Nehru had with Gandhi on 3 October 1936 when he visited Sevagram along with Vallabhbhai Patel. He compared Gandhi's insistence on personally nursing patients to the effort of King Canute to hold back the tide. "That is why," Gandhi quipped, "we have made you King Canute so that you may do it better than the others." Gandhi was referring to the fact that Nehru had been elected Congress president for the year. "But is there no better way?" Nehru asked. "Must you do all these things yourself?" "Who else is there to do it," Gandhi replied. "If you go to the village nearby, you will find that out of 600 people there, 300 are ill. Are they all to go to the hospital? We have to learn to treat ourselves. How are we to teach these poor villagers except by personal example?"'

Constructive Programme is the name Gandhi gave to all his non-political activities; indeed, he described it as 'true politics'. He regarded it as an integral part of satyagraha. It was also an inseparable element in his vision of transforming Indian society into a just and equitable society. For him, justice and equality were critically necessary for the realisation of the ideal of nonviolence. In an article he wrote in *Harijan* of 20 October 1940, in which he laid out his plan for launching a major civil disobedience movement against the British, he affirmed: 'Unless rock-bottom justice and equality pervade society, surely there is no nonviolent atmosphere'.[11] For the satyagrahi, he emphasised, 'constructive work is what arms are for the violent man'.[12]

Gandhi attached immense importance to technological innovation for the success of his Constructive Programme. He announced that he wanted an army of scientists and engineers in the villages. His only caveat was that most of them had to be suitably trained villagers. He told volunteers working in the Constructive Programme that he did not want them to be mere skilled labourers. He wanted them to become expert craftsmen and scientific researchers working collaboratively – 'I expect something unique from you'. He wanted these organisations to work like 'postgraduate institutes for research', and educate the villagers about their research. 'Under my scheme there would be more and better libraries, laboratories, and research institutes. Under it we should have an army of chemists, engineers and other experts who will be real servants of the nation and answer the varied and growing requirements of a people who are becoming increasingly conscious of their rights and wants. These experts would speak not a foreign language but the language of the people. The knowledge gained by them will be the common property of the people. Only then would there be truly original work instead of mere imitation'.[13]

What we see here is Gandhi's vision about the efflorescence of swadeshi (Indian) science and technology, not in isolation from the rest of the world, and much less an imitation of the work done in the West. As early as in 1924, he had written: 'I want to write many new things but they must all be written on the Indian slate. I would gladly borrow from the West when I can return the amount with decent interest'.[14]

Social and political activists of today have much to learn from, and be inspired by, the sheer range of activities that Gandhi conducted nationwide under the framework of his Constructive Programme: communal unity, removal of untouchability, prohibition, khadi (both hand-spun and hand-woven cloth), other village industries, village sanitation, Nayi Talim, adult education, women's empowerment, education in health, promotion of Indian languages with Hindi as the national language, economic equality, welfare of kisans, labour and adivasis, eradication of leprosy, improvement of cattle and protection of animals.

Sadly, after Gandhi's death, constructive activities never received the kind of prominence he had given them in national politics. Both the lofty philosophy and devoted practice of the Gandhian Constructive Programme took a backseat as the unhealthy ethos of competitive politics began to define the national agenda. Seva Dal, a grassroots front organisation of the Congress party, founded in 1923 by a devoted Gandhian, Dr N.S. Hardikar, lost its prestige and influence after Independence. The Gandhi *topi* (cap) worn by Seva Dal workers is the only remnant from the Gandhian era.

The other national party, Bharatiya Janata Party (BJP), adopted *sanrachana* (constructive work) as one of its three guiding mantras at its founding conference in 1980, the other two being *sangathan* (organisation-building) and *sangharsh* (struggle). However, the BJP has failed to pay serious attention to making its members adopt constructive service as their credo for organisation-building and for work among the masses.

Commendable exceptions apart, most political functionaries in today's India run educational and healthcare institutions either for commercial gain or for electoral benefit. The spirit of social service, through which Gandhi tried to give an honourable, autonomous and sovereign place to all constructive activities in his struggle for swaraj, has largely disappeared from the political landscape in India. His personal example – of cleaning toilets, nursing the sick, teaching village children, campaigning for social reforms, etc., and doing all this as an integral part of his leadership of India's battle against a mighty empire – looks quaint today.

At the same time, our country still has thousands of dedicated non-political social workers who are carrying on the legacy of the Constructive Programme in their own small and localised ways. They do not receive the kind of media publicity that politicians and celebrities from the glamour world do. They also rarely receive adequate and consistent government support. Most of them don't even have a formal association with Gandhian institutions. Nevertheless, it is in their devoted work that Gandhi continues to live even today.

PART THREE

HARMONY SEEKER

Courtesy: 'Gandhi in Cartoons', Navajivan Publishing House, Ahmedabad (1970)

Transformational music: *A Chinese friend once asked Gandhi how it was possible for him 'to find peace of mind in these troublous times'. Gandhi's reply was: 'Take to spinning. The music of the spinning wheel will be as balm to your soul. I believe that the yarn we spin is capable of mending the broken warp and woof of our life. The charkha is the symbol of nonviolence on which all life, if it is to be real life, must be based.'*

14

DECODING THE MEANING OF 'MUSIC OF THE SPINNING WHEEL'

⟶❖⟵

The essence of the great interest of art lies in the way it reveals the true feeling of the soul, the secrets of its inner life, and the world of passion that has long accumulated and fermented there before surging up to the surface. Very often, thanks to its depth and spontaneity, music is the first indication of tendencies which later translate themselves into words, and afterward into deeds...There are even cases where music is the only witness of a whole inner life which never reaches the surface...Art, like life, is inexhaustible; and nothing makes us feel the truth of this better than music's ever-welling spring, which has flowed through the centuries until it has become an ocean.

— From *Essays on Music* by Romain Rolland.

EVER SINCE I CAME ACROSS THE PHRASE 'MUSIC OF THE spinning wheel' while studying Gandhian literature, I have been intrigued by its meaning. What music can the spinning wheel possibly produce? When I first asked myself this question, I had neither understood Gandhi's philosophy of khadi and the charkha, nor knew much about his views on music. True, listening to his favourite *bhajans* (hymns) – in particular, *Vaishnava Janato Tene Kahiye Je* and *Raghupati Raghav Rajaram*, both of which he and his followers sang as they marched during the historic 241-mile Salt March to Dandi in Gujarat in 1930 – was a soul-stirring experience. But it did not shed much light on what he meant by 'music of the spinning wheel'.

One can never understand Gandhi at one go. This is true about all great personalities in history. Understanding Gandhi and his mission comes in bits and pieces, in many layers, from many different sources, and also from the specific historical circumstance in which he said or did something. The phrase 'music of the spinning wheel' appears several times in his literature, but the one that made the deepest impression on me was when he used it in one of the most trying periods of his life – in the months preceding India's independence in 1947, which was accompanied by its blood-soaked partition. He had devoted himself fully to the one task that was dearer to him than even India's freedom – the task of dousing the flames of communal violence and establishing peace and harmony between Hindus and Muslims. Even though there was turmoil all around him, and even though his own heart was full of pain at this tragic turn to the country's freedom movement, he was calm, composed and as hyperactive as ever.

In April of that year, a Chinese friend asked him how it was possible for him 'to find peace of mind in these troublous times'. His reply was: 'Take to spinning. The music of the spinning wheel will be as balm to your soul. I believe that the yarn we spin is capable of mending the broken warp and woof of our life. The charkha is the symbol of nonviolence on which all life, if it is to be real life, must be based'.[1]

Gandhi's quest for truth and nonviolence was also a quest for harmony. He believed that every manifestation of truth must be harmonious in itself and also be capable of promoting harmony in the environment. What did not have harmony was untruth, and a source of violence. He had the deepest admiration for those works of music, art and literature that reinforced the message of universal peace and harmony. This was the basis of his respect for Rabindranath Tagore and admiration for his works. This explains why he stood transfixed in front of a statue of Jesus Christ on the Cross at the Vatican museum. This is why he admired and collaborated with Nandalal Bose, one of the foremost artists in the era of India's freedom movement. This also tells us why he reached out to the best Indian musicians of his time to set the tune for the bhajans sung in his ashrams, hymnal prayers being an integral part of his socio-political campaign.

As I have explained in the Introduction, my understanding of the 'music of the spinning wheel' was further deepened by knowing about the Mahatma through two of his foreign admirers – Romain Rolland and Madeleine Slade (Mirabehn), both of whom were also admirers of the music of Beethoven.

In this part of the book, I would like to share my understanding of Gandhi's attitude towards music and art, as also my belief that this understanding is useful for any effort to promote nonviolence and harmony in our world today.

We have seen in the foregoing chapters the numerous inter-related objectives that Gandhi sought to advance by placing khadi, the charkha and village industries at the very core of his economic, social and political agenda. Although India's liberation from British rule was the proximate task to be accomplished in this agenda, his agenda was not limited by national boundaries. It was universal in the conception of its goals – such as the march towards a peaceful and cooperative world order, exploitation-free economy, dignity and justice for all human beings, goodwill and harmony between faiths and cultures, empowerment of women, and respect for Nature and all her creatures. These universal goals, he believed, could be achieved only through adherence to the eternal values of truth, nonviolence, love, justice, kindness and compassion.

However, unlike in the case of most leaders of revolutions and national liberation struggles in history, transforming the self was as important for Gandhi as transforming the world. Indeed, it was more important because, as he put it famously, one should 'be the change' that one wants to see in the world. Therefore, in his philosophy, self-purification aimed at God-realisation was a pre-requisite for success in his battles in the external world. With an inventive genius that only he could project, he transformed the spinning wheel, an ordinary village-level production tool, into a visual manifesto to publicise both his deep-going inner search and his epoch-making external agenda.

In traditional societies, the tool of production is never regarded as inert and external to the producer. It is only in the capitalist mode of production, which is based on the exploitation of man and nature that the tool of production becomes alien to the producer. Indeed, the producer becomes alienated from himself, too, because his work, working environment and working instrument are incapable of fulfilling his innate human needs and aspirations. The alienation does not disappear in communism because the system denies the worker freedom and dignity – two fundamental human aspirations – and makes him a mere cog in a mega-machine controlled by the state.

A common feature of capitalism and communism – and both, notwithstanding outward differences, are products of the West's God-denying materialistic civilisation – is that the tool of production has no moral significance either for the individual worker or for the society in general. In contrast, for the traditional Indian farmers, weavers or artisans, the plough, the loom and other implements are sacred. They carry a message that proclaims the larger purpose of life and labour. For Gandhi, the spinning wheel became not only a means of economic upliftment of the poor, and not even simply an emblem of India's freedom movement, but also a means of de-polluting one's inner being and re-connecting oneself with the Creator.

Nothing illustrates the self-uplifting power of the spinning wheel better than one of Gandhi's favourite bhajans which he had included in his daily prayer book – *Chadariya Jhini Re Jhini* by Kabir, a fifteenth century mystic saint-poet who best symbolises the syncretism of Hindu-Muslim cultures in the Indian subcontinent. A weaver by profession, Kabir explains the most profound principles of Indian philosophy in symbolism that common folks also could understand. Here is Kabir's divinely beautiful poetry, along with its translation in English.

> *kabīrā jab ham paidā hue*
> *jaga hanse ham roye*
> *aisī karanī kara chalo*
> *ham hanse jaga roye*

chadariyā jhinī re jhinī
he rāma nāma rasa bhinī

aṣṭa kamalā ka charkhā banāyā
pañca tattva kī pūnī
nava dasa māsa bunana ko lāge
mūrakha mailī kinhī
jaba moṅ chādara bana ghara āyā
raṅga reja ko dinhī
aisā raṅga raṅgā raṅgare ne
lālo lāla kar dinhī

cādara oḍha śaṅka mat kariyo
yeh do dina tumko dinhī
mūrakha loga bheda nahi jāne
din din mailī kinhī

dhruva pralhāda sudāmā ne oḍhi
śukadeva ne nirmala kinhī
dāsa kabīra ne aisī odhī
jyoṅ kī tyoṅ dhara dinhī

Says Kabir, when I was born
I cried and the world laughed.
I will do such deeds that when I die
I will laugh and the world will cry.

This body is like a delicate, transparent sheet (*chaadar*)
which should be drenched
in the holy name of Lord Rama,
the Reservoir of Divine Pleasure.

The spinning wheel that produces this *chaadar* is made from eight
lotuses, the cotton from five elements,
it takes nine-ten months to weave it fully.
The ignorant have stained it and made it unclean.

Once this sheet was completed,
it was delivered to the Dyer.

Such a strong colour was given by the Dyer
That He made it completely red.

Don't have illusions as you use this *chaadar*,
it has been given to you for a very short time.
The ignorant do not know the purpose of it,
Day after day they have stained and spoiled it.

Dhruv, Prahlad and Sudama have all worn it,
Shukdev[2] purified it,
Kabir wore it with great care.
He laid it down as such, as it had been given to him at birth.

Gandhi's attachment to his spinning wheel was like Kabir's identification with his weaver's loom. It was the indispensable aid for him in his ceaseless efforts at living a pure and God-oriented life ('drenched' constantly in the holy name of Lord Rama) amid the din and dust of politics. Like Kabir, he wanted to live his life with great care and lay down his body in as pure a state as it had been given to him at birth.

This explains why Gandhi was almost lyrical in praising the charkha. 'The music of the spinning wheel will be as balm to your soul,'[3] he told people as he appealed to the poor and the rich alike to use it. It's the 'music of universal love', he added. He found solace in its music whenever he was pained by undesirable happenings in society and unpleasant developments in politics. Once, when the internal bickering in the Congress party filled him with deep agony, he wrote in *Young India* to tell his readers how his condition was like that of Margaret, a love-lost character in Goethe's *Faust*, a book that he had read in Yeravada Jail in Poona in 1924. 'Margaret is sore at heart and troubled. She finds no relief from her misery, save by going to the spinning-wheel and to the music of the wheel giving vent to her grief. I was much struck by the whole conception. Margaret is alone in her room torn within with doubt and despair. The poet sends her to her wheel lying in a corner in the room. The reader may be sure she had a well-chosen library of books, a few paintings and a copy of a handwritten and illustrated *Bible*. She finds no solace either in the paintings or the books or, for Margaret, the book of books. She involuntarily goes to the spinning wheel'.

Gandhi then quotes Margaret's 'noble lines'.

My peace is gone, and my heart is sore:
I have lost him, and lost him, for evermore!
The place, where he is not, to me is the tomb.
The world is sadness and sorrow and gloom!
My poor sick brain is crazed with pain;
And my poor sick heart is torn in twain!
My peace is gone and my heart is sore,
For lost is my love for evermore!

He concluded the article by giving vent to his own grief: 'You may paraphrase them a little and the verses almost represent my condition. I seem to have lost my Love too and feel distracted. I feel the abiding presence of my Lover and yet He seems to be away from me. For He refuses to guide me and give clear-cut injunctions'.[4]

On another occasion, he wrote: 'I can do without food but not without sacrificial spinning'.[5] Further: 'I would like to assure those who would serve *Daridranarayana* that there is music, art, economy and joy in the spinning wheel'. 'In my dream, in my sleep, while eating, I think of the spinning wheel', he confessed. 'The spinning wheel is my sword,' he told his countrymen. 'My head daily bows in reverence to its unknown inventor' because 'the charkha is an outward symbol of Truth and Nonviolence... Just as there are signs by which you can recognise violence with the naked eye, so is the spinning wheel to me a decisive sign of Nonviolence'. And, finally, this almost unbelievable expression of attachment to his beloved instrument: 'I crave to die with my hand at the spinning wheel' because it 'is a gateway to my salvation'.

There was no dearth of people even in his own time who ridiculed him for saying and writing such things. Undeterred, he likened himself to a person 'madly bent on attaining self-realisation', and his spinning wheel to *Kamadhenu*[6] (divine cow that grants all wishes). He also likened it to *Parthiweshwar Chintamani*,[7] on which he would concentrate all the faculties of his being 'in the hope of seeing God face to face'. Here Gandhi takes his attachment to the spinning wheel to a mystical level. *Parthiweshwar Chintamani* means 'the king of kings' among wish-fulfilling philosopher's stones. Theosophists, with whom

Gandhi was in sympathetic contact, refer to the 'philosopher's stone' as a metaphor for Truth and Wisdom. According to them, 'When you carry this Truth and Wisdom in your heart, the dust of the world, which is governed by the law of Karma, cannot touch you'.

I have long wondered why Gandhi used the term 'music of the spinning wheel'. After all, he preferred the music of silence to the music of sound, except when the sound was that of devotional hymns – like the song by Kabir mentioned above – which were sung at his daily prayer meetings. Religious music appealed to him the most because of its power to create harmony in life. Moreover, he believed that devotional music also had the power to unite people because it transcended sectarian credal barriers. Calling it 'an ancient and sacred art', he wrote: 'The hymns of Samaveda are a mine of music, and no *ayat* of the Koran can be recited unmusically. David's Psalms transport you to raptures and remind you of the hymns of Samaveda. Let us revive this art and patronise the school of music'.[8] His prayer meetings were inter-religious, and he personally selected the finest hymns from different faiths to be sung at these meetings. These hymns were chosen from different languages and also from different parts of the world.[9]

Speaking with reference to other types of music and arts, he was candid in admitting that he did not attach 'such value to them as is generally done'. 'When I gaze at the star-sown heaven, and the infinite beauty it affords my eyes, that means more to me than all that human art can give me. That does not mean that I ignore the value of those works generally called artistic; but personally, in comparison with the infinite beauty of nature, I feel their unreality too intensely... Life is greater than all art'.[10]

And the art of life, Gandhi insisted, cannot be practiced without experiencing the beneficial effects of silence. While he admired modern civilisation for having 'taught us to convert night into day,' he lamented that it had also converted 'golden silence into brazen din and noise'. The radio he preferred to listen to was the Divine Radio because '(it) is always singing if we could only make ourselves ready to listen to it, but is impossible to listen to without silence'. His preferred way of spending more time listening to this Divine Radio was to observe *maun vrat*, a weekly day of silence, when he would communicate to others only through writing. 'Silence is a great help to a seeker after truth like myself',[11] he explained.

There is something deeply mystical about the phrase 'music of the spinning wheel'. On the one hand, Gandhi wanted the charkha to be completely 'noiseless'. In fact, this was one of his directions to innovators whom he invited, as we have noted earlier, to improve the spinning wheel. On the other hand, he proclaimed that his silent charkha produced the 'music of universal love'. I have found an instructive insight into this paradoxical relationship between *maun* (silence) and music, as embodied in his spinning wheel, in two sources.

In *The Mysticism of Sound and Music*, Hazrat Inayat Khan (1882-1927), who popularised Sufism in the West, writes: 'Music is nothing less than the picture of the Beloved. But the question is: What is our Beloved? Or where is our Beloved? Our Beloved is that which is our source and our goal'. For Gandhi, the goal was to find his beloved – God – by serving those in suffering, and by struggling for India's freedom.[12] He himself expressed this goal-oriented meaning of music in pithy yet profound words: 'To know music is to transfer it to life'.

To know the meaning of the phrase 'music of the spinning wheel', another helpful source is the book *Flow: The Psychology of Optimal Experience* by Mihaly Csikszentmihalyi, the celebrated Hungarian psychologist. Flow, according to him, is a mental state of complete or immersive concentration in one's activity, which, in its highest level of experience, can be mystical. Music, he explains, 'helps organise the mind that listens to it, and therefore reduces psychic entropy, or the disorder we experience when random information interferes with goals'. However, he also writes that 'greater rewards are open to those who learn to make music'. According to him, still greater rewards await those great musicians who can connect their ability to create harmony in sound to 'the more general and abstract harmony that underlies the kind of social order we call civilisation'.

Csikszentmihalyi's book (published in 1990) is a brilliant study of how 'one-pointedness' of the mind can help us experience joy and fulfilment in our work and also in other activities of life. However, I was surprised to see that, although he gives several persuasive examples to illustrate his concept, he makes no mention of the 'flow' experience of the 'music of universal love' that the spinning wheel produced for Gandhi.

Gandhi's 'flow' experience with his charkha can be better understood by turning to his revolutionary pro-poor philosophy of Karma Yoga embodied in the instrument. In a masterpiece of contemplative communication to his readers in *Young India* (1924), under the title 'Coming Nearer to the Poor', this is what he wrote:

> This spinning is growing on me. I seem daily to be coming nearer to the poorest of the poor and, to that extent, to God. I regard the four hours to be the most profitable part of the day. The fruit of my labour is visible before me. *Not an impure thought enters my mind during the four hours.* The mind wanders while I read the *Gita*, the *Quran*, the *Ramayana*. But the mind is fixed whilst I am turning the wheel or working the bow. I know that it may not mean all this to everyone. I have so identified the spinning wheel with the economic salvation of pauper India, that it has for me a fascination all its own. There is a serious competition going on in my mind between spinning and carding on the one hand and literary pursuits on the other. And I should not be surprised if in my next letter I report to you an increase in the hours of spinning and carding.[13]

What an incredible admission by the Mahatma that spinning the wheel was for him a more reliable source of self-purification than the reading of scriptures! And what an unbelievable revelation that he, whose life was so action-filled, devoted so many hours each day to spinning the charkha, which any modern politician would think to be a waste of time. The only way to understand this is by knowing that spinning was a form of prayer for him. Prayer performed as action for the poor. A perfect example of Karma Yoga, which Swami Ranganathananda (1908-2005), the most eminent disciple of Swami Vivekananda in the twentieth century, defined as '*Godward* Passion transmuted into *Manward* Love'. One-pointedness of body, mind and soul in which work and meditation are inseparably merged. When the merger takes place, it creates divine music, a mystical state best described by poet T.S. Eliot's words: 'You are the music while the music lasts'.

It is possible to conjecture that, for Gandhi, the spinning wheel had become a substitute for an icon of divinity or *ishta devata* (cherished deity). The conjecture is reinforced by the fact that, although he was a devout Hindu, he did not worship any traditional form or image of God. He believed that God is formless. 'Towards a form or image,' he said, 'I always feel *neti neti* (not this, not this)'.[14] There was no temple in his ashram. And there are hardly any photographs showing his visits to temples or him worshipping Hindu idols in traditional style. In contrast, the image of Gandhi with his spinning wheel is common all over the world. 'If one has to establish communion with God through some means, why not through the spinning wheel?'[15] he once told fellow spinners. In Hinduism, especially among followers of Bhakti Yoga, *ishta devata* is the object of one's special pious attention. Such iconification or symbolisation of the Divine is common to all religions. Worshipful and meditative attention on religious icons and symbols is believed to serve as a gateway to experiencing one's connection with the cosmos and one's own inner self, and seeing the two as one and the same. For many mystics, the icon or the symbol becomes an object of love, even if it is not an object of worship.

Gandhi had developed a mystical relationship of love with his charkha. However, his point of departure from other mystics was the fact that the spinning wheel for him was a gateway not only to his own personal salvation, but also to the salvation of his nation and its people. 'It is my conviction that with every thread I draw, I am spinning the destiny of India,'[16] he declared.

While travelling, he spun on a moving train or a rocking ship. When he kept busy the whole day in meeting people, discussing important issues with them or addressing public gatherings, he completed his quota of spinning at midnight. He presented no ornaments to his devoted wife Kasturba, but he derived immense joy in gifting her sarees made from khadi yarn spun by him. Of course, Kasturba too was a devoted

'For me there were only two, God and Bapu. And now they have become one': *This is how Mirabehn, Gandhi's devoted daughter-disciple expressed her feelings after his assassination on 30 January 1948.*

The other 'Mahatma': *Mirabehn was attracted to Beethoven's music in her youth. She spent the last phase of her life in the forest near Vienna, where she could live with the spirit of the great composer, who was described by Romain Rolland as the 'European Mahatma'.*

15

WHEN THE MUSIC OF THE SPINNING WHEEL MINGLED WITH THE MUSIC OF BEETHOVEN

❖

With boundless joy and energy, I started on the pilgrimage. Numberless times have I slipped and stumbled. Many have been the bruises and cuts. Bitter have been the tears with which I have watered the path, and once or twice the clouds have come down on the mountain and I have all but lost the way. But Bapu's love has at last led me out upon the upper pastures, where God's peace fills the sweet mountain air.

— Mirabehn, Preface to *Bapu's Letters to Mira* (1924-48).

IN THE PREVIOUS CHAPTER, WE ATTEMPTED TO DECODE THE MEANING of Gandhi's 'music of the spinning wheel'. In the attentively repetitive act of turning the spinning wheel, he attained one-pointedness of body, mind and soul in which work accompanied meditation, prayer and silent chanting, enabling him to experience music at its divine source. And having thus known the divine nature of public-spirited work as music, he transferred it to everything he did – from cleaning toilets to nursing patients in his ashram, and from urging the case of India's freedom before the British viceroy to leading massive satyagraha agitations. He thus converted spinning itself into an all-encompassing spiritual experiment in truth and nonviolence. The goal of this experiment was communion with God, which is, indeed, the purpose and promise of exalted music in all cultures around the world.

Since spinning was Gandhi's chief mode of prayer, the charkha accompanied him wherever he went, including on his travels abroad. After his return from South Africa in 1915, he went abroad only twice – to Sri Lanka in 1927 and to England and continental Europe in 1931. To explore the concept of the 'music of the spinning wheel' further, we shall now visit one of the most significant milestones in his life: his meeting with Romain Rolland, who won the 1915 Nobel Prize for Literature, at the writer's home near Geneva.

We have a special reason to bring Rolland into this discussion. No other contemporary foreigner[1] strove with as much conviction and persistence to disseminate the message of Gandhi's mission to the West as Rolland did. An ardent friend of India, Rolland had written his biography in 1924, titled *Mahatma Gandhi: The Man Who Became One With the Universal Being*. The book was largely instrumental in acquainting Europe, which had already been ravaged by one world war and was hurtling towards a deadlier new war, with Gandhi's philosophy of truth and nonviolence. This is how Rolland described his subject:

> Soft dark eyes, a small frail man, with a thin face and rather large protruding eyes, his head covered with a little white cap, his body clothed in coarse white cloth, barefooted. He lives on rice and fruit, and drinks only water. He sleeps on the floor – sleeps very little, and works incessantly. His body does not seem to count at all. There is nothing striking about him – except his whole expression of 'infinite patience and infinite love'. W.W. Pearson, who met him in South Africa, instinctively thought of St. Francis of Assisi. There is an almost childlike simplicity about him. His manner is gentle and courteous even when dealing with adversaries, and he is of immaculate sincerity. He is modest and unassuming, to the point of sometimes seeming almost timid, hesitant, in making an assertion. Yet you feel his indomitable spirit. He makes no compromises and never tries to hide a mistake. Nor is he afraid to admit having been in the wrong. Diplomacy is unknown to him; he

shuns oratorical effect or, rather, never thinks about it; and he shrinks unconsciously from the great popular demonstrations organised in his honour. Literally 'ill with the multitude that adores him,' he distrusts majorities and fears 'mobocracy' and the unbridled passions of the populace. He feels at ease only in a minority, and is happiest when, in meditative solitude, he can listen to the 'still small voice' within.

'This is the man who has stirred three hundred million people to revolt, who has shaken the foundations of the British Empire, and who has introduced into human politics the strongest religious impetus of the last two thousand years.

Rolland's admiration for Gandhi bordered on *bhakti* (devotion). He wrote that Gandhi 'awakens the sleeping Christ' among the people of Europe... '(He) himself almost seems Christ reborn'. Rolland regarded him as the 'last barrier still holding out against immense accumulated flood of violence'. On behalf of the 'intellectuals, scientists, writers and artists' of Europe, he sent a 'fervent tribute of love and veneration to Gandhi our master and brother, who in his heart and in his action realises our ideal of the humanity to come'.[2]

Gandhi too held Rolland in great respect, and called him a *rishi* – a seer.

Remarkably, without ever having visited India, Rolland also wrote two other great books: one on the teachings of Ramakrishna Paramahansa and the other on Swami Vivekananda. 'If there is one place on the face of the earth where all the dreams of living men have found a home from the very earliest days when man began the dream of existence, it is India', he wrote in his *Life of Ramakrishna*. About Vivekananda, he wrote: 'His words are great music, phrases in the style of Beethoven, stirring rhythms like the march of Handel choruses. I cannot touch these sayings of his ...without receiving a thrill through my body like an electric shock'. He described Ramakrishna and Vivekananda as 'Mozart and Beethoven', together forming 'the splendid symmetry of the Universal Soul'. An important reason behind Rolland's empathy with the Indian philosophy was his belief that it did not pit science and faith against one another and was tolerant of even atheism.

'Religious faith in the case of the Hindus', he wrote, 'has never been allowed to run counter to scientific laws, moreover the former is never made a condition for the knowledge they teach, but they are always scrupulously careful to take into consideration the possibility that by reason both the agnostic and atheist may attain truth in their own way. Such tolerance may be surprising to religious believers in the West, but it is an integral part of Vedantic belief'.[3]

Why did Rolland feel such a strong inner urge to write about Gandhi, Ramakrishna Paramahansa and Swami Vivekananda? He revealed his purpose in his address *To My Western Readers*:

> I have dedicated my whole life to the reconciliation of mankind. I have striven to bring it about among the peoples of Europe. For the last ten years I have been attempting the same task for the West and the East. I also desire to reconcile, if it is possible, the two antithetical forms of spirit for which the West and the East are wrongly supposed to stand – reason and faith – or perhaps it would be more accurate to say, the diverse forms of reason and of faith; for the West and the East share them both almost equally although few suspect it.
>
> In our days an absurd separation has been made between these two halves of the soul, and it is presumed that they are incompatible. The only incompatibility lies in the narrowness of view, which those who erroneously claim to be their representatives, share in common.[4]

Rolland's correspondence with Gandhi and his close associates, his letters about Gandhi to eminent people around the world (including Albert Einstein), and the prefaces and articles on Gandhi that he wrote for several publications fill a book of nearly 600 pages[5]. This book, an invaluable part of the huge corpus of Gandhian literature, never fails to give me contemplative moments whenever I open it. Reading it is an invitation to experience the spiritual resonance between two great men of the last century – one an Indian saint-warrior whose heart throbbed for the whole world; and the other a European internationalist and lifelong peace activist who had come to believe that the world could be saved only by the wisdom of India, as personified by its modern-day saints like Ramakrishna, Vivekananda and Gandhi.

The meeting between the Mahatma and Europe's leading pacifist writer, which was facilitated by Mirabehn, took place in December 1931. Gandhi, returning from the Second Round Table Conference in London, visited Geneva and spent five days as a guest of Rolland at the latter's villa in Villeneuve. The villa, which overlooked Lake Geneva, a valley by the Rhone river and glaciers of the Alps, was a haven of serenity. There, in between his morning and evening prayers, the singing of bhajans and chanting of hymns, his daily routine of spinning the charkha, and his speaking assignments in and around Geneva, Gandhi would sit with Rolland every day for two to three hours of intense conversation that covered both timeless issues in philosophy and the contemporary happenings in Europe and the world.

Rolland's detailed diary notes on the dialogue have given a riveting description of Gandhi's activities in Europe. Specifically, from the point of view of this book, they have immortalised a precious moment of synchronicity[6] in the lives of four individuals that destiny itself brought together – Gandhi, Rolland, Mirabehn and Beethoven (1770–1827), the German composer who remains the best-known name in Western classical music. It is a moment fragrant with the truth that men and women, even when separated by time, space, culture and customs, are ordained by a divine design to collaborate in the service of a deeper need of humanity.

After the prayers on the last evening of his Swiss sojourn, Gandhi asked Rolland to play Beethoven for him. 'I played him the Andante from the Fifth Symphony, and, on Gandhi's request, returned to the piano and played Gluck's Elysian Fields from *Orfeo*, the first orchestral piece and the flute melody', writes Rolland. 'He is very affected to the religious chants of his country, which resemble the most beautiful of our Gregorian melodies, and he has worked to assemble them. We also exchanged our ideas on art, a notion which he does not separate from his conception of truth, nor from that of joy, which he thinks truth should bring... But it goes without saying that for his heroic nature joy does not come without effort, not even life itself without hardship. The seeker after truth hath a heart tender as the lotus, and hard as granite'.[7]

Since Gandhi never showed much interest in Western classical music, we can ask ourselves the question: Why did he expressly ask Rolland to play him Beethoven? There are several disparate but mystically convergent reasons for this.[8] In 1903, Rolland had written a psychological biography of Beethoven, which remains one of the most widely read books on the life and music of the great composer. From Rolland's diary we know that both Pyarelal and Mahadev Desai, Gandhi's trusted and erudite secretaries, who accompanied him on the visit, were 'profoundly imbued with the cult of Beethoven. (They can hardly have heard much of him other than on the gramophone, but they know him by my books)'. Pyarelal had also read Rolland's ten-volume novel *Jean-Christophe*, which won him the Nobel Prize. Its protagonist is a character inspired by the life of Beethoven. He, like Gandhi, is a heroic figure, a fighter for social justice, and a courageous and uncompromising seeker of Truth. Rolland writes in his diary: 'I am deeply struck by the deep love of art among these young disciples of Gandhi; this makes all the more impressive their renunciation of all the enjoyment which art might bring them'.

Mirabehn: Her Fascinating Journey from Beethoven to Beethoven via Mahatma Gandhi

But there is another, more important, reason behind Gandhi's request to Rolland to play Beethoven for him. That reason was Mirabehn. The story of her life is too fascinating – and poignant – to permit a lengthy narration here without causing this chapter to deviate from its main theme. She was Madeleine Slade, daughter of a British admiral, before she came to India to join Gandhi's ashram at Sabarmati.

Strange though it may seem, Beethoven had played a pivotal role in bringing Madeleine Slade to Gandhi. She fell in love with Beethoven's music when, at the age of fifteen, she first heard a composition by him, Sonata Opus 31 No. 2. She writes in her autobiography, *The Spirit's Pilgrimage,* that her whole being was stirred by it; she played it over and over again. It was something beyond music that she had discovered, and which lingered in her. She felt as if she was in communion with the spirit of Beethoven. But she also felt deep anguish within herself at not being able to meet the great musician in person. In these moments of anguish, she threw herself down on her knees in the seclusion of her room and prayed to God: 'Why have I been born over a century too late? Why hast thou given me realisation of him and yet put all these years in between?' She went on a pilgrimage to Beethoven's birthplace in Germany and to his grave in Austria. She organised Beethoven concerts in England. She also learnt French so that she could read about Beethoven's life in Romain Rolland's *Jean-Christophe*. The book inspired her so much that she sought, in 1923, a meeting with the author.

She met Rolland in Villeneuve, where he lived with his sister, also named Madeleine. The two Madeleines would later forge a deep friendship. Rolland writes in his diary that 'her [Madeleine Slade's] mind was prey to a violent and passionate disturbance, and she could not find a way out'. In this meeting he mentioned India in the context of a small book he had then just written, on the life of Gandhi. When she looked blank, he asked her: 'You have never heard of him?' Madeleine replied in the negative. 'He is another Christ,' he told her, adding: 'The only living person worthy of the sort of veneration you have felt for Beethoven is Mahatma Gandhi.' These words went deep, but she stored them away and went on her voyage to Alexandria in Egypt. Back from Alexandria, she went to Paris, bought Rolland's book from a bookshop, and finished reading it on the same day. Then she realised what that 'something', which had lingered in her after her first tryst with Beethoven's music, was. It was a call to go to Gandhi.

This is how she describes her first meeting with the Mahatma when she arrived at Sabarmati Ashram in November 1925.

> I entered [the room]. A slight, brown figure rose up and came
> towards me. I was conscious of nothing but a sense of light.
> I fell on my knees. Hands gently raised me up, and a voice
> said, 'You shall be my daughter'.[9]

Gandhi gave her the name 'Mirabehn', after Mirabai, the great devotee of Lord Krishna. Mirabai's association with mystical poetry and music probably played a role in Gandhi choosing this name for his new disciple, who sacrificed her all to serve her master as an ascetic. Though Mira was a Hindu-sounding name, he made no attempt to convert her to Hinduism. A severe critic of proselytisation, he wanted her to become a model Christian. She, on the other hand, dived deep into a study of the Vedas, Upanishads and the Hindu epics. She tells us in her autobiography that the effect they had on her was 'profound'.

> For here I discovered various things that seemed to be part of my inmost self, part of something I had known long before and lost. Here there was no nightmare of the unanswerable, but instead a vast illumination of the Unknown making its contemplation not a horror, but an infinite inspiration. While reading the Upanishads and a few extracts from the Vedas, I heard the same notes as in the music of Beethoven.[10]

Rolland, who was the cause for Madeleine Slade to go to Gandhi, called her 'a Holy Woman to this new Savior'. However, he had been himself craving deeply for many years to receive Gandhi in Villeneuve and to let him experience Beethoven's sublime music. In a letter to Mirabehn on 25 April 1927 (that is, four years before Gandhi came to meet Rolland), he had written: 'If Gandhi knew him (Beethoven), he would recognise in him our European Mahatma, our strongest mediator between the life of the senses and eternal Life. And he would bless this music which perhaps, for us, is the highest form of prayer, a permanent communion with the Divinity'. Earlier, too, in his letter to Mahadev Desai on 24 February 1924, Rolland had described Beethoven as 'our European Mahatma' who 'sings in his Ode to Joy: Let us – millions of human beings – embrace each other'.

We must understand here why music, and art in general, served as the path for the best men and women of Europe to seek answers to the deepest questions posed by the troubled times they lived in. Organised religion had done little to stem the tide of violence and war in Europe. The church's stand on colonial exploitation and violence was, at best, neutral and, at worst, collusive. The Pope, in fact, refused to grant an audience to Gandhi when he visited the Vatican in 1931. Europe was clearly passing through a painful spiritual crisis. The crisis caused sensitive souls such as Romain Rolland and Madeleine Slade to turn to art, literature and music to satisfy their quest. Tolstoy, who had a profound influence on Gandhi, is quoted in Rolland's biography of the Russian writer as saying: 'Art must suppress violence, and only art can do so...All that tends to unify mankind belongs to the good and beautiful. All that tends to disunite is evil and ugly'. Rolland found solace in music because, he said: 'Nothing better than music shows me what I am and what we will be, what will be the future of our humanity.' In his novel *Jean-Christophe*, its Beethoven-like protagonist says: 'There is only one soul for all mankind; and though each one of the millions of beings seems to be different from the others like the worlds that revolve in the sky, it is the same flash of love that blazes simultaneously in the hearts which are separated by centuries'.

Thus, Madeleine Slade, whose agonised soul had been pining for Beethoven with the lament 'Why have I been born over a century too late?', found her Beethoven in Gandhi. During the twenty-three years that she lived in his presence, she rarely heard Beethoven's music. But she, who had taken to the religion of khadi and charka with utmost devotion and commitment, did experience the Mahatma's blissful 'music of spinning wheel' each day.

After Gandhi's assassination, Mirabehn wrote: 'For me there were only two, God and Bapu. And now they have become one'. She continued to live in India for another eleven years at her own ashram in the foothills of the Himalayas. Her passion was to save the environment from destruction in the name of mindless development. In agony, she wrote letters to Prime Minister Nehru and other Indian leaders highlighting the apathy and ignorance of the bureaucracy.

Nevertheless, India without her master, and the India that had strayed from the master's path, made Mirabehn deeply lonely. The call of 'something' in her that had made her come to Gandhi now urged her to go back to Beethoven. She left India in 1959 to spend the rest of her life in seclusion, solitude and Gandhian simplicity with the spirit of the composer – in a small country cottage on the wooded and calm outskirts of Vienna, where Beethoven had lived and composed many of his masterworks. She was familiar with the place since she had visited it in her youth.

The forests that inspired Beethoven to compose his heavenly music also inspired Mirabehn to pen many meditative reflections on human life.

> We inhabit the limitless Universe, and we must expand our horizons until they blend into the vastness and the Almighty Spirit with which it is pervaded.
>
> And it is not only contemplation of the celestial expanse surrounding us that awakens that sense. How often, on a summer's day, have I flung myself down on a meadow to look deep into the grass to watch there a world of tiny living creatures, each one perfect in design and colour, and each one busy fulfilling its life's calling when, at such moments, comes over me a vision of Creation's oneness from the tiniest creatures to the mightiest stars in space.
>
> We are all one family – watched over by the Creator.

How wonderfully this resonates with what Beethoven himself has written about Nature's inspiration on his music! 'No one can conceive,' he once wrote, 'the intense happiness I feel in getting into the country, among the woods, my dear trees, shrubs, hills, and dales. I am convinced that no one loves country life as I do. It is as if every tree and every bush could understand my mute inquiries and respond to them'.

Apart from publishing her autobiography in 1960, Mirabehn also wrote a precious book *Beethoven's Mystical Vision,* which portrayed the composer's life and spiritual voyage in music. The book highlighted for the first time his acquaintance with ancient Hindu scriptures, which 'profoundly stirred the mystic nature in his spirit'. One of the many long quotations that Beethoven jotted down in his sketchbooks is the teaching of the second chapter of the *Bhagavad Gita,* 'the most treasured spiritual poem of Hinduism, verses of which were recited daily at four o'clock in the morning prayer of Mahatma Gandhi'.

> Blessed is he who has overcome all passion and then with energy performs all the affairs of life without concern for

the outcome. Let the motive be in the deed and not in the result... for such unconcern means attention to the spiritual. Do not let your life pass in inactivity. Be active, fulfil your duty... Endeavour, therefore, that your reason may obtain this habit, for such a habit is in life a precious art.

Mirabehn then writes: 'The depth of feeling with which Beethoven reacted to Eastern wisdom was more than intellectual. It seems to have been the stirring of an echo from earlier spiritual experience, and with this his passionate devotion to Nature was in perfect harmony. The sages who have left us their thoughts in Sanskrit dwelt with their disciples in forest centres, and their wisdom was nourished by continual contact with Nature'.

Yehudi Menuhin (1916-99), the celebrated violinist and conductor, in his foreword to Mirabehn's book, writes: 'It is fitting that this insight should have been bequeathed to us through the lifelong adoration of a European woman who spent 33 years of her life in India, the land of mysticism and of union with the eternal, with that remarkable human being, Mahatma Gandhi'.

The cycle of Mirabehn's life had thus taken a full circle – from Beethoven to Beethoven via Mahatma Gandhi! To recall her own autobiographical lines: 'My life had been devoted to the service of two great souls with the loftiest ideals – one expressing himself through the perpetual activity in moral, social and political reform, and the other through the perpetual expression of the spiritual voice that came to him through music. In Beethoven's own words – "...it is only through untiring use of the powers with which he has been endowed that man can reverence the Creator and Preserver of Nature".'

This extraordinary ambassador of understanding and solidarity between the West and the East, this daughter-disciple of the Mahatma who had also devoted her soul to the European Mahatma, died in Vienna in 1982 at the ripe old age of ninety. But what is death for a person who lived for the music of the two Mahatmas and who then merged into the immortal music of which her own transient life on earth was but a small but intensely soulful score?

When two great Truth-seekers met: *Gandhi visited Nobel laureate writer Romain Rolland, whom he described as 'Rishi' or 'Sage', at his villa near Geneva in December 1931. There, in between his morning and evening prayers, between bhajans and Beethoven, and between his charkha-spinning sessions, Gandhi would sit with Rolland to discuss timeless issues in philosophy.* 'Mahatma Gandhi: The Man Who Became One With the Universal Being' *is how Rolland titled his highly popular 1924 biography of Gandhi.*

16

'TRUTH IS GOD' AND 'GOD IS JOY'
An Illuminating Dialogue Between
Gandhi and Romain Rolland

·→¦·◦◇◇◇◦·¦←·

My dear Madeleine, I have been trying to find out a suitable adjective
for your brother. 'Mons. Rolland' or 'your brother' sounds too prosaic and
distant. The two words that come to me are 'Rishi' or the 'Sage'. They are
almost synonymous terms but not identical in meaning. Subject, therefore,
to his and your approval, I am going to henceforth describe him as the
Rishi…Please tell the Rishi that some months ago I had read for the first
time his volumes on Ramakrishna and Vivekananda. The reading gave
me great joy and enabled me more fully than before to get a measure of
his love for India. – Love to you both from us both.

— Gandhi's letter to Madeleine Rolland, sister of Romain Rolland, from Yeravada Central
Prison, Poona, on 6 January 1933; 'from us both' in the last line refers to Gandhi and
Mirabehn, who was imprisoned in Arthur Road Jail in Bombay at the time.

THE MYSTICAL CONNECTION BETWEEN GANDHI, MIRABEHN, ROMAIN
Rolland and Beethoven is not the only reason why Gandhi's
visit to Rolland's villa near Geneva became a milestone in
both their lives. It is also because of a deeply insightful dialogue that
took place between the two great minds on the subject of Truth and
God. This subject also dominated the interaction that Gandhi had
with some Swiss intellectuals at a church in nearby Lausanne. There
is no better way of getting a peep into the Mahatma's mind than to

visit the following record in Rolland's diary. I am quoting this almost in its entirety because I regard this to be the most lucid articulation of Gandhi's seminal, and in some ways unique, contribution to the philosophy of God and Truth.

Gandhi is asked the question – 'Why do you regard God as Truth?' He replies:

'In my very early youth I was taught that the Hindu scriptures knew almost a thousand names of God, but these thousand names are not nearly enough. I believe that God has as many names as there are living creatures, and this is why we also say that God is without name. And since God has many forms, we also consider him as being without form. And since he speaks to us in many tongues, we consider him speechless. When I came to study Islam, I saw that Islam too had many names for God. With those who say that God is Love, I too say that God is Love. But in my heart I thought that though God may be Love, God is, above all, Truth. If it is possible for human language to give its complete description of God, my conclusion is that for me, God is Truth. But two years ago I made a step further, to say that Truth is God'.

Gandhi explains that he came to this conclusion after an 'incessant search for Truth' which had begun about fifty years earlier. He had felt then that the nearest approach to Truth was made by 'love', but he had recognised that the word 'love' has many meanings in the English language. Moreover, human love, in the sense of passion, could also become 'a degrading thing'. He had also recognised that love in the sense of ahimsa has only a small number of adherents in the world. 'But I have never found a double meaning to the word "Truth". Even the atheists do not doubt the necessity or the power of Truth. In their passion to discover Truth, the atheists have not hesitated to deny the existence of God – and from their point of view they are right'.

Gandhi then continues to give more reasons for his belief that 'Truth is God'.

'I might add that millions have used the name of God and committed atrocities in his name. This is not to say that scientists, too, do not very often commit cruelties in the name of Truth; I know how in the name of science and truth, all sorts of frightful cruelties are perpetrated on animals by vivisection. So there are a certain number of difficulties on the way, however one describes God. But the human mind has its limitations, and we must work within these limitations when we try to conceive of a Being or an Entity beyond our powers of apprehension. Then we have another saying in Hindu philosophy: "God alone is, and nothing else is." You will find the same truth emphasised and illustrated in the Kalma of Islam. The Sanskrit word for Truth means literally "that which exists – *Sat*". For this and several other reasons I have come to the conclusion that the definition "Truth is God" satisfies me best. And when you want to find the Truth which is God, the only infallible way to it is by Love, which means Nonviolence.'

At this point, Rolland interjects to put a question – 'But what is Truth?' Gandhi answers it with the same steady reflection:

'A difficult question. But I have solved it for myself by saying that it is what the inner voice tells us. You will ask: "How is it then that different people think different and contrary truths?" Well, we see that the human spirit works through innumerable media, and that the evolution of the human mind is not the same for all men. It follows that what may be truth for one man is non-truth for another. Those who seek truth in this way have come to the conclusion that certain conditions must first be observed. In the same way that there are indispensable courses of scientific instruction to be undergone before anyone can carry out scientific experiments, a strict preliminary discipline is necessary before a person can be qualified to make experiments in the spiritual domain. This is why everyone should reach an exact knowledge of his limitations before speaking of his inner voice. We have a belief, based on experience, that those who wish to make their individual search for the Truth which is God must undergo certain vows, for instance the vow of

Truth and the vow of Brahmacharya (chastity)...There are several other prescribed conditions, but I cannot speak of all of them. It is enough to say that those who have carried out these experiments know that it is not fitting for everyone to claim that he hears the voice of conscience. And since nowadays everyone demands the right to speak of his conscience without having undergone any kind of discipline at all, and since there are so many non-truths in this disorientated world, all I can say to you in all true humility is that Truth cannot be found by anyone who has not achieved an abundant sense of humility. If you want to swim in the bosom of the Ocean of Truth, you must reduce yourself to zero. I can go no further along this fascinating path.'

Here, Rolland expresses certain reservations about Gandhi's explanation about the attributes of Truth. In doing so, he introduces an important new element in their discussion: art.

Rolland: 'If it is true that "Truth is God", it seems to me that it lacks a very important attribute of God, which is Joy. For – and I insist on this – I cannot conceive of a God without joy. If I have been made out to be an apostle of grief because I have extolled Beethoven's conquest of joy through suffering, then my thought has been misunderstood and so has Beethoven's. Suffering cannot be an end in itself, merely a road to something else, a road which is forced on us, which we do not go out of our way to seek. I found this joy, which truth was not sufficient to prove to me, in beauty, and this is where I found myself in opposition to Tolstoy; I attribute a capital importance to art and beauty. By this I mean true art and healthy beauty.

'Great art has harmony as its essence, and it brings peace, health and equilibrium to the soul. It communicates them at once by the senses and by the mind, for both senses and mind have the right to joy. Beauty manifests itself in many ways; beauty of line, beauty of sound, beauty of colours, etc., and at the bottom of them all, the inner order, the hidden harmony,

which is in essence moral. The troubles of the soul are filtered
and sublimated through it. Art is the bread of thousands of
souls, above all in some refined races, who without beauty
(either in nature or in art) would be destitute. All the different
routes leading to peace and harmony are good; none of them
must be closed, and the ideal would be to associate them all:
– which happens in history at some supreme moments when
all the inner forces of a people run together, producing books
of religion, beauty, science and dreams for whole peoples'.

Rolland adds in his diary: 'All this expose has an unexpressed double
aim – to fight against the notion attributed to Gandhi that suffering is
pleasing to God, and to assert the rights, which he seems sometimes
to neglect, of beauty and the natural and exalting love which healthy
men have for her'.

Rolland's thoughts on art prompt Gandhi to explain his own views
on the subject.

'For me, the definition of Truth is a universal one. The Truth
is made manifest in many ways. Any art which is inconsistent
with Truth, which is not linked to Truth, is no art. I would
not classify art as a thing distinct from Truth. I am against
the formula "art for art's sake"; for me, art must be based on
Truth. I reject beautiful things which pass for art if they express
non-truth instead of Truth. I would subscribe to the formula:
"Art brings joy and is good", – but on the condition I have
stated. By Truth in art I do not mean the exact reproduction
of exterior objects; it is the living object which brings living
joy to the soul and which must elevate the soul. If a work does
not achieve this, it is worthless. If Truth does not bring joy, it
is because Truth is not in you....'

Then Gandhi speaks of a Hindu religious song of morning prayers, and
the holy formula 'sat-chit-ananda': 'sat' meaning 'truth', 'chit' 'that which
lives' and 'true knowledge' (knowledge that is not void of true perception),
and 'ananda' 'ineffable joy'. In this conception, Truth is inseparable from
joy. 'Yet,' Gandhi insists, 'one must suffer in the search for Truth; one

must undergo disappointments, fatigues and afflictions without number; but despite everything you draw joy and felicity from it.'

In support of his argument, Gandhi also quotes a Persian novel in which Shirin, the beloved, represents Truth. Her lover, in order to reach her, has to cut through a mountain with a blunt instrument; he has to spend years at the task but he does not complain; his effort is joy, and he knows that at the end he will find Shirin.

> Rolland: 'I understand that, and it is my opinion too. But it's not only about difficulties facing the seeker after Truth that I spoke; these difficulties I accept and love. I am thinking of another kind of suffering, that of responsibility. The thinker who does not fear the truth on his own account is worried about its effects on those who will be shaken by it. The great scientific discoveries made by Copernicus and the heroes of thought who followed him shook millions of people in their faith. Truth is always marching on, and not everyone can follow it without becoming breathless and apprehensive. Truth in transition is often very hard for the majority of men. This is the pain of which I speak, not my own.'
> Gandhi: 'Even in this case I would say that there must be a secret satisfaction, because that is the necessity of the thing. This is why we see in the writings of those who have gone through tortures that "the seeker after truth has a heart tender as the lotus and hard as granite".'

As the conversation between the two men goes on, they speak again of truth in art and its multiple forms. Diaryist Rolland writes:

> I say that I should like art always to be accessible to the great mass of people, and, returning to the cathedrals, I say that at the time they were built Europe was closer to the thought of India – which Gandhi admits. 'At present,' I add, 'the truth is best expressed by the scientists; they are the greatest poets.' I then allude to recent astronomical discoveries which have broken through the envelope of our universe to see other universes floating beyond the Milky Way.

Fifty years ago, in my youth, the triumph of materialism was related to that of science; now it turns out today that science itself is explaining matter in terms of energy, in other words a spiritual principle. We are living in a fine age, despite all the disorders it brings with it. Happy the man who can live in it with a healthy body and a strong heart!

According to Rolland, 'Gandhi assents, his eyes shining'. He also writes: 'I noted in him traits similar to Vivekananda'.

The Gandhi–Rolland dialogue also focussed on the menacing political situation in Europe, whose sky was already being darkened by the clouds of fascism and the approaching Second World War. Madeleine Rolland[1], the writer's sister, recorded this conversation:

They discuss the grave problems which they have at heart. My brother describes for Gandhi the tragic situation of Europe – the sufferings of the people oppressed by dictators; the drama of the proletariat who in their desperate effort to break the shackles of an anonymous and ruthless capitalism and pushed forward by their legitimate aspiration for justice and freedom, see only one way out, that of rebellion and violence. For man in the West is by education, by tradition and by temperament unprepared for the religion of ahimsa.... Gandhi listens, reflects.... When he answers, he reaffirms his unshakeable faith in the full power of nonviolence.... At times their conclusions vary; yet always they commune with each other through their common love for humanity, their identical desire to alleviate its misery, their fervent search for Truth, in its multiplicity of aspects.

Every time I read this conversation, I am awe-struck by the sheer depth, breadth, subtlety, precision and undying freshness of the thoughts expressed by both Gandhi and Rolland. What an invaluable contribution to the modern man's quest for truth! And what a touching and reassuring proof that the best of human minds, even when they are separated by continents and cultures, pulsate with the same love for mankind. Indeed, Gandhi himself had written in his letter to Rolland on 22 March 1924 (it was in reply to Rolland's letter informing him about the publication of the twenty-first edition of his book *Mahatma Gandhi* in French): 'It demonstrates once more the essential oneness of human nature though flourishing under different skies'.

As Rolland bade goodbye to Gandhi at the Geneva railway station on the evening of 11 December 1931, the great writer asked his guest: 'What would you like me to do in grateful memory of your visit? Interpret India's nonviolent struggle to the world? Learn Hindustani?'

Gandhi replied: 'Come and meet India.'[2]

Rolland, battling as much his own illness in the last years of his life as the scourge of war that had afflicted Europe, could never undertake the journey to India.

The dialogue between Gandhi and Rolland was the subject of my column in the Sunday *Indian Express* under the title 'Of Gandhi and the God Particle' (14 September 2008). The context for the column was the Large Hadron Collider experiment that physicists at the European Organisation for Nuclear Research (CERN), near Geneva, had begun in September 2006. This is what I had written:

> Everything about this biggest and costliest-ever experiment in physics is awe-inspiring. A 27-km-long, circular-shaped underground tunnel. Subatomic particles racing from opposite directions at close to the speed of light and smashing together, generating temperatures 1,00,000 times hotter than at the heart of the Sun. Creation of artificial conditions similar to what might have existed a trillionth of a second after the Big Bang, the massive cosmic explosion that created the universe some 14 billion years ago. And the search for the Higgs boson, the so-called 'God particle' that physicists believe bestows mass on everything around us.
>
> Why is the Higgs boson called 'God particle'? I do not know. But isn't it an acknowledgement that science's search for the basic truth about our universe is its way of searching for God?

Of course, Truth and God manifest in a million different ways, and the quest for them has engaged great minds from every field of human endeavour – science, spirituality, art, literature, even politics. Here I remember one of the most extraordinary conversations about Truth and God that took place some eight decades ago near Geneva, not far from the place where the 'God particle' experiment is being conducted. It was between Mahatma Gandhi and Romain Rolland...

I had ended my column with these lines:

Today the Europe that has come together to conduct the greatest scientific experiment in human history, in which scientists from the rest of the world are also collaborating, is a far cry from the Europe that fought two World Wars in the last century. In some ways, this peaceful and cooperative search for nature's secrets is a realisation of the shared vision of Gandhi and Rolland as they met, meditated, listened to Beethoven and bhajans, talked philosophy and politics, and, peering into the meaning of Truth and God, affirmed their faith in a better future for mankind.

Gandhi was deeply saddened when he heard of the death of Rolland on 30 December 1944. In his homage he wrote: 'He truly lives in his many and nameless deeds...He lived Truth and Nonviolence as he saw and believed them from time to time'.[3] He described Rolland as 'the sage of Villeneuve' and his own journey to the place as 'my pilgrimage'. He added: 'Could I have left India just to visit him and his inseparable sister, Madeleine, his interpreter and friend, I would have undertaken the voyage'.[4]

As much as this book is an exploration of Gandhi's views on Truth, it is also my grateful tribute to Romain Rolland. His words have helped me understand the Mahatma's mind and mission better than all other sources, except of course the latter's own writings.

'Bapuji' 12 April 1930: *Linocut image of the Mahatma by Nandalal Bose, one of the greatest Indian artists in the twentieth century, depicting Gandhi on his historic Salt March to Dandi. Inscribed in it are the words from a Bengali song by Rabindranath Tagore, which was Gandhi's favourite:* Ekla Chalo Re *(Walk Alone).*

17

'A TRUE ARTIST WHOSE MISSION WAS TO MAKE GODS OUT OF MEN OF CLAY'

...we have forgotten so much that was beautiful. It would seem incredible that people could want to forget the best possibilities, but this happens oftener than one can imagine. Man lost his key to the symbols of the Rig-Veda. Man forgot the meaning of the Kabala. Man mutilated the glorious word of Buddha. Man, with gold, defiled the divine word of Christ and forgot, forgot, forgot the keys to the finest gates. Men lose easily, but how to regain again? The path to recovery permits everyone to have hope. Why not, if a soldier of Napoleon discovered the Rosetta Stone in a trench, key to the understanding of the complete hieroglyphs of Egypt?

— 'Maharshi' Nicholas Roerich (1874-1947),
the legendary Russian painter who made the
Himalayas his home in the last twenty years of his life.

GANDHI'S INTRIGUING EXPRESSION — 'MUSIC OF THE SPINNING wheel' – and his spirited projection of the spinning wheel as a symbol of the search for a nonviolent socio-economic order, prompts us to ask an important question: Are nonviolence and music intrinsically compatible? To phrase the same question in another way: Are violence and music incurably incompatible?

The answer to this question has to be an emphatic 'Yes'. Music is capable of expressing a wide range of human emotions and moods, more subtly, more deeply and more authentically than any other language known to humans. However, it is incapable of expressing violence and hatred. The moment music becomes violent, it ceases to be music. It loses harmony, the most basic attribute of music.

Music is, thus, the language of nonviolence. It is the language of harmony. It is the language of morality. Precisely for this reason, it is the only pan-human language that reaches the hearts of people all over the world, making them aware of the bonds of universal brotherhood that unite them.

Music often has regional, national or community-specific connotations. For example, the tune of India's national anthem *Jana Gana Mana* appeals to the patriotism of our people. But it may not have the same effect on other people. The incomparable devotional content of Sufi singer Nusrat Fateh Ali Khan's rendering of *Allah Hu* may not appeal to non-Muslims in the same way that it does to Muslims. Gandhi's own favourite bhajan *Vaishnava jana to tene kahiye, je peed paraayee jane re...* (He is the true devotee of God who knows and feels another's suffering as his own) has an appeal to his followers which cannot be expected to touch the hearts of those who do not know its meaning and context. Numerous such examples can be given.

However, even when good music displays a local, national or community-specific personality, it never arouses narrow, chauvinistic and divisive feelings. Its universality becomes apparent on deeper reflection. It is the same as flowers of different colours and appearances having their own unique personality and yet rejoicing in their contribution to the beauty of a bouquet, which in turn enhances the beauty of individual flowers. Romain Rolland, who wrote extensively on art, extends this analogy to music by saying that the universal symphony of the music of mankind would sound incomplete if it excluded the music of even the smallest constituency of the human race.

What is true about music is also true about other forms of art. True art, whatever be its genre, can never induce violence and bigotry. For example, 'Guernica', one of the most famous paintings by Pablo Picasso, which he created in response to the 1937 bombing of this Spanish town by German-Italian warplanes during the Spanish Civil War, outwardly shows only repulsive symbols of war and violence. Nevertheless, it is regarded as one of the most powerful works of art conveying an anti-war message. This is because what the inner language of the painting conveys is the horrors and tragedies of war and the suffering it inflicts upon the innocent humanity. This brings us to a reflection on Gandhi's views on art and how they reinforce the belief of all true artists that art has both the power and the responsibility to promote peace and universal brotherhood.

Contrary to the common perception of Gandhi as an ascetic who was disinterested in art and beauty, in reality he was a connoisseur of both. His meditations on art[1] are as profound as those on any other subject. True art, he affirmed, reveals an intrinsic and inseparable relationship between truth, divinity and beauty – what the Indian science of aesthetics calls *satyam, shivam, sundaram.* Nevertheless, he gave primacy to truth over beauty.

> I see and find beauty in Truth or through Truth. All Truths, not merely true ideas, but truthful pictures, or songs are highly beautiful. People generally fail to see Beauty in Truth. The ordinary man runs away from and becomes blind to the beauty in it. Whenever men begin to see Beauty in Truth, then true art will arise.
>
> Truth is the first thing to be sought for, and Beauty and Goodness will then be added unto you. That is what Christ really taught in the Sermon on the Mount. Jesus was, to my mind, a supreme artist because he saw and expressed Truth; and so was Muhammad, the Koran being the most perfect composition in all Arabic literature – at any rate, that is what scholars say. It is because both of them strove first for Truth that the grace of expression naturally came in and yet neither Jesus nor Muhammad wrote on art. That is the Truth and Beauty I crave for, live for, and would die for.

Gandhi further elaborates his thought about the intrinsic bond between satyam and sundaram in the following words:

To a true artist only that face is beautiful which, quite apart from its exterior, shines with the Truth within the soul. There is...no Beauty apart from Truth. On the other hand, Truth may manifest itself in forms which may not be outwardly beautiful at all. Socrates, we are told, was the most truthful man of his time, and yet his features are said to have been the ugliest in Greece. To my mind he was beautiful because all his life was a striving after Truth, and you may remember that this outward form did not prevent Phidias[2] from appreciating the beauty of Truth in him, though as an artist he was accustomed to see Beauty in outward forms also.

The outward has no meaning except in so far as it helps the inward. All true art is thus the expression of the soul. The outward forms have value only in so far as they are the expression of the inner spirit in man. Art of that nature has the greatest possible appeal for me. But I know that many call themselves artists, and are recognised as such, and yet in their works there is absolutely no trace of the soul's upward urge and unrest.

'True art,' Gandhi remarked, 'takes note not merely of form but also of what lies behind.' Talking about himself, he said:

I find that I can do entirely without external forms in my soul's realisation. I can claim, therefore, that there is truly efficient art in my life, though you might not see what you call works of art about me. My room may have blank walls; and I may even dispense with the roof, so that I may gaze out at the starry heavens overhead that stretch in an unending expanse of beauty. What conscious art of man can give me the panoramic scenes that open out before me, when I look up to the sky above with all its shining stars? This, however, does not mean that I refuse to accept the value of production of arts, generally accepted as such, but only that I personally feel how inadequate these are compared with the eternal symbols of beauty in Nature. These productions of man's art have their value only in so far as they help the soul onward towards self-realisation.

Just as he was ever vigilant about anything untrue or ugly entering his thoughts and feelings, he felt that artists should exercise similar watchfulness. And the way to cultivate this quality, according to him, was faith in God.

> We have somehow accustomed ourselves to the belief that art is independent of the purity of private life. I can say with all the experience at my command that nothing could be more untrue. As I am nearing the end of my earthly life I can say that purity of life is the highest and truest art. The art of producing good music from a cultivated voice can be achieved by many, but the art of producing that music from the harmony of a pure life is achieved very rarely.

Here again – in his affirmation about 'the art of producing music from the harmony of a pure life' – we see what Gandhi meant by the 'music of the spinning wheel'. Spinning the charkha, insofar as it was outwardly a form of service to humanity and inwardly a form of silent meditation, was, for him, a way of seeking 'the harmony of a pure life'. That sublime harmony expressed itself to him as music. But let us continue to listen to Gandhi's views on art:

> Truth and untruth often co-exist; good and evil are often found together. In an artist also, not seldom, the right perception of things and the wrong co-exist. Truly beautiful creations come when right perception is at work. If these moments are rare in life they are also rare in art. These beauties ('a sunset or a crescent moon that shines amid the stars at night') are truthful, inasmuch as they make me think of the Creator at the back of them. How else could these be beautiful, but for the Truth that is in the centre of creation? When I admire the wonder of a sunset or the beauty of the moon, my soul expands in worship of the Creator. I try to see Him and His mercies in all these creations. But even the sunsets and sunrises would be mere hindrances if they did not help me to think of Him.

For Gandhi, the greatest works of art were those that served as a means of communion with God. He saw one such work of art when he visited the Vatican in 1931. After his five-day stay at Romain Rolland's villa in Switzerland, he left, by train, for Italy, then reeling under the dictatorial rule of Mussolini. The Pope's refusal to meet him was a proof of how far the church, then a silent ally of Mussolini, had moved away from the essential message of Christianity. Gandhi was not much impressed by the outward grandeur of the Vatican, which for many centuries had remained the seat of power of both the church and the state in Europe. But he was spellbound by a particular statue of Jesus Christ on the Cross in the art collection in the Vatican museum

Three decades later, Mirabehn, who had accompanied him on this visit, described the profound effect that the statue of Christ on the Cross had on him: 'He remained perfectly silent, and it was only when he left that he spoke, and then as if still in contemplation – "That was a very wonderful crucifix" – and again silence. "So deep an impression did that scene make on me that it stands out all alone in my mind, and I remember nothing else of the visit to the Vatican".'

Why did the statue of Christ's crucifixion have such a profound effect on Gandhi? Did it produce in him premonition of his own martyrdom? We don't know. But one thing we do know: there was uncanny resemblance between Jesus and Gandhi in the hand-spun and blood-stained loin cloth they both wore when they died.

Gandhi referred to his Vatican experience in his address to the Gujarati Literature Society in 1936, and said: 'Why should I need an artist to explain a work of art to me? Why should it not speak out to me itself?'[3]

Gandhi's thoughts on art are not divorced from his egalitarian economic philosophy. As we have seen earlier, he did not believe in the concept of 'art for art's sake'. According to him, art, like every other calling in life, must have a lofty purpose: of alleviating human suffering and elevating human beings to higher evolutionary possibilities, besides helping them in their quest for self-realisation. To achieve this purpose, art cannot remain a monopoly of the elite; it must speak to the millions.

Here (in art) too, just as elsewhere, I must think in terms of the millions. And to the millions we cannot give that training to acquire a perception of Beauty in such a way as to see Truth in it. Show them Truth first and they will see Beauty afterwards... Whatever can be useful to...starving millions is beautiful to my mind. Let us give today first the vital things of life and all the graces and ornaments of life will follow.

We see here how Gandhi equated Truth (which is God) with 'the vital things of life' – such as clean drinking water, sanitation, decent housing, hygienic environment, good education, and a source of gainful livelihood that can alleviate hunger. 'God comes to the hungry in the form of food,' he believed. And universalisation of the spinning wheel was his answer to the problem of widespread hunger. We begin to discern here why the spinning wheel for him was both an artistic instrument – producer of 'music of universal love' – and also a spiritual machine, since it served the poor by serving *Daridranarayan*, Gandhi's highly evocative description of God as the protector of the unprotected.

What a remarkable internal consistency there was in his economic philosophy, spiritual philosophy, scientific philosophy and artistic philosophy!

Gandhi had deep appreciation for good works of art and literature, and frequently recommended them to his colleagues and to readers of his journals. 'Why would he ask his readers to read Tolstoy and Ruskin on art unless he placed a link between the arts and his own main project in life – the regeneration of Indian society'? writes Anthony J. Parel in his book *Gandhi's Philosophy and the Quest for Harmony*. 'Artistic revival required economic and political revival also – a thought that fitted perfectly with Gandhi's theory of the *purusharthas*[4]. Swaraj was not just a political condition; it was also a moral and psychological condition of the consciousness of freedom from alien domination'.[5]

Music being his passion, it became an integral part of life in his ashrams. Soon after establishing the Sabarmati Ashram in 1915, he appointed a music teacher, Pandit Narayan Moreshwar Khare, who was a disciple of Pandit Vishnu Digambar Paluskar, a legendary name in Indian classical music. He held Pandit Paluskar in high esteem not only because of his mastery in music but also on account of his high moral calibre. Like Gandhi, Paluskar also believed that musical excellence without the cultivation of a moral character does not amount to much. It may captivate listeners for a while, but creates no lasting impact on them. In collaboration with Paluskar and Khare, Gandhi organised the first All India Music Conference in Ahmedabad in 1921. Under his inspiration, the greatest personalities in music participated in the customary music festivals coinciding with the annual sessions of the INC.

With Khare's help, Gandhi compiled the *Ashram Bhajanmala* (hymnal for the daily prayer meetings at his commune), which had over 250 hymns from different regions and languages of India – and also some from abroad. He personally translated many of them into English. His focus on devotional music was on account of his belief, which is also the belief of saints and mystics from all religious traditions in the world, that bhajans, kirtans and hymns sung or heard with a prayerful attitude clear the mind of the accumulated impurities of one's life. He regarded sacred music as a remedy for many ills of the individual and society, since it removes the root of selfishness – man's false ego – and makes him experience harmony with society, Nature and God. The very first hymn in the *Ashram Bhajanmala* encapsulated Gandhi's thought on the true nature of human beings: 'Early in the morning I call to mind that Being which is felt in the heart, which is *sat, chit,* and *ananda,* which is the state reached by perfect men and which is the super-state. I have to reach that state, and not think that I am this body made up of five perishable elements of nature'.

Gandhi was highly impressed by Anand Coomaraswamy's *Essays on National Idealism,* which was published soon after his own *Hind Swaraj* was published in Gujarati (1909), and recommended it to his colleagues. Coomaraswamy (1877-1947), a Sri Lankan Tamil, was a renowned historian and philosopher of Indian art who introduced ancient Indian art to the West. Parel writes that *Essays on National*

Idealism 'confirmed many ideas brewing in Gandhi's own mind'. Like Gandhi, Coomaraswamy 'did not believe that the national regeneration of the Indian people could take place without the support of the arts. Art contains in itself the deepest principles of life, the truest guide to the greatest art, the Art of Living'.

Coomaraswamy had immense respect for Gandhi. In 1947, shortly before India attained freedom, he remarked that Gandhi's advocacy of satyagraha made him not only a teacher of India but a *jagat-guru* (teacher of the world): 'Nonviolence, as he knows, is not only refraining from visibly violent actions; it is a matter of making peace with ourselves, one of learning to obey our Inner Man; for none but the outer man or ego is aggressive'.[6]

Gandhi's writings in both Gujarati and English, besides radiating the soul of his personality, have great literary quality. He served as the president of both the Gujarat Sahitya Parishad (Association of Gujarati Literature) and the Hindi Sahitya Sammelan (Association of Hindi Literature). He believed that India's linguistic diversity, far from being a source of its weakness, was a badge of its unique artistic, cultural and literary strengths. *Indian Opinion*, the newspaper that he founded in South Africa, was published simultaneously in four languages – English, Hindi, Gujarati and Tamil. He was a strong votary of Hindi (or, rather, Hindustani, a derivative of Hindi and Urdu) becoming India's principal link language. He made special efforts to popularise it in South India, especially among the Tamil-speaking people of Madras state (now Tamil Nadu). 'So long as you do not learn Hindi you will remain totally separate from the rest of India,' he told them in 1919.[7] He encouraged the establishment of Dakshina Bharat Hindi Prachar Sabha in 1927 as an independent organisation, of which he remained president till he breathed his last. But unlike many proponents of Hindi, he urged Hindi-speaking people to learn languages of other parts of the country.

In order to promote national integration, he himself learnt several Indian languages such as Urdu, Sindhi, Marathi, Bengali and Tamil. When I visited the birthplace of Rashtrakavi Subramania Bharati, the greatest Tamil poet in modern times, at Ettayapuram in Tamil Nadu in 1997, I found an amazing exhibit at his house (now converted into a museum). It was a letter that Gandhi had written to Bharati in June 1945 – in Tamil, and in his own handwriting!

Although Gandhi opposed the British colonial rule, and fervently promoted Indian languages, he loved the English language deeply. 'If I have given up anything for national service,' he told Kaka Kalelkar, a close associate, 'it is my interest in English literature. Renouncing wealth and career was no sacrifice; I wasn't really interested in them. But I was completely fascinated by English literature.'[8]

Gandhi interacted closely with many great contemporary writers and artists who served the cause of India's freedom movement, praising them for promoting national awakening through their art. He especially admired Rabindranath Tagore, whom he called 'Gurudev', and Nandalal Bose (1883-1966), the legendary artist from Santiniketan. He had liked Bose's painting of the Buddha carrying a lamb that he had saved from being sacrificed in a *yajna* (a ritual of sacrifice), and displayed it in his Sevagram Ashram. He frequently invited Bose to organise art exhibitions at the venues of Congress sessions. Bose's linocut image of Gandhi leading the Salt Satyagraha at Dandi (he titled it 'Bapuji' 12 April 1930) is one of the most haunting artistic representations of the apostle of truth and nonviolence.

Gandhi was – and continues to be – a source of inspiration for artists in India and abroad, as is evident from the following heartfelt tribute that Bose paid to him:

> Mahatmaji may not be an artist in the same sense that we professional artists are. Nevertheless, I cannot but consider him to be a true artist. All his life he has spent in creating his own personality and in fashioning others after his high ideals. His mission is to make Gods out of men of clay. I am sure his ideal will inspire the artists of the world.[9]

Albert Einstein once observed: 'The best scientists are also artists'. Gandhi was neither a scientist nor an artist in the conventional sense. Nevertheless, from the higher standpoint of science and art, he was both – and much more.

PART FOUR

A BEACON FOR
THE PRESENT
AND
THE FUTURE

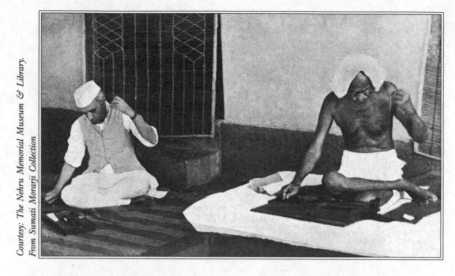

The Mahatma and his heir: *Gandhi had repeatedly affirmed that khadi was not merely a* vastra *(cloth) but a* vichaar *(an idea and an ideal). Pandit Jawaharlal Nehru, India's first prime minister, poetically described that khadi had become 'the livery of India's freedom'. However, he neither believed in nor promoted the Gandhian vision of development.*

(Left) Dr J.C. Kumarappa, architect of Gandhi's rural economics progamme; (right) Pandit Deendayal Upadhyaya, ideological guru of the Bharatiya Janata Party, whose socio-economic thoughts had much in common with the Gandhian vision.

18

NONVIOLENT ECONOMIC GROWTH:
Imperative of Aligning Money
with Morality and Justice

❖⸻◈◈◈⸻❖

In studying human institutions we should never lose sight of that great teacher, Mother Nature. Anything that we may devise if it is contrary to her ways, she will ruthlessly annihilate sooner or later. Everything in nature seems to follow a cyclic movement. Water from the sea rises as vapour and falls on land in refreshing showers and returns back to the sea again ... A nation that forgets or ignores this fundamental process in forming its institutions will disintegrate.

— Joseph Cornelius Kumarappa (1892-1960), economic philosopher and architect of the Gandhian rural economics programme.

Shall the body triumph over and stifle the soul or shall the latter triumph over and express itself through a perishable body which, with its few wants healthily satisfied, will be free to subserve the end of the imperishable soul? This is 'Plain living and high thinking'.

— From Mahatma Gandhi's Foreword to Dr J.C. Kumarappa's book *The Economy of Permanence.*

MANY GREAT HUMANIST THINKERS IN MODERN TIMES HAVE preached nonviolence. All of them are worthy of veneration. However, what is distinctive about Gandhi is that his 'science of nonviolence' explored, among other things, the economic basis of violence. It also enunciated a new ethics-based and peace-promoting way of economic development consistent with the higher possibilities in human evolution. The spinning wheel and village industries were the implementing tools of this science, albeit for a specific situation and a limited historical period in India. The choice of his tools was guided by his belief, which he had arrived at during his formative years in South Africa, that the West's industrial economy was the chief source of violence, war and exploitation. In his fiery essay *Sarvodaya* (1908) paraphrasing John Ruskin's *Unto This Last*, which was written six years before the outbreak of the First World War (1914–18), Gandhi had accurately predicted that Europe was heading towards a catastrophic war. Moreover, he had pointed out that the main cause of the war would be the West's industrialism, whose inherent predilection towards overproduction created an almost limitless appetite for new sources of cheap raw materials as well as new markets for its finished goods. He prophesied:

> Western civilisation is a mere baby, a hundred or only fifty years old. And yet it has reduced Europe to a sorry plight. Let us pray that India is saved from the fate that has overtaken Europe, where the nations are poised for an attack on one another, and are silent only because of the stockpiling of armaments. *Some day there will be an explosion, and then Europe will be a veritable hell on earth.* Non-white races are looked upon as legitimate prey by every European state. What else can we expect where covetousness is the ruling passion in the breasts of men? Europeans pounce upon new territories like crows upon a piece of meat. I am inclined to think that this is due to their mass-production factories. *(Emphasis added)*

A lot has changed in the world in the hundred years since Gandhi wrote this indictment of Western imperialism, the most notable change being the end of colonial subjugation of non-white races by European nations. Nevertheless, there has also been a striking continuity. The Western model of economic growth with some variations has spread to most parts of the world. The big and powerful nations' instinct to aggressively capture sources of raw materials, especially energy resources, near and far, and their equally aggressive attempts to capture markets for their finished products, is very much a part of the commercial culture in the age of globalisation. Slowly, India too is following the wrong footsteps of other powerful nations in this regard.

This essentially Western, but lately globalised, model of economic growth has also given rise to new forms of violence. Economic 'progress' has resulted in – nay, it has actually necessitated – the most virulent attacks on the environment, the likes of which had never been seen in human history. Forests, one of the most beautiful and benevolent creations of Mother Nature, have been felled with impunity. Oceans, rivers and other water bodies have been polluted, their effluents often reaching toxic levels and killing countless number of aquatic creatures. Even though we have not, fortunately, witnessed in the past few decades mass killings of human beings on a scale seen during the two World Wars and other smaller wars in the twentieth century, man's savagery on the other species on Planet Earth can only be described as an unending holocaust. The irony is that other species are being exterminated in the name of the 'development' of the human species. Clearly, Nature's highest creation has turned out to be the worst destroyer of its other creations.

Another new form of violence in the modern era has been the massive disruption of that most basic, civilising, and naturally created institution of mankind: family. It is in the institution of family that man is most human. It is here that humanising values such as love, mutual affection and care, and cooperation without seeking anything in return from the close members of one's family, are more freely active than in other areas of social interaction. The laws of modern economics have no place within the family unit because human labour here is non-monetised and freely offered. Traditional societies in the past had ensured extension of this caring ethos of the family to neighbourhoods and communities to a substantial degree. Sadly, in modern times, this ethos has come under relentless attack by the forces of lopsided economic growth. The rapid disintegration of family and communities has led to atomisation of society. Paradoxically, countries where family and community values have got most eroded are regarded as 'developed', worthy of being emulated by the developing and underdeveloped countries!

This degenerative process is no longer limited to countries of the West. We can also see it in India and China, the two large ancient civilisations that have achieved high rates of GDP growth by following essentially the Western model of development. The widening rural-urban divide, the forced separation of migrant workers from their families, the dehumanising living conditions for the urban poor, the separation of ageing parents from their children in middle-class families, the inhospitable, and even hostile, nature of the urban environment for senior citizens, children and people suffering from disabilities, and the growing scarcity of living space and other basic amenities for all but the rich minority – are all these not manifestations of violence? For example, healthcare, a basic need and an inalienable right of every human being, now comes with a price tag – and the price tag has made it unaffordable to the common people even in rich countries. Isn't it systemic violence when the sick go unattended, not for want of medical facilities in the vicinity but for want of money? And isn't it systemic violence when the undignified and hazardous living and working conditions for a large section of the global population increases their vulnerability to disease and death?[1]

The compulsions of crass commerce have brought violence even into the realm of culture. The function of culture is to refine the higher senses of human beings, enrich human relationships and thus enhance joy in life. However, by converting culture into a marketable commodity, tempting human beings into becoming consumers of this commodity, deadening their capacity for refined aesthetic experience, and reducing joy itself to instant and yet momentary pleasure, the business of mass entertainment has only created an illusion of 'good life'. Worse still, the giant entertainment industry in the West, which in turn is aped by entertainment businesses run by the westernised elites in India and other countries, has actually inflicted violence on a huge scale on the diversity of arts, culture, literature, languages, dialects and spiritual traditions around the world.

All these multiple manifestations of violence have caused a moral vacuum and alienation in modern societies. Crime in many new and sophisticated ways, which has increased in almost every part of the world, is also a form and an outcome of alienation.

There is another, oft-neglected, form of alienation in the modern world caused by the economic and cultural tyranny of industrialism: man's alienation from his past as well as from his future. Increasingly, we are obsessed only with the short-term considerations and aspirations of our finite existence on this planet – with the 'here' and 'now'. We have little concern either for our ancestors' expectations from us or for our own obligations towards the generations to come. This has resulted in a cognitive and behavioural disorder in the modern man. Edward Goldsmith (1928–2009), a renowned Anglo-French philosopher of sustainable development and a passionate votary of the Gandhian model of development, remarks: 'The notion that we owe nothing to posterity seems to justify, in the eyes of many people, our terrible egotism and the deliberate pillaging of the world's natural resources to which our society is so committed in order to satisfy the requirements of the corporations that control it'.[2]

Does Gandhi's philosophy offer readymade formulas to overcome the multiple maladies of the modern world? No. However, it does help us understand that the source of these maladies lies in the reigning economic system, which in turn has distorted the systems of politics, education, science and technology, and even religion, prevailing in countries around the world. It also provides a medicine-kit of ideas and insights that can help cure many of these maladies. One can find a good selection of them engraved on the walled enclosure surrounding Raj Ghat, Gandhi's serenely verdant *samadhi* (cremation site) in New Delhi. Among them is this pithy but profound aphorism, penned by Gandhi himself, explaining the 'seven social sins', which he regarded as the roots of all kinds of violence in society:

Wealth *without* Work,
Pleasure *without* Conscience,
Knowledge *without* Character,

Commerce *without* Morality,
Science *without* Humanity,
Worship *without* Sacrifice,
Politics *without* Principles.[3]

The introduction of justice and moral values as a factor to be considered in regulating international commerce was, according to Gandhi, the touchstone of 'the extension of law of nonviolence in the domain of economics'. He declares: 'Economics that hurts the moral well-being of an individual or a nation are immoral and therefore sinful'. Much of what Gandhi said or wrote about economics negates the foundational principles of modern economic theory and practice. 'True economics,' he affirms, 'is the economics of justice'. He calls it the first principle of every religion. His castigation of colonial Britain was on account of the fact that the economics it practiced was a violation of the religion of Jesus that it preached. 'I know no previous instance in history of a nation's establishing a systematic disobedience to the first principle of its professed religion'.[4] He reminds us that all the scriptures of the world, 'which we (verbally) esteem as divine' denounce 'the love of money as the source of all evil, and as an idolatry abhorred of the deity'. They also declare 'mammon service to be the accurate and irreconcilable opposite of God's service'.[5]

Gandhi questions the 'absurd assumption' of capitalist economics that inequity and injustice are inevitable. He likens the circulation of wealth in a nation to the circulation of blood in the natural body. Using this scientific analogy, he explains how inequalities of wealth, 'unjustly established' are harmful to the health of society and its members, both rich and poor. (It is necessary to record here that Gandhi makes a distinction between inequalities of wealth 'justly' and 'unjustly' established. He considers the former to be natural.)

Using the language of mathematics, Gandhi explains the moral and immoral ways of wealth creation:

The real value of acquired wealth depends on the moral sign attached to it, just as sternly as that of a mathematical quantity depends on the algebraical sign attached to it. Any given accumulation of commercial wealth may be indicative, on the one hand, of faithful industries, progressive energies and productive ingenuities; or on the other hand, it may be indicative of mortal luxury, merciless tyranny, ruinous chicanery. ...One mass of money is the outcome of action which has created, – another, of action which has annihilated, – ten times as much in the gathering of it. Therefore the idea that directions can be given for the gaining of wealth, irrespective of the consideration of its moral sources, is perhaps the most insolently futile of all that ever beguiled men through their vices.

As in everything else, Gandhi places greater responsibility on big powers (which now includes India) than on small and weak nations to promote nonviolence and peace in international commerce. 'Great nations (must cease) to believe in soul-destroying competition and to multiply wants and thereby increasing their material possessions'.[6] Do leaders of India and other powerful nations, who ritualistically pay homage to Gandhi, pay heed to these words while devising their policies and strategies for economic growth?

Trusteeship: Science of Nonviolence Applied to Business

Three peace-promoting operative points emerge out of the Gandhian economic thought as sketched above.

Firstly, a key requirement is the adoption of the virtue of cooperation, in the place of unhealthy and destructive competition, in all economic activities. Secondly, both societies and individuals should move away from an economy of acquisition to an economy of human needs. Thirdly, Gandhi attached the highest importance to voluntary limiting of man's material needs through self-control. 'Our civilisation, our culture, our Swaraj depend not upon multiplying our wants – self-indulgence, but upon restricting our wants – self-denial. That you cannot serve God and Mammon is an economic truth of the highest value'.[7] It is apt to emphasise here that Gandhi enlarged the meaning of two key principles of Hinduism through his economic philosophy – *asteya* (non-stealing) and *aparigraha* (non-greed). He held that if a man accumulates more than what he and his family reasonably require for the fulfilment of their needs, it amounts to greed and stealing from society. Out of this understanding arose his concept of trusteeship.

Gandhi's belief in trusteeship came from a pearl of wisdom in the first verse of the *Isha Upanishad*, which states: 'Everything animate or inanimate that is within the universe is controlled and owned by the Lord. One should therefore accept only those things necessary for oneself, which are set aside as one's quota, and must not accept other things, knowing well to Whom they belong'. He extolled this verse for conveying a message of universal brotherhood – not only brotherhood of all human beings, but of all living things. Indeed, this Upanishadic verse inspired him to formulate the idea of trusteeship, which can be called the kernel of Gandhian socialism: 'When an individual has more than his proportionate portion, he becomes a trustee of that portion for other creations of God'.[8] We can see here how beautifully ancient Indian philosophy has linked the concepts of non-stealing, nonviolence, trusteeship and socialism ('each for all and all for each').

Trusteeship was Gandhi's creative application of the 'science of nonviolence' in the economic sphere. The ideal of egalitarianism that he propounded was different from both capitalism and communism. 'Economic equality,' he argued, 'is the master key to nonviolent independence. Working for economic equality means abolishing the eternal conflict between capital and labour. It means the leveling down of the few rich in whose hands is concentrated the bulk of the nation's wealth on the one hand, and the leveling up of the semi-starved naked millions on the other.'[9]

Gandhi made a distinction between capitalism and the capitalist. 'By the nonviolent method, we seek not to destroy the capitalist, we seek to destroy capitalism'. He invited the rich to become trustees by telling them that 'it is possible to acquire riches without consciously doing wrong'. At the same time, he also emphasised that labour must be regarded as an equal partner of capital. 'If capital is power, so is work. Either is dependent on the other. Immediately the worker realises his strength, he is in a position to become a co-sharer with the capitalist instead of remaining his slave'.[10] He put his enlightened views on trade union activities into practice when, in 1918, he organised the textile workers of Ahmedabad. He called trusteeship 'a laboratory of human relations', and succeeded in winning the hearts of both workers and employers.

Gandhi was confident that his theory of trusteeship would 'survive all other theories' because 'it has the sanction of philosophy and religion behind it' and also because 'no other theory is compatible with nonviolence.' (As we shall see in Chapter 23, Gandhi had extended the concept of trusteeship beyond economics to the realm of the environment; human beings, he declared, 'are the trustees of the lower animal kingdom.') When his critics mentioned that his appeal to businessmen fell mostly on deaf ears, he retorted: 'That possessors of wealth have not acted up to the theory does not prove its falsity; it proves the weakness of the wealthy... The question how many can be real trustees is beside the point. If the theory is true, it is immaterial whether many live up to it or only one man lives up to it. The question is of conviction. If you accept the principle of *ahimsa*, you have to strive to live up to it, no matter whether you succeed or fail. There is nothing in this theory which can be said to be beyond the grasp of intellect, though you may say it is difficult of practice'.[11]

He again used a scientific concept to drive home his point. 'Absolute trusteeship is an abstraction like Euclid's definition of a point, and is equally unattainable. But if we strive for it, we shall be able to go further in realising a state of equality on earth than by any other method'.[12]

Gandhi had warned, in the sternest possible language, about the serious consequences of the rich-poor divide in independent India. 'A nonviolent system of government is clearly an impossibility, so long as the wide gulf between the rich and the hungry millions persists. The contrast between the palaces of New Delhi and the miserable hovels of the poor, labouring class nearby cannot last one day in a free India in which the poor will enjoy the same power as the richest in the land... A violent and bloody revolution is a certainty one day unless there is a voluntary abdication of riches and the power that riches give and sharing them for the common good'.[13]

Has India heeded Gandhi's warning? The answer is obvious. The wealth gap in today's India, compared to what it was in the colonial era, has widened to an extent that was unimaginable in his time. Concomitantly, violence due to economic inequality, social injustice and regional imbalance in development has also increased. 'A bloody revolution' may not have happened, but that cannot make either our government or our society complacent. The numerous mass protests resulting in bloodshed in the six decades since Independence have proved Gandhi right in his prognosis that inequity inevitably breeds violence.

We must note here that independent India never made a serious attempt – rather, it made no attempt at all – to introduce trusteeship in economic planning and legislation. The business class and the political-bureaucratic leadership colluded in giving this key Gandhian concept a deep burial. However, the blame rests not only with the Indian state. It also rests with Indian society, especially the Hindu society. Although Hinduism has inherited the timeless wisdom of the Vedas, Upanishads, epics and other scriptures, the elite – the economic, social political and religious leadership of the Hindu society – has chosen not to be energised by this wisdom. This is evident from the slow pace of reforms in Hindu society, its disinclination to cast away the influence of the Western capitalist ideology, and its failure to carry forward the campaign for 'trusteeship', a quintessentially Indian economic thought, which Gandhi had launched.

However, there is no point in simply diagnosing the problem and apportioning blame. It is far more important to strive to resurrect the philosophy of trusteeship in the conduct of individuals and institutions. Such efforts have a chance to succeed because of two helpful developments in the post-Gandhian history of India and the world. Firstly, communism has collapsed – and this is something Gandhi had foreseen as early as in the 1930s. Secondly, capitalism has not proved its success in fulfilling its own promises. Indeed, its failures are all too glaring. The self-realisation of many Western societies about the limitations of their economic model has prompted them to seek far-reaching reforms in their economies. Hence, both the Indian experience and the global experience have placed the search for an alternative economic system – that is nonviolent – right on top of the agenda of the twenty-first century. A large part of the answer to this search can be found in the concept of trusteeship, whose validity is universal. Gandhi was, perhaps, far ahead of his time in advocating it. The time for trusteeship was perhaps not then. But it certainly is now.

'Antyodaya' and 'Integral Humanism': Convergence Between the Ideas of Gandhi and Deendayal Upadhyaya

One of the last notes that Gandhi left behind in January 1948, in which he, in a way, gave a directive to independent India's democratic government and also to all the wealthy and privileged people in society, has since become a widely quoted aphorism: 'I will give you a talisman. Whenever you are in doubt, or when the self becomes too much with you, apply the following test. Recall the face of the poorest and the weakest man [woman] whom you may have seen, and ask yourself, if the step you contemplate is going to be of any use to him [her]. Will he [she] gain anything by it? Will it restore him [her] to a control over his [her] own life and destiny? In other words, will it lead to swaraj for the hungry and spiritually starving millions? Then you will find your doubts and your self melt away'.[14]

It is worth mentioning here that Kumarappa, who crystallised Gandhi's economic philosophy in his book *The Economy of Permanence*, which we have cited earlier, lived his life by the dictates of this talisman. In *J.C. Kumarappa: Mahatma Gandhi's Economist*, his biographer Mark Lindley writes: 'Kumarappa in his last seven years resided in a one-room house, the interior decoration of which consisted of a picture of a poor man. When asked who it was, he would say, "My master's master. My master is Mahatma Gandhi, and Gandhi's master is this villager"'.

Among the political thinkers and activists in independent India, in whom the Gandhian socio-economic thinking found a strong resonance, was Pandit Deendayal Upadhyaya (1916-68). A man of impeccable integrity, he too, like Gandhi, *lived* his philosophy. He was the leader of the Bharatiya Jana Sangh from 1953 till his tragic death in 1968. His concept of *Antyodaya* (institutional commitment to give the first priority to the last person in society in all policies and programmes) echoes Gandhi's own vision of *Sarvodaya* (equitable progress of all), which was later amplified by Acharya Vinoba Bhave, Gandhi's 'spiritual heir'.

In his treatise *Integral Humanism,* Upadhyaya offers a highly persuasive critique of both communism and capitalism, and, like Gandhi, presents a holistic alternative perspective essentially rooted in the Indian *darshan* (world-view). I shall summarise here the key economic ideas in *Integral Humanism*:[15]

- The object of our economic system should be, not extravagant use of available resources, but a well regulated use. The physical objects necessary for a purposeful, happy and progressive life must be obtained. The Almighty has provided as much. It will not be wise, however, to engage in a blind rat-race of consumption and production as if man is created for the sole purpose of consumption.

- It is essential to use up that portion of the available natural resources which Nature will be able to recoup easily. When the fruits are taken, the fruit tree is not injured: it may even be helpful to the tree. However, in the effort to take a greater harvest from the land, chemical fertilisers are used which in a few years time render the land altogether infertile. How long can this dance of destruction go on?

- Keeping in view the aim of human life, we must endeavour to see how with the minimum of fuel, man proceeds to his goal with the maximum speed. Such a system alone can be called civilisation. This system will not think of merely a single aspect of human life but of all its aspects including its ultimate aim.

- The right to food is a birthright. In a society even those who do not earn must have food. The children and the old, the diseased and the invalids, all must be cared for by the society. The social and cultural progress of mankind lies in the readiness to fulfill this responsibility.

- To educate a child is in the interest of the society itself. We know that when the tree grows, we shall reap fruits. Education is a similar investment. An educated individual will indeed serve the society.

- According to the Bharatiya traditions, a nation is an organic living entity which has come into existence on its own and has not been made up or created by any group of persons. A nation brings forth a variety of institutions to fulfill its needs, as well as to give concrete shape to its inner fundamental nature. The state is one of these institutions which, though being an important institution, is not supreme. Dharma is supreme.

- The economic system must achieve the production of all the basic things essential for the maintenance and development of people as well as the protection and development of the nation. Having satisfied the basic minimum requirements, the question naturally arises, whether there should be more production for greater prosperity and happiness. Western societies consider it most essential and even desirable to go on continuously and systematically increasing the desires and needs of man. There is no upper limit in this context. Normally desire precedes the efforts at producing the things desired. But now the position is reverse. People are induced to desire and use the things that have been and are being produced. If the demand does not exist, systematic efforts are made to create demand. This has become the chief characteristic of the Western economic movement.

- The present economic system and system of production are fast disturbing the equilibrium of Nature. As a result, on the one hand new products are manufactured for satisfying ever-increasing desires; on the other hand, new problems arise every day, threatening the very existence of the entire humanity and civilisation.

- The guarantee of work to every able-bodied member of society, should be the aim of our economic system. God has given hands to every man but by themselves hands have a limited capacity to produce. They need assistance of capital in the form of machines. Labour and capital bear the same relation to each other as that between man and Nature. The world is a creation of these two. Neither of them can be neglected.

- The advantage in decentralisation is in the fact that the workers have a sense of direct participation in the management of this surplus value or capital. Machine is the most common form of capital. Machine was created in order to reduce the content of physical labour in production and to increase the productivity of the worker. Machine, therefore, is an assistant of the worker and not his competitor. The principal drawback of the capitalist viewpoint is the fact that by making the machine a competitor of human labour and thereby displacing and subjecting human beings to privations, the very purpose of creating machine has been defeated.

- Scientific knowledge is not a monopoly of any particular country. But its application has to take into account the particular conditions of each country and its requirements. Our machines must not only be tailored for our specific economic means, but also must, at least, avoid conflict with our socio-political and cultural objectives, if not support them.

- The capitalist system which boasts of giving the highest importance to the individual has ironically destroyed all individuality. Clearly, it is incapable of helping the development of an integral human being.

- Socialism arose as a reaction to capitalism. But even socialism failed to establish the importance of the human being. Socialists contented themselves by merely transferring the ownership of capital in the hands of the state. But the state is even more of an impersonal institution. All the business of the state is conducted through rigid rules and regulations. Generally, there is no place for individual discretion, but corruption and favouritism on the part of the administrators is rampant. There is no such thing as individual freedom in the socialist system.

- The state is made the supreme and sole authority in all matters in the socialist system. Individual citizen is reduced to a mere cog in this giant wheel. There are no provisions to inspire the individual to fulfill his role. As Milovan Djilas[16] states, the class of old-fashioned exploiters has been eliminated, but a new class of bureaucratic exploiters has come into existence.
- Both these systems, capitalist as well as communist, have failed to take account of the Integral Man, his true and complete personality and his aspirations. One considers him a mere selfish being hankering after money, having only one law, the law of fierce competition, in essence the law of the jungle; whereas the other has viewed him as a feeble lifeless cog in the whole scheme of things, regulated by rigid rules, and incapable of any good unless directed. The centralisation of power, economic and political, is implied in both. Both, therefore, result in dehumanisation of man. Man, the highest creation of God, is losing his own identity. We must re-establish him in his rightful position, bring him the realisation of his greatness, reawaken his abilities and encourage him to exert for attaining the divine heights of his latent personality. This is possible only through a decentralised economy.
- We want neither capitalism nor communism. We aim at the progress and happiness of 'Man', the Integral Man.

Upadhyaya wrote *Integral Humanism* in the mid-1960s, when the rivalry between the two rival ideologically driven economic and political systems, capitalism and communism, was at its peak globally. The situation has changed significantly since then. Nevertheless, the basic concepts and concerns contained in his philosophical treatise remain fully valid.

On a personal note, I read *Integral Humanism,* and started reading about Upadhyaya, at a time when I had become disillusioned with Marxism. I wasn't disillusioned with capitalism, because I was never attracted to it in the first place. I had been searching for new thought systems to answer my questions and to remove the doubts that had agitated my mind. As I have mentioned in Chapter 1, I rediscovered Mahatma Gandhi then. Several years later, I discovered Deendayal

Upadhyaya, who became one of the reasons for my joining the BJP, the ideological successor to the Bharatiya Jana Sangh. I strongly believe that Upadhyaya's socio-economic and political thoughts belong not only to the BJP, but also to all progressive organisations and activists in India and elsewhere. Speaking about the BJP, I wish my party studied, understood and practiced Upadhyaya's philosophy far more seriously than it is doing today.

Gandhi repeatedly emphasises that his advocacy of nonviolence is a necessary by-product of his faith in truth. Since he recognised science to be an important and reliable way of finding truth, he called his advocacy of nonviolence the 'science of nonviolence'. As we have noted above, he was one of the few saintly voices of peace who uncovered the economic roots of violence. Nevertheless, his 'science of nonviolence' was comprehensive. It addressed three fundamental questions that have agitated the minds of thinking people all over the world.

Firstly, is man inherently violent? If violence is an inseparable part of human nature, then the dream of a nonviolent world remains just that – an unrealisable dream. On the contrary, if, as Gandhi believed, man is not by nature violent, then the question that begets itself is: How can individuals, societies and nations progress along the path of peace?

Specifically, how can our world rid itself of wars and weapons of mass destruction? Can science and technology, which have so far come to the aid of man's instinct to kill fellow man, become the means to promote the virtue of non-killing? Can the rhetoric of 'a world without nuclear weapons' be converted into reality – and how soon? Peace-lovers in all ages have dreamt of beating 'swords into plowshares'. Realisation of this dream demands a drastic reduction in military expenditures of national governments, especially big powers, and diverting the saved resources to eliminate poverty, hunger, disease and homelessness from our beautiful planet. How can this be achieved?

Secondly, how can we protect the priceless eco-wealth of our planet? In other words, can man become nonviolent towards the natural ecology of which he is an integral part? Can *Homo sapiens* become a reliable trustee to other living species that are cohabiting this beautiful but fragile planet? Like the challenge of nuclear disarmament, this challenge too has become far more pressing in the post-Gandhi era. Indeed, the biggest task here is to first heal the wounds man has already inflicted on Gaia[17], Greek for Mother Earth. Science and technology can no doubt serve as the healing agents, but man needs something more – the wisdom to know why he committed the crime of assaulting the environment in the first place, the readiness to repent, and the knowledge to save both himself and the wondrous web of life on this planet.

Thirdly, are women more capable of making our world a safer and better place than men? Are they inherently more predisposed towards peace and caring than men? Gandhi's answer was resoundingly in the affirmative. Astonishingly, latest scientific research – the theory of 'survival of the kindest' as against the theory of 'survival of the fittest' – is yet again proving him right.

As the next five chapters will show, Gandhi's 'science of nonviolence' casts its light of wisdom on our exploration of these critical questions.

Photo by Bob Fitch (1966). Courtesy: Steven Kasher Gallery, NY

Gandhi never travelled to America, but his influence did: *Dr Martin Luther King Jr. in the Atlanta office of the Southern Christian Leadership Conference (SCLC), which played a pivotal role in the American Civil Rights Movement.*

'The odd thing about assassins, Dr King, is that they think that they've killed you!'

Courtesy: The Chicago Sun-Times (April 1968)

19

GANDHI AND THE SCIENCE OF
EVOLUTIONARY BIOLOGY
From Man the Brute to Man the God

My study of Gandhi convinced me that true pacifism is not nonresistance to evil, but nonviolent resistance to evil. Between the two positions, there is a world of difference. Gandhi resisted evil with as much vigour and power as the violent resister, but he resisted with love instead of hate... 'Rivers of blood may have to flow before we gain our freedom, but it must be our blood,' he told his countrymen.

— Martin Luther King Jr, in *My Pilgrimage to Nonviolence* (1958).

IN DECEMBER 2007, *TIME* MAGAZINE CARRIED A COVER FEATURE titled 'What Makes Us Good/Evil'. Its subscript read: 'Humans are the planet's most noble creatures – and its most savage. Science is discovering why'. Revealingly, its message was sought to be conveyed by the photographs, on the magazine's cover, of Gandhi and Hitler, representatives of the two contrasting human specimens. Its scholarly author Jeffery Kluger wrote: 'We're a species that is capable of almost dumbfounding kindness. We nurse one another, romance one another, weep for one another. Ever since science taught us how, we willingly tear the very organs from our bodies and give them to one another. And at the same time, we slaughter one another...That we're also the lowest, cruelest, most blood-drenched species is our shame – and our paradox'.

Thanks to the rapidly progressing science of evolutionary biology – of neuroscience in particular – our understanding of what makes man both kind and cruel has undoubtedly increased. Nevertheless, many people continue to harbour the doubt that the shame and paradox that Kluger alludes to can ever be eliminated. They believe that savagery is as much a part of the sourcecode of the human DNA as sympathy – that Hitler is not an aberration in humanity's evolution but, sadly, an inevitable, recurring and pre-destined phenomenon. In this chapter, I shall try to dispel this pessimism-promoting belief by presenting Gandhi's seminal thoughts on the 'science of nonviolence'.

Resurrection of the age-old ethical principle of nonviolence in trying to reorder international relations has been Gandhi's unique achievement in history. Many have practiced nonviolence in their personal lives, and many have even succeeded in changing life in small neighbourhoods and communities. However, Gandhi was the first statesman in modern times to confront a mighty empire by mobilising an entire nation – a nation of continental size at that – on the principle of nonviolence. It was an audacious, even impossible-looking undertaking, unparalleled in the annals of mankind. Of course, several other factors also contributed to the ultimate success of India's freedom movement, including the struggles and sacrifices of those Indians who were not his followers. Nevertheless, the super-human saga of how he remained steadfast on the path of truth and nonviolence, and how he inspired a large majority of Indians to support his mission, cannot but go down in human history as a significant success.

We must acknowledge here that, in the case of many of Gandhi's admirers, such admiration sits alongside disbelief. Even those who hold him in high esteem generally do not fully believe in his affirmation that nonviolence will someday triumph over violence. They want to be optimistic, but their hope is punctured by awareness about the endless episodes of wars and violence in world history. The ordinary human mind faces a peculiar dilemma here. On the one hand, thinking about the indispensability of violence in human life is not a happy thought. It breeds pessimism, cynicism and helplessness. On the other hand, man cannot live without dreaming of a violence-free world. It is not in human nature to rejoice in bloodshed, notwithstanding the bestiality that has often surfaced in human conduct.

For Gandhi, this belief in the essentially peaceful nature of human beings is not merely an ethical concept. It is also scientific. The bedrock of this science is his simple but insightful thought: 'Man as animal is violent, but as spirit is nonviolent'. If we are prepared to think beyond the narrow Western understanding of scientific truth, and view Truth as the all-pervasive governing and sustaining principle of the universe as well as human life, then the phrase 'science of nonviolence' becomes self-explanatory in the following words of Gandhi: '*Ahimsa* is my God, and Truth is my God. When I look for *Ahimsa*, Truth says, "Find it through me." When I look for Truth, *Ahimsa* says, "Find it out through me."'[1]

Gandhi frequently used scientific terminology to explain his belief. '*Ahimsa* is a science, and the word "failure" has no place in the vocabulary of science,' he affirmed. In 1931, when he was sailing from Bombay to London to participate in the Second Round Table Conference organised by the British government, a group of Egyptian journalists met him on the steamer while at a halt in Alexandria, and asked him about nonviolence and truth. His reply was: 'The law of love will work, just as the law of gravitation will work, whether we accept it or not. For, the force of nonviolence is infinitely more wonderful and subtle than the material forces of Nature, like for instance electricity.'[2]

On another occasion, he said: 'All society is held together by nonviolence even as the earth is held in her position by the force of gravitation.' This thought has been validated by Brian Swimme, a mathematical cosmologist at the California Institute of Integral Studies in San Francisco, who avers: 'Gravity is love'.[3] Swimme, author of *The Hidden Heart of the Cosmos* says: 'We are the first species that actually has the possibility of caring about *all* of the other species. You see, chimpanzees are our closest relatives, and they certainly care about one another, but their care doesn't extend over in any visible way to other species, even though they may share territories with baboons. But with humans, suddenly you have the possibility, largely through the human imagination, of actually caring. My point is that the human being is that space in which the comprehensive compassion that pervades the universe from the very beginning now begins to surface *within consciousness*. We didn't *invent* compassion, but it's flowing through us – or it could.'

About the power of ahimsa to spread from one person to another in a chain reaction, Gandhi said: 'Nonviolence is like the radium in action.' Indeed, there were many instances in India's freedom movement showing the radium-like effect of Gandhi's appeal for peace in situations of conflict, the most notable being his successes in containing the fire of Hindu-Muslim violence in Calcutta, Noakhali (now in Bangladesh) and Delhi during the traumatic time of India's Partition in 1947.

To doubters, he said: 'My nonviolence is made of stern stuff. It is firmer than the firmest metal known to the scientists...I have been practising with scientific precision nonviolence and its possibilities for an unbroken period of over fifty years.'[4] He further avowed: 'If intellect plays a large part in the field of violence, I hold that it plays a larger part in the field of nonviolence.'[5] When intellect begins to promote nonviolence, it transforms itself into love. Thus, Gandhi made a distinction between intellect and love by saying: 'There is a limit to the development of the intellect, but none to that of the heart.'[6]

Gandhi was often asked: 'On what basis do you affirm that love conquers hatred, and that nonviolence triumphs over violence? Where are historical precedents to prove this?' His answer provides a highly unorthodox, and immensely hopeful, understanding of human history. He said: 'History is only a record of every interruption of the even working of the force of love.'[7] What he meant by this was that love, compassion, cooperation and mutual accommodation govern, and are reflected to varying degrees in, most day-to-day interactions in society. If this were not so, all human relationships would have become battlegrounds for permanent strife, and there would be nothing like progress in human cultures and civilisations. This simply is not true. History, unfortunately, does not record this reality – what Gandhi calls 'the even working of the force of love'. What it records are mostly mega incidents of violence, thereby giving a distorted picture of the basic human nature.

'Brute nature,' Gandhi contended, 'has been known to yield to the influence of love'. In contrast to the doctrine of 'original sin', he put forward the doctrine of 'original goodness'. In his mind, there were no good men and evil men, and even Hitler[8], he had heroically hoped, was not beyond redemption. 'We are all tarred with the same brush, and the children of one and the same Creator, and as such the divine powers within us are infinite'.[9]

The clearest exposition of his 'science of nonviolence' can be found in an article Gandhi wrote in *Young India* of 11 August 1920, not long after the end of the First World War: 'In this age of the rule of brute force', he observed, 'it is almost impossible for anyone to believe that anyone else could possibly reject the law of the final supremacy of brute force'. The article was titled 'The Doctrine of the Sword'. It is one of the most important writings in Gandhi's works, and therefore deserves to be read in its entirety. Its purpose was to explain to doubting Indians (and also to Britishers who doubted his true motive behind starting the Non-Cooperation Movement) that the 'sword of nonviolence' was more powerful than the 'sword of violence'. In words that have imperishable purity and persuasive power, Gandhi wrote:

> The religion of nonviolence is not meant merely for the *rishis* and saints. It is meant for the common people as well.

Nonviolence is the law of our species as violence is the law of the brute. The spirit lies dormant in the brute and he knows no law but that of physical might. The dignity of man requires obedience to a higher law – to the strength of the spirit.

Strength does not come from physical capacity. It comes from an indomitable will...I have therefore ventured to place before India the ancient law of self-sacrifice. For *satyagraha* and its offshoots, non-cooperation and civil resistance, are nothing but new names for the law of suffering. The *rishis*, who discovered the law of nonviolence in the midst of violence, were greater geniuses than Newton. They were themselves greater warriors than Wellington. Having themselves known the use of arms, they realised their uselessness and taught a weary world that its salvation lay not through violence but through nonviolence.

Many people believed, as they do even now, that Gandhi's doctrine of nonviolence was a prescription for the meek to surrender before the strong. In other words, it was a doctrine fit for cowards. Gandhi's understanding, however, was radically different.

Nonviolence in its dynamic condition means conscious suffering. It does not mean meek submission to the will of the evildoer, but it means the putting of one's soul against the will of the tyrant. Working under this law of our being, it is possible for a single individual to defy the whole might of an unjust empire to save his honour, his religion, his soul and lay the foundation for that empire's fall or its *regeneration*.

We feel too downtrodden not to be angry and revengeful. But I must not refrain from saying that India can gain more by waiving the right of punishment. *We have better work to do, a better mission to deliver to the world.*

I am not pleading for India to practise nonviolence because it is weak. I want her to practise nonviolence being conscious of her strength and power. No training in arms is required for realisation of her strength. We seem to need it because we seem to think that we are but a lump of flesh. I want India to recognise that she has a soul that cannot perish and that can rise triumphant above every physical weakness and defy the physical combination of whole world. *(Emphasis added)*

Gandhi then expressed, with unmatched candour, his thoughts and feelings if India abandoned the path of nonviolence.

If India takes up the doctrine of the sword, she may gain momentary victory. Then India will cease to be pride of my heart. I am wedded to India because I owe my all to her. I believe absolutely that she has a mission for the world. She is not to copy Europe blindly. India's acceptance of the doctrine of the sword will be the hour of my trial. I hope I shall not be found wanting. My religion has no geographical limits. If I have a living faith in it, it will transcend my love for India herself. My life is dedicated to service of India through the religion of nonviolence which I believe to be the root of Hinduism.

Precisely because Gandhi understood nonviolence to be governed by a law as immutable as the fundamental scientific laws of Nature – hence his audacious term 'science of nonviolence' to describe it – he also laid enormous emphasis on the application of this science. The use of any science becomes manifest only when its laws are applied in the right manner. Therefore, Gandhi said: 'Unless you go on discovering new applications of the law of nonviolence, you do not profit from it'.[10]

It is necessary to emphasise here that, being a realist, Gandhi recognised that practice of perfect nonviolence in every situation in life was impossible. A certain degree of violence in many basic human activities – eating, breathing, moving about on foot or by a vehicle – is unavoidable. In certain rare cases, he even justifies conscious use of violence to save life. 'Nonviolence is not an easy thing to understand, still less to practice, weak as we are'.[11] With characteristic humility, he also writes: 'I have never claimed to present the complete science of nonviolence. It does not lend itself to such treatment'.[12] His ideal was to reduce voluntary violence to the barest minimum as a precondition for humanity's self-advancement.

His own prescription for reaching this ideal was to follow the route of justice. 'The first condition of nonviolence is justice all round in every department of life'.[13] We see here how Gandhi makes truth, nonviolence, love and justice synonyms of each other. Emphasising the indivisible nature of these four ideals, both in theory and practice, is Gandhi's unique contribution to modern man's quest for true progress. Building a just society thus becomes imperative for giving full play to nonviolence and love. At the same time – and this is where Gandhi departs radically from Marxist and some other proponents of justice – violent means to secure justice in society never achieve the desired end. They only end up making social conditions more unjust, and men in power more brutish.

Swami Ranganathananda saw in Gandhi's 'science of nonviolence' the path for 'the evolution of man the brute into Man the God'. In a perceptive essay titled *Mahatma Gandhi: The Abiding Elements in His Life and Work,* which he contributed for the commemorative volume to mark Gandhi's birth centenary in 1969, the venerable Swamiji wrote:

> The central core of his message, and what is imperishable in it is satya and ahimsa, truth and nonviolence, as he has himself expressed it on innumerable occasions. Gandhi's uniqueness lies in projecting these sterling moral virtues on to the wider fields of collective socio-political life and action. He translated his passionate spiritual quest into an equally passionate struggle to ensure the freedom and dignity of the human spirit everywhere. He sought the incorporation of these values in the body-politic as the only means to advance the cause of human evolution, the evolution of man the brute into Man the God.

According to Ranganathananda, Gandhi saw humanity at the crossroads of destiny.

> During the past few centuries human intelligence has become disciplined and sharpened, and man has become master of vast resources, of energy and power. In the absence of a spiritual orientation, all this has led to the sharpening of man's animal

appetites and the deepening of his inner conflicts and tensions, leading to hatred, violence and war.

Gandhi, says Ranganathananda, acutely recognised the need to match the growth of man in the tangible fields of his physical and intellectual life with a corresponding growth in the not-so-obvious field of spiritual life. 'And this is the specifically human field of evolutionary biology. It is only when man's life energy gets this spiritual direction that he becomes truly human and his life becomes true life.'[14]

Ranganathananda's allusion above to 'evolutionary biology' is highly significant, for it conforms to what Gandhi himself had said: 'In our present state, we are partly men and partly beasts.'[15] Evolutionary biology holds that the evolution of modern man to higher levels of capability is not a biological but a psycho-social process.[16] It depends on 'breakthroughs to new dominant patterns' of inter-human relationships brought about by a new 'mental organisation' of individuals and institutions. This new science of evolution of human life into life divine was well understood by Indian philosophers. One of the foremost among them in modern times, Yogi Aurobindo (1872-1955),[17] whom Gandhi respectfully addressed as 'Rishi Aurobindo', writes:

> Man is a transitional being. He is not final. The step from man to superman is the next approaching achievement in the earth evolution. It is inevitable because it is at once the intention of the inner spirit and the logic of nature's process.
>
> If the bodily life is what Nature has firmly evolved for us as our base and first instrument, it is our mental life that she is evolving as her immediate next aim and superior instrument.... Man is there to affirm himself in the universe, that is his first business, but also to evolve and finally to exceed himself: he has to enlarge his partial being into a complete being, his partial consciousness into an integral consciousness; he has to achieve mastery of his environment but also achieve world-union and world-harmony... The natural man has to evolve himself into the divine man. This hope is the justification of his life upon earth amidst the phenomena of the cosmos.[18]

Like Gandhi, Aurobindo avers that violence is not the innate and defining trait of man – 'Barbarism is an intermediate sleep, not an original darkness'[19] in human evolution. The cause of this 'evolutionary sleep' is the imbalance in the progress of human life. 'At present mankind is undergoing an evolutionary crisis in which is concealed a choice of its destiny; for a stage has been reached in which the human mind has achieved in certain directions an enormous development while in others it stands arrested and bewildered and can no longer find a way.'[20]

How to correct this evolutionary imbalance? According to Swami Ranganathananda, the remedy lies in the society-wide application of Gandhi's message of truth, nonviolence, universal brotherhood, mutual cooperation, mutual caring and self-controlled cultivation of inner human possibilities. Besides removing the imbalance, the result of this effort will also mark a new 'breakthrough' in man's future progress. If recurrent eruptions of science-assisted violence in the past millennia have stunted human evolution, the science of nonviolence offers the certainty of accelerating man's progress along the upward path of evolution. Aurobindo signals this new evolutionary destiny of man in a marvellous sentence: 'Man has been less than human' today, but 'he can be more than human' tomorrow.[21]

Swami Ranganathananda describes Gandhi's science of nonviolence as the 'science of human possibilities'. As proof of this, he cites the following profound prophesy made by Gandhi:

> In this age of wonders no one will say that a thing or idea is worthless because it is new. To say it is impossible because it is difficult, is again not in consonance with the spirit of the age. Things undreamt of are daily being seen, the impossible is ever becoming possible. We are constantly being astonished these days at the amazing discoveries in the field of violence. But I maintain that far more undreamt of and seemingly impossible

discoveries will be made in the field of nonviolence.

Gandhi wrote these luminous lines of hope in *Harijan* on 25 August 1940, amid the gloom created by the outbreak of the Second World War. They show his unwavering confidence in the power of science to redress a humungous problem created, partly, by science itself.

Can the science of nonviolence succeed? Yes, it can! When the sword of violence is confronted by the sword of nonviolence (which entails self-suffering and self-sacrifice), a point must come when the former feels powerless. This is because, as Gandhi reminds us, nonviolence is the law of the human species, whereas violence is the law of the brute. The brute may follow the law of physical might, because he knows no other law. But 'a man of dignity must obey a higher law' – and be obedient to the strength of the spirit. Gandhi makes an extremely important observation here that 'the spirit lies dormant in the brute'. This dormant spirit of humanity or divinity is inevitably awakened when it is confronted by the self-suffering and self-sacrifice of nonviolent satyagrahis, who use their faith in God as their shield and practice the canon of 'Hate the sin, not the sinner'. That is the moment of defeat for the brute. Actually, it is not the moment of defeat, because it is also the moment of regeneration for the brute. Note Gandhi's deliberate use of the words '...empire's fall or its *regeneration*' in his article 'The Doctrine of the Sword'.

When the sword of violence thus gets defeated and regenerated in its battle with the sword of nonviolence, not once nor twice but repeatedly, that is when a new breakthrough occurs in man's evolutionary biology, causing the transformation of *haivaniyat* (bestiality) into *insaaniyat* (humanity). Or, to borrow the words of Ranganathananada, it causes 'the evolution of Man the brute into Man the God'.

This, I think, is the basis of Gandhi's bold and hope-giving prediction that 'far more undreamt of and seemingly impossible discoveries will be made in the field of nonviolence.'

Courtesy: 'A Requiem for Hiroshima' by Hideshima Yukio; 'No More Hiroshima, Nagasaki', Nihon Tosho Center Co., Ltd.

A 'Hell on Earth': *On 6 August 1945, at 8.15 a.m. the United States' military dropped the world's first nuclear weapon on Hiroshima in Japan. In an instant, ninety percent of the city was destroyed. By the end of 1945, over 1,40,000 people had died and there was an equal number of 'hibakusha', individuals exposed to the bomb's radiation. One of the few buildings that survived the attack, albeit in ghostly skeletal form, was the Hiroshima Prefectural Industrial Promotional Hall, which came to be known as the 'Atomic Bomb Dome'. Three days later, on 9 August, Nagasaki became a victim of the second atomic bomb dropped by the US, and lost nearly 80,000 of its citizens. The two bombs brought the Second World War to a quick end. However, they also marked the dawn of a global race for nuclear arms, which threatens the very existence of human life on our planet.*

As members of the human race, we nurture a desperate hope: 'NO MORE HIROSHIMA, NAGASAKI'.

20

NUCLEAR WEAPONS
A Diabolical and Sinful
use of Science

***

We (scientists) are speaking on this occasion, not as members of this or that nation, continent, or creed, but as human beings, members of the species Man, whose continued existence is in doubt…There lies before us, if we choose, continual progress in happiness, knowledge, and wisdom. Shall we, instead, choose death, because we cannot forget our quarrels? We appeal as human beings to human beings: Remember your humanity, and forget the rest. If you can do so, the way lies open to a new Paradise; if you cannot, there lies before you the risk of universal death…(We) urge the governments of the world to …find peaceful means for the settlement of all matters of dispute between them.

— From the Russell–Einstein Manifesto, issued in London on 9 July 1955. This impassioned appeal for the elimination of all nuclear and other weapons of mass destruction was signed by Max Born, Percy W. Bridgman, Albert Einstein, Leopold Infeld, Frédéric Joliot-Curie, Herman J. Muller, Linus Pauling, Cecil F. Powell, Joseph Rotblat, Bertrand Russell, Hideki Yukawa. The manifesto called for an international conference, which was originally planned by Jawaharlal Nehru to be held in India. It was held in Pugwash, Canada, in July 1957.

AN EXAMINATION OF GANDHI'S ADVOCACY OF NONVIOLENCE cannot overlook his reflections on the most violent weapon ever invented by man using the power of science. When the United States dropped atomic bombs on Hiroshima and Nagasaki in

Japan in August 1945, he lent his voice to an outraged humanity's condemnation of this barbaric act. This nuclear genocide was a severe test of his faith in the superior power of nonviolence over that of violence. In an article in *Harijan* of 7 July 1946, titled 'Atom Bomb and Ahimsa', he wrote in anguish: 'The atomic bomb has deadened the finest feeling that has sustained mankind for ages. There used to be the so-called laws of war which made it tolerable. Now we know the naked truth. War knows no law except that of might'.[1]

Gripped by a sombre and contemplative mood, he reaffirmed his faith in man:

> There have been cataclysmic changes in the world. Do I still adhere to my faith in Truth and Nonviolence? Has not the atom bomb exploded that faith? Not only has it not done so, but it has clearly demonstrated to me that the twins constitute the mightiest force in the world. Before it the atom bomb is of no effect. The two opposing forces are wholly different in kind, the one moral and spiritual, the other physical and material. The one is infinitely superior to the other which by its very nature has an end. The force of the spirit is ever progressive and endless. Its full expression makes it unconquerable in the world. In saying this I know that I have said nothing new. I merely bear witness to the fact. What is more, the force resides in everybody, man, woman and child, irrespective of the colour of the skin. Only, in many it lies dormant. But it is capable of being awakened by judicious training. It is further to be observed that, without the recognition of this truth and due effort to realise it, there is no escape from self-destruction. The remedy lies in every individual training himself for self-expression in every walk of life, irrespective of response by the neighbours.[2]

When a British journalist asked him in 1946 for his views on nuclear weapons, Gandhi reiterated his conviction: 'I regard the employment of the atom bomb for the wholesale destruction of men, women and children as the most diabolical use of science.' The journalist asked him if the atom bomb had antiquated nonviolence. 'No. *It is the only thing the atom bomb cannot destroy.* I did not move a muscle when I first heard that the atom bomb had wiped out Hiroshima. On the contrary, I said to myself, "Unless now the world adopts nonviolence, it will spell certain suicide for mankind".'[3] *(Emphasis added)*

The era of nuclear weapons was still in its infancy when Gandhi died. Only one country in the world, USA, possessed nuclear weapons at the time. Nevertheless, Gandhi had already foreseen, and warned against, the logic of deterrence that would dominate the nuclear debate decades later. In the aforementioned article titled 'Atom Bomb and Ahimsa' he wrote:

> The moral to be legitimately drawn from the supreme tragedy of the bomb is that it will not be destroyed by counter-bombs even as violence cannot be by counter-violence. Mankind has to get out of violence only through nonviolence. Hatred can be overcome only by love. Counter-hatred only increases the surface as well as the depth of hatred. I am aware that I am repeating what I have many times stated before and practiced to the best of my ability and capacity. What I first stated itself was nothing new. It was as old as the hills... It is the central truth by which one can stand alone without flinching. I believe in what Max Muller said years ago, namely, that truth needed to be repeated as long as there were men who disbelieved it.[4]

Writing in *Harijan* again on 23 July 1946, he posed the questions that supporters of the cynical theory of Mutually Assured Destruction (MAD) in USA, erstwhile USSR and elsewhere raised much later: 'Won't the very frightfulness of the atom bomb force nonviolence on the world? If all nations are armed with the atom bomb, won't they refrain from using it as it will mean absolute destruction for all concerned'? His answer to these arguments was an emphatic 'No'. When more and more countries possessed nuclear weapons, far from the MAD theory deterring all of them, 'the violent man's eye would be lit up with the prospect of the much greater amount of destruction and death which he could now wreak'.[5]

'OK, Mr President, let's talk'

A cartoon in a British newspaper of 29 October 1962 showing Soviet leader Nikita Khrushchev and US President John F. Kennedy arm-wrestling during the Cuban Missile Crisis.

Gandhi's warning has become more relevant with the passage of time. It completely delegitimises the stockpiling of nuclear weapons by nation-states that have also been spending unconscionably huge amounts of money on delivery systems and other military hardware. These stockpiles are capable of killing the entire human race and also a large part of living beings on earth – the only planet in the universe known to nurture life. Nuclear arms race can also lead to nuclear arm-twisting. Recall the eyeball-to-eyeball rhetoric between the Soviet leader Nikita Khrushchev and US President John F. Kennedy during the Cuban Missile Crisis in 1962 at the height of the Cold War.

Indeed, the world now faces the additional threat of the technology of producing nuclear weapons being acquired by non-state terrorist entities. Therefore, to know about Gandhi's views on nuclear weapons is to be reminded about the imperative of immediately and irreversibly eliminating all the weapons of mass destruction in the world.

But there is yet another reason why the world must heed Gandhi's warning. Military spending by big powers, India included, is one of the biggest causes for the prevalence of poverty and want in large parts of the world. It is also responsible for the large-scale degradation of the environment. Most seriously, the unprecedented militarisation of international relations has warped political thought across the globe and has become the greatest obstacle to peace, cultural renaissance and genuine people-to-people relations amongst the countries of the world. Indeed, militarisation of international relations defeats the very purpose and potential of globalisation. It must therefore be defeated by the collective actions of peace-loving people all over the world.

The nuclear disarmament movements across the globe, which had gained considerable strength in the 1980s and 1990s, should be further intensified. The goal of complete annihilation of all weapons of mass destruction, possessed by all countries, must be brought on the practical and time-bound agenda of governments of the world and global organisations like the UN. No doubt, Gandhi's philosophy of satya and ahimsa will continue to serve as a source of inspiration for this noble and urgent mission.

Is this only a pious thought, or can the idea of nonviolence actually influence international relations and the thinking as well as the conduct of political institutions in the age of globalisation? In finding the answer to this question, we would do well to view globalisation as an ally of global peace. On account of the growing inter-dependence that globalisation has created among nations, nonviolence has become both a necessity and a real possibility. This helpful insight was succinctly expressed more than four decades ago by Werner Heisenberg (1901–76), a Nobel laureate and German scientist who propounded the famous 'Uncertainty Principle' of Quantum Physics, in an article titled 'Nonviolence in Politics'. It was Heisenberg's tribute to Gandhi on the occasion of his birth centenary in 1969, and was published by the Gandhi Peace Foundation. The article is so persuasive and impassioned that it deserves to be presented in full. *(See Annexure III.)*

To sum up, nuclear disarmament – total, universal and irreversible – is the first and foremost peace-promoting point in Gandhi's manifesto for our times.

Hiroshima Peace Memorial Museum

*'It may have been a mistake the first time
But it's a betrayal the second time.
We'll not forget
The promise we've made to the dead'.*

21

WHAT WOULD GANDHI HAVE SAID ABOUT INDIA'S NUCLEAR WEAPONS?
'We Indians Have a Better Mission
to Deliver to the World'

❖

But the inventors
of that ultimate weapon
which, on the dark night of the Sixth
of August, Nineteen Forty-Five,
danced the dance of death in
Hiroshima-Nagasaki
and took the sacrifice of over two
hundred thousand people,
crippled thousands of people for life,

Did they, for a second even,
get the feeling that what they had
done was not right?
If so, then time will not put them in
the dock,
but if not then history will never
forgive them.

— Atal Bihari Vajpayee, from the English translation of his poem *Hiroshima ki Peeda*
(The Pain of Hiroshima), which was published in the collection of his Hindi poems,
Meri Ikyavan Kavitaein (My Fifty-One Poems); Kitab Ghar, New Delhi, 1995.

A T THIS POINT IN MY LONG REVIEW OF GANDHI'S THOUGHTS ON nonviolence, I would be guilty of being dishonest if I skirted the question posed in the title of this chapter. To say why the rest of the world should be free of nuclear arms, and yet remain silent on what Gandhi would have said about India's own recent entry into the club of nuclear-weapon states, would not be in keeping with the spirit of writing this book.

The government of Atal Bihari Vajpayee, of which I was a part, conducted nuclear tests at Pokharan, Rajasthan, in May 1998, and declared: 'India is now a nuclear-weapon state'. It justified the move as having been necessitated by the regional and global security scenario. India, surrounded by unfriendly and nuclear-powered neighbours, needed a minimum nuclear deterrence for its self-defence. International opinion has found no basis to question the defensive nature of this programme. After all, India's nuclear doctrine is unambiguous: the avowal of no-first use of nuclear weapons and no-use-ever against a non-nuclear nation.

However, it is equally irrefutable that the global campaign for universal and total nuclear disarmament has suffered a setback on account of two factors. Firstly, the five countries – USA, USSR (now Russia), United Kingdom, France and China – which are recognised as nuclear-weapon states by the Nuclear Non-Proliferation Treaty (NPT) of 1970, have accepted no obligation to eliminate all their nuclear arsenal within a specified time frame. Thus, one of NPT's prime objectives – to further the goal of achieving 'general and complete disarmament' – has been brazenly ignored by the five original nuclear-weapon states, which are also permanent members of the UN Security Council (UNSC). This shows how the NPT and the present structure of UNSC are both flawed, and must be reformed.

Secondly – and this is a direct consequence of the first factor – the NPT has also failed in its non-proliferation objective. After India, Pakistan and North Korea have also conducted nuclear tests and declared that they possess nuclear weapons. Israel is an undeclared nuclear-weapon state, even though it has not conducted a nuclear test. The likelihood of more nations wanting to possess nuclear weapons is real, and so is the even more ominous possibility of non-state actors and terrorist organisations gaining the capability and resources to make nuclear weapons.

Thus, whatever be the justification of certain nations to have nuclear weapons, it is undeniable that they have collectively caused a nuclear sword of Damocles to hang over the world.

If the world fails in achieving the twin objectives of nuclear disarmament and non-proliferation, the premise of nuclear defence and deterrence will seem even more unreliable than now. Nuclear weapons, being weapons of mass destruction, are never meant to be used. There will be no winners in a nuclear war, including those countries which are neutral to the combat. All are losers. The idea of a nuclear weapon as an offensive sword is of course sheer insanity. However, even the idea of a nuclear weapon as a defensive shield will become more questionable in the time to come.

The more I think about this matter, the more I am convinced about the moral weight of Gandhi's message: '*We Indians have better work to do, a better mission to deliver to the world*'.[1]

It is a message that he conveyed repeatedly and insistently throughout his leadership of India's freedom movement. In his 1920 article titled 'The Doctrine of the Sword' *(cited in Chapter 19)*, we have seen how, with extraordinary prescience and long before nuclear weapons came on the global scene, Gandhi had warned against India treading the militaristic path of Western powers. He returned to this theme again, in *Young India* of 6 April 1921:

> If India makes violence her creed, and I have survived, I would not care to live in India. She will cease to evoke any pride in me. My patriotism is subservient to my religion. I cling to India like a child to its mother's breast because I feel that she gives me the spiritual nourishment I need. She has the environment that responds to my highest aspirations. When that faith is gone, I shall feel like an orphan without hope of ever finding a guardian.

Only a saint with the good of the whole world at heart, and only an enlightened patriot with the good of his own country at heart, could have uttered such bold words. No leader in modern history has so categorically and courageously subordinated his love for his own nation to his love for truth.

I have often wondered in the course of researching for this book: If reading Gandhi today, sixty-four years after his death, can be so profoundly reassuring, how might the experience have been for those who had the privilege of seeing and meeting him? I found one answer in an article in *The New York Times* in 1930, titled 'Gandhi – The Prophet Who Sways India', by Upton Close, an American expert in foreign affairs who had met and admired the Mahatma.

> What was his secret? I think my wife discovered it. She said, 'In his presence I felt a new capability and power in *myself* rather than a consciousness of *his* power. I felt equal, good for anything – an assurance I had never known before, as if some consciousness within me had newly awakened.'
> A man who can do this to people can mold his age.[2]

Gandhi never visited America. But what he said in his only radio message to the people of USA, on 13 September 1931, is of timeless significance. The message – 'On God' – was broadcast live by the Columbia Broadcasting Service (CBS) from London, where he had gone to attend the Second Round Table Conference.

> I personally would wait, if need be, for ages rather than seek to attain the freedom of my country through bloody means. I feel in the innermost recesses of my heart, after a political experience extending over an unbroken period of close upon thirty-five years, that the world is sick unto death of blood-spilling. The world is seeking a way out, and I flatter myself with the belief that perhaps it will be the privilege of the ancient land of India to show that way out to the hungering world.

In *Young India* of 9 May 1929, Gandhi hoped that if India gained independence through nonviolent means, it would 'never want to carry a vast army, an equally grand navy and a grander air force'. His hope was for the benefit of not only India but also the entire world. And it was indeed a grand hope. 'If India's self-consciousness rises to the height necessary to give her a nonviolent victory in her fight for freedom, the world values will have changed and most of the paraphernalia of war would be found to be useless. Such an India may be a mere day-dream, a childish folly. But such, in my opinion, is undoubtedly the implication of an India becoming free through nonviolence....Hers will be the voice of a powerful nation seeking to keep under restraint all the violent forces of the world.'

In one of the finest orations of his life, Gandhi articulated India's – nay, renascent Asia's – message to the world when he addressed the closing session of the Inter-Asian Relations Conference held on 2 April 1947 in New Delhi. This important conference was held in the backdrop of the victory, or impending victory, of the national liberation struggles of many countries in Asia and Africa. (Gandhi did not omit Africa in his message, which was, as almost all his talks were, delivered extempore.) It was time for the newly liberated people of Asia to think of their future path of development. Should they imitate the goals and methods of their colonial masters? Or should they rediscover their own civilisational goals and find their own 'Asian' ways to achieve those goals?

Gandhi joined this debate by first reminding the delegations that 'wisdom came to the West from the East'. Who were the carriers of this wisdom? All of them were the great prophets of the world, and all were from Asia.

> Zoroaster. He belonged to the East. He was followed by Buddha. He belonged to the East, he belonged to India. Who followed Buddha? Jesus, again from Asia. Before Jesus was Musa, Moses, also belonging to Palestine, though... he was born in Egypt.

The East's message to the West: *Gandhi at the Inter-Asian Relations Conference, New Delhi, 2 April 1947. Sharing the dais him with him was Jawaharlal Nehru. In his speech, Gandhi said: 'The message of the East, the message of Asia, is not to be learnt through European spectacles, not by imitating the tinsel of the West, the gunpowder of the West, the atom bomb of the West. If you want to give a message again to the West, it must be a message of "Love", it must be a message of "Truth".'*

And then came Jesus, then came Mohammad. I omit Krishna, I omit Mahavir, I omit the other lights, I won't call them lesser lights, but unknown to the West, unknown to the literary world. All the same, I don't know a single person to match these men of Asia. And then what happened? Christianity became disfigured when it went to the West. I am sorry to have to say that, but that is my reading. I won't take you any further through this.

After reminding the delegates about Asia's great and unique prophetic heritage, Gandhi urged them to remain faithful to this heritage and not to blindly copy the West's path of economic growth or militarisation.

...what I want you to understand, if you can, is that the message of the East, the message of Asia, is not to be learnt through European spectacles, through the Western spectacles, not by imitating the tinsel of the West, the gun-powder of the West, the atom bomb of the West. If you want to give a message again to the West, it must be a message of 'Love', it must be a message of 'Truth'. There must be a conquest ... *(clapping).*

When the delegates applauded, Gandhi, the master of silence, interjected, 'Please, please, please. That will interfere with my speech, and that will interfere with your understanding also. I want to capture your hearts and don't want to receive your claps. Let your hearts clap in unison with what I'm saying, and I think, I shall have finished my work. Therefore, I want you to go away with the thought that Asia has to conquer the West.'

Gandhi was, of course, talking about the moral conquest of the West by the East – so fundamentally different from the West's economic, political and military conquest of the East. He went on to say that the East had to 'conquer' the West for the West's own recovery from its illness. Indeed, it was no longer 'East and West', nor, much less, East vs. West; in the dawn of the new era, Gandhi gave a resounding message for the realisation of the dream of One World:

Then, the question that a friend asked yesterday, 'Did I believe in one world?' Of course, I believe in one world. And how can I possibly do otherwise, when I become an inheritor of the message of love that these great un-conquerable teachers left for us? You can redeliver that message now, in this age of democracy, in the age of awakening of the poorest of the poor, you can redeliver this message with the greatest emphasis. Then you will complete the conquest of the whole of the West, not through vengeance because you have been exploited, and in the exploitation, of course, I want to include Africa. And I hope that when next you meet in India, by that time there aren't any exploited nations on the Earth. I am so sanguine that if all of you put your hearts together, not merely your heads, but hearts together and understand the secret of the messages of all these wise men of the East have left to us, and if we really become, deserve, are worthy of that great message, then you will easily understand that the conquest of the West will be completed and that conquest will be loved by the West itself. West is today pining for wisdom. West today is in despair of multiplication of atom bombs, because a multiplication of atom bombs means utter destruction, not merely of the West, but it will be a destruction of the world, as if the prophecy of the *Bible* is going to be fulfilled and there is to be a perfect deluge. Heaven forbid that there be that deluge, and through man's wrongs against himself. It is up to you to deliver the whole world, not merely Asia but deliver the whole world from that wickedness, from that sin. That is the precious heritage your teachers, my teachers, have left to us.

These resonant lines, even after the passage of so many decades, speak to us as if Gandhi were addressing us face-to-face today. After listening to them, which thinking Indian, Asian, or Westerner, and which believer in the dream of One World, would remain unmoved?

Gandhi felt it necessary to remind his countrymen about India's moral responsibility in the new world again in *Harijan* of 7 December 1947 – after India had gained independence and after humanity had lost its innocence with regard to the sin of using nuclear weapons.

I am only hoping and praying [that....there] will rise a new and robust India – not warlike, basely imitating the West in all its hideousness, but a new India learning the best that the West has to give and becoming the hope not only of Asia and Africa, but the whole of aching world....In spite, however, of the madness and the vain imitation of the tinsel of the West, the hope lingers in me and many others that India shall survive this death dance and occupy the moral

Courtesy: The WAKE, a student magazine, University of Minnesota

The Doomsday Clock: *Developed by the Bulletin of the Atomic Scientists, it conveys how close humanity is to catastrophic destruction – the figurative midnight – because of the existence of nuclear weapons.*

height that should belong to her after the training, however imperfect, in nonviolence for an unbroken period of thirty-two years since 1915.

My Musings at the Hiroshima Peace Memorial

It is these wise Gandhian thoughts that have caused my re-conversion to the idea of India becoming a leading campaigner, through self-example, for the goal of a nuclear weapons-free world. This reconversion got further solidified when I visited Hiroshima, the Japanese city that bears the birthmark of the nuclear age. As I stood before the Atomic Bomb Dome, a mute and mutilated witness to the barbaric devastation caused by the first-ever nuclear weapon used by man against man, I could feel a sorrowful silence in the air that has remained undisturbed since the fateful morning of 6 August 1945. The sorrow turned to horror when I walked through the Hiroshima Peace Memorial Museum. Its exhibits carry a grim warning about what could happen to our world if the fate of Hiroshima and Nagasaki were to befall any other places in a future nuclear war – or even in the event of an accidental nuclear explosion. In the museum's souvenir shop, I bought a book of poems on Hiroshima and Nagasaki. One of the poems is by Hiroshima-born Sadako Kurihara (1913-2005), who lived in the city and was exposed to radiation. With haiku-like brevity and simplicity, her poem conveys a message of unyielding resolve:

> *It may have been a mistake the first time,*
> *But it's a betrayal the second time.*
> *We'll not forget*
> *The promise we've made to the dead.*

I was benumbed when I came out of the museum. As I took a slow stroll in the Hiroshima Peace Memorial Park, I wondered: What will it be if there is a *third time*?

A mistake?

A betrayal?

No, it'll be a suicidal folly by the human race.

At the centre of the park is an arch-shaped concrete monument covering a cenotaph that bears the names of all the people who perished in the bomb attack. The epitaph on the cenotaph reads: 'Rest in Peace, for the error shall not be repeated'. Whose error was it? Certainly, dropping the atomic bomb was a deliberate decision taken by the then American government. However, at a deeper level, the error – rather, crime – was committed by the entire human race. America's action was the handiwork of the brute in man, a continuation of the long tradition of war and violence that has marred human history. All countries and all races in the world have contributed to this dishonourable tradition to a greater or a lesser degree.

Hiroshima's Peace Park also has an Eternal Peace Flame that memorialises the nearly 2,00,000 people who died due to the bomb attack and its horrible after-effects. The flame will remain lit until all nuclear weapons in the world are destroyed and our planet becomes free from the threat of nuclear suicide.

The message of this Eternal Flame must never be forgotten. We must strive with redoubled conviction and vigour for the irreversible elimination of all nuclear weapons, and all other weapons of mass destruction, from the face of our beautiful planet. The main responsibility in achieving this goal undoubtedly rests with those nations that have stockpiled a huge armoury of such weapons. Nevertheless, India should set an example by strengthening her moral voice for universal nuclear disarmament.

Going further, peace-loving people all over the world must advocate for deep cuts in the indefensible overspending on military infrastructure by USA and other powers, including China and India. As noted in the previous chapter, military spending is the single biggest factor contributing to mass poverty in the world (North Korea is a good example) and also to destruction of the environment. What humanity is crying for is demilitarisation of both international relations and scientific and technological research, so that its collective natural, intellectual and political resources can be deployed for solving the gigantic problems facing our world.

In short, a new Thought Revolution – rooted in the imperishable ideals of truth and nonviolence, which India, more than any other country has devotedly served since time immemorial – is what the world is waiting for in the twenty-first century.

Who can be torch-bearers of this thought revolution? Women, according to Gandhi, as we shall see in the next chapter.

Courtesy: Gandhi Smriti

Gandhi being greeted by British women workers in Lancashire on 21 September 1931: *He once said, 'If only the women of the world come together, they could display such heroic nonviolence as to kick away the atom bomb like a mere ball.'*

Courtesy: Gandhi Smriti

Two women who influenced Gandhi's personality the most:
mother Putlibai (left) and wife Kasturba.

22

SURVIVAL OF THE KINDEST
Women and the Science of Nonviolence

⇥⚡◇⚡◈⚡◇⚡⚡⇤

Gandhi taught that nonviolence does not mean passivity. No. It is the most daring, creative, and courageous way of living, and it is the only hope for our world. Nonviolence is an active way of life which always rejects violence and killing, and instead applies the force of love and truth as a means to transform conflict and the root causes of conflict. Nonviolence demands creativity. It pursues dialogue, seeks reconciliation, listens to the truth in our opponents, rejects militarism, and allows God's spirit to transform us socially and politically.

— Mairead Maguire, Northern Irish peace activist, winner of the 1976 Nobel Peace Prize.

IN GANDHI'S LIFE, AS WELL AS IN HIS VOLUMINOUS WRITINGS, THE loftiest place was reserved for women. The respect and reverence with which he viewed women, and the enthusiasm with which they became active in his movement by responding to his saintly nature, is a narrative that has no parallel in the biography of any other leader in modern history. The relationship was unorthodox and non-sexist, but full of pure love, from both sides. Precisely for this reason, it has some interesting pointers to how the man-woman matrix might develop in tomorrow's nonviolent world. We have discussed it in a subsequent chapter (on his brahmacharya experiments) in this book. Here we shall see why he believed women to be superior to men in practising the science of nonviolence.

If we study Gandhi's views on women, it is easy to foresee that many of the 'undreamt of and seemingly impossible discoveries in the field of nonviolence', which he predicted, would be made by those whom ignorant and arrogant men have called 'the weaker sex'. A feminist in both thought and action, he remarked: 'To call women the weaker sex is a libel. It is man's injustice to woman...If by strength is meant moral power, then woman is immeasurably man's superior.'[1]

In a message to Chinese women that he sent on 18 July 1947, Gandhi said: 'If only the women of the world could come together, they could display such heroic nonviolence as to kick away the atom bomb like a mere ball. Women have been so gifted by God. If an ancestral treasure lying buried in a corner of the house unknown to the members of the family were suddenly discovered, what a celebration it would occasion. Similarly, women's marvelous power is lying dormant. If the women of Asia wake up, they will dazzle the world. My experiment in nonviolence would be instantly successful if I could secure women's help.'[2]

The tribute that the Mahatma paid to the power of women was perfectly in tune with his moral philosophy. 'Woman is more fitted than man to make explorations and take bolder action in ahimsa,'[3] he said. He regarded women as the incarnation of ahimsa because 'ahimsa means infinite love, which again means infinite capacity for suffering'.[4] He described woman as 'the embodiment of sacrifice and suffering'.[5] He strongly advocated feminisation of public life because of his belief that it would result in 'purifying' politics and governance. 'Women are special custodians of all that is pure and religious in life'.[6] He went to the extent of confessing: 'I have always counted myself as a woman' and 'I have mentally become a woman in order to steal into her heart'.[7]

After this effusive praise for the stronger sex, the only thing left for him was to make this prophesy – 'If nonviolence is the law of our being, the future is with woman'.

Gandhi walked the talk by fully encouraging women to play prominent roles in all the political and social campaigns he led. 'He was a super strategist, and his strategy to fight for freedom could not ignore women,' writes Ela Bhatt, a widely respected Gandhian activist and founder of the Ahmedabad-based Self Employed Women's Association (SEWA), in her foreword to the book *Gandhi on Women*. 'He had more faith in his women soldiers than the men soldiers, because he really considered women to be superior to men, particularly when the weapons in the struggle were love and nonviolence. He believed women to be stronger because their hearts contained, as mothers, qualities of love and peace. No other public leader has ever put such positive confidence in the women of the country. He realised a very strong need for support and participation from women in creating a society based on justice'.[8]

Is there a scientific basis to his prophesy about women representing the future of the human race or is it merely the expression of a pious hope and wish? To probe this question, it is again useful to return to the framework of evolutionary biology. If it is true, as evolutionary biologists like Julian Huxley argue, that the evolution of modern man to higher possibilities is not biological, but psycho-social, then it is a foregone conclusion that women, and not men, will be the trail-blazers of the future progress of the human race. For who can deny women's superiority over men in the psychological and social life of the species, and in the possession of higher human qualities such as love, kindness, compassion, cooperation, self-sacrifice and faith?

Gandhi experienced this superiority early on in his own marital life. He recounts how he learnt the lesson of nonviolence from his wife Kasturba's practice of 'domestic satyagraha'. During their initial years in South Africa, he was quite a demanding and domineering husband, believing that he had the right to impose his will upon his wife. Kasturba's response was a fine combination of nonviolent resistance and a loving readiness to suffer. It soon opened his eyes and changed his conduct. 'I learnt the lesson of nonviolence from my wife, when I tried to bend her to my will. Her determined resistance to my will, on the one hand, and her quiet submission to the suffering my stupidity involved, on the other, ultimately made me ashamed of myself and cured me of my stupidity...in the end, she became my teacher in nonviolence'.[9]

Gandhi tells us in his autobiography about the profound influence that his mother, Putlibai, had on him in his childhood years. She didn't have any formal education, but she imparted to her son values that form the bedrock of human civilisation – truthfulness, kindness, piety, nonviolence, readiness to serve others and to suffer in the process, and commitment to keep one's word irrespective of the consequences. She was a devout Hindu who was taught by her faith, and who in turn taught her son to give equal respect to all religions, sects, prophets, and to their teachings.

In her book *Women, Power, and the Biology of Peace,* Dr Judith L. Hand, a reputed evolutionary biologist, contends that women are naturally more nonviolent. They are better suited to conflict prevention and resolution because of their innate inclination for negotiation, mediation, compromise – all nonviolent tools – as opposed to shedding blood. She writes: 'In my view, while human males may have evolved often under an imperative to invade and conquer, a basic reproductive imperative for females has been to do whatever they can to foster social stability. I propose that a female inclination to facilitate social stability is as deeply evolved in humans as the well-known and frequently discussed male inclination for group aggression. This is why things would be different if women ran the world – specifically, society would be more socially stable. Because of a female's unavoidable and costly commitment to her offspring, basic human female biological priorities are different from those of males'.[10]

Dr Hand, a pioneer in the emerging field of peace ethology, which studies human conflicts and peacemaking, argues that the differences between men and women are not merely cultural. Their origins are deeply rooted in our evolutionary past. 'We inherit them from our pre-human primate ancestors. Given free rein and uncurbed by social or ecological forces, these opposed tendencies, with males ready to bond together in acts of aggression and females more inclined to seek social stability, will play themselves out in our group behaviour. Not to take them into consideration when discussing the question of war and how to make a lasting peace is a profound error'.

In the other book by Dr Hand, titled *A Future Without War* – her website also bears the same name – she writes that a major pre-requisite for abolition of war is the global empowerment of women – educational, financial, legal, political and religious. 'If women around the world in the twenty-first century would get their act together they could, partnered with men of like mind, shift the direction of world history to create a future without war'.

Gandhi would have certainly endorsed this optimistic view.

Not surprisingly, scientists like Dr Hand are influenced by the life and teachings of Gandhi. In an essay called 'Essential Human Goodness: Our hope for abolishing war and ushering in the next great shift in human history', Dr Hand states: 'Mohandas Gandhi, the master student of social transformation, built his program for nonviolent social transformation on a fundamental belief about us: that humans are essentially good. His *satyagraha* technique relies on using love and understanding to bring out the best in others, to win them over to a better, less violent way, to empathise with them and in return gain their empathy'.

Many social scientists today are asserting that 'feminine' qualities like empathy are more fundamental to human nature, and are challenging entrenched beliefs that human beings are wired to be aggressive and selfish. There is a growing body of research to show that human societies have survived, and thrived, better when they have practiced the virtues of compassion, collaboration and altruism. Dr Dacher Keltner, a renowned psychologist at the University of California, Berkeley, and author of the bestselling book *Born to Be Good: The Science of a Meaningful Life,* contends that this trend will be even more pronounced in mankind's future evolution. He calls it 'Survival of the Kindest'.[11]

Dr Keltner writes: 'Human beings have survived as a species because we have evolved the capacities to care for those in need and to cooperate. "Born to be good" for me means that our mammalian and hominid evolution have crafted a species – us – with remarkable tendencies toward kindness, play, generosity, reverence and self-sacrifice, which are vital to the classic tasks of evolution–survival, gene replication and smooth functioning groups. These tendencies are felt in the wonderful realm of emotion – emotions such as compassion that promote ethical action and are the fabric of cooperative societies... Sympathy is indeed wired into our brains and bodies'.

If nonviolent and life-enriching emotions such as love, sympathy, kindness and cooperation are going to be the survival tools for tomorrow, the world will have to accept women's all-round empowerment, indeed their leadership in various fields, as a prime necessity. This is what Gandhi meant when he affirmed: 'If nonviolence is the law of our being, the future is with woman'.

And now, modern science itself is proving the validity of his affirmation by positing the theory of 'Survival of the Kindest' in the future evolution of the human species.

If there is one institution that has played a crucial role not only in the survival of the human species but also in civilising it, it is the family. Gandhi recognised its importance. He praised women's contribution to the protection and nurturing of family values, calling it sacred. Although he was second to none in advocating full scope for women to play their part in public life, he nevertheless underscored their natural duty towards their families. 'I believe in complete equality for women, and in the India I seek to build, they will have it,' he wrote in an article titled 'Myself, My Spinning Wheel and Women', which was published in the *Daily Herald* during his visit to Britain in 1931. 'What I want to see is the opening of all offices, professions and employments to women; otherwise there can be no real equality'.

What he further said was, and continues to be, equally significant:

> But I most sincerely hope that woman will retain and exercise her ancient prerogative as queen of the household. From this position she must never be dethroned. It would indeed be a dreary home of which a woman was not the centre. I cannot, for instance, imagine a really happy home in which the wife is a typist and scarcely ever in it. Who would look after the children? What, after all, is a home without children, the brightest jewels in the poorest household?

Gandhi saw the highest value in women's role as family-builders. Some modern-day feminists may not concur with him when he says that 'equality of the sexes does not mean equality of occupations'. But the modernity of this traditionalist has a timeless appeal, as can be seen from the following lines.

> It is a woman's work to bring up her little ones and mould their character. A precious work, too. Equality of status with men, I desire for women, but if the mother fails in her sacred trust towards her children, then nothing can atone for the loss. Whatever the race, family life is the first and greatest thing. Its sanctity must remain. Upon it rests the welfare of the nation. For good or for ill home influence persists. Of that there can be no possible doubt, and no State can survive unless the sacred security of its home life is preserved. Individuals there may be who in pursuit of some great principle or ideal forgo, like myself, the solace of family life, choosing instead one of self-sacrifice and celibacy; but for the mass of the people the preservation of home life is essential.[12]

The life-creating and life-nurturing role of a mother had a unique fascination for Gandhi. It was so central to his philosophy of nonviolence that, as we shall see later in the chapter on his brahmacharya experiments, his aspiration in the final decade of his life was to become a mother who would do everything possible, including risking her own life, to save her child in danger – in this case, the humanity in India threatened by communal violence. Let us read the following lines he wrote in *Harijan* of 12 February 1940:

> I have suggested in these columns that woman is the incarnation of ahimsa. Ahimsa means infinite love, which again means infinite capacity for suffering. Who but woman, the mother of man, shows this capacity in the largest measure? She shows it as she carries the infant and feeds it during nine months and derives joy in the suffering involved. What can beat the suffering caused by the pangs of labour? But she forgets them in the joy of creation. Who again suffers daily so that her baby may wax from day to day?

Gandhi, who had the amazing ability to extrapolate the personal to the universal, then says:

> Let her transfer that love to the whole of humanity, let her forget she ever was or can be the object of man's lust. And she will occupy her proud position by the side of man as his mother, maker and silent leader. It is given to her to teach the art of peace to the warring world thirsting for that nectar. She can become the leader in satyagraha which does not require the learning that books give but does require the stout heart that comes from suffering and faith.

To drive home his point that women alone can save the world, he narrates a telling personal experience.

> My good nurse in the Sassoon Hospital, Poona, as I was lying on a sick bed years ago, told me the story of a woman who refused to take chloroform because she would not risk the life of the baby she was carrying. She had to undergo a painful operation. The only anaesthetic she had was her love for the babe, to save whom no suffering was too great. Let not women, who can count many such heroines among them, ever despise their sex or deplore that they were not born men. The contemplation of that heroine often makes me envy woman the status that is hers, if only she knew. There is as much reason for man to wish that he was born a woman as for woman to do otherwise. But the wish is fruitless. Let us be happy in the state to which we are born and do the duty for which nature has destined us.

Gender equality, both at home and in public life, was an article of faith for Gandhi. He ensured scrupulous adherence to this principle in his ashrams as well as in his mass campaigns. But he also insisted on inculcating it among children at a young age. The book *Gandhi on Women* illustrates this by narrating an instructive episode from his life. Once, while he was on his way to prison, Kakasaheb Kalelkar, his senior aide in the ashram asked him to write a primer for the children of primary schools. Gandhi wrote it in jail. It was in the form of a mother teaching her young son never to regard women to be inferior to men. Here is a dialogue in the chapter on housework.

Mother: Dear son, you should also help in household chores as your sister does.

Son: But she is a girl, I am a boy. A boy plays and studies.

Daughter: How come? I also love to play and study!

Son: I do not deny that, but, dear sister, you have to do housework as well.

Mother: Why should a boy not do housework?

Son: Because the boy has to earn money when he grows up. Therefore he must study well.

Mother: You are wrong, my son. Women also can earn for the family. And, there is a lot to learn in housework – cleaning, cooking, dish-washing, laundry, etc. By doing these chores you will develop various skills of the body and will become self-reliant. In good housework you need to use your eyes, hands and brain. Therefore, these activities are educative and they build your character. Men and women both need to be educated equally in housework because the home belongs to both.

Gandhi's non-sexist approach irked many male readers. As was always his wont, he listened to people's criticisms and used his journals to educate them about his philosophy. 'I am building a new society,' he audaciously wrote.

For Gandhi the virtue of kindness entailed being kind not only to fellow human beings, but also to all living creatures and to the natural ecology. He regarded it to be the moral duty of human beings to act as trustees of the natural environment and also all the non-human creatures that it nurtures. Therefore, we now turn to an examination of the relevance of his all-encompassing conception of nonviolence to an issue – protection and regeneration of the environment – which has come to occupy the centre stage of contemporary global concern, debate and activism.

'It is an arrogant assumption to say that human beings are lords and masters of the lower creatures': *Gandhi, Mirabehn (centre) and Pandit Madan Mohan Malaviya (to her right) inspecting goats when they visited the Dairy Exhibition at the Royal Agricultural Hall, Islington, London, on 23 October 1931.*

Two great Gandhian environmentalists: *(left) E.F. Schumacher, author of the highly influential book* Small is Beautiful: Economics as if People Mattered; *and Arne Naess, originator of the Deep Ecology movement.*

23

A PIONEER OF THE GREEN MOVEMENT

⟶⟨◈◈◈⟩⟵

I reflect on my childhood experience when I would visit a stream next to our home to fetch water for my mother. I would drink water straight from the stream. Playing among the arrowroot leaves I tried in vain to pick up the strands of frogs' eggs, believing they were beads. But every time I put my little fingers under them they would break. Later, I saw thousands of tadpoles: black, energetic and wriggling through the clear water against the background of the brown earth. This is the world I inherited from my parents.

Today, over 50 years later, the stream has dried up, women walk long distances for water, which is not always clean, and children will never know what they have lost. The challenge is to restore the home of the tadpoles and give back to our children a world of beauty and wonder.

— Wangari Maathai (1940–2011), Kenyan environmental activist and winner of the 2004 Nobel Peace Prize. She was inspired by the ideals of Mahatma Gandhi.

PROTECTION OF THE ENVIRONMENT AND SUSTAINABLE DEVELOPMENT were not quite on the global or India's agenda when Gandhi was alive. Nevertheless, we see how he was far ahead of his time in warning the world about the potentially disastrous consequences of the Western model of economic growth, which has, alas, now become, with some local variations, the globally accepted model. When asked if he wanted India to enjoy the same kind of lifestyle as in Britain, his incisive reply was: 'It took Britain half the resources of the planet to achieve this prosperity. How many planets will a country like India require?'[1]

Gandhi had not only foreseen the unsustainability of Western patterns of production, marketing and consumption, but he had also warned India about the danger inherent in imitating them. He wrote in *Young India* on 20 December 1928: 'God forbid that India should ever take to industrialisation after the manner of the West. The economic imperialism of a single tiny island kingdom (England) is today keeping the world in chains. If an entire nation of 300 million took to similar economic exploitation, it would strip the world bare like locusts'.

Gandhian environmentalism is integrally linked to his world-view of nonviolence. 'It is an arrogant assumption,' he wrote, 'to say that human beings are lords and masters of the lower creatures. On the contrary, being endowed with greater things in life, they are the trustees of the lower animal kingdom'. He wanted 'to realise identity with even the crawling things upon earth, because we claim descent from the same God, and that being so, all life in whatever form it appears must essentially be so'.[2] In a highly original re-interpretation of colonialism, he affirmed that lording over nature and lording over other 'inferior' people are both manifestations of colonialism.[3]

To know the shocking extent of violence that man has perpetrated through his 'colonialism' of other species on planet Earth – paradoxically, this eco-colonialism has gained momentum after the era of conventional colonialism came to an end in the second half of the twentieth century – let us turn to some irrefutable evidence. A recent study by the International Union for Conservation of Nature (IUCN), the world's oldest and largest global environmental network, has concluded that Nature's very 'backbone is at risk'. The most comprehensive assessment of the world's vertebrates confirms 'an extinction crisis' with one-fifth of species threatened. 'On average, fifty species of mammal, bird and amphibian move closer to extinction each year'. Another study conducted by IUCN partners suggests that over one-fifth of all plant species are threatened. 'Most threatened plant species are found in the tropics and that the most threatening process is man-induced habitat loss'.

Yet another study sponsored by the United Nations, called 'The Economics of Ecosystems and Biodiversity (TEEB)' calculates 'the cost of losing nature at US$2-5 trillion per year, predominantly in poorer parts of the world... putting the livelihoods of millions of people dependent on these vital resources at risk'.[4]

Kenneth E. Boulding (1910–93), an American economist and peace activist who was greatly influenced by the life and teachings of Gandhi, posed a pertinent question: 'Are we to regard the world of nature simply as a storehouse to be robbed for the immediate benefit of man?...Does man have any responsibility for the preservation of a decent balance in nature, for the preservation of rare species, or even for the indefinite continuance of his race?' Since Boulding was also a poet, he expressed the same concern in the following limerick:

With laissez-faire and price atomic,
Ecology's Uneconomic,
But with another kind of logic
Economy's Unecologic.

Gandhi had recognised this inherent conflict between economics and ecology in the modern era of limitless consumption fed by limitless exploitation of nature. Today environmentalists all over the world have come to recognise the profound truth in the Gandhian tenet: '*The earth provides enough to satisfy everyone's need, but not for anyone's greed*'. This statement is now universally quoted in the manifestos of environmental movements around the world. The operative part of this message is the need to rediscover the environmental wisdom inherent in all religions of the world. This wisdom places welfare of all above aggrandisement of the few. It also affirms that material progress is simply a means for man to achieve the far more rewarding progress in social, cultural, artistic and spiritual spheres. It cannot reconcile with the modern paradigm of development which, according to Gandhi, 'attaches undue importance to the body rather than the soul, which is infinitely more real than the body'.[5]

It is not difficult to see that this religion-embedded wisdom spells a mortal threat to the culture of consumerism, which keeps Western-type capitalism alive to the detriment of both the environment and human happiness. Gandhi's prescription for sustainable development is the very antithesis of consumerism, for he says: 'Civilisation consists not in the multiplication of wants but in the deliberate and voluntary reduction of wants'. It emphasises the need for voluntary control of bodily wants, for the balanced development of individuals, society and the environment. 'A certain degree of physical harmony and comfort is necessary,' Gandhi concedes. 'But above a certain level it becomes hindrance instead of help. Therefore the ideal of creating an unlimited number of wants and satisfying them seems to be a delusion and a snare ...The incessant search for material comforts and their multiplication is an evil. I make bold to say that the Europeans will have to remodel their outlook, if they are not to perish under the weight of the comforts to which they are becoming slaves... A time is coming when those who are in mad rush today of multiplying their wants, will retrace their steps and say: what have we done?'[6]

Prescient words, indeed, because many progressive thinkers in the West have also asked: 'What have we done?' Erich Fromm (1900–80), a widely respected American psychoanalyst, echoed Gandhi's concerns when he observed:

> Material production was once supposed to be a means for a more dignified, happier life and the aim was clearly the fuller, more dignified and more human life. Today production and consumption have become ends in themselves. Nobody asks any longer, why or what for? We are happy discovering how we can produce more. In fact, our economic system is based on ever increasing consumption and production. But why we want to produce more, why we want this, that, and the other... is a question which is not asked.[7]

Gandhi's advocacy of vegetarianism and animal care was deeply anchored in his ethics of nonviolence. 'Man has no power to create life, therefore has no right to kill any life also...A society can be judged by the way it treats its animals'. It is not surprising that scholars of the modern science of human ecology, which rests on the principle that man has responsibility towards fellow human beings and also towards all forms of life on Planet Earth, regard Mahatma Gandhi as a 'Human Ecologist'[8]. Robert Hart, in his essay 'Gandhi and the Greens: Road to Survival', writes: 'In today's world, generally Gandhi's truest political heirs are the Greens.'

As a matter of fact, during Gandhi's own lifetime, the fledgling green movement in the West had sought his blessings and guidance. In 1945, Mrs M.H. Morrison, secretary of the London-based Green Cross Society, wrote a letter to him seeking his support for the organisation's 'Ten Don'ts' campaign aimed at preventing destruction of wildlife and nature. Gandhi's reply was enthusiastic: 'It may interest and even please you to know that I have enforced in my own life now for years your Ten Don'ts and invited my neighbours to do likewise.' Then, echoing a line from a famous poem by William Wordsworth, he said, 'For I have long believed that there is a "Spirit in the wood", using the word "wood" in a double sense.'[9]

Gandhi, a man of extraordinary tolerance, was nonetheless highly intolerant in respect of wastage of any God-given resource, including, and especially, time. Long before the 3-R principle of reduce-recycle-reuse became popular in the discourse on sustainable development, he had made its compliance mandatory in his ashrams. Most of the letters he wrote were on the blank side of the reusable paper that came to him. He made the utmost use of the pencils he wrote with, until they became one-inch stubs and hence incapable of being gripped by his fingers. His ashrams were exemplars of zero-waste, the modern principle of sustainable development. His dictum: 'You may not waste a grain of rice or a scrap of paper, and similarly a minute of your time. It is not ours. It belongs to the nation and we are trustees for the use of it'.[10] Look how he extended his concept of trusteeship even to inanimate things used by men.

In a touching tribute to Gandhi's passion for precision that Mirabehn wrote just a week before his demise, she describes the immaculate manner in which he arranged and used his stationery wherever he sat and worked. '...I am never tired of watching him handle his writing work. Nothing is ruffled or damaged by his hands, and nothing is wasted....Such times are for me infinitely precious, infinitely sweet, and filled with a profound teaching which could never be conveyed in words'. Mirabehn concludes her essay with these words: 'There is only one real Gandhi Ashram in the whole world, and that is the few square feet containing Bapu's *gaddi* (floor mat) and the little writing desk'.[11]

Gandhian environmentalism has had a deep impact on the thinking of many progressive thinkers around the world. One of them was E.F. Schumacher (1911–77), author of the highly influential book *Small is Beautiful: Economics as if People Mattered.* He wrote: 'Gandhi abhorred the industrial civilisation because it was based on callous exploitation of non-renewable resources. It made bodily welfare the sole object of life, which reduced man to nothing but a clever animal'. He adds: 'As in agriculture, so in industry and in every other walk of life, we need to give our attention to the developing and perfection of nonviolent methods to find answers to the threefold crises of the modern world – the crisis of resource exhaustion, the ecological crisis and the crisis of man's alienation and disorientation. All this requires work – that is, Gandhian work with a spirit of truth and nonviolence which inspired Gandhi'.

Petra Kelly (1947-92), a founder of the German Green Party, acknowledged: 'In one particular area of our political work we have been greatly inspired by Mahatma Gandhi. That is in our belief that a life style and method of production which rely on an endless supply and a lavish use of raw materials generates the motive for the violent appropriation of these raw materials from other countries. In contrast, a responsible use of raw materials, as part of an ecologically oriented life style and economy, reduces the risk that policies of violence will be pursued in our name'.[12]

Another pioneer of the green movement in Europe was Arne Naess (1912–2009), who is internationally known as the originator of a sub-movement called Deep Ecology. His spiritual vision, which affirms the unity and sacredness of nature, was deeply influenced by Buddha, Spinoza and Mahatma Gandhi. The latter's philosophy and practice of nonviolence strongly endorsed his own concept of the unity of all living beings, and of self-realisation as an approach to truth. 'Nature conservation,' Naess stated, 'is nonviolent at its very core.' He found wellsprings of inspiration for his movement in Gandhi's thoughts on the man-environment relationship – 'I believe in *advaita* (non-duality), I believe in the essential unity of man and, for that matter, of all that lives. Therefore I believe that if one man gains spiritually, the whole world gains with him and, if one man fails, the whole world fails to that extent.'[13]; 'If our sense of right and wrong had not become blunt, we would recognise that animals had rights, no less than men'[14]; 'I do believe that all God's creatures have the right to live as much as we have'.[15]

Bringing these Gandhian insights into the current debate on sustainable development, Naess wrote: 'In a major victory for the global ecology movement, the World Commission for Environment and Development announced clearly that sustainable development unconditionally requires ecological sustainability. The consequences of this admission are far-reaching because ecological sustainability requires significant economic, technological, social, political and cultural changes in most or all countries'. Among other changes, he said: 'The term developed country' must mean 'ecologically developed country'.[16]

Naess made a distinction between his concept of Deep Ecology and what he called the Shallow Ecology movement, which fought against pollution and resource depletion for anthropocentric (human-centric) reasons – namely, that they were wrong because they threatened human health and affluence. The Deep Ecology movement, in contrast, champions 'biocentric egalitarianism' as a guideline for environmental action. 'This distinction between anthropocentric and biocentric environmentalism is at the heart of Deep Ecology'.[17] Thus, Deep Ecology meant understanding that industrialism and the culture of consumerism are the root causes of the earth-threatening ecological crisis. Naess's writings on Gandhi, such as his books *Gandhi and the Nuclear Age* (1965) and *Gandhi and Group Conflict: An Exploration of Satyagraha* (1974), shaped the thinking of both the green and peace movements around the world.

It is a welcome sign that protection of the environment has now come to the centre stage of the political and developmental discourse. National governments and multilateral agencies are forced to evaluate all technology and policy alternatives from the perspective of sustainable development. The debate on sustainable development itself has transcended local and national boundaries to acquire global scale and sweep. The evolution of this debate from the UN-sponsored global summits in Stockholm (1972), Rio de Janeiro (1992) and Copenhagen (2009) clearly shows that concern over the catastrophic impact of economic growth on the environment has been rising with each passing year. There is still greater concern among thinking people around the world that governments, big business groups and influential economic institutions are not doing enough to save the environment, even though the warning bell had been sounded at the Stockholm Summit itself: 'A point has been reached in history when we must shape our actions throughout the world with a more prudent care for their environmental consequences'. The collapse of the Climate Summit in Copenhagen in 2009 is only the latest proof of the alarming gap between the rhetoric and action.

If our world has to meet the rhetoric with right action, it has to pay heed to Gandhi's environmental wisdom. Until now, only non-governmental institutions, activists and some enlightened business organisations have been experimenting with Gandhian environmentalism[18]. The real challenge is to integrate it in the thinking and actions of governments, multilateral agencies and corporates, and also in the lifestyles of the people, especially wealthy people.

In Indian philosophy and culture, respect for, and protection of, ecology stems from a belief that a cosmic principle governs the totality of the happenings in Nature. There is harmony and rhythm in everything that happens in the universe. This rhythm is best expressed by the seasons in Nature, the Sanskrit word for which is *ritu*. I once found the following description of the incredible beauty of the rhythmic changes in nature in an exhibition called 'Rta-Ritu' on the 'Cosmic Order and Cycle of Seasons', organised by the Indira Gandhi National Centre for the Arts (IGNCA) in New Delhi. 'Each gorgeous short-lived butterfly, each symmetrical flight of migrating cranes, each burst of sea-foam at high tide, each flash thunder-storm, each swollen river spilling from hill onto plain, each love-lorn peacock in full finery, each meditating forest reassures us that in spite of death, decay and irreversible change all is part of an inextricable rhythm of the world. We may participate in this pervasive harmony as children partake of the mother's bounty'.[19]

However, after reading this, I thought: 'Should we decide to destroy this harmony by trying to go against Mother Nature, mankind itself will ultimately be destroyed.'

Human birth and death are as much a part of the rhythmic order of Nature as anything else. However, this rhythm and harmony is broken when death is an outcome of violence. Natural death is a part of the nonviolent order of the cosmos, but death due to killing is not. Significantly, there is no deliberate violence in the non-human universe; when killing happens in the animal world, it is only instinctual.

This begets some important questions. Are violence and nonviolence, understood in their broadest sense, also associated with the act that causes human birth – sexual union between man and woman? What is the place of sex in human life? Can sexuality, one of the greatest mysteries ever to have seized the human mind and heart, be reoriented to create a nonviolent world?

Gandhi confronted these questions about human sexuality squarely, and in his own uniquely personal way, as we shall examine in the next chapter.

Brahmacharya as a self-purification *yajna* **(sacrifice):** *Gandhi intensified his brahmacharya in Noakhali (now in Bangladesh), where he went on a two-month-long peace pilgrimage in November 1946 to end communal violence. About his peace mission, Lord Mountbatten, Britain's last viceroy in India, would later say: 'While a 55,000-man boundary force in Punjab was swamped by riots, the One-Man Boundary Force brought peace to Bengal'. India's partition in 1947 resulted in the deaths of nearly 1.5 million people and in the trans-border displacement of 12.5 million people, the largest ever in world history.*

24

EXPERIMENTS IN THE SCIENCE OF BRAHMACHARYA
How Gandhi Sought to Divinise Sexual Energy for Nonviolence

→·≪≫·←

When the disorderly sexual life spreads among a large part of the members of a society, then mental diseases, emotional storms and crises, and paralysis of will begin to mount. Through volitional paralysis, there is a growing inability of the society to control biological and emotional drives; to resist the temptations of flesh and of material wealth and comfort; to curb the lust for power; to discharge painful duties and to make necessary sacrifices; and to chart and to follow its own historical course. From a self-determining and self-controlling collectivity, the society deteriorates into a passive drifter until it is brought to the brink of an historical Niagara.

— Pitirim Alexandrovitch Sorokin (1889–1968) in *Sane Sex Order*. A victim of communist persecution in his native country, Russia, he migrated to USA and founded the Department of Sociology at Harvard University. He viewed Gandhi's brahmacharya experiments sympathetically.

WHY DOES A CHAPTER ON GANDHI'S SEXUALITY – THIS IS, indeed, the longest of all the chapters – find a place in this book? The reasons are compelling. Firstly, the purpose of this book is to explore all those test points in Gandhi's life that contributed to his mission of truth and nonviolence. Brahmacharya – popularly, but wrongly, described by its partial meaning of sexual abstinence – was inseparably interlinked with his pursuit of truth and nonviolence. They formed a trinity in his worldview. Therefore, his mission of truth and nonviolence cannot be adequately understood without reference to his brahmacharya.

Secondly, as we have seen earlier in this book, Gandhi adopted a highly scientific approach in his pursuit of truth and nonviolence – of course, in his own unique understanding of science in which science is compatible with faith, and vice-versa. His approach to sex and other aspects of brahmacharya was similarly a blend of science and faith, both having the common purpose of eliminating human indignities, enhancing human happiness and giving a God-ward reorientation to human life. When brahmacharya is thus understood comprehensively as a spiritual science and scientific spirituality, it has the potential to transform human sexuality itself into a mighty new stream of energy that can heal man's divided self, reduce human suffering, and assist humanity to enter a new stage of its nonviolent evolution. This hypothesis forms the last section of this chapter, in which we discuss the question: 'Is Gandhi's brahmacharya relevant today?' Many readers are bound to disagree with some or all aspects of his views as expressed in this chapter, but it is equally certain that he provokes all of us into thinking about the complex issues involved in human sexuality seriously.

Thirdly, Gandhi's approach to sex is one of the most superficially debated, but least understood, dimensions of his life. Indeed, no aspect of his life is more misrepresented in the lay mind than his thoughts on, and his experiments in, brahmacharya. Even much of the voluminous Gandhian literature published since his demise has somehow only skimmed the surface of this important subject. And this is odd, considering the uncompromising consistency and regularity with which Gandhi articulated his views on brahmacharya right from the time he returned from South Africa till his tragic demise. There have been very few attempts to recognise brahmacharya as he did – that is, as an important discipline for God-realisation for himself and for the realisation of the ideal of nonviolence in the world. One of them is *Mahatma Gandhi: The Last Phase*, an acclaimed book by

Pyarelal, who joined Gandhi as one of his personal secretaries in 1925, and became his chief secretary after the sudden demise of his predecessor, the venerable Mahadev Desai, in 1942. Besides giving the finest narration of the final climactic years of Gandhi's life, it presents the most honest and insightful account of his brahmacharya. I must gratefully acknowledge that, in writing this chapter, I have benefitted considerably from Pyarelal's magnum opus.

Man cannot be fully known without knowing how sex shapes his psychic life. Our sexuality reveals a large part of who we are and what we make of ourselves. What we feel, think, dream, say and do in matters sexual, mirrors the strengths, weaknesses and dark ambiguities of our personalities. 'To thine own self be true' is the first commandment of moral living. Nowhere is our adherence to it tested more severely than in our conscious and subconscious experience of sex. A man-woman relationship is one of the greatest mysteries of human life, on par with birth and death. But what is mysterious often becomes mundane with the passage of time as our capacity to love, trust, care, reflect and wonder, weakens under the weight of habit and the social environment. Not many of us make serious attempts to understand our own sexuality because doing so demands introspection with utmost honesty, transparency and understanding a task we fear and avoid. Rarer still are those who, like Gandhi, not only examine the mystery of sex, but also harness its power to the pursuit of a larger social goal.

'The unexamined life is not worth living,' states Socrates, who, as we have seen in Chapter 3, had deeply influenced Gandhi during his long stay in South Africa. Gandhi examined his own sexuality, and human sexuality in general, with the rigour and single-mindedness of a scientist. What he discovered – rather, rediscovered from the ancient Indian science of brahmacharya – was startling. The power of sex lies not in its limitless indulgence but in its scrupulous self-restraint, sublimation and transmutation, along with self-control of all the other sense-faculties. His experiment-based self-searching had led him to conclude that a seeker must pursue truth, nonviolence and brahmacharya simultaneously – truth as the ultimate and inviolable goal, nonviolence as the path to reach the goal, and brahmacharya as a way of making oneself fit to travel along that path. However, never a blind imitator of knowledge and beliefs inherited from the past, Gandhi introduced several astonishing innovations in his practice of brahmacharya to suit his goal. He did so even at the risk of inviting societal criticism and disapproval by some of his close colleagues.

Many people find one such innovation, Gandhi's concept of 'married brahmacharya', difficult to comprehend. Far more incomprehensible for his admirers and critics alike are his unusual experiments in brahmacharya, which sometimes involved sleeping in a naked state near a naked woman associate. Indeed, the line separating his admirers from his critics frequently becomes blurred when they encounter this particular subject, as can be gauged from the surfeit of negative opinions expressed by both sides on the Internet. Many of his ardent admirers cannot understand, much less endorse, his highly non-conformist brahmacharya practices. They generally tend to respond to any debate on this subject with embarrassed silence, which suggests that even though they regard him as a Mahatma in many other astonishing things he did in his life, they believe that he tripped from the pedestal of mahatmahood in this particular matter. As for his critics, they view his preaching and practice of brahmacharya as perverse, indeed proof of him being a fake Mahatma.

The fact is that Gandhi's sexuality was as unique, audacious and goal-oriented as the man himself. In mankind's modern history, Gandhi is the only political leader who tried to use the power of sex – rather, sexual celibacy within the larger matrix of brahmacharya – to counter large-scale violence and bring about peace, reconciliation and unity in turbulence-hit India. There have been many saints in the past, belonging to different faiths, who successfully practiced celibacy in order to perfect their own saintliness as a precondition for God-realisation. But Gandhi is the only saintly political personality in modern history for whom celibacy was not merely a means to achieve self-realisation, which is a personal goal. Rather, God-realisation through brahmcharya

Gerald Heard, a philosopher who wrote many influential books, believed, like Gandhi, that overcoming of lust and transmutation of sexual energy could mark a new step in human evolution. In a tribute to Gandhi on his seventieth birthday in 1939, Heard wrote: 'To meet such a convergence of two madnesses – the blind submission of free men to the power of murderous machines and then to the dictates of group-folly as blind as and even more destructive than the murder-machines themselves, there was needed a man as ingenious as the inventors of the diabolic instruments of destruction and as dynamic as the demonic leaders who were stampeding their peoples into mutual massacre. There can be little doubt that this man will be recognised by historians as M.K. Gandhi'.

was for him a moral means to achieve, among other things, a larger goal – to prevent India's tragic partition and the inferno of Hindu-Muslim riots that preceded and followed it. His innovative experiments in brahmacharya were never a means of sexual gratification for him. Instead, they were an essential part of his sustained effort, an unceasing *yajna* (sacrifice), for divinisation of sex, so that he could become a more effective 'warrior' of nonviolence. As has been pointed by Gerald Heard (1889–1971), a British philosopher whose book *Pain, Sex and Time: A New Outlook on Evolution and the Future of Man* remains one of the most influential works on human sexuality: 'The world-wide and age-long interest of Mr Gandhi's experiment lies in the fact that he has attempted to make the method work on what may be called the wholesale or national scale'.[1]

Sex and Nonviolence: A Marriage
Made in Heaven, Tested on Earth

We begin our exploration of Gandhi's brahmacharya by asking a basic question: Is there a correlation between sex and nonviolence? How can there not be? The primary function of sex in human life is procreation. Insofar as giving birth to new life is the most nonviolent act imaginable – killing, its antithesis, being the most extreme act of violence – sex in its procreative function is quintessentially a messenger of nonviolence. Indeed, it is also a messenger of divinity. Anything that can create new life must be regarded as having a miraculous power and worthy of highest reverence.

The plethora of fertility rites in all the cultures in the world since ancient times show that sex was never a casual affair as, unfortunately, it has tended to become in the culture of consumerism prevailing in modern times. It is thanks to the reproductive power of sex that, although individual man dies, mankind lives with relative immortality from generation to generation. The power of sex is comparable, in an illustrative though not in a real sense, to God's own limitless creative power, which has created the universe and all the countless self-reproducing living beings in it. Thus, there is something divine in the primary reproductive function of sex.

Sex is a messenger of nonviolence in another self-evident and profoundly significant sense. Nonviolence is integral to not only human birth but also to every subsequent stage of human life. This is because whatever creates life must also sustain life. Sustenance of new life requires unselfish love, affection, care, kindness, nurturing, dedicated labour to secure the material means of nurturing, and parental protection even at the cost of suffering, self-denial and sacrifice of one kind or the other on the part of mother and father. All these are multiple forms of nonviolence. These are the uplifting emotions and actions through which nonviolence works.

Just as sex is a derivative of the creative attribute of God, all forms of nonviolence are also human derivates of the life-sustaining attributes of God. After all, He is the source of infinite love, compassion, mercy, care, nurturing, protection and harmony. The universe cannot survive even for a second without God's boundless love and care. Man has been ordained by Nature to internalise these qualities into his life for his own survival and growth. It is for this reason that, as Gandhi says, of all His infinite creations 'Man alone is made in the image of God'.[2] Gandhi also says: 'When you want to find Truth as God, the only inevitable means is love, that is, nonviolence.'[3] This establishes that sex, whose power approximates God's own creative power, albeit on a decidedly limited scale and on a different plane, cannot at all be dissociated from pure love, which is the highest and most active form of nonviolence. Loveless sex, or sex with lust only, is an act of violence. It neither humanises nor, much less, divinises man. It signifies man's fall from his own higher evolutionary possibilities.

If sex is nonviolent and divine in its essence, how does one account for the fact that so much of humans' sexual activity undeniably takes place without the involvement of pure love, and, worse still, with the accompaniment of various degrees of violence – lack of mutual trust, respect, responsibility, care and commitment, insensitivity towards one another's emotions and needs, dishonesty and deceit, selfishness, possessive power play and, not infrequently, physical aggression? The answer lies in our inability, especially the inability of the male members of the species, to understand the true nature, power and place of sex in God's design for human life. The marriage between sex and nonviolence has taken place in heaven, blessed by God Himself. However, on earth, sex has a propensity, when driven by lust, to routinely ditch its soul-partner, nonviolence, and have dalliance with violence in its various subtle and not-so-subtle forms. This duality had a major bearing on Gandhi's attitude toward sex.

There is further evidence of the existence of an unbreakable bond between sex and nonviolence. It can be seen in another great attribute of God – namely, beauty – which is inseparably associated with human sexuality. Beauty is the most abstract, most incomprehensible and yet most intensely experienceable among all the attributes of divinity. Both the journey towards, and the actual act of, sexual union is an intense experience of beauty in all its visible and felt manifestations. Beauty is, essentially and entirely, nonviolent in nature. There cannot even be an iota of the aesthetic in any violent feeling, speech or action. Indeed, beauty registers its strongest protest by withdrawing itself completely wherever there is untruth.

Thus, falsehood, violence, aggression and hatred are the bitter foes of beauty, just as truth and nonviolence are the bywords for beauty. This is the basis of the Hindu understanding of God as the divinity enfolded in the trinity of *Satyam, Shivam, Sundaram* – Truth, Goodness and Beauty. The concept of this trinity is universal in nature. It appears prominently in scriptures, philosophies and works of great artists around the world. St. Augustine, in repentance for the wayward ways in his youth, tells God in his autobiographical classic *Confessions*: 'Late have I loved you, beauty so old and so new'. There is Plato's declaration: 'Beauty is the splendor of Truth' (*Veritatis Splendor*). John Keats, the romantic bard whose poetry is suffused with sensual imagery, says: 'Beauty is Truth, Truth Beauty – that is all/Ye know on earth, and all ye need to know'. Leo Tolstoy, Gandhi's teacher in nonviolence, wrote in a letter to Romain Rolland: 'All that tends to unify mankind belongs to the Good and the Beautiful. All that tends to disunite it is evil and ugly'.

In India, *Soundarya Lahari* ('Waves of Beauty') is sage Adi Shankara's great poetic work on the philosophy of mantra, yantra and kundalini. Its very first verse is an ode to the power of divine sex. It asserts: 'Only when Shiva is united with Shakti does he have the power to create. Without her, even an inch he cannot move. And so how can one who does not do good deeds, Or one who does not sing your praise, Become adequate to worship you, Oh, Goddess mine?'

Gandhian Overtones in Dostoyevsky's Maxim 'Beauty Will Save the World'

Precisely because it is an attribute and manifestation of the Divine, true beauty heals. True beauty vitalises and revitalises. It affirms the self-renewing resolve of life. 'Beauty will save the world,' Russian novelist Fyodor Dostoyevsky famously wrote in his novel *The Idiot*. Nobody has ever crafted a more authentic, more arresting, and also a more enigmatic,[4] tribute to the nonviolent character of beauty. It is not easy to comprehend what the great writer, an empathetic illuminator of the darkest corners of man's psychic, and sexual, life, meant by saying 'Beauty will save the world'. However, we are helped here by the understanding that Gandhi provides. Replace 'beauty' with 'nonviolence' in the Dostoyevskian maxim, and we get the most perfectly authentic Gandhian aphorism: 'Nonviolence will save the world'.

In his Nobel lecture, Alexander Solzhenitsyn, the dissident writer from the erstwhile Soviet Union who won the Nobel Prize in Literature in 1970, brings a profound insight into Dostoyevsky's tribute to the nonviolent character of beauty. In the process, he also sheds useful light on the trinity of *satyam, shivam, sundaram*:

> One day Dostoyevsky wrote the enigmatic remark: 'Beauty will save the world'. What sort of a statement is that? For a long time I considered it mere words. How could that be possible? When in bloodthirsty history did beauty ever save anyone from anything? Ennobled, uplifted, yes – but whom has it saved?
>
> There is, however, a certain peculiarity in the essence of beauty, a peculiarity in the status of art: namely, the convincingness of a true work of art is completely irrefutable and it forces even an opposing heart to surrender. It is possible to compose an outwardly smooth and elegant political speech, a headstrong article, a social program, or a philosophical system on the basis of both a mistake and a lie. What is hidden, what is distorted, will not immediately become obvious.
>
> Then a contradictory speech, article, program, a differently constructed philosophy rallies in opposition – and all just as elegant and smooth, and once again it works. Which is why such things are both trusted and mistrusted.
>
> But a work of art bears within itself its own verification: conceptions which are devised or stretched do not stand being portrayed in images, they all come crashing down, appear sickly and pale, convince no one. But those works of art which have scooped up the truth and presented it to us as a living

force – they take hold of us, compel us, and nobody ever, not even in ages to come, will appear to refute them.

So perhaps that ancient trinity of Truth, Goodness and Beauty is not simply an empty, faded formula as we thought in the days of our self-confident, materialistic youth? If the tops of these three trees converge, as the scholars maintained, but the too blatant, too direct stems of Truth and Goodness are crushed, cut down, not allowed through – then perhaps the fantastic, unpredictable, unexpected stem of Beauty will push through and soar TO THAT VERY SAME PLACE, and in so doing will fulfill the work of all three?

In that case Dostoyevsky's remark, 'Beauty will save the world,' was not a careless phrase but a prophecy? After all HE was granted to see much, a man of fantastic illumination.

And in that case art, literature might really be able to help the world today?

Solzhenitsyn's Nobel lecture was given only to the Swedish Academy and not actually delivered as a lecture, since he was not allowed by the Soviet Union's communist authorities to receive the Nobel Prize.

At the risk of digressing into literary criticism, I wish to show here how Dostoyevsky's popular tribute to beauty resonates with the Gandhian understanding of nonviolence.

The protagonist of *The Idiot* is Prince Myshkin, truly an 'idiot' in the sense that this young, pure-hearted but epileptic man with Christ-like spiritual attributes is a total misfit in the nineteenth century aristocratic Russian society corroded by greed, dishonesty and moral corruption. The novel is a tale of his inner torment arising out of the conflict between his natural goodness – he believes that love and compassion can transform our world into a heaven of harmony – and a society given to soul-destroying ways of sexual conquest, vain display of power and wealth, and superficial intellectualism. He is in love with

Nastasya Filippovna, but his attraction, devoid of sexual desire, for this beautiful but emotionally scarred woman is more out of compassion for her condition of unmitigated suffering. She is held in contempt by society because, as a young girl, she had been sexually exploited by her wealthy guardian. Myshkin, who has returned to Russia after spending several years in a Swiss sanatorium meant for curing insane people, first sees her face as the subject of a portrait.

'So you admire this kind of beauty, do you?' his hostess in St. Petersburg, who considers Nastasya a fallen woman, asks Myshkin.

'Yes, I do – this kind.'

'Do you mean especially this kind?'

'Yes, *especially this kind.*'

'Why?'

'There is much suffering in this face,' murmured the prince, more as though talking to himself than answering the question.

Myshkin believed that supreme beauty, an attribute of godliness, lies in one's ability to experience, and have empathy for, others' suffering. This echoes Gandhi's own conception of beauty. 'To a true artist', he writes, 'only that face is beautiful which, quite apart from its exterior, shines with the truth within the soul'.[5] One of Gandhi's many descriptions of God is that He is 'long-suffering' because of the injustice and violence perpetrated by man on man. In other words, beauty lies not so much in the eye of the beholder, but in the soul of the beholder. Beauty experienced by the senses has finite existence and appeal. But beauty that touches the spirit and is internalised by it has great transformational power. As one of the characters in Dostoyevsky's novel remarks: 'With such beauty as that one might overthrow the world'.

There is a persuasive explanation of how this happens in the essay 'Will Beauty Save the World?' by Michael D. O'Brien, a Canadian writer of strong Christian beliefs. He notes that the oft-quoted maxim, 'Beauty will save the world', is widely misunderstood and misused in our times. 'As Dostoyevsky demonstrates throughout the novel, beauty alone cannot save the world. However, one of his primary insights is that beauty and suffering can seize the human heart of the observer for reasons other than carnality or even romanticised and idealised attraction, though these may be present at the early stages of a relationship. As the lover grows in love of the beloved, he must continuously seek the ultimate good of the beloved. If his "love" is to avoid degenerating into selfishness, it must steadily become more and more Christ-like'.

O'Brien further explains: 'Toward the end of the story Myshkin's Christ-like love for Nastasya is put to a supreme test. He is asked to show mercy, to be a presence of Christ, to the very person who kills his beloved. This mercy, made possible only by the power of indwelling divine Mercy, is the beauty that will save the world'.[6]

There is something profoundly Gandhian in Dostoyevsky's portrayal of suffering Nastasya's beauty, Prince Myshkin's selfless and non-carnal love for her, and in his final act of showing mercy to the person who stabs her to death.

Gandhi's 'Celibate Sexuality'

There is no further need to belabour the point that sex and nonviolence are correlated by an umbilical cord of heavenly make. This, however, leads us to an important conclusion. If sex and nonviolence have a correlation, and if Gandhi was a votary of nonviolence, it follows that he could not really have been ill-disposed towards sex. Strangely, both popular and much of scholarly opinion holds that he had strongly negative views about sex. This is just not true. He made a sharp distinction between two types of sexuality. One degrades women, enslaves man to lustful desires, makes him commit subtle or gross acts of violence, disables him in his effort to do good to society and also blocks his path to spiritual growth. The other sublimates and spiritualises desire for sex, promotes nonviolence, empowers man to achieve both self-growth and render extraordinary service to society, and, most importantly, holds women in the highest esteem. Gandhi was a practitioner of sexuality of the latter kind. His relation with women in general, and with his close female associates in particular, were marked by utmost naturalness, emotional richness and even physical intimacy – but without a trace of carnality. In a truly original insight into this aspect of his brahmacharya, Prof.

Vinay Lal of the University of California, Los Angeles, has described it as Gandhi's 'Celibate Sexuality'.[7]

These two contrary aspects of sex, one as a source of spiritual light and the other as the road to psychic darkness, have been well recognised by the Hindu philosophy. On the one hand, *kaama* (satisfaction of sensual needs) is recognised as one of the four *purusharthas* or desirable goals of human life. The other three are *dharma* (the path of righteousness), *artha* (satisfaction of material needs), and *moksha* (liberation through renunciation). However, *kaama* is also regarded as the first among *shadripus* (six enemies) that human beings should overcome through self-restraint. These are: *kaama* (when satisfaction of sensual needs becomes lust); *krodha* (anger); *lobha* (greed); *mada* (pride); *moha* (attachment) and *matsara* (covetousness).

About these internal foes of man, Gandhi observes: 'It is easier to conquer the entire world than to subdue the enemies in our body. And, therefore, for the man who succeeds in this conquest, the former will be easy enough. The self-government [swaraj] which you, I and others have to attain is in fact this'.[8] We see here how Gandhi, unlike other leaders of India's freedom struggle or of the national liberation struggles of other countries, puts forth a completely radical concept of swaraj, one in which not only the nation has to be free from external yoke but every citizen also has to endeavour to be free from his own internal enemies.

I must admit here that Gandhi's views on sex are problematic in one specific respect. On the one hand, he affirms: 'Sex urge is a fine and noble thing. There is nothing to be ashamed of in it.' However, he says this with a crucial caveat: 'But it [sex urge] is meant only for the act of procreation. Any other use of it is a sin against God and humanity.'[9] Gandhi's insistence that sexual desire and intercourse are good only when they are meant for procreation has subjected him to a lot of criticism. Some of this criticism is indeed justified, as I shall discuss later. However, many scholars have wrongly surmised from this that he viewed sex to be inherently violent. Suffice it to say that Gandhi was a proponent and practitioner of alternative sexuality of a highly unconventional kind.

Gandhi has been severely criticised by many people, including his admirers, for stating that he 'cannot imagine a thing as ugly as the intercourse of man and woman'. Based on this one sentence, some critics have jumped to the conclusion that he viewed sex itself as a source of violence. The sentence appears in a letter that he wrote in 1922 to his South Africa-based second son Manilal, who had had illicit sex with a female ashramite a decade earlier. This incident had agonised Gandhi so much that he even contemplated committing suicide. As penance he undertook a fast for seven days and thereafter ate only one meal a day for four-and-a-half months. This was the first instance of his using fast as a way of self-purification and influencing the conduct of others. Manilal, as a mark of repentance, took a vow of celibacy till he was released from the vow by his father. The letter that Gandhi wrote, from Sabarmati Jail, was in response to Manilal's keen desire to obtain his father's permission to marry. Gandhi advised his son to follow the dictate of his conscience, adding, however, that 'there is no happiness in marriage'.

Although it is impossible to agree with Gandhi's characterisation of coitus as ugly, it would be wrong to conclude that this was his final opinion about sex. On a few rare occasions in his life, Gandhi is known to have made sweeping and misleading statements on subjects that he felt strongly about. His castigation of railways in *Hind Swaraj*, which he later revised, belongs to this category. In this particular case, he later changed his view about sex being 'ugly', as can be attested by his 1936 affirmation: 'Sex urge is a fine and noble thing. There is nothing to be ashamed of in it.' Most thinkers and social reformers have exhibited such intellectual inconsistency. In Gandhi's case, as mentioned elsewhere in this book *(see p. 93)*, all his writings published by Navajivan Publishing House, which he founded, carry the standard prefatory statement to his readers: '[w]hen anybody finds any inconsistency between any two writings of mine, if he has still faith in my sanity, he would do well to choose the later of the two on the same subject'.

To use the term 'alternative sexuality' in the Mahatma's case might sound heretical to many people, most of all to devout Gandhians.

Conventionally, alternative sexuality refers to homosexuality or bisexuality. Indeed, some ignorant and sensationalist sections of the media have portrayed Gandhi as gay or bisexual in the wake of the publication of Joseph Lelyveld's *Great Soul: Mahatma Gandhi and his Struggle with India.*[10] Lelyveld's own superbly written study (2011) says no such thing. But there is further evidence to show that such a portrayal of Gandhi is baseless. His relations with his close associates, male or female, had the highest levels of emotional intensity and spiritual bonding. Precisely for this reason, these relations are susceptible to being easily misunderstood. For example, when Maganlal Gandhi, his chief comrade-in-arms from his South African days and the 'soul' of the Sabarmati Ashram, suddenly died in 1928, a grief-stricken Gandhi remarked: 'I have been widowed'. This does not mean that the two had a homosexual relationship.

Gandhi's Goal-Oriented Celibacy

Celibacy has a long and lofty tradition in almost all religions of the world. Many prophets and saints were either lifelong celibates or embraced celibacy at some decisive point in their lives. The popular mind generally sees saintliness and spiritual pursuit to be incompatible with indulgence of sexual passion. Gandhi believed likewise. But he went a step further. He concluded that satisfaction of sexual passion was incompatible not only with his own spiritual seeking but also with his socio-political mission and the principles that underpinned it. In 1906 – significantly, in the same year that he launched the satyagraha movement – he took a lifelong vow to 'sacrifice' sexual relations with his wife or any other woman. He kept his vow.

There is a memorable scene in Richard Attenborough's film *Gandhi*, in which Margaret Bourke-White, an American photo-journalist working for *LIFE* magazine, is interviewing Kasturba about the Mahatma's celibacy. The scene is shot in Aga Khan Palace in Poona, where Gandhi, along with Kasturba, Mahadev Desai, Mirabehn and other associates was imprisoned by the British after he launched the Quit India Movement in Bombay on 9 August 1942. The reporter, full of curiosity and amazement, asks Kasturba about her husband's vow of celibacy that he had taken decades earlier.

Bourke-White: You mean he...he...gave up... married life?

Kasturba (with a smile): Four times he tried – and failed. But then he took a solemn vow...

Bourke-White: And he has never broken it?

Kasturba (with a twinkle in her eye): Not yet.

Bourke-White looks at Kasturba incredulously and they both (along with Mirabehn, who is present during the interview) burst into laughter.

The distinctiveness of Gandhi's sexuality appears in several other ways, too. No other personality of global stature comes anywhere close to him in terms of the unimaginable levels of transparency and honesty that he brought to bear on discussing his sexual life publicly or in altogether erasing the dividing line between the private and public domains of his life. He was completely untainted by hypocrisy in sexual matters. He subjected his private feelings and actions to the same rigorous test of truthfulness and public scrutiny as he did any other subject of national or international importance. Having chosen to become a servant of God and humanity, Gandhi ceased to belong to his family. Indeed, many sympathetic Gandhian scholars fault him for having neglected his fatherly duties towards his four sons, especially his eldest son Harilal, whose life was an unending series of tragedies.

With the dissolution of his personal self and its total dedication to the promotion of public good, Gandhi came to regard secrecy in any matter as a sin. Indeed, all his political negotiations with the British were conducted in the public sphere. He conducted the most unorthodox experiments in sexual celibacy, which were an integral part of his experiments with truth, also in the public sphere. He shared his successes and failures candidly in letters written to his colleagues, including close women associates such as Mirabehn, Sushila Nayyar, Rajkumari Amrit Kaur, Premaben Kantak and Prabhavati (wife of the great socialist leader Jayaprakash Narayan). Moreover, he shared them also with the readers of his journals. At times, public knowledge of these experiments threatened to 'damage' his national and global reputation.

However, since he was indifferent to considerations of gain or loss of personal reputation in any of his activities, he continued undeterred by criticism and controversy to perfect his own brahmacharya till the end of his life.

There is a remarkable passage on Gandhi's transparent lifestyle in the chapter on Brahmacharya in Pyarelal's *Mahatma Gandhi: The Last Phase*.

> There were no 'walls' in his Ashram, either at Sevagram or at Sabarmati. He had no 'private life'. His most intimate functions were performed not in privacy. Thus, he had his massage (an important component of nature cure) practically naked, with young girls very often as masseurs. He often received visitors and even members of the (Congress) Working Committee while stretched on the massage table. Similarly, while having hydropathic treatment, he allowed both men and women to assist him and any and almost everybody had free access to him in his bath. In his celebrated letter to Churchill, while appropriating as a compliment the disparaging epithet of the 'half-naked fakir', which the Tory leader had applied to him, he went on to say that it was his ambition to become completely naked – literally as well as metaphorically – *the latter being of course more difficult.*[11] *(Emphasis added)*

Ever since he embarked on the path of satyagraha, his means of self-purification were four-fold: complete and uncompromising practice of austerities, which involved extreme levels of simplicity; selfless and ceaseless service of humanity; regular prayers, fasts, observance of silence for one day in a week, and mandatory daily spinning of the wheel; and, lastly, strictest practice of celibacy. This last discipline meant not only abstinence from any kind of sexual act, but also elimination of the last trace of sexual desire from his mind and heart. In other words, his aim was to become sexless – 'spiritual eunuch' is the term he uses to describe that state.

Brahmacharya for him meant total purity of the body, mind, heart and soul, and was an inseparable part of his larger endeavour to achieve the goal of God-realisation. But, unlike a yogi in a Himalayan cave, absolute brahmacharya was not something he wanted for his own personal spiritual elevation. Rather, he endeavoured to gain the enormous powers of a true brahmachari so that by becoming a perfect slave and instrument of God, he could use those God-given powers to stop India's descent into the dark abyss of barbarism just when it was approaching the light of long-awaited freedom. Nobody in modern human history has ever dared to do something as extraordinarily ambitious as this.

An Impending Tragedy in the Life of India and Gandhi

To know why Gandhi aligned his brahmacharya to a larger, seemingly impossible-to-achieve, goal, it is necessary to take a brief look at India in the last and most agonising years of his life. Just as India was hurtling towards a tragedy waiting to happen, so was Gandhi's own heroic life. Nobody was more aware of this than the Mahatma himself. The mission that he had undertaken had made him a targeted man for the forces of religious extremism. But he was not afraid of facing death at the hands of an assassin, having chosen the credo of fearlessness during the difficult years of his internship in South Africa. Indeed, in the final months of his life, he had on several occasions shown clairvoyance about how he was going to embrace death with the name of God on his lips. He had lived his life in a self-willed and self-directed way, something that ordinary human beings are incapable of since our lives are pulled and pushed in different directions by the currents of chance and circumstance. Remarkably, his death was also self-willed and self-directed, a voluntary act of sacrifice, a longed-for reunion with his Creator whom he was faithfully serving through his mission. 'Death is at any time blessed', he had once written, 'but it is twice blessed for a warrior who dies for his cause, that is, Truth'.[12]

Gandhi conducted his bravest brahmacharya experiments in the decade of the 1940s, which unfolded with portentous developments both in India and the world. Another World War, more horrific than the previous one in which Gandhi had volunteered to assist the British, had broken out in 1939. Aided by the advancements in science and technology, it had unleashed violence on a scale never before witnessed in human history. Its culmination with America dropping two atom bombs on Hiroshima and Nagasaki in Japan had singed the conscience of humanity. The war had also raised the spectre of worse catastrophes to come in the future if progress in the technology of armaments manufacturing continued in tandem with moral bankruptcy in the economic and political systems dominating the world.

But these were developments over which neither Indian people nor Gandhi had any control. The same, however, could not be said about the happenings in India. He was determined to guide the destiny of his motherland, driven as he was by the wish to see a nonviolently liberated India become a beacon of light and hope to a world that was descending into the depths of destruction and darkness.

Dark and ominous clouds could indeed be seen in the Indian sky at the dawn of the decade of 1940s. India's freedom movement suffered a mortal blow when the Muslim League adopted a resolution in Lahore in March 1940 demanding India's partition and creation of a separate Muslim state called Pakistan. Gandhi was deeply saddened by this demand. After all, he had devoted his entire public life to the cause of preserving and strengthening Hindu-Muslim unity, to which he indeed assigned a higher priority than to securing immediate political freedom for India.

The Muslim League's demand filled Gandhi's mind with gloomy forebodings about what might happen if India was actually divided on communal lines. He feared communal bloodshed and strife on a humungous scale. His worst fears began coming true, as events in the succeeding years unfolded. His dream of a united India, free from the colonial yoke and offering a bright and secure future to all its Hindus, Muslims and people of other faiths, without any distinction or discrimination, was going to be shattered. At his prayer meeting on 20 July 1947, he explained why he was not going to 'rejoice' on 15 August. 'I do not want to deceive you,' he said. 'Unfortunately, the kind of freedom we have got today contains also the seeds of future conflict between India and Pakistan'.

Prescient words, indeed!

The situation created by the Muslim League's obdurate and violently pursued demand required him to spare no efforts to prevent the looming calamity. His response was two-pronged. On the one hand, he convinced the Congress party to launch a decisive final battle to end the British Raj in India. He believed that once the British left India, Hindus and Muslims, who had lived together on the same land for over a millennium, could sort out among themselves the many issues involved in democratically governing a free nation in a spirit of mutual concern and accommodation. He was also convinced that this was not possible so long as the British colonial rule, which had its own self-serving agenda, continued. Therefore, the Congress party's historic session in Bombay on 8-9 August 1942, meeting under his leadership, gave the clarion call of Quit India. He appealed to the people of India to make it a nonviolent movement by following the mantra of Do or Die. In what came to be regarded as one of the greatest speeches in world history, Gandhi said:

> There are people who ask me whether I am the same man that I was in 1920, or whether there has been any change in me. You are right in asking that question. Let me, however, hasten to assure that I am the same Gandhi as I was in 1920. I have not changed in any fundamental respect. I attach the same importance to nonviolence that I did then. If at all, my emphasis on it has grown stronger.
>
> Occasions like the present do not occur in everybody's and but rarely in anybody's life. I want you to know and feel that there is nothing but purest Ahimsa in all that I am saying and doing today...If there is any among you who has lost faith in Ahimsa or is wearied of it, let him not vote for this resolution. Let me explain my position clearly. God has vouchsafed to me a priceless gift in the weapon of Ahimsa. I and my Ahimsa are on our trial today. If in the present crisis, when the earth is being scorched by the flames of Himsa and crying for deliverance, I failed to make use of the God given talent, God will not forgive me and I shall be judged unworthy of the great gift. I must act now.

I know how imperfect our Ahimsa is and how far away we are still from the ideal, but in Ahimsa there is no final failure or defeat. I have faith, therefore, that if, in spite of our shortcomings, the big thing does happen, it will be because God wanted to help us by crowning with success our silent, unremitting Sadhana for the last twenty-two years.

Gandhi went on to say that the world had never witnessed a 'more genuinely democratic struggle for freedom than ours'. He had read Thomas Carlyle's *French Revolution* while he was in prison. It was a violent revolution. So was the Bolshevik revolution in Russia in 1917. The stated goals of these revolutions were indeed lofty. However, inasmuch as these struggles were fought with the weapon of violence, they failed to realise the democratic ideal. In the democracy which Gandhi had envisaged, 'a democracy established by nonviolence', there would be equal freedom for all. 'Everybody will be his own master. It is to join a struggle for such democracy that I invite you today. Once you realise this you will forget the differences between the Hindus and Muslims, and think of yourselves as Indians only, engaged in the common struggle for independence'.

He then spoke candidly about what the Indian people's attitude towards the British should be.

I have noticed that there is hatred towards the British among the people. The people say they are disgusted with their behaviour. The people make no distinction between British imperialism and the British people. To them, the two are one... We must get rid of this feeling. Our quarrel is not with the British people, we fight their imperialism...We must, therefore, purge ourselves of hatred. Speaking for myself, I can say that I have never felt any hatred. As a matter of fact, I feel myself to be a greater friend of the British now than ever before. One reason is that they are today in distress. My very friendship, therefore, demands that I should try to save them from their mistakes. As I view the situation, they are on the brink of an abyss. It, therefore, becomes my duty to warn them of their danger even though it may, for the time being, anger them to the point of cutting off the friendly hand that is stretched out to help them. People may laugh. Nevertheless, that is my claim. At a time when I may have to launch the biggest struggle of my life, I may not harbour hatred against anybody.

Gandhi's profession of non-hatred towards India's colonial rulers, even when he was about to launch the biggest ever mass-struggle against them, was a direct result of his adherence to truth, nonviolence and brahmacharya.

If a nonviolent mass movement to force the British to quit India was the one prong of his mission in the 1940s, the other was his earnest appeal to the Muslim League, especially its leader Mohammad Ali Jinnah, to give up the demand for India's partition. His eighteen-day-long patient dialogue with Jinnah on this issue, which was held at his initiative at the latter's palatial mansion, Jinnah House, in Malabar Hill, the richest part of Bombay, makes for mandatory reading for all those who want to seriously study, and act upon, Hindu-Muslim and India-Pakistan rapprochement in our times. It shows the stark contrast between the two men.

Both Gandhi and Jinnah hailed from the same Kathiawad part of Gujarat. In their formative years in public life, both were influenced by the same Congress leader, Gopal Krishna Gokhale (1866–1915). Both went on to create history. But they created history in diametrically opposite ways. This is because, Gandhi, though not a Muslim, was more knowledgeable about, and more deeply devoted to, the core teachings of Islam than Jinnah. Jinnah was a Muslim, but he had neither studied Islam nor practiced it. After having fervently championed the cause of united India as a Congressman until the end of the 1920s – Gokhale once hailed him as the 'ambassador of Hindu-Muslim unity' – he cynically used the card of Muslim separatism to pursue his own personal, and the Muslim clerical-trading elite's, ambitions for power.

Therefore, predictably, Jinnah and his Muslim League spurned Gandhi's appeal for keeping India's unity intact with undisguised contempt. Indeed, they took a menacingly aggressive step forward by giving a call for Direct Action Day on 16 August 1946 in order to secure their demand for the creation of Pakistan on the basis of the spurious Two-Nation theory. It was a thinly veiled instigation for communal violence. In Calcutta, it set off what came to be known as the 'Week of Long Knives'. More than 6,000 people, mostly innocent Hindus, were killed and over 1,00,000 people were displaced from their homes.

In Noakhali district in East Bengal (now in Bangladesh), Muslim hooligans did likewise with a view to driving away the minority Hindu population. From early October 1946, the media started carrying reports of mass murder, rape, forcible conversions, attacks on temples and burning down of villages. In November, Gandhi journeyed to Noakhali, an almost entirely rural district steeped in Bengal's centuries-old tradition of Hindu-Muslim amity, on what turned out to be a historic peacemaking mission. For two months, he, now seventy-seven years old, walked mostly barefoot from village to village, armed with nothing but his walking stick, a set of holy books, and his favourite Bengali song, *Ekla Chalo Re* (Walk Alone), composed by Rabindranath Tagore:

Jodi Tor Dak Shune Keu Na Ashe
Tobe Ekla Chalo re
Ekla Chalo Ekla Chalo Ekla Chalo re
Jodi Keu Katha Na Kai Ore Ore O Abhaga
Jodi Sabai Thake Mukh Firae Sabai Kare Bhay
Tabe Paran Khule
O Tui Mukh Phute Tor Maner Katha Ekla Bolo re
Jodi Sabai Phire Jai Ore Ore O Abhaga
Jodi Gahan Pathe Jabar Kale Keu Feere Na Chay
Tobe Pather Kanta
O Tui Rakta Makha Charan Tale Ekla Dalo re
Jodi Alo Na Dhare Ore Ore O Abhaga
Jodi Jharr Badale Andhar Rate Duar Deay Ghare
Tobe Bajranale
Apaan Buker Panjar Jaliye Nieye Ekla Jalo re

If they answer not to thy call, walk alone,
If they are afraid and cower mutely facing the wall,
O thou of ill luck,
open thy mind and speak out alone.

If they turn away, and desert you when crossing the wilderness,
O thou of ill luck,
trample the thorns under thy tread,
and along the blood-lined track travel alone.
If they do not hold up the light when the night is troubled with
storm,
O thou of ill luck,
with the thunder flame of pain ignite thy own heart
and let it burn alone.

Gandhi suffered immense physical hardships during the trek – his feet frequently bled walking through thick foliage and post-harvest paddy fields. He also encountered a hostile response in many places. 'Accept Pakistan or go back', Muslim League supporters shouted at him. Lumps of human faeces were thrown on the paths he walked, which he sometimes removed himself, saying to his colleagues: 'You don't know the joy it gives me'. He conducted inter-faith prayers in every village. His post-prayer discourses touched upon his many pet themes – eradication of the sin of untouchability, village sanitation, nature cure, mutual help, empowerment of women and, above all, communal peace and harmony. He made Muslims and Hindus alike take a pledge not to kill or in any way harm each other.

At one such meeting, an angry Muslim villager pounced on him and caught his throat. Gandhi almost collapsed, but while falling down he recited a message of peace from the *Quran*. Verses from the *Quran* were a part of his daily prayer meetings that were held wherever he went. Hearing the Quranic words, the Muslim, instead of throttling Gandhi, touched his feet and asked to be pardoned. Gandhi had 'stabbed' his attacker with the weapon of love.[13] He called his journey in Noakhali's villages a 'pilgrimage'. He had gone there in search of God, whom he sought to find by serving the most sacred (from his point of view), and also most pressing (from India's point of view), cause of Hindu-Muslim unity.

His appeal for restoration of peace and amity was not limited to the people of Noakhali, but to Hindus and Muslims all over the then undivided India. Hindus were a minority in Noakhali and the rest of East Bengal, which later became East Pakistan. They were also a minority in West Punjab, Sindh, Baluchistan and the North-Western Frontier Province – all of which areas were to become parts of West Pakistan. Muslims were a minority in most of the rest of India, except in Kashmir Valley. He urged Hindus and Muslims to remember that they were both children of the same God. Neither Hinduism nor Islam sanctioned bestiality by brother upon brother; irrespective of whether one community was bigger than the other in any part of India, it had a duty towards God to protect the other.

After Noakhali, he decided to go on a similar peacemaking mission to Bihar, where extremist Hindus had unleashed a reign of terror on innocent Muslims. We have an eye-witness account of what he did and achieved in Bihar from Manu Gandhi, his young grandniece who, as his personal attendant, was his constant companion from Noakhali days till the moment of his assassination in Delhi on the evening of 30 January 1948. (She also participated in his brahmacharya experiments in Noakhali, about which a little later.) She wrote this in her diary, later published under the title *The End of an Epoch*[14]:

> But as soon as order was restored in Noakhali, Bihar went mad. Stories of communal atrocities there sorely wounded Bapuji's heart. He was a devout Hindu and could not stand any atrocities being done in the name of Hinduism. Therefore, in March 1946, Bapuji rushed to Bihar. The situation there was as bad as it had been in Noakhali. Under a scorching sun, we toured the villages of Bihar. There was trouble everywhere, and this meant more work for Bapuji. On some days he worked for eighteen hours. Any ordinary man's health would have given way. But the amazing control that Bapuji exercised over himself and the remarkable manner in which he overcame various ills, gave him superhuman strength to go through the rigours of the journey. Very often I would shave his beard with a safety razor and he would pop off to sleep and sleep very soundly for ten minutes after which he would suddenly wake up, as fresh as ever. Wonderful, indeed!

The work in Bihar was extremely difficult as we had to face much hostility. But Bapuji of course treated everyone with kindness and affection. Several guilty persons came and confessed their sins to Bapu. Some Hindus opened a Muslim Relief Fund as a token of their freshly awakened sympathy for the aggrieved Musalmans.

Gandhi's courageous exertions in Noakhali and Bihar, and the significant success that they achieved, were hailed by peace-loving Hindus and Muslims all over India. It was just the kind of balm from a saintly personality that India's deeply wounded psyche had been waiting for.

Gandhi's 'Mahatma' touch produced another major success in Calcutta in August-September 1947. The city, which was the scene of grisly mass killings a year earlier, had relapsed into communal mayhem. Therefore, instead of participating in the Independence Day festivities in New Delhi on 15 August, Gandhi was once again out on his holy pilgrimage, this time travelling, at grave risk to his own life, through the riot-hit lanes and bylanes of Calcutta. He appealed to the conscience of the warring sections of Hindus and Muslims to end bloodshed. His action had a spectacular effect. We have this authentic account of it in Manu Gandhi's diary:

It was in such an atmosphere that, on the 15th of August, India heralded her Independence. The chains of slavery that had bound India for centuries were at last broken, and the golden dawn of freedom appeared on the Indian horizon. The entire population of Calcutta that day, went mad in jubilation. The people flocked into our house to have darshan of Bapu. It was the month of Ramzan, a period of festivity and fasting for the Musalmans. So on the 15th of August, many Musalmans had decided first to catch a glimpse of Bapuji and then alone break their day's fast.

On the night of the 14th of August, the eve of Independence, crowds of happy people, irrespective of caste or religion, flocked to our Beliaghat house, to be with Bapu.

But what was Bapu's condition then? His visage was grave. While the people in his room rejoiced, his mind kept thinking of the suffering people in riot-torn regions. Bapuji – the Shankara of our age – spent the day fasting and spinning. He observed silence that day and his mind was immersed in deep meditation. Thousands of people rushed to Bapuji and fell at his feet. But he was calm. He was all sobriety and humility. At times Bapuji would join his palms together in a grateful *namaskar*, as if thanking the people for the co-operation they offered to him during the struggle for liberation.

However, the peace in Calcutta proved to be short-lived. Within a fortnight, large-scale violence again erupted in the city, raising the spectre of a repeat, this time by Hindu extremists, of the Great Calcutta Killings of 1946. A deeply anguished Gandhi responded to the situation by going on an indefinite fast, his moral weapon of self-suffering to induce heart-transformation among the mutually hostile multitudes. Its impact was palpable. Many of the same frenzied Hindus and Muslims who were earlier spilling blood started fraternising at each other's homes and in places of worship, shouting *'Mahatma Gandhi ki jai'* (Victory be to Mahatma Gandhi). Leaders of the two communities pledged to him that they would work jointly to prevent recurrence of such violence. So quick and decisive was the transformation that Gandhi ended his fast after three days. Calcutta's history has recorded this event as a 'miracle'. Manu's description of it is matchless.

But by God's infinite grace, the passions did subside. God cleansed the hearts of the people. Numerous dangerous weapons were surrendered at Bapuji's feet by miscreants who confessed their guilt. These weapons representing brute violence, looked miserable in front of that small frail human being – that apostle of peace. It was a sanctifying spectacle. Bapuji had triumphed. I thanked God for giving me this opportunity of being near Bapuji during his most triumphant moments.

About Gandhi's peace mission in Bengal, Lord Louis Mountbatten, Britain's last viceroy in India, would later, memorably, say: *'While a*

55,000-man boundary force in Punjab was swamped by riots, the One-Man Boundary Force brought peace to Bengal'. (Emphasis added)

The Mahatma had saved West Bengal and East Pakistan from a holocaust of the kind that took place in Sindh and the Punjab. This success, however, could not hide the greatest failure of Gandhi's life, and also of the nationalist movement of which he was the tallest leader – namely, the partition of India. Gandhi had once declared, 'If the Congress accepts partition, it will be over my dead body.'[15] Initially, the Congress party was opposed to the partition plan. However, it later changed its position, unable to deal with a civil war-like situation that had begun to slip out of anybody's control. A complex interplay of factors, in which the collusion between the Muslim League and the British government proved to be the most decisive, was pushing India's break-up towards inevitability. Sadly, Gandhi was getting increasingly isolated within the Congress, which was not slow in wanting power, and his appeal for keeping India's unity intact was beginning to sound like a call in the wilderness. Ultimately, with a heavy and defeated heart, he acceded to the partition plan in the hope that it would stop further bloodshed – but without giving up the hope to bring about a reconciliation between India and Pakistan after the departure of the British.

The flames of communal violence, however, were not extinguished by the birth of Pakistan on 14 August 1947 and India's independence a day later. Hundreds of thousands of people in neighbouring Punjab, now divided between India and Pakistan, were forced to flee their homes – Hindus and Sikhs from West Punjab were migrating to East Punjab and Delhi, and Muslims in Delhi and West Punjab were migrating to West Pakistan. On a relatively lower scale, Hindus from East Bengal, now a part of Pakistan (and later to become Bangladesh in 1971) migrated to West Bengal. In the orgy of violence that ensued, large numbers of innocent people belonging to the Hindu, Sikh and Muslim communities were killed, mostly in the two Punjabs. In all, India's vivisection resulted in the deaths of as many as 1.5 million people and in the trans-border displacement of 12.5 million people, the largest ever in world history. A heartbroken Gandhi wrote: 'I do not remember to have experienced such darkness in my life ever before, and the night seems long. My only consolation is that I have not accepted defeat or given way to despair'.

India celebrated Gandhi's seventy-eighth birthday on 2 October 1947 with an outpouring of joy and veneration. After all, it was the first birthday of the Father of the Nation after India had gained independence. But, at his daily all-faith prayer meeting on that day, he said: 'There is nothing but anguish in my heart.' His religious faith, best formulated in his favourite Ashram song *Vaishnava janato tene kahiye, je peed parayi jane re,* composed by the fifteenth century saint from Gujarat, had taught him that a true believer in God is one who understands and feels others' suffering. Now his heart was filled with nothing but suffering on account of the suffering of millions of ordinary Hindus and Muslims, who had lost their near and dear ones in a communal tornado and were driven out of their homes to live the miserable life of refugees at distant places in either Pakistan or India. He was also concerned that a section of the refugees had fallen prey to the feelings of bigotry and revenge.

All this made Gandhi even more determined to work for the safety and protection of dignity of the minorities in the two countries – Muslims in India and Hindus in Pakistan. In January 1948, just over a fortnight before his assassination, Gandhi again undertook an indefinite fast in a heroic bid to stop the communal madness that had gripped Delhi, India's capital city. The fast, which lasted six days, drew the attention of the entire world, which started to look at this saint-warrior's peace-making endeavours in awe, comparing him to Jesus Christ who had similarly taken the responsibility for mankind's sins and sufferings upon himself.

In the chaotic, hate-filled, and blood-drenched atmosphere that prevailed before and in the immediate aftermath of India's partition, it was common knowledge that Gandhi's life was in danger. Both the British administration before independence, and the Indian government after independence, urged him to accept police protection or at least bodyguards in plain clothes. He flatly refused. Since he considered himself a servant of God, he believed that he must have complete trust in God, who alone could protect him. His argument was: 'The day I seek physical protection, I would rather not live'. He did not change his mind even when there were attempts on his life. At a prayer meeting on 20 January 1948, a bomb was thrown and the congregation began to disperse. Gandhi sat unmoved. 'Don't be frightened,' he told his devotees and continued with his prayer.

Why Gandhi Intensified his Brahmacharya Experiment

Gandhi was always convinced that, in remaining unshaken in his commitment to nonviolence, he was only following God's divine will. Nevertheless, in the final years of his life he was deeply troubled by a question: Why am I failing to put an end to the ongoing dance of death? His 'sword of nonviolence', which was locked in a dangerous battle with the 'sword of violence', was proving to be wanting in its efficacy. His own firm belief was that the failure lay not in the principle of ahimsa, but in the soldier wielding it as his weapon. 'Even if my mission here should fail, it will not be the failure of ahimsa itself. It will be the failure of *my* ahimsa,' he declared.[16] He also admitted: 'The hardest fibre must melt in the fire of love. If it does not melt, it is because the fire is not strong enough.'[17] He felt that there must be something impure and inadequate in himself, causing the failure of his mission. This led him to conclude that he had to first succeed in his parallel – and primary – mission of self-purification for God-realisation, where complete success had eluded him. Hence, even though he continued to work ceaselessly in the most turbulent external environment that he had ever experienced in his life, he intensified his efforts to achieve complete internal purity. He did so by carrying on his silent dialogue with the Almighty, by spinning the wheel, and by performing prayers and fasts. He described this practice as the 'yearning of my soul to merge in the divine essence', to be 'in tune with the Infinite'.[18]

He also intensified yet another observance in his self-purification endeavour – brahmacharya. As he had himself candidly admitted on several occasions, he had yet to achieve the goal of perfection as a brahmachari. Pursuit of this goal became his highest priority in the last few years of his life.

Indeed, the aim of his brahmacharya experiments now was even more daring. Gandhi wanted to become, psychologically, a woman – more specifically, a mother – in the sense of fully internalising the ahimsa nature of the female half of the human species. As we have seen in Chapter 22, he frequently said that women were the true torchbearers of nonviolence. Although India after independence would honour him as the Father of the Nation, Gandhi's own desire and ambition was to become one of the all-caring, all-loving and all-protective Mothers of Humanity. If he succeeded in acquiring such powerful spiritual influence, he would be able, he hoped, to stop Hindus and Muslims from continuing their fratricidal conflict and to prod them to seek peace, reconciliation and unity. I am reminded here of a miniature painting in Salarjung Museum in Hyderabad, which shows a spiritually evolved yogini or brahmacharini (female brahmachari) in a forest with miraculous powers to tame and transform the violent instincts of animals. This is depicted metaphorically by a lion meekly prostrating himself before the compassionate saintly woman. The moot point of difference is that, unlike the forest-dwelling yogini, Gandhi in the last years of his life was endeavouring to become a brahmachari and, hopefully, with miraculous powers to tame the violent instincts of a section of the Indian population that had become beastly. His hope and belief were anchored in the promise of brahmacharya that a perfectly sexless, passionless and egoless spiritual seeker attains miraculous powers, which can be effectively deployed for achieving a larger social good.

How does perfect brahmacharya promise superhuman powers? What is the science of brahmacharya? How did the attainment of its powers become an inseparable part of Gandhi's mission for satya and ahimsa – the *leitmotif* of his life? These questions demand in-depth discussion. For this, we need to take a philosophical detour to understand some basic principles on which the concept of brahmacharya rests, and which operate at the cosmic level as well as at the level of an individual human being.

Satya and Rta — An Essential Interconnectedness Between Cosmic Order and Human Order

SATYAMEVA JAYATE. This Sanskrit aphorism, which means 'Truth Alone Triumphs', is familiar to Indians. It is the official credo of our Republic. What most people do not know is that it is an abridgement of a line that says: *Satyameva jayate naanritam.* It is taken from a mantra in the *Mundaka Upanishad* (3.1.6), which reads:

> *Satyameva jayate naanritam*
> *Satyena pantha vitato devayanah*
> *Yenakramantyrishayo hyaptakama*
> *Yatra tat satyasya paramam nidhanam*

Truth alone triumphs, not falsehood.
Through Truth the divine path is spread out
By which the sages, whose desires have been completely fulfilled,
Reach where that supreme treasure of Truth resides.

We must truly bow our heads before the wisdom of India's Constitution makers who chose our national motto from an Upanishad which literally means the Head of all Upanishads. (*Munda* in Sanskrit means head). *Mundaka Upanishad* is all about how man may attain self-knowledge or self-realisation. Its message of enlightenment is further reinforced by where it appears – on our national emblem with its Dharmachakra or the Wheel of the Eternal Law dating back to the great Buddhist empire of Emperor Ashok, who embraced the credo of nonviolence after seeing the futility of a bloody war he had won. The Dharmachakra sanctifies our national flag. The leaders of India's freedom movement who framed our Constitution clearly intended that our ancient nation should yet again attain self-knowledge and realise the purpose of its existence in the family of nations by following the path of dharma in the modern era. Gandhi's concept of Rama Rajya (the ideal model of governance, as exemplified by the reign of God King Rama) was synonymous with Dharma Rajya or the rule of dharma. It is not a coincidence that our national motto echoes the quintessential message of Gandhi, the Father of the Nation.

The same message is further reinforced by the hidden part of our national motto, *naanritam*, which proclaims that falsehood shall never prevail. The literal translation of *naanritam* is not what is opposed to *rta*. In this root word *rta* is hidden a treasure of philosophical knowledge about human life and the cosmos. Hence, *rta* is the starting point of our exploration of the most controversial aspect of Gandhi's life – his brahmacharya.

Rta, a Sanskrit word, connotes the right order of things and events in Nature and in the wider cosmos, as conceptualised by the Rigvedic rishis. It means 'that which is properly joined' or 'fixed order'. A manifestation of Truth, which for Gandhi was the same as God, it describes the fundamental unity, order, harmony and balance that exist in the universe. The word *rtu* or *ritu* is one of the many derivates of *rta*, and refers to the seasons through which Nature displays its inner harmony, interdependence, and that thrilling and hope-giving phenomenon – cyclical self-renewal. *Rta* is born afresh in each *ritu* by unerringly succeeding in maintaining the mystifying balance between disorder (entropy) and order (negative entropy), between destruction and creation, in the cosmos.

The rishis or sages of ancient India extrapolated the concept of *rta* from the non-human to the human domain by establishing the principle of dharma – the law that secures the moral order in human life. The human species being a creation of Nature, its life cannot be at variance with *rta*. After all, there are ritus in human existence, too, as is evident from the successive events and periods in our lives – birth, childhood, adulthood, married and worldly life, old age that is meant to devote oneself to the virtue of detachment and social-spiritual service, and death. There must, therefore, be a fundamental moral principle sustaining and regulating human life in its various phases and it must be in consonance with that eternal principle – Truth – which sustains *rta* itself. Derived from the root *dhr*, which means 'to hold together', dharma imparts order and cohesion to society, prevents entropy, chaos and disintegration, and aids its progressive evolution. The ancient aphorism *Ahimsa paramo dharmah* – nonviolence is the highest dharma – further buttresses the moral foundations upon which our sages sought to build the superstructure of dharma and all the associated human institutions.

This Vedic understanding of the interconnection between satya, *rta* and dharma has travelled intact through the Buddhist, Islamic and British eras to be enshrined in modern India's national emblem, motto and flag. However, the message of this interconnection is universal, not merely national. If humankind follows its dharma, it evolves upwards to acquire the higher potential and realise the greater possibilities that are in store for it. On the other hand, if it violates its dharma, it slides downwards, making retribution and suffering inevitable.

The responsibility of following the ordinances of dharma, loosely translated as 'religion', rests principally with the individual. Individual as the primary unit of humankind is the unalterable architecture of both biology and theology. The individual human being's karma, which means the sum total of his 'actions' during his life, ensures his own progressive evolution if his karma is along the path of dharma. If karma is in breach of dharma, the individual is bound to suffer not only in this life but also in the next life. Hence the constant refrain of all our scriptures – and also of religious scriptures all around the world – that individuals should live a life of goodness, purity and service. This is best expressed by the three moral commandments of Zoroastrianism, which I learnt from my Parsi friends: *Humata, Hukhta, Huvarshta* (Good Thoughts, Good Words, Good Deeds). It is also echoed in the message of one of the mantras that I had learnt from my father during early childhood:

> *Kaayena vacha manasendriyairva*
> *Buddhyatmana va prakrite swabhavah*
> *Karomi yadyad sakalam parasmai*
> *Narayanayeti samarpayami*

> Whatever I do with my mind, body, speech or with other senses of my body,
> Or with my intellect or with my innate natural tendencies,
> I offer everything to Narayana, the Almighty.

The defining part of this mantra is 'Whatever I do' – *karomi yadyad*. A man becomes what he does. And doing includes man's doings with his feelings and thoughts, and not just his words and deeds. This is an ancient theme of Christianity also. It has great import on our understanding of the Gandhian dialectic between sex and nonviolence.

Sex, Lust and Celibacy in Various Faith Traditions

The Hindu way of life does not reject, belittle, marginalise or stigmatise, sensual desire, known as kaama. As mentioned earlier, it regards *kaama* as the third of the four goals (*purusharthas*) of life. It insists, however, that man should rise above lower-level desires to higher-level desires, which converge at their summit in the desire for self-realisation. Climbing this summit unfalteringly is not easy for anybody, except the rarest of rare individuals. Our lives are hostage to many negative desires and emotions – selfishness, untruthfulness, dishonesty, anger, arrogance, aggression, jealousy, acquisitiveness, covetousness, vanity, the urge to exercise power over others, and suchlike. These instincts and desires both manifest consciously and also lie hidden in our dark, unconscious self. Attaining freedom from them is never easy, not even for great and gifted personalities. The most difficult part of the effort is in the way we seek to satisfy our sexual desires, the strongest of all sense-desires. The fumbles and falls in this effort may not trouble the conscience of ordinary human beings, but they act as some of the severest test points in the path of spiritual seekers.

Although religions of the world differ on the do's and don'ts about sex – Islam, for example, does not support celibacy – they are unanimous in proscribing impure passions for all human beings and in prescribing sexual self-restraint for seekers of the highest levels of spiritual growth and service. The Buddha, who had himself chosen the path of celibacy, exhorted his close followers: 'Cut down the whole forest (of lust), not a tree only! Danger comes out of the forest (of lust). When you have cut down both the forest and its undergrowth, then, Bhikshus, you will be free!' Further, Dhammapada says: 'The fields are damaged by weeds, mankind is damaged by passions'.

Judaism does not sanctify celibacy, nor is it among the special restrictions prescribed for the priesthood. Its precept to 'be fruitful and multiply' is seen as a cardinal duty to perpetuate life. Nevertheless, there is the example of the widely revered second century Palestinian teacher, Simeon ben Azzai, who remained unmarried and explained his celibacy with the words: 'My soul is fond of the Law; the world will be perpetuated by others' (Yev. 63b). As far as lust is concerned, Judaism, like other Abrahamic religions, considers it a sin.

The *Bible* holds that one 'who looks at a woman with lustful intent has already committed adultery with her in his heart' (Matthew 5:27-28). The Catholic catechism states: 'Lust is disordered desire for or inordinate enjoyment of sexual pleasure. Sexual pleasure is morally disordered when sought for itself, isolated from its procreative and unitive purposes'. (Verse 2351)

The *Quran* and the Hadith, which are sayings of the Prophet, prohibit lust, which can impinge on a person's path to Allah. The *Quran* states: 'Follow not the lusts (of your hearts), lest ye swerve' (Surah 4:135). People who act on lust are not among the true believers. The *Quran* says: 'Allah doth wish to turn to you, but the wish of those who follow their lusts is that ye should turn away (from Him), far, far away'. (4:27) Pious Muslims, who undertake the mandatory month-long fast in the month of Ramadan, are not permitted to have sexual intercourse during the fasting period. Religious fasting is regarded as a way of 'cooling sexual passion'.

The *Bhagavad Gita* teaches that lust is a 'mighty enemy (3:43)', a selfish desire that is an obstacle in the path of self-realisation. Krishna exhorts Arjuna: 'Pleasures conceived in the world of the senses have a beginning and an end and give birth to misery, Arjuna. The wise do not look for happiness in them. But those who overcome the impulses of lust and anger which arise in the body are made whole and live in joy. They find their joy, their rest, and their light completely within themselves. United with the Lord, they attain nirvana in Brahman'. (*Bhagavad Gita* 5:22-24).

Hinduism enjoins upon spiritual seekers to know that purity of kaama determines the purity of karma. As mentioned earlier, sex being the strongest of all sensual urges, its satisfaction routinely attracts impurities. Avoiding wrongdoings in one's sexual life, and ridding it of impurities that one has gathered along the way, is strongly recommended for spiritual seekers. Hindu scriptures have prescribed self-purification yajna for them. Yajna in Indian society has often degenerated into indefensible and superstitious acts. However, if it is understood in the true sense of the term, it connotes acts of penance performed in the spirit of service and sacrifice for the benefit of one and all. Using a phrase from folk language, it can be described as *'karma dhulai'* – that is, washing away, of the impurities one collects on account of one's bad deeds by doing good deeds.

We thus see that there is an essential interconnectedness between satya, *rta*, dharma, karma, kaama, yajna and brahmacharya. This conceptual backdrop is necessary to understand the brahmacharya experiments conducted by Gandhi, who had made a deep study of all the scriptures of world religions. For him, these experiments were a part of his determined endeavour to bring his own life, and the life of the newly independent India, in harmony with the divine order or the *rta* of the universe.

Science of Brahmacharya: Practice of the Spiritual Six-Sigma Principle

Gandhi's belief in brahmacharya was as scientific as any other aspect of life that he searched for and commented on, based on study and self-practice. He wrote on this subject with such regularity in his journals that his writings fill a big volume.[19] Since brahmacharya was central to his concept of holistic health, a concise elucidation of it appears in a booklet titled *Key to Health*, which he penned within a fortnight of his imprisonment at the Aga Khan Palace, Poona, upon the launch of the historic Quit India movement in August 1942.[20] He begins this posthumously published treatise with his thoughts on the human body.

> What is the use of the human body? Everything in the world can be used and abused. This applies to the body also. We abuse it when we use it for selfish purposes, for self-indulgence

or in order to harm another. It is put to its right use if we exercise self-restraint and dedicate ourselves to the service of the whole world. The human soul is a part of the universal spirit or God. When all our activity is directed towards the realisation of this link, the body becomes a temple worthy for the spirit to live in.

The body has been described as a mine of dirt. Looked at in its proper perspective, there is no exaggeration in this statement. If the body was nothing else but this, there could be no point in taking such pains to look after it. But if this so-called mine of dirt can be put to its proper use, it becomes our first duty to cleanse it and keep it in a fit condition. The mines of precious stones and gold also have the look of ordinary earth on the surface. The knowledge that there are gold and precious stones underneath, induces men to spend millions and engage scientific brains in order to get at what lies in those mines. Similarly, we cannot take too much pains over keeping in a fit condition the temple of the spirit–the human body.

Man came into the world in order to pay off the debt owed by him to it, that is to say, in order to serve God and (or through) His creation. Keeping this point of view in front of him, man acts as a guardian of his body. It becomes his duty to take such care of his body as to enable it to practise the ideal of service to the best of its ability.

This shows that brahmacharya and yoga, which was highly commended by Gandhi, was a scientific way of mining, refining, extracting and using the 'gold and precious stones' hidden in the human body. However, the purpose of this exercise was not self-enrichment and self-aggrandisement. Rather, brahmacharya for Gandhi was a way of making his body a fit instrument for pursuing God-ward search through man-ward service.

Gandhi described his own experiments in brahmacharya as inspired by 'the scientists of old' who had put 'great value upon the vital fluid' and had 'insisted upon its strong transmutation into the highest form of energy for the benefit of society'.[21] His belief in brahmacharya had its roots in the ancient traditions of yoga. Satya (Truth), ahimsa (nonviolence), *asteya* (non-stealing), *aparigraha* (absence of avarice) and brahmacharya are the five *yamas* or codes of right living prescribed in Patanjali's *Yoga Sutras*[22], which he had read in South Africa in 1903. Brahman is the Supreme Being, and *'charya'* means conduct.

Thus, brahmacharya means conducting one's life in such a way that it is oriented towards the search of Brahman or Truth. This requires simultaneous self-restraint of all the sense-organs of the mind, speech and body – particularly, sex, which produces the strongest sensual desire. Gandhi's whole life and his philosophy of satyagraha were built on these five pillars. 'As faith in God is essential in a satyagrahi, even so is brahmacharya. Without brahmacharya the satyagrahi will have no lustre, no inner strength to stand unarmed against the whole world... His strength will fail him at the right moment'.[23] Brahmacharya 'is one of the greatest disciplines without which the mind cannot attain the requisite firmness. A man who is unchaste loses stamina, becomes emasculated and cowardly. He whose mind is given to animal passions is not capable of any great effort'.[24]

'Mere abstention from sexual intercourse,' according to Gandhi, 'cannot be termed brahmacharya. So long as the desire for intercourse is there, one cannot be said to have attained brahmacharya. Only he who has burned away the sexual desire in its entirety may be said to have attained control over his sexual organ. The absence of seminal discharges is a straightforward result of brahmacharya, but it is not all. There is something very striking about a brahmachari. His speech, his thought, and his actions, all bespeak possession of vital force ... His conception of beauty alters. He will not look at the external form. He or she whose character is beautiful will be beautiful in his eyes... Such a man has so controlled his sexual instinct that he never gets erections... He does not become impotent for lack of the necessary secretion of sexual glands. But these secretions in his case are sublimated into a vital force pervading his whole being. It is said that an impotent man is not free from the sexual desire. ...But the cultivated impotency of the man, whose sexual desire has been burnt up and his sexual secretions are being converted into vital force, is wholly different. It is to be desired by everybody. It is true that such a brahmachari is rare to find'.[25]

Along with brahmacharya and the other four yamas, Patanjali also prescribes five *niyamas* or observances that are necessary for achieving a healthy order and balance within oneself. These are *shaucha* (cleanliness or purity to clear away the negative physical and mental states of being), *santosha* (cultivation of contentment by finding happiness and tranquility with what we have and what we are), *tapas* (austerity by showing discipline in body, speech and mind), *swadhyaya* (study of the Self through study of sacred texts) and *Ishwar Pranidhana* (the final act of surrender to a Higher Power by living one's life with an awareness of the Divine in all).

In addition to yamas and niyamas, Patanjali's philosophy of *Ashtanga Yoga* or the Eight-Limb system of yoga (in Sanskrit *ashta* means eight and *anga* is limbs), prescribes six other observances. These are (1) *aasana* – postures of yoga, mastering of which frees the body and mind from tension and restlessness and prepares them for meditation on the Infinite; (2) *praanayaama* – control of breath to direct *praana* or life-force for perfecting concentration of mind; (3) *pratyahara* – withdrawal of the senses and directing one's attention inwards; (4) *dharana* – effortless stilling of the mind by pushing away superfluous thoughts and making it focussed on a single point or goal; (5) *dhyana* – uninterrupted meditation leading to heightened self-awareness and oneness with the universe; and (6) *samadhi* – absolute bliss, super consciousness, enlightenment or God-Union, which is the ultimate goal of the eight-fold path to yoga. (In modern usage, samadhi refers to the place where a person regarded as holy is interred or cremated.)

When an individual performs the eight-fold yogic practices consistently and unerringly, his *atman* (individual self) receives the powers of Brahman (cosmic self). Patanjali's *Yoga Sutras* describe these powers as *ashta mahasiddhis* – Eight Great Abilities[26], which in their totality are achieved only by perfect yogis. These are:

1. *Anima:* the ability to become minute in size and thus to penetrate an atom or molecule and perceive its inner structure. This siddhi

(ability) would give complete knowledge of the working of the world in its microcosm.

2. *Mahima:* the ability to become gigantic in size and be able to penetrate beyond our solar system and the universe. This siddhi would give complete knowledge of the working of the world in its macrocosm.

3. *Laghima:* the ability to become weightless or assume lightness at will. Apart from levitation, this siddhi would include the power to leave one's body at will and travel in astral form.

4. *Garima:* the ability to gain excessive weightiness and the power that accrues from this.

5. *Prakamya:* the ability to exercise moral power over others, compelling them to do one's wishes.

6. *Isitva:* the ability to control one's body and mind, both one's own and that of others – including the bodies of animals.

7. *Vasitva:* the ability to control the natural elements, such as the power to produce rain, stop floods, prevent an earthquake, etc.

8. *Kaamavasayita:* the ability to have all one's desires fulfilled.

Patanjali states that when an aspirant of yoga has become established in ahimsa, as a result of the continuous practice of yamas and niyamas, all beings (men as well as animals) give up enmity in his presence. When he is well grounded in the practice of abstinence from falsehood, his speech comes out to be unfailingly effective. Similarly, he gains superhuman powers when he is firmly fixed in brahmacharya and conserves his semen. The Sanskrit word for semen is *veerya* (vital energy, a term commonly alluded to in all ancient civilisations), which has profound social, cultural and spiritual connotations.[27] It is the root word for *veer*, one who possesses courage and self-controlled gallantry.

Yogi Aurobindo supports this thought:

The sex-energy utilised by Nature for the purpose of reproduction is in its real nature a fundamental energy of Life. It can be used not for heightening but for a certain intensification of the vital-emotional life; it can be controlled and diverted from the sex-purpose and used for aesthetic and artistic or other creation and productiveness or preserved for heightening of the intellectual or other energies. Entirely controlled it can be turned into a force of spiritual energy also. This was well known in ancient India and was described as the conversion of *retas* [sexual fluid] into *ojas* [spiritual vigor which is felt after union with and immersion into cosmic energies] by Brahmacharya. Sex-energy misused turns to disorder and disintegration of the life-energy and its powers.[28]

The science of ayurveda explains that semen is the last, most refined and most power-embedded, product of the seven-stage metabolism in the human body. 'From the consumption of food comes juice; from juice comes blood; from blood, flesh; from flesh, fat; from fat, bones; from bones, marrow; and lastly, from marrow, semen,' writes Swami Sivananda in his *Practice of Brahmacharya*. A revered guru of ayurveda, yoga and Vedanta, Swami Sivananda (1887–1963) founded the Divine Life Society in the foothills of the Himalayas. Out of the *sapta dhatus* (seven refined products of food) that support the human body and life, he describes veerya as the 'essence of essences'. Although veerya comes out of the bone marrow, 'it is found in a subtle state in all the cells of the body'.

Veerya, when it is retained with the practice of yoga and brahmacharya, flows up from the cells, is converted into *tejas* or *ojas* (vital energy), and nourishes the brain-cells. When that happens, 'the brahmachari shines with brahmic aura in his face. Brahmacharya is the bright light that shines in the house of human body. It is the fully blossomed flower of life around which the bees of strength, patience, knowledge, purity and *dhriti* (firmness) wander about hither and thither....A man who has the power of brahmacharya can turn out immense mental, physical and intellectual work. He can influence the people by speaking a few words, or even by his very presence. Look at Mahatma Gandhi! Physically he was frail. But he wielded the world through the power of Ahimsa, Satya and Brahmacharya'.[29]

Gandhi's own explanation of the power of semen retention through brahmacharya echoed the understanding of India's great yoga gurus:

The sexual glands are all the time secreting the semen. This secretion should be utilised for enhancing one's mental, physical and spiritual energy. He, who learns to utilise it thus, will find that he will be as capable as any of undertaking physical labour. Mental exertion will not tire him easily nor will he show the ordinary signs of old age. Just as a ripe fruit or an old leaf falls off naturally, so will such a brahmachari when his time comes pass away with all his faculties intact.[30]

In a bold new interpretation of 'sexual liberation' – which actually turns upside down its prevailing meaning and practice not only in the West but also in contemporary India – Gandhi wrote:

Restraint self-imposed is no compulsion. A man, who chooses the path of freedom from restraint, i.e., of self-indulgence, will be a bondslave of passions, whilst the man who binds himself to rules and restraints releases himself. All things in the universe, including the sun and the moon and the stars, obey certain laws. Without the restraining influence of these laws, the world would not go on for a single moment.[31]

In other words, brahmacharya is not a practice necessitated by sexual dysfunction. On the contrary, it is conscious transmutation of the sexual function, along with the regulation of all the bodily, mental and emotional functions, aimed at achieving the fundamental unity of the life force. It is the highest point of the self-directed growth of a human being attained through a number of disciplines and observances.

Gandhi firmly believed that 'nothing is impossible' for a brahmachari who has reached the highest point of perfection and achieved complete control over all his senses and organs. 'But it is an ideal state which is rarely realised.' Is the non-attainability of the perfect, then, a cause for despair? No. A true scientist never gives up his quest for truth even though he knows that the ultimate or complete Truth is beyond his grasp. He derives hope from the conviction that future generations of scientists will progress further along the path of quest. Gandhi explains, using his pet mathematical analogy: 'It [the ideal state of brahmacharya] is almost like Euclid's line which exists only in imagination, never capable of being physically drawn. It is nevertheless an important definition in geometry yielding great results. So may a perfect brahmachari exist only in imagination. But if we did not keep him constantly before our mind's eye, we should be like a rudderless ship. The nearer the approach to the imaginary state, the greater the perfection'.[32]

These words will find ready resonance among modern-day research and development (R&D) professionals in precision instrumentation. They know that the more demanding the purpose for which they are devising an instrument – for example, a space mission to Mars and beyond, or the functioning of a critical component in a nuclear power plant – the smaller is the 'tolerance' in its design specifications. They define 'tolerance' as 'the unwanted but acceptable deviation from a desired dimension'. As the acceptable tolerance decreases, the performance level of the precision instrument increases.

Gandhi in his writings on brahmacharya tells us repeatedly that the human body is also an instrument that can be perfected for pursuing impossible-looking tasks. Since he was himself engaged in a seemingly impossible mission – making India free from British rule through nonviolent means and converting India's freedom into swaraj of his conception – the 'tolerance' he allowed himself, as he began perfecting his body-instrument from the day he took the brahmacharya pledge, grew smaller and smaller. He attained total control over his palate, which he regarded as the first unavoidable step in the pursuit of brahmacharya, not only by drastically reducing his intake of food, but also by keeping a precise watch on its weight and composition. Since control of the mind is the stiffest of all challenges in brahmacharya, his mind-control experiments through fasting, prayer, observance of a weekly day-of-silence, daily spinning and social service activities became more and more precise.

When his mission became more challenging in the last years of his life – averting India's partition and the communal carnage that it brought in its trail – his brahmacharya experiments became even more precise and sharply focussed. He now wanted not only his own body-instrument but also those of his entire team of satyagrahi associates to reduce their 'tolerance' standards for the minutest task in their daily routines. Since he regarded time to be the most precious among all the natural resources, of chief concern to him now was to ensure that everyone worked in perfect unison and that every minute of everyone's time was used for achieving the best possible result in the task assigned to them. Whenever there was even the slightest delay due to lack of diligence, he would exhort his colleagues that wasting time is akin to 'stealing' the most precious resource God has made available to man. Long before the modern business management strategy evolved the 'Six Sigma' principle in manufacturing and service provision – this principle seeks to make 99.99966 percent of the products or outcomes defect-free – Gandhi had been practising a paradigm of spiritual 'Six Sigma' that aspired for one hundred percent freedom from defects. It was as if he was endeavouring to make the functioning of his, and his colleagues', body-mind continuum emulate the functioning of the cosmos, in which all its constituent parts follow *rta* – that is, work in perfect order and harmony.

Tales of Brahmacharis with Extraordinary Powers

The Hindu epics and puranas have numerous stories of yogis and brahmacharis performing extraordinary feats with the abilities proffered by near-perfect brahmacharya. There are also stories of spiritually empowered seers losing some or all of their powers when they misused them for wrong ends. Significantly, many such tales revolve around rishis being tested on their ability to control their sexual urges. These have formed part of the living folklore of Indians, generation after generation. Gandhi himself mentions a story about Samarth Ramdas Swami, a seventeenth century saint in Maharashtra who was regarded by the legendary king Shivaji as his spiritual guru. This life-long brahmachari was so sensitive to the suffering of others that he experienced the lashes given to someone else on his own back. 'Such should be the condition,' Gandhi remarks.

One of the most popular and revered figures in Indian mythology is Hanuman, the loyal and celibate servant of Rama, who had acquired

Brahmacharya's power to promote nonviolence: *Swami Krishnananda, at the 1936 Kumbh Mela in Prayag (Allahabad), with his tame vegetarian lioness. Reproduced from Paramahansa Yogananda's* Autobiography of a Yogi. *Yogananda writes:* 'Gandhi has described his life with devastating candour in The Story of My Experiments with Truth... *Many autobiographies replete with famous names and colorful events are almost completely silent on any phase of inner analysis or development. One lays down each of these books with a certain dissatisfaction, as though saying:* "Here is a man who knew many notable persons, but who never knew himself". *This reaction is impossible with Gandhi's autobiography; he exposes his faults and subterfuges with an impersonal devotion to truth rare in annals of any age'.*

divine powers on account of his brahmacharya. He is regarded as the bravest of the brave, one for whom no task was difficult to accomplish. The *Ramayana* tells the tale of how, when Laxman, Rama's younger brother, became critically ill in the battle against Ravana, Hanuman lifted an entire mountain containing the life-restoring *sanjivani* herb, and delivered it across the sea to the battlefield in Lanka. This, like numerous other such tales about Hanuman, no doubt has a strong element of mythological exaggeration. However, no myth in any culture around the world, survives without some correlation with the ancient or even the current reality.

Incidentally, Hanuman has always been the source of inspiration for *pehalwans* who practice Indian-style wrestling called *kushti,* which puts a premium on brahmacharya. They are taught by their gurus in specially sanctified *akhaaras* (gymnasiums) that wrestling is about sublimation of aggression and violence by gaining self-control over physical strength. For this, they are required to follow an elaborate regimen to retain their semen, the essence of their bodily and mental prowess.

Another legend is that of Maharshi Dadhichi, an ancient seer who is said to have had his ashram on the banks of the Sabarmati River in present-day Ahmedabad, where, incidentally, Gandhi also set up his ashram after his return from South Africa. Dadhichi, through his yogic austerities, had mastered a rare rite which gave him superhuman powers. He was once approached by the gods to safeguard their most powerful weapons as they were being constantly attacked by demons, headed by Vritra, who wanted to capture those weapons. Dadhichi kept them with him for a long time. However, one day, tired of the task of keeping a watch over them, he dissolved them in sacred water and drank it.

Meanwhile, the gods in heaven, who were finding it increasingly difficult to beat back the demons' assaults, decided to defeat Vritra once and for all and, hence, asked Dadhichi to return their weapons. Dadhichi told them what he had done and informed them that their weapons were now a part of his bones. Panic-stricken gods then sought guidance from Lord Vishnu, who told him that only a weapon produced by the bones of Dadhichi would overpower Vritra. When Dadhichi learnt this, he told the gods: 'This body will anyway wither away one day. If it can serve some useful purpose, so be it.' He willingly sacrificed his life and enabled the gods to prepare a large number of weapons using his bones, including the most powerful *vajrayudha*, which was as strong and unbreakable as diamond. The tormentors of the gods were vanquished.

Sage Dadhichi thus became a highly revered embodiment of the spirit of self-sacrifice for the larger good of the world. India's highest gallantry award for soldiers, Paramveer Chakra, carries the symbol of his bones. In one of his most inspiring poems (*Aao Phir Se Diya Jalayen* – Let us light the lamp again), former Prime Minister Atal Bihari Vajpayee calls upon leading socio-political activists in India to become 'new Dadhichis' and set fresh examples of sacrifice for national progress, so that the darkness of despair can be dispelled and the lamp of hope relit.[33]

The modern age also has produced great brahmacharis who were spiritual adepts possessing seemingly unbelievable powers. Their feats have been narrated by several acclaimed authors, two of whom can be mentioned here.

The first is Paul Brunton (1898-1981), one of the foremost spiritual explorers of the modern age. He has given in his book *A Search in Secret India*, eye-witness accounts of yogis who demonstrated the power to stop their heart-beat, pulse and breathing at will. He also encountered yogis who possessed incredible healing powers. About Gandhi's brahmacharya, he writes: 'Gandhi demonstrated in his own person the foolishness of the belief that absolute continence leads to mental disorder. He was sane enough to lead his countrymen to freedom. He also demonstrated the falsity of the belief that it was impossible. For forty years he practised it successfully. He said: "The ability properly to conserve, assimilate, and transmute the vital fluid comes with long training. It strengthens the body and the mind." His spiritual career further indicated that mastery of sex by those who have experienced it is more likely to be real and lasting than in the case of those who have starved it'.[34]

The other author that we turn to, Paramahansa Yogananda (1893–1952), was a great yogi himself. In his *Autobiography of a Yogi*, an international bestseller, he describes his encounters with an adept who lived in two bodies, another who could tame a tiger, and yet another who could levitate. Yogananda was an exponent of Kriya Yoga, an ancient science extolled by Patanjali, of body discipline, mental control, and meditation. It aims at achieving harmony with God as perceived by the cosmic creative sound of *aum*. According to Yogananda, its psychophysiological method, as performed by its highest practitioners, results in decarbonisation of human blood and transmutation of all body cells into pure energy. 'A yogi who faithfully follows its technique is gradually freed from karma or the universal chain of causation'.

Hindu scriptures affirm that 'man requires a million years of normal, diseaseless evolution to perfect his human brain sufficiently to express cosmic consciousness'. However, 'human evolution can be quickened' with the practice of Kriya Yoga, writes Yogananda. 'The ancient yogis discovered that the secret of cosmic consciousness is intimately linked with breath mastery. This is India's unique and deathless contribution to the world's treasury of knowledge. The life force, which is ordinarily absorbed in maintaining the heart-pump, must be freed for higher activities by a method of calming and stilling the ceaseless demands of the breath'. He further adds: 'Elijah, Jesus, Kabir and other prophets were past masters in the use of *Kriya* or a similar technique, by which they caused their bodies to dematerialise at will'.[35]

> The *Kriya Yogi* mentally directs his life energy to revolve, upward and downward, around the six spinal centers (medullary, cervical, dorsal, lumbar, sacral, and coccygeal plexuses) which correspond to the twelve astral signs of the zodiac, the symbolic Cosmic Man. One-half minute of revolution of energy around the sensitive spinal cord of man effects subtle progress in his evolution; that half-minute of *Kriya* equals one year of natural spiritual unfoldment.
>
> The astral system of a human being, with six (twelve by polarity) inner constellations revolving around the sun of the omniscient spiritual eye, is interrelated with the physical sun and the twelve zodiacal signs. All men are thus affected by an inner and an outer universe. The ancient rishis discovered that man's earthly and heavenly environment, in twelve-year cycles, push him forward on his natural path. The scriptures aver that man requires a million years of normal, diseaseless evolution to perfect his human brain sufficiently to express cosmic consciousness.
>
> One thousand *Kriya* practiced in eight hours gives the yogi, in one day, the equivalent of one thousand years of natural evolution: 365,000 years of evolution in one year. In three years, a *Kriya Yogi* can thus accomplish by intelligent self-effort the same result which nature brings to pass in a million years. The *Kriya* short cut, of course, can be taken only by deeply developed yogis. With the guidance of a guru, such yogis have carefully prepared their bodies and brains to receive the power created by intensive practice.

Yogananda's autobiography is pertinent to our discussion for an additional reason. It contains a lengthy and illuminating chapter about the three days he spent with Gandhi at the Sevagram Ashram in August 1935. Gandhi expressed a wish to learn the Kriya Yoga from him. 'I was touched by the Mahatma's open-mindedness and spirit of inquiry,' writes Yogananda. 'He is childlike in his divine quest, revealing that pure receptivity which Jesus praised in children, "...of such is the kingdom of heaven".' Yogananda taught Gandhi and his fellow satyagrahis the various *kriya* techniques and exercises, explaining to them that 'the body is visualised as divided into twenty parts; the will directs energy in turn to each section'. Gandhi and his colleagues were quick learners. 'Soon everyone was vibrating before me like a human motor. It was easy to observe the rippling effect on Gandhi's twenty body parts, at all times completely exposed to view! Though very thin, he is not unpleasingly so; the skin of his body is smooth and unwrinkled. Later I initiated the group into the liberating technique of Kriya Yoga'.

One of my favourite photographs of Gandhi shows him sharing a meal with Swami Yogananda at the Sevagram Ashram, both sitting, Indian style, on the floor. The food served was frugal, and what Gandhi ate was even more so – a chapati, boiled beets, some raw vegetables, and oranges. Yogananda writes: 'On the side of his plate was a large lump of very bitter *neem* leaves, a notable blood cleanser. With his spoon he separated a portion and placed it on my dish. I bolted it down with water, remembering childhood days when Mother had forced me to swallow the disagreeable dose. Gandhi, however, bit by bit was eating the *neem* paste with as much relish as if it had been a delicious sweetmeat. In this trifling incident I noted the Mahatma's ability to detach his mind from the senses at will. I recalled the famous appendectomy performed on him some years ago. Refusing anesthetics, the saint had chatted cheerfully with his disciples throughout the operation, his infectious smile revealing his unawareness of pain'.

Later, Yogananda remarked on 'several very recent Western books on diet' which lay on Gandhi's desk. 'Yes, diet is important in the Satyagraha movement – as everywhere else,' Gandhi responded. 'Because I advocate complete continence for satyagrahis, I am always trying to find out the best diet for the celibate. One must conquer the palate before he can control the procreative instinct. Semi-starvation or unbalanced diets are not the answer. After overcoming the inward *greed* for food, a satyagrahi must continue to follow a rational vegetarian diet with all necessary vitamins, minerals, calories, and so forth. By inward and outward wisdom in regard to eating, the satyagrahi's sexual fluid is easily turned into vital energy for the whole body'.

A question that is often debated in Gandhian studies is this: Did Gandhi practice yoga? If so, what system of yoga did he practice?

Of course, Gandhi practiced yoga, but the full answer to the above question goes to show what a great innovator he was in everything he did. He made satyagraha his path of yoga. For him, unlike most yogis, yoga was not something for one's own spiritual advancement. It had to be an instrument of social transformation on a mega scale. Students of yoga, many of whom initially mistake it for different kind of physical exercises, soon learn that it is impossible to tell where the bodily focus ends and the mental focus begins. More advanced practitioners of yoga are aware of its spiritual dimension.

But, in Gandhi's system of yoga, there was no dividing line between the physical, mental, spiritual, societal and political dimensions. This is most strikingly evident from how he innovatively expanded the five basic *yamas* of Patanjali to eleven mandatory observances (*ekadasha sutras*) to be strictly followed by all the inmates of his Sevagram Ashram. These were: truth; nonviolence; non-stealing; brahmacharya; non-possession; body-labour; control of the palate; fearlessness; equal respect for all religions; swadeshi (use of home manufactures); and freedom from untouchability.

Gandhi's uniqueness with regard to yoga is also evident in another way. The *Bhagavad Gita* extols three major *margas* or paths of yoga which enable their practitioners to reach the highest goal – namely, realisation and union with Brahman. These are: (1) karma yoga or the path of selfless action; (2) jnana yoga or the path of self-transcending knowledge; and (3) bhakti yoga or the path of devotion. Aspirants are advised to follow any of these three paths according to their personal inclinations, capabilities and circumstances. Gandhi was unique in the sense that he was simultaneously a karma yogi, jnana yogi and bhakti yogi. He was an activist, scientist and devotee all at the same time. And he brought to bear all the three dimensions of his yogic personality on his innovative experiments in brahmacharya.

Gandhi's Innovations in Brahmacharya

Gandhi married Kasturba in 1883, when he was fourteen years old and she only six months younger. As he would write in his autobiography, they were 'two innocent children' being pushed into 'the ocean of life'. Gandhi left for his law studies in London, in 1888, leaving behind his wife and their newly born son Harilal. He returned to India in 1891, and their second son Manilal was born a year later. In 1893, he left for South Africa. Kasturba joined him there in 1897, along with their two sons. They were later to have two more sons – Ramdas (1897) and Devdas (1900).

Gandhi had been preparing himself for a life of brahmacharya since 1900, but the resolve became stronger after he established the Phoenix Settlement, his first ashram in South Africa, as a nucleus of all his multifarious activities – political, social, scientific and spiritual. After a few failed attempts, he finally took the oath in 1906. Kasturba obediently consented to his decision.[36] Gandhi writes that 'Ba, as she was affectionately called, accepted it as her own', adding that brahmacharya was 'more natural for her than for me'. Thereafter, his wife became his close and enthusiastic associate in all his social and political activities. They had their moments of friction, but these mostly had to do with her complaints that Gandhi was neglecting his responsibilities towards their children. Paying tribute to his wife's selfless support to his work, Gandhi wrote: 'What developed the self-abnegation in her to the highest level was our Brahmacharya'.[37]

Gandhi has described his wife as 'a tranquil heroine in the intense drama' that had been their life together. However, the tribute that Kasturba has paid to her husband is even more fulsome:

> I thank you for having had the privilege of being your lifelong companion and helpmate. I thank you for the most perfect

marriage in the world, based on Brahmacharya and not on sex. I thank you for having considered me your equal in your life work for India. I thank you for not being one of those husbands who spend their time in gambling, racing, women, wine, and song, tiring of their wives and children as the little boy quickly tires of his childhood toys.

How thankful I am that you were not one of those husbands who devote their time to growing rich on the exploitation of the labor of others. How thankful I am that you put God and country before bribes, that you had the courage of your convictions and a complete and implicit faith in God. How thankful I am for a husband that put God and his country before me. I am grateful to you for your tolerance of me and my shortcomings of youth, when I grumbled and rebelled against the change you made in our mode of living, from so much to so little.

As a young child, I lived in your parents' home; your mother was a great and good woman; she trained me, taught me how to be a brave, courageous wife and how to keep the love and respect of her son, my future husband. As the years passed and you became India's most beloved leader, I had none of the fears that beset the wife who may be cast aside when her husband has climbed the ladder of success, as so often happens in other countries. I knew that death would still find us husband and wife.

Although Gandhi built his life on the pillars of yamas and niyamas, his approach to these observances, especially to Brahmacharya, was radically different from how numerous pious personalities in the Hindu tradition had practiced it. As Pyarelal, his secretary, tells us, he made several innovations which were at variance with what the Hindu *shastras* (scriptures) had prescribed.

His approach to these ideals (satya, ahimsa, *aparigraha, asteya* and brahmacharya) was not that of the orthodox moralist – he refused to accept the traditional interpretation of these disciplines – but of a scientific searcher after truth. He poured into them a meaning and content which sometimes left the orthodox gasping for breath....brahmacharya in his case was a natural corollary to the law of love 'which sublimates all desire as well as all possessiveness', the five basic disciplines being 'five test points in what is a single commandment – to love all mankind as oneself.' To treat one of them, namely sex, on the highest level of the law, viz., the law of love, and the rest on the pedestrian level of practical convenience, would be, as Gerald Heard points out, 'to make an inconsistent reply and so produce an inconsistent life.' All the five constitute an integral whole and are of equal importance. Gandhi's striving for Truth consisted in full practice of all of them.

Gandhi was critical of those proponents and practitioners of brahmacharya who only talked of sexual abstinence. For him, control of anger, greed, pride, fear, hatred and all such negative emotions was as critical for the practice of brahmacharya as control of sexual passion. Being himself free from any form of morbid self-mortification – indeed, he was a picture of calm serenity, cheerfulness and joviality even in times of external turmoil – he disapproved of it among celibates. 'The so-called brahmacharis that one comes across, behave as if their one occupation in life was the display of bad temper. One notices that these people disregard the ordinary rules of brahmacharya and merely aim at and expect to prevent seminal discharges.'[38]

Another innovation he introduced in the practice of brahmacharya was that it was neither a private pursuit for him – we have seen earlier how the private dimension of his life had all but vanished – nor a solitary practice for him. His close associates became his partners, bound by an ethic of mutual trust, support and consultation. Indeed, by sharing his experiments with the readers of his journals, he made himself open to benefitting even from their criticisms and constructive suggestions. Gandhi explains the collective and cooperative nature of the practice of brahmacharya again with the help of the analogy of mining 'gold and precious stones' from the human body. He writes that no human being alone can discover these precious metals in the bowels of the earth, bring them up in the form of ores, and refine them to desired levels of purity. Just as this is a cooperative endeavour, so is attainment of brahmacharya in its wider sense.

Thirdly, brahmacharya was a mandatory observance for all who joined his ashrams at Sabarmati and Sevagram. Indian society had known about religious orders and ashrams whose members had to take the oath of, and diligently practice, brahmacharya. Such ashrams and establishments exist even today. But here was the first example in modern Indian history of brahmacharya becoming an integral part of an ashram dedicated to a socio-political agenda, albeit a spiritually guided one. There were many married individuals and couples in Gandhi's ashrams. For them, he coined the concept of 'married brahmacharya'. Married couples could have sexual intercourse, but only for the purpose of procreation. Otherwise, brahmacharya commanded married people to behave as though they were unmarried.

The most radical innovation Gandhi introduced in his practice of brahmacharya was that he conducted it not by avoiding the company of women but by being in their close company. Sexual segregation in some form or the other is common among the religious establishments of almost all faiths. In some, it takes the extreme form of male monks not even seeing or talking to women. However, Gandhi was of the opinion that 'brahmacharya that could not be practiced except in strict segregation was not worth much'. According to him, a brahmachari does not go seeking the company of women. He may not hanker after it, but he does not flee from it either when he is required to render some necessary service to society. In his *Key to Health*, he wrote: 'For him (brahmachari), the distinction between men and women almost disappears. No one should distort my words to use them as an argument in favour of licentiousness. What I mean to say is that, a man whose sexual desire has been burnt up ceases to make a distinction between men and women'.[39]

Gandhi believed that 'even the sight of a nude woman will not affect a perfect brahmachari and vice versa'.[40] His ideal in this regard was Saint Shukadeva, the celibate son of Vyasa, the author of the epic

Mahabharata. In a letter to a close female associate in 1938, Gandhi revealed that although he had been 'striving to attain to Shukadeva's condition', he had not succeeded in that goal yet. 'If I succeed, I would become a eunuch though possessed of the vital fluid, and discharges would become impossible'.[41]

Shukadeva, an elevated soul, was a *bala* brahmachari – he led a passionless life from birth to death. He made no distinction between male or female. He wandered around naked through the forests, where he conducted rigorous yogic observances. His father once spotted him walking past a group of naked women bathing in a lake. They looked at him attentively but without covering their bodies even though he was in a naked state. However, when Vyasa, one of the greatest saints in the Indian pantheon, followed his son along the same route, they quickly grabbed their clothes to hide their nudity. When a puzzled Vyasa asked them about this, the women replied that they did not see the young man as a man at all, nor did he look at them with a male gaze. They were blind to his maleness, but were affected by his spiritual lustre. In contrast, they felt that Vyasa was a married man who, despite his age, viewed them with sex-consciousness, prompting them to react differently to his presence.

Attainment of a state of sexlessness for spiritually exalted persons has been lauded also in other cultures. For example, Lao Tsu, the mystic philosopher of ancient China and the father of Taoism, states: 'The man of Tao is free from the consciousness of sex'. It is the state of evolving beyond the sexual duality of male and female, and attaining the 'totality that lies beyond duality' or the 'bi-unity of male and female in God', as signifed by the concept of *ardhanarishvara*. It represents the synthesis of masculine (*purusha*) and feminine (*prakriti*) energies of the universe. For Gandhi's pursuit of brahmacharya, this implied his becoming one with womankind through the conquest and sublimation of sex. He described himself as 'half a woman'. To Sarojini Naidu, one of the leading personalities in India's freedom movement, a noted poetess in English, and his devoted follower, he once wrote: 'I hope you have not missed the woman in me'. Indeed, he had attained considerable progress in attaining freedom from sex-consciousness even in his South Africa years, as is clear from the following amazing observation by Millie Graham Polak, who, along with her husband Henry Polak, was a close associate of Gandhi in both the Phoenix and Tolstoy ashrams.

> Most women love men for such attributes as are usually considered masculine. Yet, Mahatma Gandhi has been given the love of many women for his womanliness; for all those qualities that are associated with women...Women would sense that in him they had found a fellow-traveller, one who had passed ahead along the road they, too, were travelling, and could give him an affection deep, pure and untouched by any play of sex-emotion. Women of all kinds have turned to him in perplexity and trouble, and no problem of their lives but could be discussed with absolute frankness, if they desired to do so. They could be sure that some light would be thrown upon their difficulties and the path made to look not too arduous to travel.[42]

A highly educated, aristocratic, Indian society lady once remarked: 'There are some things relating to our lives which we, women, can speak of to, or discuss with, no man. But while speaking to Gandhi we somehow forgot the fact that he was a *man.*'[43]

As in every other walk of life, Gandhi regarded self-cultivated internal restraint to be superior to externally imposed discipline. In his ashrams he deliberately encouraged men and women of all ages to live and work together. There was always the risk of failure in such efforts, but this, he maintained, 'applies to all my experiments...Those who have joined the Ashram after due deliberation have joined ... fully conscious of all the risks involved therein. As for the young boys and girls, I look upon them as my own children, and as such they are automatically drawn within the pale of my experiments. These experiments are undertaken in the name of the God of Truth. He is the Master Potter while we are mere clay in His all-powerful hands'.[44]

The result of these experiments, he declared, had been encouraging, since both 'men as well as women have on the whole derived benefit from it.... The greatest benefit has in my opinion accrued to women'. In the process, 'some of us have fallen, some have risen after sustaining a fall'. The possibility of stumbling, he maintained, was implicit in all such experimentation. 'Where there is cent per cent success, it is not an experiment but a characteristic of omniscience'.[45]

Coping with Failures

Gandhi was frank and honest enough to admit that he counted himself among those who had often fallen – and 'risen after sustaining a fall' – in the course of their brahmacharya practice. As is widely known, his first self-confessed 'fall' occurred in the pre-brahmacharya phase of his life, but the sense of guilt associated with it stayed with him throughout his life. That catastrophic incident took place at his home in Porbandar, Gujarat, when he was sixteen years old, and his father was critically ill. Gandhi used to nurse him with deep care and filial love, massaging his legs, giving him medication and attending to all his needs. He writes in his autobiography that one evening, in the middle of rendering nursing service to his father, he was overcome by lust for his wife. Even though Kasturba was pregnant at the time, he could not control himself and he left his duty by his father and went to satisfy his passion – 'that too at a time when religion, medical science and commonsense alike forbade sexual intercourse'. Within less than ten minutes, a servant called him out to say that his father had died. Recounting the shame arising out his lustful act, he writes in his autobiography:

> (It) was a blot I have never been able to efface or forget, and I have always thought that, although my devotion to my parents knew no bounds and I would have given up anything for it, yet it was weighed and found unpardonably wanting because my mind was at the moment in the grip of lust. I have therefore always regarded myself as a lustful, though faithful, husband. It took me long to get free from the shackles of lust, and I had to pass through many ordeals before I could overcome it.

There were also a few other episodes in the post-brahmacharya phase of his life which, though for him far less calamitous in nature, found him wanting in his *sadhana* (spiritual pursuit) as a celibate. Although he never had a sexual relationship either with his wife (or with any other woman) after he took the oath of brahmacharya, he confessed to the readers of his journals that 'impure thoughts' had surfaced in his mind on a few occasions. He wrote that on one occasion, in 1920, he was on the verge of falling into the 'hell-fire' of adultery with a married woman who had become his associate in the Sabarmati Ashram and was a well-known name in the initial phase of his khadi campaign. '(A)lthough the flesh was pulling hard enough to tear the chains to bits', he says that he was miraculously saved by his close comrades, and also by 'the thought of my wife', from 'going to perdition'.[46]

In 1936, he informed the readers of his weekly journal *Harijan* that his 'darkest' hour came to him when in his dream he desired to have sex with a woman. How much he was tormented by this episode becomes clear from his own words:

> (a) man who had tried to rise superior to the instinct for nearly forty years was bound to be intensely pained when he had this frightful experience. I ultimately conquered the feeling, but I was face to face with the blackest moment of my life and if I had succumbed to it, it would have been my absolute undoing.[47]

On another occasion, in 1938, he was so shocked and shaken when he experienced an erection in a waking state that he felt that his entire *tapasya* of many decades had suffered a severe setback. He described his state of mind in a letter to Mirabehn.

> That degrading, dirty, torturing experience of 14th April shook me to bits and made me feel as if I was hurled by God from an imaginary paradise where I had no right to be in my uncleanliness.[48]

Gandhi was frank in telling people who wanted to join his ashram that they should have no illusion that he was a perfect Mahatma. To one such person, he wrote:

What do you gain by placing so much faith in me? I am not perfect, nor am I free of passion. Only last night, I had a dirty dream. This is not a good thing. What can you hope to gain by living with such a person? Know me as I am. A Bapu who exists only in your imagination will not be of any use to you. Whatever I have in me is known to the world. You can draw from it a good deal wherever you may be. You know my definition of freedom from passion, don't you? Such a man, even though virile, does not become sexually roused in thought word or deed, whether waking or asleep. I am striving to become such in this very life. If I succeed you will benefit by being with me. Let us see what God wills.[49]

In Gandhi's own self-analysis, he attributed his inability to attain complete perfection in celibacy to the fact that he had adopted brahmacharya after leading a married life for some years. After his 1936 experience of having an erotic dream, he wrote to a woman associate in the satyagraha movement:

(i)t seems practically impossible that a person who has indulged in sex gratification from the age of 15 to 30, maybe with his wife only, can, on taking the vow of brahmacharya, control the discharge of his vital fluid completely. One whose capacity for retention has progressively weakened from day to day for fifteen years cannot recover it fully all at once. Both his body and mind will have become too weak for that. I, therefore, consider myself a very imperfect brahmachari. But my position is like that of a castor oil plant which looks big on a heath where there are no trees.[50]

Gandhi, in a remarkable confessional to Vinoba Bhave, whom he regarded as his spiritual heir, also spoke about his shortcomings in the non-sexual aspects of brahmacharya.

My *sadhana* is not matchless. I know the anger that lies buried within me. I have no hatred for the English, but when I think of them, I cannot but feel, why are they so dangerous? They are human, not dangerous. If I recognise that their attitude is perilous, I must melt with love for them.

The same self-critical quality can be seen again in the following lines:

> It is my full conviction, that if only I had lived a life of unbroken brahmacharya all through, my energy and enthusiasm would have been a thousand-fold greater and I should have been able to devote them all to the furtherance of my country's cause as my own. If an imperfect brahmachari like myself can reap such benefit, how much more wonderful must be the gain of power, – physical, mental, as well as moral, – that unbroken brahmacharya can bring to us![51]

Gandhi was aware that the success of the Satyagraha movement launched by him depended on the moral strength of his leadership. After all, he considered himself the general of the army of satyagrahis. He also felt that the success of his leadership depended on the success in his efforts at perfection in brahmacharya. 'There must be power in the word of a Satyagraha General – not the power that the possession of limitless arms gives but the power that purity of life, strict vigilance and ceaseless application produces. This is impossible without the observance of brahmacharya...All power comes from the preservation of and sublimation of the vitality that is responsible for the creation of life. This vitality is continuously or even unconsciously dissipated by evil or ever rambling, disorderly, unwanted thoughts. And since thought is the root of all speech and action, the quality of the latter corresponds to the quality of the former. *Hence, perfectly controlled thought is itself power of the highest potency and becomes self-acting* ...If man is after the image of God, he has but to will a thing in the limited sphere allotted to him and it becomes. *Such power is impossible in one who dissipates his energy in any way whatsoever.*'[52] *(Emphasis added)*

In the course of his socio-political activities, whenever violence flared up or undesirable developments that were against his plans and wishes took place, Gandhi was troubled by the thought: why he lacked the power that could enable him to achieve what he wished.

He traced the answer to his imperfection in brahmacharya. As he wrote in *Harijan* on 23 July 1938; 'I have not acquired that control over my thoughts that I need for my researches in nonviolence. If my nonviolence is to be contagious and infectious, I must acquire greater control over my thoughts. There is perhaps a flaw somewhere which accounts for the apparent failure of my leadership'.

Overcoming the 'flaw' meant that he had to subject himself to more rigorous tests in brahmacharya. We have seen earlier that he did not subscribe to the traditional injunction that a brahmachari should never see, much less touch, a woman. He had also rejected the view that perfect brahmacharya can be observed only by ascetics living in the Himalayas without any association with worldly affairs. He was a karmayogi whose arena of action was where millions of Indians lived and whose purpose of action was swaraj for India and all-round transformation of the Indian society. Therefore, he had to succeed in his brahmacharya in the turbulence of worldly affairs and while working closely with his trusted companions, many of whom were women. This prompted him, in 1938, to write an introspective article in *Harijan*:

> Doubtless, a brahmachari may not think of, speak of, see or touch a woman *lustfully*. But the prohibition one finds in books on brahmacharya is without this important adverb ('lustfully'). The reason for the omission seems to be that a man is no impartial judge in such matters. ...It is not woman whose touch defiles man, but he is often himself too impure to touch her. But recently a doubt has seized me as to the nature of the limitations that a brahmachari or brahmacharini should not put upon himself or herself, regarding contacts with the opposite sex. *I have set limitations which do not satisfy me. What they should be, I do not know.*[53] (Emphasis added)

The italicised lines hold the key to understanding Gandhi's brahmacharya experiments in Noakhali in 1946-7. Further proof of this can be found in his 1942 treatise *Key to Health*. It contains a remarkable admission by Gandhi that he was conducting his experiments in sexual celibacy with the spirit and rigour of a scientific researcher, and that his research had reached a higher stage.

I cannot say I have attained the full brahmacharya of my definition but, in my opinion, I have made substantial progress towards it. If God wills it, I might attain even perfection in this life. Anyway, there is no relaxation of effort nor is there any despondence in me. I do not consider thirty-six years too long a period for the effort. The richer the prize, the greater the effort must be. Meanwhile, my ideas regarding the necessity for brahmacharya have become stronger. *Some of my experiments have not reached a stage when they might be placed before the public with advantage. I hope to do so some day if they succeed to my satisfaction.* Success might make the attainment of brahmacharya (by others) comparatively easier.[54] *(Emphasis added)*

Which experiments of his was Gandhi referring to in 1942 that, in his words, 'have not reached a stage that might be placed before the public with advantage'? What did he mean by hoping that, God-willing, he 'might attain perfection in this life'? We now turn to these questions.

Brahmacharya Experiment with Grandniece, Manu, in Noakhali

As we have seen earlier, the mass killings in Calcutta in August 1946, after the Muslim League's call for Direct Action to press its demand for the creation of Pakistan, triggered the outbreak of communal violence on a ghastly scale in many parts of northern, north-western and eastern India. The desire to become effective in stopping this bloodbath and preventing India's partition prompted Gandhi to intensify his experiments in brahmacharya. Previously, especially after the death of his wife Kasturba in 1944, he had subjected himself to experiments involving physical nakedness with a few of his consenting women associates. When his peace mission in Noakhali initially failed to elicit the desired response, he was filled with intense agony, which he shared with an old associate of his. 'If I temporise in the matter of brahmacharya, would it not blunt the edge of my brahmacharya and vitiate my practice of Truth? Ever since my coming to Noakhali, I have been asking myself the question: "What is it that is choking the action of my Ahimsa? Why does not the spell work? May it not be because I have temporised in the matter of brahmacharya?"'[55]

It is in this painful and self-questioning state of mind that Gandhi decided to continue his experiments of sleeping at night with his nineteen-year-old grandniece Manu, both in a state of nakedness, during his peacemaking journey in Noakhali district. He began the experiments with Manu's prior consent, and only after she agreed to tell him in full honesty if she found the slightest trace of improper conduct on his part and also if she herself experienced any sexual desire on account of his nearness to him. He also bound himself by the same condition. As soon as either of them discovered that the condition was not met, he said, the experiments would be terminated.

There is no record of what exactly these experiments entailed. However, in a significant re-characterisation, Gandhi in Noakhali repeatedly describes them no longer as *prayog* (experiments) but as *yajna* (sacrifice). This means that Gandhi had mentally reached a stage in Noakhali when he was aware that the time for making the supreme sacrifice in the battle against violence had come. His condition was not dissimilar to that of a brave soldier engaged in a just war who, when he finds himself in a hopeless situation, prays to the Almighty either to help him to become victorious or accept his life as a martyr's sacrifice.

There was another significant aspect of Gandhi's brahmacharya practice in Noakhali. We have earlier alluded to his desire to inculcate within himself feminine – indeed, motherly – qualities. The presence of Manu in Noakhali provided a natural opportunity for him to play the role of a mother. Manu had lost her mother in her childhood. She looked upon Kasturba as her mother and nursed her with great devotion in the prison at Aga Khan Palace in Poona. Kasturba, who did not have a daughter of her own, developed deep affection for her and gave her motherly love and care. Just before her death, Kasturba entrusted Manu to Gandhi by saying: 'After me, you have to become a mother to her'. The fact that his brahmacharya practice with Manu in no way affected his motherly disposition towards her till the end of his life is evident from her own remarkable account of her relationship

Courtesy: Gandhi Smriti

Gandhi is seen here with his grandniece Manu Gandhi (left) and another of his devoted disciples, Rajkumari Amrit Kaur.

with the Mahatma, titled, tellingly, as *Bapu: My Mother*. She begins this booklet, published in 1949, with these lines:

'Bapu was father to innumerable men and women and the guru of many. There were many to whom he ministered as their doctor or even as a nurse. He was a dear friend to many colleagues. Countless people looked up to him as their redeemer. All this is aptly included in the term "Father of the Nation". For me, however, he was a mother. Generally, it is not possible for a man to become a mother to anyone because he has not been endowed by God with the mother's loving heart which a woman is blessed with. But Bapu appropriated for himself a share of even this divine gift'.[56]

Gandhi did not hide his brahmacharya practice with Manu in Noakhali from his close associates. Indeed, he mentioned its purpose even to the villagers and others attending his post-prayer discourses. Not surprisingly, his decision caused a great deal of controversy and also prompted a few of his associates to leave him. Gandhi, however, stood firm while respectfully listening to every point of view. The most authentic account of this aspect of his pilgrimage to Noakhali is given by his loyal secretary Pyarelal. His own sister and Gandhi's personal physician, Dr Sushila Nayyar, had sometimes participated in his brahmacharya experiments in Delhi.

> Friends asked Gandhi how he could afford to lavish his time and attention on this when he was engaged in his great mission. 'They think it is a sign of infatuation on my part,' he remarked to Manu. 'I laugh at their ignorance. They do not understand. I regard the time and energy spent on you as time and energy well spent. If out of India's millions of daughters, I can train even one into an ideal woman by becoming an ideal mother to you, I shall thereby have rendered a unique service to womankind. Only by becoming a perfect brahmachari can one truly serve the woman.'
>
> He spent anxious days and nights turning the searchlight inward. He gave patient and earnest consideration to every viewpoint, every argument addressed to him. In his search for the Great Truth, he let all concerned understand that he needed the help and cooperation of all, particularly the dissenters and critics.
>
> If his sincerity could impress itself upon her and evoke in her all the excellences that he aimed at, it would show that his quest of truth had been successful. His sincerity should then impress itself upon the Muslims, his opponents in the Muslim League, and even Jinnah, who doubted his sincerity to their own and India's harm.
>
> He explained: 'My meaning of brahmacharya is this – "One who never has any lustful intention, who, by constant attendance upon God, had become ... capable of lying naked with naked women, however beautiful they may be, without being in any manner whatsoever sexually excited. Such a person should be incapable of lying, incapable of intending doing harm to a single man or woman in the whole world, free from anger and malice and detached in the sense of the *Bhagavad Gita*. Such a person is

a full brahmachari. Brahmachari literally means a person who is making daily and steady progress towards God and whose every act is done in pursuance of that end and no other.'"

According to his wont, he took the public into confidence. In one of his prayer addresses he referred to 'small-talks, whispers and innuendos' going round him of which he had become aware. He was already in the midst of so much suspicion and distrust, he told the gathering, that he did not want his most innocent acts to be misunderstood and misrepresented. He had his grand-daughter with him. She shared the same bed with him. The Prophet had discounted eunuchs who became such by an operation. But he welcomed eunuchs made such through prayer by God. His (Gandhi's) was that aspiration. It was in the spirit of God's eunuch that he had approached what he considered was his duty. It was an integral part of the *yajna* he was performing and he invited them to bless the effort. He knew that his action had excited criticism even among his friends. But a duty could not be shirked even for the sake of the most intimate friends. In a letter to Mirabehn he wrote: 'The way to truth is paved with skeletons over which we dare to walk.'

Speaking on the same topic the next day, he told them, he had deliberately referred to his private life because he had never thought that the private life of individuals did not affect the course of the public activities. Thus, he did not believe that he could be immoral in private life and yet be an efficient public servant. His public conduct was bound to be affected by his private. He held that much mischief was made in the world by divorce between public and private conduct. When he was engaged in the supreme test of nonviolence in his life, he wished to be judged before God and man by the sum total of his activities both private and public. He had said years ago that nonviolent life was an act of self-examination and self-purification whether by an individual, a group, or a nation.

He sounded a note of warning on the third day. What he had said about his private life was not for blind imitation. He never claimed to have extraordinary powers. What he did was for all to do if they conformed to the conditions observed by him. If that was not done those who pretended to imitate his practice were doomed to perdition. What he was doing was undoubtedly dangerous but it ceased to be so if the conditions were rigidly observed. What those conditions were, he had summed up in his *Key to Health*: 'The glorious fruit of perfect brahmacharya is not to be had from the observance of... limited brahmacharya (i.e., continence in the physical sense alone). But no one can reach perfect brahmacharya without reaching the limited variety.'

Bapu explained further: 'There is first the innocence of the child. He had no knowledge or consciousness of sex-distinction. It is innocence rooted in ignorance. But the perfect innocence of a grown-up person, who has full knowledge and understanding of sex, is true brahmacharya. Such a perfect brahmachari will be proclaimed by the luster on his face, he will be a stranger to infirmity or disease. He will manifest in full measure all the marks of a *sthitaprajna*. And when finally he dies, it will not be as a result of sickness, his death will be a "sleep and a forgetting". He will retain his faculties unimpaired till the end and keep on doing His work and taking His name with his last breath. These are some of the signs by which a perfect brahmachari will be known.'

Prajna in Sanskrit is mind, intellect, wisdom. *Sthita* means stable or in a state of equilibrium. *Sthitaprajna*, as described by Krishna in the *Bhagavad Gita*, is a person whose mental faculties are in an evolved state of perfect equilibrium without any negative traits while facing the ups and downs of life. This is the state that Gandhi's brahmacharya experiments were elevating him to, as is evident from what he wrote: 'I am experiencing an equanimity, steadiness and firmness of purpose that I never did before. It fills me with ineffable peace and joy. It shows that I am coming nearer and nearer to my ideal of *sthitaprajna*'.

Once Manu asked Gandhi why Partition-related strife and violence in the country made him unhappy if he was trying to become a sthitaprajna. His reply was revealing: 'If I did not feel unhappy I would be a person with a heart of stone. It is easy to become a saint and sainthood gives greater satisfaction. Sitting in a forest or in solitude and pursuing knowledge is no doubt a kind of spiritual living, but to practise goodness while living in the world is, in my opinion, a more difficult kind of spiritual living. One may not be a scholar but one must show sympathy towards the poor and the afflicted. Yes, it is a sign of a *sthitaprajna* to remain calm in the face of a calamity or illness or the death of a dear one. But it is the duty of a man to show sympathy towards those who suffer and to endeavour to lighten their suffering'.[57]

Countless eyebrows have been raised by Gandhi's brahmacharya practice with Manu in Noakhali, and by similar less-publicised practice with his other close women associates before and after Noakhali. It has also invited many condemnatory comments. Most of this condemnation originates in ignorance about the purpose behind the practice. A scientist perhaps never shies away from conducting an experiment that he or she considers indispensable for the purpose of finding the truth. In the kind of experiments that Gandhi conducted, what mattered, above all, is how he viewed his women associates and how they viewed him. Significantly, none of these women ever complained that what the Mahatma did, or what they did by participating in his experiments, was improper. Their respect for him remained undiminished and unaffected by all the controversy that raged in society. This is indeed a tribute to the elevated character of his women associates, who stood by him even when some of his close male comrades became either uneasy or disapproving.

In any case, as Pyarelal mentions in his book, there is sanction for such esoteric practices in Hindu scriptures. *Srimad Bhagavata* states:

Masters [those possessed of extraordinary power of self-control] are sometimes seen courageously to transgress the prescribed rules of conduct. This is not a blemish in those with *tejas* or radiance, even as the all-devouring fire is not affected [by what it consumes]. He who is lacking in such control should not even think of imitating such conduct, for it can only bring destruction to him like swallowing poison in imitation of Shiva. The teachings of the great hold true for all, not always their actions. So, a wise person should imitate only such conduct of the Masters as conforms to their precepts.

Pyarelal concludes his chapter on Gandhi's brahmacharya with an honest comment. 'I must add here that although my study of Gandhi's brahmacharya experiments further raised him in my estimation, particularly because of the purpose for which he conducted them, I have not been persuaded to fully agree with his views on the role of sex in human life. His summary rejection of sex for anything other than the purpose of procreation is unconvincing. It is inconsistent with the human beings' exalted, ennobling and life-enriching experience of non-procreative sex down the ages.[58]

Most admirers of the Mahatma will agree with Pyarelal.

Is the Mahatma's Brahmacharya Relevant Today?

What is the relevance of Gandhi's philosophy and practice of brahmacharya to our times, and the times to come? The question is pertinent because what he advocated – and he never wavered or compromised in the advocacy of brahmacharya as he understood it – is evidently at variance with the prevailing sexual ethos not only in India but also in many parts of the world. After all, we live in an age when sex has been extensively commodified and commercialised. The attitudes that a consumerism-driven economy fosters have deeply, and deleteriously, affected the way human beings seek to gratify their diverse needs, including sexual needs. People are encouraged to consume sex, rather than experience it in life-enriching, socially stabilising and spiritually elevating ways. They are being goaded daily by a flood of messages and images from the businesses of entertainment, advertising and ad-driven journalism into believing that there is nothing wrong in the excitement of sexual passion, nor in its limitless indulgence. By inciting consumers to seek newness and instantaneous pleasure in almost every product or service they buy, these messages have influenced the people to demand the same in their sex life.

Knowing well that sex is the strongest human desire, and hence easily arousable, the hidden persuaders of the advertising industry expend most of their creativity on stimulating desire for a wide range of products by subliminally associating their acquisition and consumption with sex. Ask the editors of glossy magazines, organisers of sports spectacles, producers of music videos on television channels, movie-makers looking for box-office hits, and the marketing brains for lifestyle goods, and all of them unanimously proclaim their faith in the time-tested formula: 'sex sells'. Thus, demeaned and enslaved by market forces, sex has been made the universal seductress, an ubiquitous brand ambassador indeed, for the modern consumption-dependent economy.

Sex is not only a seductress for the sale of other commodities, but it is itself on sale as a commodity – never more in human history than now. The crime of human trafficking, mainly for the purpose of commercial sexual exploitation, has reached unprecedented levels both within nations and trans-nationally. Pornography, riding on the near-universal reach of the digital media, has become a multi-billion dollar industry. This is where the enslavement of sex by market forces assumes extreme forms.

All this cannot but strain and stain the social fabric of humanity. Thanks mainly to urbanisation, with the concomitant onslaught of Westernisation, the restraints and regulations that traditional societies and cultures had placed on sex – on premarital and extramarital sex, sex within marriage, discussion and depiction of sex in the public space, and so on – have been largely torn asunder, with little concern for the long-term consequences of such destruction. The current paradigm of globalisation, driven almost solely by chaotic economic forces, has endangered not only the precious bio-diversity on our planet but also the equally precious cultural diversity in our world.

The numerous rites, rituals, customs and cultural-spiritual anchors that regulated the role of sex in traditional societies are vanishing as rapidly as the vulnerable non-human species on earth. This change is often defended or rationalised by its supporters by invoking the concepts of individual choice, sexual liberation and tradition-as-an-obstacle-to-progress. But its two-fold disintegrating effect on the psychological state of individuals is undeniable. Firstly, more and more people today find that their sexual life fails in its promise of providing genuinely joyful, fulfilling and re-integrating experiences. Secondly, and this is a result of the first malaise, they feel increasingly atomised and lonely, even though they live in the midst of large human populations.

Pyarelal, in the chapter on Gandhi's 'Brahmacharya', writes, quoting from the book *The Living Brain* by Dr Grey Walter, a well-known neurophysiologist and robotician.

> This unstaunched primal energy – far in excess of our procreative requirements – is an evolutionary force waiting to be transformed into a new faculty....When this store of energy is transmuted into a higher form of creative activity man transcends sex consciousness. In the case of the modern man this reserve is dissipated in aimless sexuality, not only through physical abuse but also through 'psychic haemorrhage' helped by the 'entertainment industry', which seems to be largely devised 'with the express purpose of keeping his veins open'. This 'psychic bleeding' of the modern man, induced by pornography, voyeurism, erotic art, obscene advertising, etc., Dr Grey Walter warns, 'is evolution in the reverse gear and fraught with the most far reaching consequences to the human race'.[59]

This warning has become vastly more serious in the age of the Internet, which has opened the floodgates of pornography. Nevertheless, we must hasten to accept here that, not all the changes in social and sexual mores have been caused by the negative influences of the market and the mass media. This is because not everything about the traditional understandings about sex and its regulation was sound and worthy of being preserved. Every society in every era has seen some of its traditions become ossified and even detrimental to human dignity and freedom. These traditions must be either discarded or reformed. Dynamic societies do so by continually transforming themselves from within and absorbing positive influences from without. Therefore, the desire to break free from such shackles, adopt new norms and customs, or at least to experiment, is natural. This desire is not to be condemned so long as it is within the parameters of basic human ethics as determined by the individual's own conscience.

In such a contemporary sexual landscape, does Gandhi's advocacy of brahmacharya, with its insistence on sex only within the sacred institution of marriage and only for the purpose of procreation, have any chance of being viewed other than as the anachronistic stance of an otherwise venerable personality who refused to recognise the value of a fundamental human need?

Any exploration of the contemporary relevance of Gandhi's advocacy of brahmacharya must address three basic issues. Firstly, is the *ideal* of brahmacharya intrinsically meaningful, defensible and worth pursuing? Secondly, even if the ideal is right, did Gandhi fail to recognise non-procreative sex as a natural, healthy and enriching need of human beings? Thirdly, can human sexuality be reformed in any other way to make it a more reliable pathway to progressive human evolution?

Gandhi's own life provides a resoundingly affirmative answer to the first question. His adherence to truth, nonviolence and brahmacharya was as seamless as it was total. How much importance he attached to it, vis-à-vis his political activities is clear from the following bold assertion:

> My Mahatmaship is worthless. It is due to my outward activities, due to my politics which is the least part of me and is therefore evanescent. What is of abiding worth is my insistence on Truth, Nonviolence and Brahmacharya, which is the real part of me. That permanent part of me, however small, is not to be despised. It is my all. I prize even the failures and disillusionments which are but steps towards success.[60]

Gandhi's life is by no means the sole example proclaiming the validity of the ideal of brahmacharya. All great truth-seekers in the world, irrespective of the religious or non-religious tradition they belonged to, practised self-restraint in their sexual lives. Licentiousness has never been the hallmark of spiritual personalities or those who rendered outstanding service to society by making extraordinary sacrifices. This is because one of the first sacrifices that a genuine servant of society is called upon to make – rather, feels an inner urge to make – is to sacrifice his or her sensual desires. The awareness that sensual desires bring pleasure to one's personal self, whereas selfless service of society demands subordination of personal pleasure to the needs of societal happiness, inevitably guides such persons toward efforts at self-restraint. Gandhi himself explains his reason for taking the vow of brahmacharya in these words: 'I clearly saw that one aspiring to serve humanity could not do without it. It was borne in upon me that I should have more and more occasions for service of the kind I was rendering, and that I should find myself unequal to the task if I were engaged in the pleasure of family life...In a word, I could not live both after the flesh and the spirit'.[61]

Success in gaining control over the flesh generally becomes the touchstone of progress both for the spiritual seeker as well as for his or her followers. Indian society has admired, but never revered, those spiritual personalities who had intellectual brilliance and even possessed some minor occult or miracle-making powers, but led promiscuous sexual lives. Its highest reverence is reserved for those ascetics who reduced themselves to zero in service of God and society. Humanity in every age has progressed only by seeking inspiration and guidance from the lives and teachings of such holy personalities.

Gandhi's Unconvincing Views About Non-procreative Sex

Such evolved personalities, who embody an ideal, are necessarily rare in any era. Not all members of a society can be expected to live up to the highest ideal. Gandhi himself concedes that practice of perfect brahmacharya is as elusive as the writing of a 'Euclidian line'.

Therefore, the sexual norms for the multitudes are understandably less exacting than those for the social and spiritual leaders in any society. So long as the common people follow the less demanding injunctions of dharma prescribed for them, they too contribute substantially to the society's progress. Hence, our discussion on the contemporary relevance of Gandhi's advocacy of brahmacharya, which brooked no relaxations from the ideal, leads us to the second question – was he wrong in not recognising the intrinsic virtues and beneficial effects of non-procreative sex for non-brahmacharis? Yes, he was wrong.

Gandhi's was a maximalist approach to brahmacharya. It did not allow any distinction to be made between the mandate and the message of brahmacharya. The mandate for an avowed brahmachari is clear: He has to observe complete abstinence from sex, if he is unmarried, and, if married, to have sex with the consent of his spouse only for bringing a new life into the world. However, several spiritual gurus in the Hindu tradition have stated that the message of brahmacharya for the multitudes is one of moderation in sexual activity within the institution of marriage and the performance of the act as an offering to the divine. In other words, what the Hindu way of life lauds and recommends for the multitudes is a harmonious balance between the sensual and the spiritual, between happiness in this world (*iha-loka*) and in the world beyond our material existence (*para-loka*). This is evident from the inclusion of *artha* (satisfaction of life's material needs) and *kaama* (satisfaction of life's sensual needs) within the rubric of the four *purusharthas* or goals of human life. It is noteworthy that these two goals are flanked, in the order of their location, by the other two goals of dharma (righteous living) and *moksha* (seeking divine grace for a fulfilled end to one's material existence). The message of the four *purusharthas* is that *artha* and *kaama*, pursued under the light of dharma, lead a person to *moksha*.

The message of moderation is also contained in the Hindu concept of four *ashramas*[62] (stages) in human life. The very first stage is *brahmacharya ashrama*, in which a person is expected to observe celibacy for the first twenty-five years of his life, while devoting himself to gaining knowledge and acquiring various skills. The second stage of twenty-five years is *grihastha ashrama*, when a person lives the married life of a householder and provides for the material needs of his family, which is his primary responsibility. In the next stage of twenty-five years, *vanaprastha ashrama*, he is expected to turn the focus of his life from his immediate family to the larger family – namely, society – and render voluntary service to it. The final stage of *sanyasa ashrama* is meant to be devoted to detachment from worldly ties and preparation for the journey to after-life. It is clear from this responsibility-based division of life that strict celibacy is limited only to the first twenty-five years of brahmacharya stage. Thereafter, there is no bar on householders to have sex for procreative as well as non-procreative purposes. Rather, pursuit of sensual happiness during the *grihastha* stage, within the bounds of moderation and dharmic regulation, is regarded as necessary for the husband and wife to harmonise their lives, know each other better, jointly raise their children with love and care, and lead a happy family life. Happy and cohesive families are *sine qua non* for a happy and cohesive society.

The spirit of the concept of the 'four stages and four goals' of human life is not unique to Hinduism. It is articulated in different ways in all the faiths and ancient cultures of the world. If more and more people in India and elsewhere follow the spirit of this concept, sex in moderation and with ethical self-restraints is bound to aid individuals' self-development and also become a major contributor to making our world a better, more beautiful and more peaceful place. In his voluminous and extremely educative writings on human sexuality, Gandhi somehow refuses to recognise this important point.

Gandhi is also unconvincing, like the rigid Christian edict, in his extreme views on contraceptives, whose use was taboo for him in all circumstances. 'Self-control is the surest and the only method of regulating the birth-rate,' he insists. 'Persons who use contraceptives will never learn the virtue of self-restraint...Self-indulgence with contraceptives may prevent the coming of children but will sap the vitality of both men and women – perhaps more of men than of women. It is unmanly to refuse battle with the devil'.[63] There is indeed some merit in his message, especially insofar as it is aimed at men.

However, it overlooks the pain, tension and hardships that women, who often are in no position to say 'no' to their demanding partners in today's male-dominated world, have to go through in the event of an unwanted pregnancy.

Here is another strong argument that underscores the virtues of conscientiously practiced non-procreative sex. Every era of human history is witness to the truth that sensual love between man and woman, which seeks consummation in sexual union, has been a powerful inspiration for self-discovery, self-growth and creativity. Through the institution of marriage, sensual love brings husband and wife together in joint service of family and other institutions of society. In many cases, it also serves as an entry point for the individual's or couple's spiritual journey. The world would be deprived of much of its priceless wealth in music, art, literature, poetry, sculpture, dance, theatre and cinema if quest for the beauty, universality and eternality of sensual love were prohibited. Experience, appreciation and acculturation of beauty – which appears in its most concentrated, consecrated, sublime and divine form in the female body – is indispensable for the aesthetic evolution of man and mankind. It is a precondition for understanding and internalising the profound meaning of the trinity of *satyam, shivam, sundaram.*

The world of sensual pleasure can, of course, too easily drag a person into excess, betrayal, dishonesty, self-deceit, straying from the path of responsibility and commitment and causing deep psychological injury to one's beloved and to oneself. Who can say that there is no truth in Gandhi's cautionary observation that 'love based upon indulgence of animal passion is at best a selfish affair and likely to snap under the slightest strain'?[64] A lot of suffering and tragedy in the unending human drama is on account of sensual pleasure-seeking gone astray.

Gandhi never changed his view about the impermissibility of sex outside marriage and sex for non-procreative purposes within marriage. But it must be admitted that he came to regard sex as a noble desire. Moreover, inflexible though he was in his belief in brahmacharya, he never imposed upon others his views on sex. Only those who voluntarily chose to join his ashrams had to follow brahmacharya and other injunctions. About others' sexual views and conduct, including those of his closest colleagues in the Congress party, he remained tolerant and non-judgmental.

The Future of Sex: Glimpses of Gandhi's Vision

We now come to discussing the third issue concerning the relevance of Gandhi's philosophy and practice of brahmacharya: Can human sexuality be reformed to make it a more effective promoter of the ideal of a nonviolent world? Our affirmative answer to this question rests on the belief that it is possible to harmonise the invaluable lessons from Gandhi's – and other such spiritual adepts' – brahmacharya practice with the no less valuable learnings from the ennobling effect of sex in the life of common people. The life of adepts shows us the ideal, and makes us believe in its seemingly limitless possibilities for human progress. By approximating one's conduct to the conduct of Brahma, the creator of the cosmos, it is indeed possible for the individual self to acquire a substantial part of the powers of the Cosmic Self. Gandhi's own life, almost every minute aspect of which has been authentically recorded for posterity, is proof positive of the incredible power of brahmacharya to promote nonviolence and universal love.

However, no major social transformation ever takes place solely due to the actions of the personifiers of the ideal. For any positive change to yield the desired fruit, the multitudes must participate in it with enthusiasm and self-awareness. But the multitudes cannot be expected to practice Gandhi's maximalist brahmacharya. Their contribution to the making of a world of nonviolence and universal brotherhood can come not through the rejection of sex, but through its gradual spiritual elevation.

This necessitates, first and foremost, liberation of human sexuality from the manipulative and exploitative influence of lust, commerce and custom. Men and women should become free agents to experience mutual love, which of course comes with the obligation of mutual trust, respect, care, commitment and, equally importantly, responsibility towards society. Social traditions should be reformed to encourage such love-based relationships. In his own time, Gandhi promoted several such reforms by championing inter-caste marriage, widow remarriage and women's empowerment. He did so also by relentlessly flaying men's aggressive behaviour, which is a cause of both domestic violence and violence in society, and urging men to shun their prejudices about women. For example, he admonished:

> [w]hy is there all this morbid anxiety about female purity? Have women any say in the matter of male purity? We hear nothing of women's anxiety about men's chastity. Why should men arrogate to themselves the right to regulate female purity? It cannot be superimposed from without. It is a matter of evolution from within and therefore of individual self effort.[65]

Another important contribution by Gandhi to sexual reforms comes in the form of the absolute honesty and openness that he brought to bear on discussing sex-related matters. Hypocrisy and prudery were totally alien to him. Whether he was discussing his own sexuality or the sexual matters in society, his sole guiding principle was Truth, which manifested itself in his concern for human welfare. These virtues shine brightly against the backdrop of the prurient superficiality and hypocrisy that dominates the discourse on sex in our society.

Perhaps Gandhi's greatest contribution to the debate on human sexuality is that he envisioned a future when sex – indeed, the human body itself – will have undergone a radical transformation by acquiring greater qualities of divinity. This also explains why he remained inflexible in his advocacy of maximalist brahmacharya. To know his mind on this issue, let us examine the following thought:

> It is no argument against the possibility or desirability of abstinence to say that it is difficult for the vast majority of mankind. What was not possible for the vast majority a hundred years ago has been found possible today. And what is a hundred years in the cycle of time open to us for making infinite progress? *If scientists are right, it was but yesterday that we found ourselves with the human body. Who knows, who dare prescribe, its limitation? Indeed, every day we are discovering the infiniteness of its capacity for good as well evil. (Emphasis added)*

The science of human evolution tells us that it took seven billion years for hominids to give birth to *Homo sapiens*. Numerous hominid species arose and then died out during this long process. Even the journey from *Homo erectus* to *Homo sapiens* lasted over a million years. If, believing in the Big Bang theory, we look back at our universe's journey of nearly fourteen billion years, we find that Gandhi was right in reminding us that 'it was but yesterday that we found ourselves with the human body'. Procreation, of course, has been a biological necessity to ensure the continuity of our species. It is something that we have inherited from our animal past, and continue to share with animal species. Non-procreative sex too has been man's necessity and it too has contributed immensely to humanity's evolution.

However, sex – procreative or otherwise – is often not freed from animal passion, made worse with the addition of many negative emotions that are not to be found in animal behavior. Our body and mind are thus working as per a design, with its positive and negative features that we have acquired from our animal as well as civilisational past. But is this design permanent and unchangeable? Certainly not! It can be changed, and man has the ability to gradually change it for the better. Therefore, as Gandhi tells us, none can prescribe the limitations of the human body – and, thus, of human sexuality – in the future. If the human body's infinite capacity for evil is significantly curbed, and if its infinite potential for good is substantially realised, then the man-woman relationship in all its aspects, including sexual, will become as unrecognisably different in the future as the sexual act of Neanderthal Man 1,00,000 years ago was from the sublime sex of our own times as depicted, for example, in Rodin's timeless sculpture 'The Kiss', now placed in his museum in Paris.

Gandhi expresses the imperative necessity – and also the definite possibility – of transforming human sexuality and human life in general in the following words:

> Birth as a human being is declared by all religions as a rare privilege – as a state of probation. And Hinduism says that if we are weighed and found wanting, we should have to be reborn as beasts.[66]

Again:

> Man is not a brute. He has risen to the higher state after countless births in the brute creation. *He is born to stand, not to walk on all fours or crawl. Bestiality is as far removed from manhood as matter from spirit.*[67] (Emphasis added)

Here Gandhi is alluding to three extremely important stages of disruptive discontinuity in natural and human evolution. The first such point of discontinuity came at the origin of the universe – spirit giving birth to matter. The next was matter giving birth to life in its various forms. The third was the brute life-form giving birth to man. But is this the final stage in human evolution? Gandhi's answer – indeed, the answer given by all the great visionaries of the world – is an emphatic 'No'.

A new point of evolutionary discontinuity is beckoning man. It is the stage when man will re-enter the world of spirit, free himself from all the influences of Satan, and prove that he is indeed a higher life-form that is made in the image of God. This is when Truth and Nonviolence will reign supreme. Gandhi, however, introduces a note of caution: He tells us that this is a long struggle, which may take 'thousands of years' to bear success.[68] He repeatedly advises us that we should be in no hurry to see the desired results in our own lifetime. Rather, he urges patience and devoted effort, leaving the outcome, as per the *Bhagavad Gita's* teaching of Karma Yoga, to God.

When Gandhi says metaphorically that man '*is born to stand, not to walk on all fours or crawl*', he is not referring to today's man who, of course, stands erect anatomically. He is urging that man must learn to stand erect *ethically*. Every impurity in our emotions, thoughts and actions makes us bend, and impedes our march towards our evolutionary destiny. Which is why, brahmacharya, in its broadest sense, was chosen by Gandhi as a method of constant self-purification of body and mind. He says:

> Our body has been given to us on the understanding that we should render devoted service to God with its aid. It is our duty to keep it pure and unstained from within as well as without,

so as to render it back to the Giver when the time comes for it, in the state of purity in which we got it.[69]

How beautifully this passage echoes the message contained in Kabir's bhajan, which was Gandhi's favourite, *Chadariya Jhini Re Jhini*, which we visited in Chapter 14 in our attempt to decode the meaning of the 'music of the spinning wheel'!

Gandhi's belief that human sexuality is transformable is supported by Gerald Heard. According to Heard, man owes his primacy in nature to the fact that he alone seems to have an immense store of still unused, undifferentiated primal energy. The sex energy with which man is endowed is many times greater than that of animals. This unused energy, far in excess of human beings' reproductive needs, is a reserve resource which if wisely harnessed can greatly aid human evolution. Heard asks: 'Can we find spiritual powers equal to our unbalanced physical powers, the finding of which is a matter of life and death for civilisation?' He answers it thus: 'We have today a society which must capsise unless our psychic knowledge can equal our physics...This can only be done by a specific training whereby the latent energy for this creative task and act, an energy which lurks inside us and manifests itself in pain and lust, individual neurosis and mass neurosis, be made to express itself in advanced and purely psychological activities. ...By this advance in psychological power we may at last achieve a nonviolent sanction for all human relationships and a new approach in our relationships with animal life and a new insight into the inanimate'.[70]

Heard sums up his call for the transmutation of sexual energy in a profoundly perceptive thought: 'Man has transmuted the atom...He must now transmute himself'.

Gandhi's brahmacharya experiment for transmuting his sexual energy for a noble cause has no less significance for the modern world than the harnessing of the energy of the atom for peaceful purposes. Its relevance to our times is beyond doubt. Indeed, it is as relevant as his satyagraha itself, both having been embraced by him in the same year – and, revealingly, the latter as a result of the former. If it is true that Gandhi was ahead of his times on many salient issues concerning the wellbeing of humanity, it is equally true that he was also ahead of his times in preaching and practicing brahmacharya. Even though his admirers, like me, may disagree over certain aspects of his views on sex, there is no denying that Gandhi provokes us to think seriously about the following future possibilities in human sexuality.

- Can we envision sex in the future as a source of pure joy and happiness, untainted by any of the weaknesses – selfishness, jealousy, dishonesty, betrayal of trust, insensitivity, apathy, aggression, violence on women, etc. – that we have acquired from our animal past and historical heritage?
- How can sensual love, which is today mostly person-specific, get transmuted into universal love for all human beings and for all the creations in Nature, without losing its anchor in man-woman love?
- Since experience of beauty is integrally associated with our sexual experience, how can human beings broaden, deepen and refine their aesthetic capabilities in all walks of life, free from commercial, socially exploitative and all other false trappings? Can we get close to attaining Plato's ideal of Beauty, which was also Gandhi's? Plato states: 'He [man] should begin by loving earthly things for the sake of the absolute loveliness, ascending to that as it were by degrees or steps, from the first to the second, and thence to all fair forms; and from fair forms to fair conduct; and from fair conduct to fair principles, until from fair principles he finally arrive at the ultimate principle of all, and learn what absolute Beauty is'.
- Human beings' biological evolution is certain to be accelerated in the coming decades and centuries by technological evolution – a point that Ray Kurzweil, inventor and futurist of information technology (IT), makes elsewhere in this book. Isn't it reasonable then to think that our bodies, our minds, our sexual lives and our psychic selves will also undergo as yet unimaginable transformation in the future?

This future evolution of sex as an integral part of man's evolution to superman, is what Maharshi Aurobindo had alluded to when he wrote[71]:

> When we have passed beyond enjoying, then we shall have Bliss.
> *Desire was the helper; Desire is the bar.*
> When we have passed beyond individualising, then we shall be real Persons.
> *Ego was the helper; Ego is the bar.*
> When we have passed beyond humanity, then we shall be the Man.
> *The Animal was the helper; the Animal is the bar.*

These are the mind-expanding meditations on Gandhi's philosophy and practice of brahmacharya that prompted me to write this long chapter. I have devoted many pages to it for a simple reason. The Internet age, more than any other age in human history has vastly enhanced both the possibilities and perils of sex.

We now turn to the final section of this book that looks specifically at how Gandhi's vision can help us minimise the perils of the Internet age and maximise its promise of ushering in a nonviolent tomorrow.

PART FIVE

PROMISE
OF
THE INTERNET

TOM STANDAGE

AUTHOR OF THE NEW YORK TIMES BESTSELLER A HISTORY OF THE WORLD IN 6 GLASSES

THE VICTORIAN INTERNET

THE REMARKABLE STORY OF THE TELEGRAPH AND THE NINETEENTH CENTURY'S ONLINE PIONEERS

An enthusiastic user of the 'Victorian Internet': *Gandhi received and sent a large number of telegrams. Tom Standage in his book has described telegraph as 'The Victorian Internet', a precursor to today's Internet. If Gandhi embraced what were the state-of-the-art communication technologies in his time, he would have certainly done so now.*

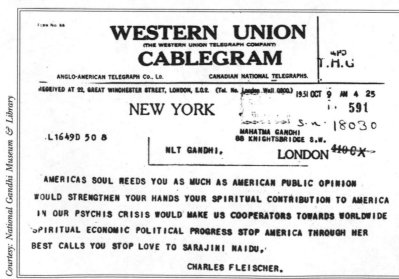

FORM No. 68

WESTERN UNION
(THE WESTERN UNION TELEGRAPH COMPANY)
CABLEGRAM

ANGLO-AMERICAN TELEGRAPH Co., Ld.   CANADIAN NATIONAL TELEGRAPHS.

RECEIVED AT 22, GREAT WINCHESTER STREET, LONDON, E.C.2.   (Tel. No. London Wall 0800.)   1931 OCT 9 AM 4 25

NEW YORK

591

S. n. 18030

.L1649D 50 8

MAHATMA GANDHI
88 KNIGHTSBRIDGE S.W.

NLT GANDHI,   LONDON

AMERICAS SOUL NEEDS YOU AS MUCH AS AMERICAN PUBLIC OPINION
WOULD STRENGTHEN YOUR HANDS YOUR SPIRITUAL CONTRIBUTION TO AMERICA
IN OUR PSYCHIS CRISIS WOULD MAKE US COOPERATORS TOWARDS WORLDWIDE
SPIRITUAL ECONOMIC POLITICAL PROGRESS STOP AMERICA THROUGH HER
BEST CALLS YOU STOP LOVE TO SARAJINI NAIDU,

CHARLES FLEISCHER.

A telegram Gandhi received from an American well-wisher in 1931. Many foreigners wrote letters and sent telegrams inviting him to visit their countries.

25

WHY GANDHI WOULD HAVE EMBRACED THE INTERNET
A Dreamer who Wanted Modern Science to Re-clothe Ageless India

—⋙⟡⋘—

Here's to the crazy ones. The misfits. The rebels...The ones who see things differently... And they have no respect for the status quo. You can quote them, disagree with them, glorify or vilify them. About the only thing you can't do is ignore them. Because they change things. They push the human race forward. And while some may see them as the crazy ones, we see genius. Because the people who are crazy enough to think they can change the world, are the ones who do.

— From Apple's 'THINK DIFFERENT' advertising campaign (1997), conceived by Steve Jobs, which featured his personal heroes, among them Mahatma Gandhi.

THE PRECEDING PAGES OF THIS BOOK WERE DEVOTED TO EXAMINING several salient questions which those people with non-trivial interest in Mahatma Gandhi often ask themselves. Why did khadi and the charkha mean so much to him? Did his insistence upon self-reliant development of village-centric industries during India's freedom movement, with the spinning wheel as its pivot, mean that he was opposed to modern science and technology? Why did he make the spinning wheel a carrier of his larger message about truth and nonviolence? What is satyagraha? Does it provide a strong enough anchor for the 'science of nonviolence', which individuals and societies can successfully practice in our times? How, in practical terms, is Gandhi relevant to the current global debate on democracy, disarmament, social justice, gender justice, economic justice, sexual ethics, and ecologically and socially sustainable development?

It is for the readers to judge whether the author's examination of these questions in the previous chapters passes muster.

However, as far as I am concerned, a paradoxical question has remained unexplored. The moral message of khadi and the charkha, as I have argued earlier, is still undoubtedly relevant to India and the modern world. But at a time when the spinning wheel itself has all but disappeared in India, hasn't the Mahatma's charkha been reduced to mere symbolism? And when the medium of the message becomes irrelevant and nonexistent, doesn't the message itself face the danger of losing its potency in a fast-changing world?

After all, any discussion on khadi and the charkha to demonstrate the relevance of Gandhi's philosophy for today's world runs the risk of sounding archaic, even hypocritical. The reason is obvious: very few people in India wear khadi these days. I rarely do so myself. And almost none of us spin the charkha. The last time I did was in my sixth and seventh standards, when we had weekly spinning sessions in our school. And the school, too, stopped charkha-teaching long ago. Trying one's hand at the spinning provides a good photo-op for VIPs visiting Sabarmati Ashram in Ahmedabad, Sevagram Ashram near Wardha or Mani Bhavan in Mumbai, where Gandhi lived whenever he visited the city. But it doesn't in any way revive large-scale use of the charkha. So why pay tribute to a relic of the past? The charkha undoubtedly was a powerful symbol of mass education and mass mobilisation during India's struggle for independence. But why invoke something that neither has any practical value now nor, we must admit, strikes an emotional chord in a large section of the Indian society today?

For a long time, I, as a devotee of the Mahatma, wrestled with this paradox of an ever-relevant message symbolised by a no-longer-relevant medium. However, a paradox, it is said, is always pregnant with the possibility of producing new knowledge. As it happened, Gandhi himself has provided an insight for me to begin a new line of thinking.

The good thing about Gandhi is that he rarely disappoints you if you hurl a question at him or place your dilemma before him. All he demands of you is to judge his views with an open mind and come to your own conclusions. Reading Gandhi is indeed like having an animated conversation with a wise friend. He speaks to his readers directly, without any pretensions, and in a language that is as simple, sincere and transparent as the man himself. His words come across as the words of a living man, eager to listen to you and also to share his thoughts with you. If you remain unconvinced and choose to disagree, he respects your choice. Which is why, whenever I have had doubts about any of his ideas and arguments, I have felt like the protagonist in the widely acclaimed, entertaining and educative Bollywood film *Lage Raho Munnabhai,* made by Rajkumar Hirani and Vidhu Vinod Chopra, and starring Sanjay Dutt. Circumstances compel the film's bumbling hero to become – or, rather, pretend to be – a Gandhi scholar. But whenever he is in a quandary, or has a query, the ever helpful Mahatma comes to him as a ghost to show the way. And without his knowing, this small-time criminal in a big city gets transformed into a genuine servant of society and fighter for justice.

The quandary I found myself in, as I began seriously studying Gandhi's thoughts on science, technology and development, was this: Khadi and the charkha simply cannot be resurrected now in the way Gandhi wanted it in his time, but the *spirit of khadi and the charkha* most certainly, and most urgently, is in need of a rebirth. How can this happen? Is there a *new medium* capable of broadcasting and promoting the Mahatma's message of Truth and Nonviolence, which he famously said are 'as old as the hills'?

Then I came across several startling statements from Gandhi himself that the 'spirit of khadi' cannot, and need not, be located in any particular device or technology for all time to come. In an article titled 'Is Hand-Spinning Opposed to Machinery?' in *Young India* in 1921, he had written: 'I would favour the use of the most elaborate machinery if thereby India's pauperism can be avoided'.[1] Writing again in *Young India* in 1926, he had stated that he would discard the spinning wheel 'if someone shows a better and more universal political programme than hand-spinning...I am anxious to know if there is any'. In the same article, he went on to say: 'I have not contemplated, much less advised, the abandonment of a single healthy industrial activity for the sake of hand-spinning. The entire foundation of the spinning wheel rests on the fact that there are crores of semi-unemployed people in India. And I should admit that if there were none such there would be no room for the spinning wheel'.[2] He returns to this theme in 1929, when he says: 'The moment these [poor] millions can have a better substitute, they are at liberty to give up the spinning wheel, and no one would be more glad than I to see these millions possess a better substitute'.[3]

Also: 'The message of the spinning wheel is much wider than its circumference. Its message is one of simplicity, service of mankind, living so as not to hurt others, creating an indissoluble bond between the rich and the poor, capital and labour, the prince and the peasant. That larger message is naturally for all'.[4] He often took pains to urge both his followers and his critics to understand what khadi and the charkha '*stood for*' and what they '*connoted*'.

All this shows that the spinning wheel was not a permanent and unchanging element in his social and economic philosophy.

Gandhi's non-dogmatic approach to the issue of modern machines is also evident from the conversation that the famous English comedian and filmmaker, Charlie Chaplin, had with him in London in September 1931. After enquiring about his health, Chaplin said: 'I am all for the freedom of your country and its people. But there is one thing that I don't understand. Why do you oppose the use of machines? Don't you think that a lot of work would come to a standstill if machines are not used? What do you feel about the rapid technological advancements?'

Gandhi said: 'My primary concern is the chronic unemployment of millions of people in India's villages'.

This prompted Chaplin to ask: 'But if you could find other work for your unemployed and ensure equitable distribution of wealth, you would welcome machinery?'

'Certainly,' replied Gandhi.[5]

In other words, Gandhi was open to the idea of a 'better substitute' for the spinning wheel. His only caveat was that the substitute should embody and promote the three-pronged message of khadi and the charkha – economic, cultural and spiritual – as explained in Chapter 6. There was a specific socio-historical context that dictated his choice of the charkha for carrying this message during India's freedom struggle. Now the context is significantly different in many respects – both in India and the world. Therefore, our search for a superior alternative to the spinning wheel is perfectly in order.

But what could that alternative be?

The alternative to the spinning wheel in the twenty-first century is the INTERNET. And all the other Internet-enabled revolutionary technologies.

Gandhi's Historic Correspondence with Jawaharlal Nehru

My discovery of the Internet as the potentially worthy successor to the spinning wheel came from reading Gandhi's own writings – in particular, his correspondence with Jawaharlal Nehru in the 1940s. With the imminent departure of the British from India, Gandhi wanted to discuss with Nehru the strategy of socio-economic development suitable for independent India. It was well known to all even then that the two leaders had serious differences on this issue. Gandhi's faith was in a bottom-up approach to India's all-round development, based on 'gram swaraj' or revival of villages as vibrant and self-governing socio-economic units, a non-exploitative relationship between cities and villages, welfare of labour and decentralised democratic governance.

Nehru, however, did not share his mentor's faith in India's villages and villagers, nor did he believe that decentralised development and governance was critical for the country's progress. 'We cannot stop the river of change', he wrote in his autobiography (1936), 'or cut ourselves adrift from it, and psychologically, we who have eaten the apple of Eden cannot forget the taste and go back to primitiveness'. He was strongly in favour of large-scale industrialisation. He believed that the ills of capitalism could be obviated by keeping the ownership and management of all major industries in the hands of the state. 'Pandit Nehru wants industrialisation,' Gandhi told an American businessman in 1940, 'because he thinks that if it is socialised (along the Soviet pattern), it would be free from the evils of capitalism. My own view is that the evils are inherent in industrialism, and no amount of socialisation can eradicate them.'[6]

Gandhi's views on the development model for independent India form the centrepiece of an extremely important debate that took place in 1945 between him and Nehru – through that quaint medium of communication, letter-writing, which has all but vanished from the contemporary practice of political leaders. Those of us who read Gandhi's letters today will not fail to be mesmerised by the depth of concern that he showed for the future of India and the world. He wanted India to revive, and build on, the best of its own age-old heritage of village-centred civilisation without rejecting the best that the modern world had to offer. The impatient Nehru, however, had neither Gandhi's deep understanding of, nor faith in, India's rich rural civilisation. The model of socio-economic and political development that he was attracted to was essentially Western, a combination of the communist pattern then being practiced in the Soviet Union and the one advocated by Fabian Socialists in Britain. Gandhi knew this.

Therefore, it was Gandhi who initiated the debate by writing to Nehru a lengthy letter on 5 October, in which he candidly mentioned the 'difference of outlook between us'. Reiterating the main themes of *Hind Swaraj* that he had written thirty-six years earlier, he warned against the certainty of the emergence of inequality-breeding big cities, in which some would live in 'palaces' and many more in 'huts'. He therefore insisted on self-reliant village-centric development, one in which villages and cities would have a healthy and mutually supportive relationship. It is better to let Gandhi speak to us in his own inimitable words:

> I hold that without Truth and Nonviolence, there can be nothing but destruction of humanity. We can realise Truth and Nonviolence only in the simplicity of village life and this simplicity can best be found in the Charkha and all that the

Charkha connotes. I must not fear if the world is going the opposite way.[7] It may be that India too will go that way and like the proverbial moth burn itself eventually in the flame round which it dances more and more furiously. But it is my bounden duty up to my last breath to try to protect India and through India the entire world from such a doom. The essence of what I want to say is that man should rest content with what are his real needs and have control over the things that are necessary for the sustenance of life. If he cannot have this control, the individual cannot survive. Ultimately, the world is made up only of individuals. If there were no drops, there would be no ocean.[8]

Gandhi's letter to Nehru is significant for another reason. It reveals yet again that he was not a dogmatic leader, but a self-evolving person who was ever ready to revise his own views (or, rather, revise the earlier formulation of his views). It explicitly affirms his faith in modern technology for the success of his village-centric model of development in a free India. 'I do not think I have stated this in *Hind Swaraj*,' he first admits, and goes on to craft the following exquisite lines that carry a resonant policy message, even today.

While I admire modern science, I find that it is the old looked at in the true light of modern science which should be reclothed and refashioned aright. You must not imagine that I am envisaging our village life as it is today. The village of my dreams is still in my mind. After all, every man lives in the world of his dreams. My ideal village will contain intelligent human beings. They will not live in dirt and darkness as animals. Men and women will live in freedom and be able to face the whole world. There will be neither plague, nor cholera nor small-pox; nobody will be allowed to be idle, nor to wallow in luxury. Everyone will have to contribute his quota of manual labour. Granting all this, I can still envisage a number of things that will have to be organised on a large scale. I do not want to draw a large scale picture in detail. It is possible to envisage railways[9], *post and telegraph offices*, etc. ...I do not know what things there will be or will not be. Nor am I bothered about it. If I can make sure of the essential thing, other things will follow in due course. But if I give up the essential thing, I give up everything.[10] *(Emphasis added)*

Telegraph? I must confess that I was completely bowled over by this passage when I first read it and found a mention of telegraph. And with a great sense of joy, I said to myself: 'I now know why Gandhi would have embraced the Internet, if he were alive today.'

It was a Eureka moment for me.

Telegraph, which was developed almost simultaneously in America and Britain in the 1840s, was in many ways a precursor to the Internet, a point persuasively made in the book *The Victorian Internet* by Tom Standage. Telegraph was the first machine-enabled, near-instantaneous, long-distance communication system invented by man. If Gandhi was a votary and a regular user of telegraph, which was the extant state-of-the-art online communication technology in the early part of

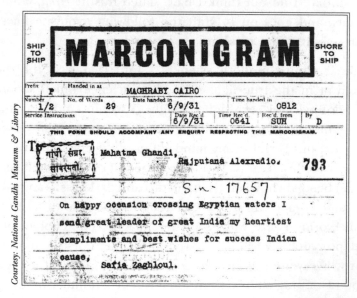

An Egyptian lady sent this telegram to Gandhi when his ship, the S.S. Rajputana, *was sailing by Alexandria en route to London in September 1931.*

the twentieth century, he would certainly have been an enthusiastic champion of information and communication technology in the twenty-first century.

I actually started imagining that the Father of the Nation, if he were living amidst us, would be publishing his *Young India* and *Harijan* on the Internet, writing e-mails to people near and far more prolifically than the scores of postcards he used to pen each day, urging scientists to develop technologies that would de pollute the planet and conserve natural resources, and insisting that policy makers bridge the digital divide in hundred different ways, including through promotion of IT in Indian languages, so necessary to empower the common masses. I was convinced that he would hail the Internet as one of the greatest creations of the human mind.

Why?

Because, didn't he say in his letter to Nehru that he wanted the denizens of the ideal Indian village of his dreams to be able to hold their own against anyone in the global village? Hadn't he often said that he wanted inventions that served the masses, and not just the classes? 'Whatever cannot be shared with the masses is taboo to me', he had written in *Harijan* in 1934[11]. Now, here he would have found an affordable and universally owned technology that reaches billions of people almost instantaneously, in every corner of the earth, a technology that has actually transformed the entire world into a Global Village. Wouldn't all this have made Gandhi an ardent user and a spirited backer of the Internet?

Most certainly!

To know why Gandhi would have been enthusiastic about the Internet, we shall now explore how the Internet promotes several ideals dear to his heart. Similarly, in the following chapters we shall attempt to show that the future evolution of the Internet, which is the most human-like of all the scientific inventions in history, can assist mankind's own evolution towards a better future – a Gandhian future – provided it is used wisely.

A Better World Is Possible! – *Gandhi was a supreme techno-optimist. In an appreciative and anticipative comment about the advancements in science and technology in his time, he wrote in 1925: 'Many things are impossible and yet are the only things right. A reformer's business is to make the impossible possible by giving an ocular demonstration of the possibility in his own conduct. Whoever thought it possible before Edison to speak to people hundreds of miles away from us? Marconi went a step further and made wireless communication possible. We are daily witnessing the phenomenon of the impossible of yesterday becoming the possible of today. As in physical science, so in psychological.'*

The Mahatma, who used Marconi's 'Victorian Internet', would have certainly embraced the Internet for effecting mankind's socio-psychological transformation.

Illustration: Riddhi Chokhawala

26

CAN THE INTERNET SERVE THE 'KHADI SPIRIT'?
The Answer Lies in what the Net is Doing

❖

Technomanifestos is the story of computer scientists, engineers, mathematicians, and other visionaries who raised profound questions of how technology relates to human beings, redefining who and what we are and where we are going. Fueling these revolutionaries is the conviction that computers are tools for communication, creativity and community, not just computation and capitalism…At the beginning of the twenty-first century, humans have reached symbiosis with their information technologies. The ethical, political, and economic decisions that thinking people must now face are some of the most difficult… The spirit of humanism underlies the convictions of the information revolutionaries.

— Introduction to *Technomanifestos: Visions from the Information Revolutionaries* by Adam Brate. The book features the works and ideas of the wizards in information technology — Vannevar Bush, Alan Turing, John von Neumann, J.C.R. Licklider, Doug Engelbart, Marvin Minsky, Tim Berners-Lee, Richard M. Stallman, Lawrence Lessig, K. Eric Drexler, Bill Joy, Jaron Lanier and others.

THE IDEA OF THE INTERNET AS A TWENTY-FIRST CENTURY substitute for the spinning wheel may seem far-fetched, but only on a superficial consideration. A deeper inquiry will reveal many layers of the truth of this proposition.

Our inquiry should begin by asking ourselves mainly three pertinent questions.

1. Is there any machine or technology that is changing, or is capable of changing, our world in a manner that is fundamentally different from the industrialism of the West that Gandhi had vehemently opposed?
2. As we have seen in the previous chapter, Gandhi himself was open to the idea of a substitute for the spinning wheel if it promoted the latter's three-pronged economic, cultural and moral-spiritual message rooted in truth and nonviolence. Therefore, does any other machine or technology come close to fulfilling this criterion?
3. The world situation, as also India's own national situation, has changed incomparably in the post-Gandhi era. Many new challenges and problems have arisen before the world during this period. Is there any machine or technology, or a developmental paradigm based on that technology, which can potentially meet these new challenges in a manner consistent with the Gandhian philosophy?

Three questions, but only one answer: Internet!

The Internet, and the breathtaking advances in other technologies that it is facilitating, have been transforming our world, especially the global economy and culture, in fundamentally new ways. Much of this transformation has been positive, and of a kind that would have pleased Gandhi. Of course, these positive transformations have not been effected by technology alone. Many important socio-political developments since the latter half of the last century have also contributed decisively to making our world a relatively better place to live in. Some of these developments are – end of colonialism, end of the Cold War, spread of democracy to more and more parts of the globe, and the rise of Asia, Africa and Latin America. Significantly, the Internet has positively and catalytically impacted even these progressive socio-political developments. No invention in human history has ever had such simultaneous influence on almost all aspects of human life – that too, on a global scale.

Lest my hypothesis that the Internet is the successor to the spinning wheel of the Gandhian conception be misunderstood and countered as pure fantasy, I must add a few caveats here. Firstly, the Internet – here, let me repeat, I include all the digitial technologies and all the advances in human knowledge generated by these technologies – has the *potential* to fulfil the triple expectations that Gandhi had from his ultra-simple artefact. However, much of the Internet's potential is yet to be realised. We are still in the infancy of the Internet age. There are too many unjust, iniquitous, exploitative and dehumanising remnants of the industrial age that are still surviving. These may yet survive for a long time to come. But the Internet's contribution to mitigating them has already become incontrovertible.

My second caveat: whether, how soon, and to what extent, these remnants of the industrial age can be banished by unleashing the Internet's transformative potential depends on the conscious socio-political and ethical choices made by individuals, institutions, nations and the international community. If we do not make the right choices and initiate right actions, the Internet by itself will be powerless to remove the injustices, inequities and dehumanising practices that humankind has inherited from the past.

This leads me to my third caveat. A new band of revolutionaries are needed to guide and lead the society to unlock the Internet's revolutionary potential. No society in history has ever moved in a progressive direction without members of a leading segment of its population dedicating themselves to the task, and performing that task by becoming moral exemplars to the rest of society. This has required them to be selfless, self-motivated, and willing to make sacrifices for the larger societal good. Such change-agents also have to be knowledgeable, skilled, always eager to learn, alive to the need for introspection, self-correction and self-purification, and ever-ready to work in cooperation and in a well-organised manner with other likeminded fellow men. Gandhi's khadi, charkha and satyagraha could become a social movement only because tens of thousands of idealistic men and women in his time consciously chose to become satyagrahis who embodied the afore-mentioned qualities. The Internet age similarly needs Internet Satyagrahis to realise its full potential – this time on a global, and not merely national, scale.

To appreciate how the Internet has the potential to transform our world in essentially Gandhian ways, it is first necessary to take a brief look at the major global challenges that call for effective responses – and how the Internet is providing many of these responses.

- In spite of the spectacular rise in prosperity in some parts of the world and also India since the end of the Second World War, there has been no satisfactory solution to the problems of poverty and unemployment, and all their attendant negative effects on human development. Today, more than two billion people, accounting for over one-fourth of the global population, live in conditions of extreme poverty, deprived of housing, sanitation, clean drinking water, etc.
- Communism has almost collapsed. And capitalism has changed its complexion. However, exploitation of man by man in the economic sphere has not ceased. The divide between rich and poor was never as extreme as it is today – and it is widening.
- Exploitation of Nature to meet the insatiable demands of the dominant economic system in the world has indeed advanced to levels that were unthinkable during Gandhi's time. Prosperity for the few has been achieved by endangering the planet for all – for the human as well as non-human species. Oceans, rivers, lakes, mountains, forests, farm lands and air, deemed sacred by all the ancient cultures around the world, have been poisoned in the name of 'development'. Desertification is spreading rapidly. Life of incredible diversity in the oceans is also slowly perishing. Global warming threatens to lead to climate change with unpredictably harmful consequences, including a change in the basic control mechanisms of the Earth.
- Human migration of unprecedented proportions, both within and across countries, is taking place. This is accentuating the problems of urbanisation and placing impossible demands on available natural resources. It is also creating social instability, cultural alienation and spiritual stress on a large scale.
- There is growing realisation that this model of economic growth is simply unsustainable. Its very survival depends on creating limitless

desire and demand for goods and services, most of which Gandhi and other enlightened thinkers in modern times would put beyond the orbit of the 'real needs' of human beings. One need not be an ascetic like Gandhi to realise the soundness of his warning that 'the modern mad rush for adding material comfort upon comfort' is making life 'so complicated as to make one doubly unfit for knowing oneself and one's God'.

- The use of science and technology for the production of weapons of mass destruction, far deadlier than those in Gandhi's time, has not stopped.
- New forms of violence, such as terrorism that is inspired by religious fanaticism but is adept at the use of modern technology, especially the Internet, have surfaced.

Dr James Martin, a renowned information technology scientist and founder of the 'James Martin Twenty-First Century School' at Oxford, presents a very stark prognosis of the future of humanity. In his book *The Meaning of the Twenty-First Century: The Make-or-Break Century*, he writes: 'A global cocktail of intolerable poverty and outrageous wealth, starvation, mass terrorism with nuclear/biological weapons, world war, deliberate pandemics and religious insanity, might plunge humanity into a worldwide pattern of unending hatred and violence – a new Dark Age'.[1]

Therefore, all those who are troubled by the above challenges have no option but to continue the search that characterised Gandhi's life – the search for humanising technologies and morality-promoting economic and social activities. This is where we can appreciate many virtues of the Internet, as will be evident from the following illustrations – and also from our examination of the above issues in the subsequent chapters.

Inclusive Growth Globally

The Internet is empowering ordinary people around the world, in rich as well as in not-so-rich countries. It is democratising wealth creation, making it inclusive both within countries and globally. This is happening because the power of new knowledge, which can be accessed by all those with good scientific, technological and managerial education, is prevailing over the power of old capital, which had remained the preserve of the few. The rapid spread of material prosperity outside North America and Europe to countries in Asia, Latin America and Africa, which we have seen in the past two decades, could not have been possible without this new economic paradigm of the information age proving its superiority over the old economic paradigm of the industrial age. Many countries in the so-called developing world have leapfrogged to the next level of economic growth within a few decades using the tools of the information age, India and China being prime examples. The G-7 and G-8 groups, which once dominated the world's economy and politics, have been forced to make way for the G-20 group (Argentina, Australia, Brazil, Canada, China, France, Germany, India, Indonesia, Italy, Japan, Mexico, Russia, Saudi Arabia, South Africa, South Korea, Turkey, the United Kingdom, the United States of America, and the European Union). Many more countries are bound to join these groupings, ultimately leading to maximum democratisation of the world economic and political order.

One of Gandhi's complaints against the then prevailing industrial culture of the West was that 'industrial nations have become parasitic upon agricultural nations' and 'those who live in temperate climates have become increasingly parasitic upon tropical peoples'.[2] Today the global situation has considerably changed. Parasitism may not have completely disappeared, but it has been markedly reduced by the dramatic changes brought about by information and communication technologies (ICTs). Thus, Sri Lanka with its tropical climate enjoys a level playing field with Sweden, which enjoys cold climate, as far as harnessing the power of ICTs is concerned.

Japan was the first non-Western country in modern history to prove that technological domination was not the monopoly of Europe and USA alone. It demonstrated that even a country with scarce natural resources could develop great strengths by mastering the power of computers, telecommunications and other modern technologies. But within a few decades of the Japanese miracle, several other non-Western countries emerged as technology-driven economic powerhouses. Here are a few telling examples.

Until the end of the 1950s, South Korea was a poverty-stricken country with acute food shortages. The streets of Seoul were filled with the unemployed people and beggars, while its farmers suffered from starvation. Today, it is a case study in gleaming prosperity, a giant in hi-tech industries that has a commanding global presence in everything from heavy industries, ship-building, flatscreen television sets, automobiles, mobile communication and electronics – in short, from ship to chip. Samsung and LG have become household names in India.

Similar has been the miraculous self-transformation of Taiwan, which has been leading the computer hardware industry for a long time. It has developed breathtaking capabilities in designing and manufacturing every part in the hardware value-chain, from chips to laptops. Its highly innovative and competitive companies have been manufacturing millions of computers for the 'One Laptop Per Child' project,[3] an initiative that would have gladdened Gandhi. He would have been similarly happy to see how Taiwan's Hsinchu Science-based Industrial Park, established in 1981, has helped thousands of small-scale production units to contribute to the country's spectacular rise as a hi-tech power. Taiwan's success has inspired several other countries in South-East Asia – Indonesia, Malaysia, Thailand and, of course, Mainland China – to become manufacturing hubs for technology products.

China undoubtedly presents the most striking case study of how ICTs have helped a large continent-sized country with a population of 1.3 billion modernise itself and, in the process, radically reshape the old world order. Nearly 500 million people in China are active users of the Internet, and double that number use mobile phones. ICTs have catalysed China's breathtaking expansion and modernisation of its infrastructure and its industrial, agricultural and educational base. In slightly over two decades, China has also become the world's biggest manufacturer and exporter of IT hardware. It is now racing ahead of other countries in the development of greener, cleaner technologies for harnessing solar and other renewable sources of energy.

China's rapid economic growth also presents many negative features – massive urbanisation, urban-rural divide, rich-poor divide, social atomisation, ecological destruction, rampant corruption, excessive pursuit of materialistic progress at the cost of society's moral fabric, etc. However, these features are common, in smaller or greater measure, to all newly industrialising nations, including India. Disturbing though these negative features are, they cannot negate the truth that the resurgence of countries like India and China has challenged the unacceptable imbalance in the old global order.

Another Asian country, tiny in size and population but enormous in IT-led innovation, is Israel. It has the highest number of engineers and scientists per capita in the world, who have transformed this desert nation into a hub of innovation in diverse fields. Its innovations include the pen drive, IP telephony, ingestible pill-sized camera, ZIP compression, efficient water-saving and recycling technologies, cutting-edge agricultural advancements and a range of products in defence and security. Israel's technology-driven national strength tells the story of how the spirit of innovation can grow luxuriant plants of prosperity even in desert soil.

Incidentally, Israel's chief architect and its first prime minister, David Ben Gurion (1886-1973), who initiated his country's dramatic 'make-the-desert-bloom' campaign, was an ardent admirer of Mahatma Gandhi. In the bedroom of his spartan home in the Negev desert, where he began his nation-building movement, hangs a portrait of Gandhi – the only picture in the room. Under it is a plaque with Ben Gurion's words:

> 'The moral strength of the East is perhaps embodied most of all in the great Indian leader Mahatma Gandhi, the outstanding man who is heading the war for independence and the weapon of this commander is nonviolence'.

At the other end of the world, Brazil has emerged as an economic powerhouse on the global stage, a member of the BRICS (Brazil, Russia, India, China and South Africa) conglomerate that exemplifies how much the world has changed in recent decades. It is making big strides in IT-led development. Brazil is modernising its infrastructure, improving the efficiency of its industries and agriculture, and boosting the development of its renewable energy sector.

Information technology is also empowering Africa, which has suffered the worst pillage of its natural resources and the cruellest destruction of its native spiritual and cultural traditions in the colonial and post-colonial eras. Although ICTs progress in Africa has been slower than in Asia and Latin America, there is no doubt that Africa's renaissance has already begun and the Internet is playing a big role in this renaissance. It has dramatically increased the internal communication within and between African countries, and is promoting local entrepreneurs and innovators who are dealing with the rest of the world with unprecedented self-confidence. It is also helping Africa rediscover the incredible wealth of its own intellectual, cultural and spiritual heritage.

No poor country in the world exemplifies this Internet-induced self-confidence and ambition better than Rwanda, a small land-locked nation in central and eastern Africa that is classified as one of the least developed countries (LDCs) in the world. Unlike South Africa or neighbouring Congo, it does not have diamonds and gold. It does not have oil like Sudan in the north, nor copper like Zambia in the south. But what it does not lack is imagination and ambition. Rwanda wants to become the Singapore of Africa. Towards this end, it has decided to modernise its digital infrastructure and education, and emerge as the IT hub for the resource-rich nations in the African continent. How heartening it is to know that the dream of a digital revolution has gripped a nation that witnessed a horrific ethnic genocide in the early 1990s – 800,000 people were massacred out of Rwanda's then population of seven million, which has now risen to eleven million.

The decisive contribution of the Internet and all the Internet-enabled technologies to inclusive growth globally is by no means limited to the few examples cited above. To a greater or lesser extent, their impact can be seen all over the world. The pace of technological change is accelerating everywhere, the spread of the Internet and mobile telephony being the most visible manifestations of this change. An important driver of this change is the fact that Internet-related technologies are becoming less expensive and more open-sourced; which means that a well-educated person in Bangladesh or Botswana can contribute to collaborative innovation as much as his or her counterpart in Europe or the USA. Significantly, what we are witnessing is still the early stage of the digital technology revolution. Its outcome and impact in the next few decades are going to be unimaginably more dramatic than what we have seen so far.

For the first time in world history, the dream of equitable socio-economic development in all parts of the planet – a key element of the Gandhian vision – has begun to appear realisable. This does not at all mean that inequities have ceased to exist, globally or nationally. What the paradigm of the information age does mean is that poverty and stark inequities *need* not exist, and *can be* made history soon.

Inclusive Growth in India

Isn't India itself a telling example of how digital technologies can drive inclusive development? Nothing has contributed more to the rise of India's international profile in recent years than our country's achievements in, IT. From a near-zero level in the early 1980s, the IT sector has grown so big that it accounts for nearly six percent of India's GDP. It has also become one of the biggest employment creators in India. Significantly, IT is realising an important component of the Gandhian vision: It is ending the domination of old privileged classes by enabling new sections of society, including first-generation entrepreneurs and professionals, to become wealth-creators. Many of these entrepreneurs and professionals – N.R. Narayana Murthy, founder of Infosys, being a prime example – have built a reputation for ethical business practices.

The first phase of the development of the IT sector in India was largely characterised by software exports and outsourcing of jobs from Western countries. However, IT has also immensely helped large sectors of India's own domestic manufacturing, financial and services sectors to become efficient and globally competitive. As the domestic focus of India's IT industry inevitably increases in the years to come, especially its linkage with agriculture and the informal sector of the economy, it can make India's economic growth more resilient and create more sustainable employment opportunities – an important goal in the Gandhian paradigm of development.

Another major goal – namely, decentralised development – is also being aided by IT. Unlike the pattern of industrialisation in the previous decades, when industries and business activities were concentrated in a few big cities, the development of IT in India – and IT-led development of other industries and businesses – is fast becoming geographically inclusive. Apart from Bengaluru, Mumbai, Delhi and National Capital Region, Chennai, Hyderabad and Kolkata; smaller cities such as Poona, Ahmedabad, Thiruvananthapuram, Coimbatore, Kochi, Vijaywada, Indore, Raipur, Bhubaneshwar, Chandigarh and Jaipur have become prominent IT hubs. With a strong policy push, smaller towns and even villages can add to India's prowess in the IT sector in the years to come.

A strong stimulant to this inclusive growth is the unbelievable expansion of IT infrastructure and services almost all across the country. When India became independent in 1947, there were only 84,000 telephone lines for a population of 350 million people – a teledensity of 0.00024 percent. One of the privileged ones who had a telephone installed at his residence – which was indeed nothing more than a hut in a cluster of huts – was Gandhi, whose permanent address for the last eleven years of his life was the Sevagram Ashram. The Mahatma did not ask for the privilege. Rather, the phone connection was provided at the behest of the British viceroy, so that he could contact the leader of India's freedom movement whenever needed.

Even as recently as in 1990, India had just five million fixed phone lines installed and a teledensity of only 0.59 percent – that is, just about six out of a thousand Indians owned a phone. Owning a phone in the pre-1990s era was like owning a Toyota Lexus today! And long-distance calls, called trunk calls, were as cumbersome as reserving railway travel before the computerisation of rail ticketing.

Today, over 800 million Indians, accounting for more than half the population, have a phone. As many as 150 million Indians used the Internet in 2011, and this number could skyrocket to 500 million, with one hundred million broadband connections, by the end of 2012. Clearly, digital connectivity is no longer a luxury or a privilege in India, but a basic necessity of every citizen. Remarkably, the growth in mobile and Internet users has been faster in rural India than in urban India – a trend that opens up exciting new possibilities for inclusive growth in India. If digital, physical and market connectivity to rural areas can be rapidly improved, along with education and healthcare services, India can effect the most dramatic bridging of the urban-rural divide within the next few decades.

A major IT-led initiative with multiple benefits, including inclusive growth, is Aadhaar, an imaginative project launched by the Unique Identification Authority of India (UIDAI). Headed by Nandan Nilekani, an iconic figure in India's IT industry, it provides a twelve-digit unique number for all residents in India. The number will be stored in a centralised database and linked to the basic demographics and biometric information. It will be easily verifiable online. Aadhaar will become the single source of identity verification for Indians, thus sparing them the hassle of repeatedly providing supporting identity documents for obtaining a bank account, passport, driving licence, and so on. Aadhaar (which means base or edifice) will also become a major facilitator of financial inclusion of the poor and underprivileged people into the formal banking system. They will be able to avail services provided by the government and the private sector in a transparent manner. This will help in checking widespread corruption in the implementation of government schemes. In an era of unprecedented movement of people from one place to another in search of livelihood, Aadhaar will also give migrants hassle-free mobility of identity.

Another important dimension of the IT-driven inclusive growth in India is the slowly growing trend of social inclusivity. To be sure, it is not yet as robust as the growing trend in geographical inclusivity. Nevertheless, it is undeniable that more and more young people from underprivileged and marginalised sections of society – those belonging to the scheduled castes, scheduled tribes, other 'backward' classes (OBCs) – have begun to aspire for IT education and participation in IT-driven economic activities. This aspirational energy is bringing about a silent social revolution in India.

Although the picture above is heartening, we cannot be oblivious to the fact that IT-led inclusive development in India is facing one of its biggest hurdles in the very slow growth of the Internet in non-English Indian languages. No doubt, the number of people who speak, or study in, English is rapidly growing in India. Indeed, India is set to emerge as a country with the largest English-speaking population in the world in the latter half of this century. English, therefore, is as much an Indian language today as any of the twenty-two languages recognised by our Constitution as Scheduled Languages. Nevertheless, it is also a fact that a vast majority of Indians speak their own respective region-specific languages with very little knowledge of English. Many of these linguistic communities are very large by global standards. Indeed, each of the five big amongst them (Hindi – 422 million, Bengali – 83 million, Telugu – 74 million, Marathi – 72 million, Tamil – 61 million) is larger, in terms of population, than over 200 countries and dependent territories in the world![4] Hindi-speaking people alone outnumber the population of the United States, the third most populous country in the world. Sadly, usage of the Internet in the non-English native languages in India has remained extremely low.

Most Indians cannot use the computer in their own languages, because Indian language keyboards are hard to get. Sending e-mail and text messages on mobile phones in non-English languages is not common, because doing so is either impossible or quite cumbersome. Although the Internet offers an ocean of information and knowledge in English, what it provides in other Indian languages are mere puddles. There is very little searchable and creatively presented educational content available on the Net for students studying in non-English languages, which obviously handicaps them when they have to compete with their privileged counterparts studying in English.

Since IT remains underdeveloped in Indian languages, our country has not been able to reap its revolutionary benefits in telemedicine and other areas of healthcare; in financial inclusion through banking and insurance; in e-commerce; in e-agriculture; and in employable skill development through IT. For all the talk of e-governance in India, even the websites of governmental and semi-governmental organisations provide very little information in citizens' own languages. These websites are generally not interactive and are rarely comprehensive or updated. Indeed, much of e-governance in India has come to mean only English-governance!

Paradoxically, discrimination against Indian languages is taking place at a time when India has emerged as a leading global power in IT. India's achievement in IT certainly does us all proud. However, it is equally true that only a small section of India's population has so far contributed to, and benefited from, this success. Our farmers, workers, our people living in villages and urban slums, and our incredibly creative people in the fields of arts, crafts and culture have been IT-deprived. Despite all the talk of 'inclusive development', a vast majority of Indians are today excluded from the promise of IT-enabled educational, economic and social development. No wonder, this Digital Divide has become a new factor that is further widening the existing socio-economic divide in our society. The sad part is, this need not be so. IT itself can be a powerful tool to protect and further enrich our linguistic heritage.

This situation has produced another serious negative consequence. On the one hand, IT has created tremendous awareness and aspiration in our society, especially among the youth. On the other hand, since they cannot use the computer and the Internet in their mother-tongues, they have come to believe that English is the sole passport to prosperity and that learning in their mother tongues is pointless. Those who cannot study in English-medium schools develop an inferiority complex. Many Marathi schools in Mumbai, Kannada schools in Bengaluru, Telugu schools in Hyderabad, etc., have been closed down because of a sharp fall in enrollment. The craze for English-medium schools is fast spreading even in rural India. Thus, the very survival of native Indian languages – first as a medium of school education and ultimately in many other walks of public life – is in serious jeopardy.

This situation would have appalled Gandhi. Never a foe of English, he was nevertheless an ardent advocate of the preservation and promotion of India's rich heritage of provincial languages, in which is embedded its priceless cultural-artistic-spiritual heritage. He repeatedly stressed that people's self-expression is natural and creative only if basic education is imparted to them in their mother tongues.

Geographical inclusivity, social balance and linguistic equity in India's IT-led development are not impossible goals to achieve. With the right combination of visionary leadership, well-conceived policies, effective implementation and strong government-society partnership, these goals can be substantially realised within a couple of decades. The responsibility lies squarely with Central and state governments, business organisations, educational institutions, mass media, socio-cultural organisations and on all educated Indians. Failure to achieve these goals can have extremely negative repercussions for India.

Eradication of Mass Poverty

The combined effect of inclusive economic growth in the context of the West and the Rest, and also in the domestic context of 'developing' and 'underdeveloped' countries, is that mass poverty can certainly become history in the twenty-first century itself. This noble end can be realised primarily due to the unprecedented power of technologies of the digital age. Mass poverty, it must be remembered, is a festering wound caused by the industrial age. Although poverty in relative terms has existed throughout history, mass poverty and mass unemployment did not exist before the arrival of Western colonialism and capitalism. They came to blight human societies because the industrial age thrived on exploitation of one nation by another and of one class by another. In contrast, the information age is going to make it increasingly difficult for such exploitation to continue, either between or within nations. It holds the promise of creating productive and sustainable livelihoods in every part of the world, as Gandhi had dreamt of.

As we have seen in the earlier chapters, the principal economic reason for Gandhi's advocacy of the spinning wheel was that he saw it as a provider of self-reliant, dignified and decentralised employment to millions of poor people in rural India under the British Raj. In the changed circumstances of today, no other technology is capable of generating large-scale employment, self-employment and wealth creation opportunities for the rural as well as urban poor than the Internet. It can boost agricultural productivity by reviving traditional knowledge and combining it with the discoveries and applications of modern science. It is already helping in weather forecasting and in conservation and better management of soil, water and other natural resources. For example, Israeli companies like Netafim and Plastro have shown how IT can be used to promote micro-irrigation systems that drastically reduce water input while maximising crop yields and preserving soil fertility. Since agriculture accounts for seventy percent of worldwide water use, universal adoption of IT-supported water conservation practices has become absolutely critical for water security.

One of the major uses of IT in poverty eradication can be seen in the way the functioning of village milk producers' cooperatives, helped by the National Dairy Development Board (NDDB), are being modernised across India. Milk production as an allied activity of farming significantly enhances the incomes of rural families. Indeed, women are now running many milk cooperatives in villages. They are becoming well-versed in modern management and technology practices – such as in the use of smart cards and handheld devices that have brought banking operations to their doorsteps. Establishing traditional bank branches in every village is not possible. It is also difficult for a village woman to travel to a nearby bank for her banking needs. Now technology has helped spread the concept of 'branchless banking', which is not only providing new livelihood opportunities for rural women but also boosting their self-esteem and aiding their socio-economic empowerment.

Similarly, ICTs can help revive traditions, skills and knowledge systems in agriculture, animal husbandry, arts, crafts and other eco-friendly productive activities using locally available natural resources.

For example, developing new crop varieties through traditional hybridisation methods is more eco-friendly than genetically modified (GM) crops. But such experimentation is time-consuming. It can be speeded up dramatically through modelling and simulation. ICTs can also impart to rural populations – to women as much as to men – new skills and knowledge in these areas, sourced from the local as well as the global pool of knowledge, expertise and best practices. Besides, they can create new market linkages and efficient service delivery mechanisms. Significantly, the education and training required for all these ICT-supported economic activities can be provided by ICTs themselves – what Gandhi had envisioned as bringing the '*vidyapeeth* (university) to villages'.

I saw one such example of a world-renowned university, the MIT, going to an Indian village and attempting to benefit the villagers with a combination of high and low technologies. Dr Neil Gershenfeld, who is now the director of MIT's prestigious Centre for Bits and Atoms, began a unique initiative at Vigyan Ashram at Pabal village near Poona. Vigyan Ashram, which is guided by the Gandhian philosophy of 'learning through doing', is empowering young people, mostly high-school dropouts, through revival of native scientific and technological capabilities. Both Gershenfeld and Vigyan Ashram's founder, the late Dr Shrinath Kalbag, believed in demystifying science. Their partnership led to MIT bringing its fabrication laboratory (FAB LAB), a set of computer-operated fabrication tools such as a 3-D milling machine which can make just about any machine part. FAB LAB was customised for local needs, such as making circuit boards to be used in groundwater-locating machines, devices to test milk for purity, diesel engine tuning devices, etc. Local communities have greatly benefitted from these locally produced precision devices.

I met Gershenfeld, author of the widely acclaimed book *FAB: The Coming Revolution on Your Desktop: From Personal Computers to Personal Fabrication*[5], at his MIT office in Cambridge, USA. 'Information technology is the greatest driver of decentralisation,' he said. 'Just as personal computers have decentralised access to information, personal fabricators will decentralise capabilities to make and manufacture things. This will have a profound impact on the economy and society in the future. It will be something akin to what Mahatma Gandhi had visualised.'

Initiatives like the one at Vigyan Ashram need to be vastly replicated. However, as 'proof-of-concept', they amply prove that digital technologies have the potential to create adequate employment and income-generating opportunities in decentralised, ecologically sustainable, socially cohesive and culturally vibrant rural habitats, from which mass poverty can be banished irreversibly. Wasn't this the dream that Gandhi had conveyed in his historic letter to Nehru in October 1945? Let us re-read those infinitely inspiring lines from the letter quoted in the previous chapter:

> While I admire modern science, I find that it is the old looked at in the true light of modern science which should be reclothed and refashioned aright. You must not imagine that I am envisaging our village life *as it is today*. The village of my dreams is still in my mind. After all every man lives in the world of his dreams. My ideal village will contain intelligent human beings. They will not live in dirt and darkness as animals. Men and women will be free and able to hold their own against anyone in the world... *(Emphasis added)*

Let us make no mistake. The Internet is that super-intelligent machine which will help man 'look at the old in the true light of modern science'. It will also 'reclothe and refashion aright' humankind's limitlessly diverse intellectual and cultural resources from the past to create a better future for all.

Owned by All, Accessible to All

The Internet is serving the philosophy of khadi and the spinning wheel in several other ways, too. For Gandhi, one of the chief attractions of the charkha lay in the fact that it could be owned and used by almost one and all. Similarly, the Internet – more precisely, the World Wide Web (WWW), the most important application that runs on the

global system of interconnected computer networks and supports the
sharing of an ocean of information and other services – belongs to
all and can be used by all. Parts of the Internet infrastructure are
owned by various organisations, corporations, governments, academic
institutions, private citizens and service providers, but nobody owns
it all. *There is no centralised control, and nobody can turn the Internet off.*
(Emphasis added)

True, there are national and international organisations that oversee
and standardise the working of the Internet and assign IP addresses
and domain names, such as the International Corporation for Assigned
Names and Numbers (ICANN), National Science Foundation (NSF),
the Internet Society (ISOC) and its Internet Engineering Task Force
(IETF) and Internet Architecture Board (IAB), etc. Many of these are
nonprofit, public-benefit, and democratically governed corporations with
participants from all over the world dedicated to keep the Internet
secure, stable and interoperable, and to ensue the open development
of the Internet for the benefit of people throughout the world. Just
as Gandhi would have liked it.

The Internet is unique not only in the sense that it is owned
by all, but also for the fact that it is potentially accessible to all the
people in the world. Already, by the middle of 2011, as many as
2.5 billion people in the world, out of a global population of about
seven billion, were using it. The Internet penetration, as a percentage
of the population, was the lowest in Africa in 2010 – only eleven
percent. Significantly, however, Africa also accounted for the fastest
rate of growth of Internet usage during the decade of 2000-10 – 2353
percent! As many as forty-six percent of Internet users worldwide are
women. Access to mobile telephony is close to becoming universal.
According to the International Telecommunications Union (ITU),
ninety percent of the world's population had access to mobile services,
including eighty percent of people in rural areas, by the end of 2010.
Driving this growth is the increasing affordability of the basic mobile
and Internet services. The prices of mobile phones and computers, as
well as usage charges, are falling all over the world. With advances in
wireless technology making the Internet rapidly available on a mobile

platform, there is little doubt that the basic Internet services can be made available to the entire global population within a decade.

Until recently, the wheel and electricity were the only universally used inventions in the history of mankind. This hallowed category of history-changing inventions now has a third member: the Internet, which can be owned, accessed and used by every human being on the planet. However, unlike the other two, this new invention is interactive and also intelligent. It is well on its way to becoming the Central Nervous System of the human race. Thus, it is worthy of being regarded as the first 'Species Tool' of mankind, with enormous new possibilities for the future evolution of the human race, a concept that will be discussed in greater detail in Chapter 35.

Instantaneous and Universal Communication

E-mail or electronic mail was invented in 1971 by Ray Tomlinson, who, in a brilliant insight, used the @ sign to separate the user from their computer. E-mail is the commonest application of the Internet, instantaneous in its delivery and universal in its reach. However, its magical power can be understood by contrasting it with the archaic communication systems of the past.

This point is best illustrated by referring to Gandhi's *London Dairy*, which he had maintained during his student years in England (1888-91). It contains the following letter he wrote to his elder brother Lakshmidas, upon reaching London, in which he registered a mild complaint.

November 9, 1888

Respected Brother,

I am sorry that there has been no letter from you for the last two or three weeks. Your silence is due perhaps to your not having heard from me. But it was impossible for me to post any letters before I reached London. That you should not have written to me on that account is indeed surprising. As I am far from home we can meet only through letters. And if I do not

get letters I feel very much worried. Therefore please drop a
postcard every week without fail. ...Please give my respects to
mother and sister-in-law.[6]

How quaint Gandhi's source of worry seems to us today! This is because
we have got accustomed to the instantaneity of Internet connectivity. If
Gandhi had Internet access then, he would have had real-time e-mail
communication with his family in Porbandar and, better still, made
audio and video calls to know about the wellbeing of his mother,
brother, and his own wife and their little son Harilal. In particular,
his experience of a very sad episode in his life – the death of his
mother – would have been very different.

Gandhi's mother Putlibai, to whom he was deeply attached, passed
away when he was studying in England. However, he learnt about her
demise only after he returned to India in June 1891 – that is, nearly
six months later. Gandhi writes about this in his autobiography: 'I
was pining to see my mother (when I returned to India). I did not
know that she was no more in the flesh to receive me back into her
bosom. The sad news was not given to me...My brother had kept me
ignorant of her death, which took place whilst I was still in England.
He wanted to spare me the blow in a foreign land. The news, however,
was nonetheless a severe shock to me.'

E-mail and other communication applications of the Internet
have undoubtedly boosted social connectivity in the virtual sphere.
Nevertheless, the downside to the phenomenon of being forever
connected to the outside world by e-mail, SMS and the mobile
Internet cannot be ignored. Most knowledge workers all over the
world find that they have very few 'unconnected' hours in a day for
themselves. Besides, they also have to deal with a considerable amount
of 'information overload' which exhausts them mentally. Digital
connectivity can be no substitute for real-life social interactions, where
alone can humans experience the joy of giving and receiving warmth,
empathy, understanding and love.

Clearly, the gains of Internet-enabled communication should
not come at the expense of socialisation (which is our ability to
communicate authentically with others), contemplation (which is our

ability to communicate with our own inner selves) and meditation (which is our ability to communicate with our Creator). Therefore, one of the big challenges before individuals and societies is how to find in the digital age the right balance between different modes of communication that are necessary for human happiness.

How Social Media is Democratising the Mass Media

Gandhi was a uniquely creative and effective communicator. The power of his communication lay as much in the power of his thoughts as in his sincere and transparent personality. These very qualities made him an outstanding journalist with a radically pro-people approach to his profession. He believed that the media 'should never be prostituted for selfish ends or for the sake of merely earning a livelihood or, worse still, for amassing money'.[7] The true owners of a newspaper, he believed, were its readers and not its proprietors. Therefore, in the several journals that he founded and edited, he devoted a lot of space for ordinary readers' letters and comments. Indeed, his critics outnumbered his admirers in these contributions. He was a zealous defender of freedom of the press, which he called 'a precious privilege' of journalists and readers alike.

A lot has changed in the world of media since the time of Gandhi. Unfortunately, many of these changes have reinforced the ills that he had warned against. Mass media outlets and products in democratic societies have become commercialised to an unacceptable degree. Profit-making, rather than public service, has become the guiding criterion for both news and entertainment parts of the media. Influential newspapers, magazines, TV channels and movie production houses are owned mostly by transnational or big national corporations, whose commitment to the ethics of journalism and entertainment is, barring exceptions, either weak or non-existent. The phenomenon of 'paid news' – political parties, candidates contesting elections, and businessmen paying for space in newspapers and for airtime on TV channels for favourable coverage or even for negative coverage of their rivals – shows the extent of the malaise that has spread in the

Indian media. The products of the big media groups, apart from 'dumbing down' journalism and deadening people's sensibilities, also suppress national and local cultures. They treat the common man merely as a passive consumer, unworthy of being paid the close and fawning attention that is reserved for the rich and powerful in society. Herbert Schiller (1919-2000), a respected American media critic, had aptly described this phenomenon as 'the mass media without the masses'.

(As we go to the press, the phone-hacking scandal in the UK, in the Rupert Murdoch-owned *News of the World*, has claimed as casualty one of the world's largest circulated newspapers. It might also well wreck many reputations in British journalism and politics.)

Much, though not all, of this is now changing with the advent of the Internet. A new wave of transformation has been sweeping the mass media with considerable potential to promote Gandhian ideals. In particular, the Internet is slowly giving the mass media back to the masses by sounding the death knell of the big media owned by big money. In the process, it is also reforming the noble profession of journalism. Readers and viewers of the print and TV media are no longer passive consumers. Thanks to the Internet, they can express their views freely. Since anyone can create her or his own web journal or blog with little expense, the small media as well as the blogosphere are humming with millions of voices commenting on just about every aspect of human life. Many of these voices are more creative and incisive than those that are read in newspapers or heard on TV channels. Moreover, the Internet has also helped many ordinary citizens become 'citizen journalists'. Today anybody equipped with enthusiasm, ideas and good communication skills, and having access to a digital camera and the Internet, can produce reports and features for a global audience. Of course, such 'citizen journalists' have the responsibility to be objective, fair, accurate, careful and non-sensational in what they report or write.

The birth of social media, which enable the creation and exchange of user-generated content on a common, globally accessible platform, is by far the most stunning proof of how the Internet has been democratising the world of mass media. Social networking sites such as Facebook (which had over 800 million users all over the world in early 2012) and Twitter have become shared digital terrains on which countless borderless conversations and friendships blossom daily. People have the opportunity to make friends worldwide, and also find like-minded individuals and groups with common ideas and concerns with whom they can collaborate in socio-political activities. This has enhanced their ability to make a difference worldwide, as has been shown, for example, by the worldwide support for the pro-democracy movements in Arab countries.

More specialised social networking sites encourage voluntarism, promote philanthropy and bring micro-finance to tiny enterprises that are otherwise underserved by traditional financial institutions. These sites also facilitate professionals to make contacts, scientists to conduct collaborative research, and artists and cultural personalities to join hands across continents.

Decentralisation and democratisation of the digital media has revealed another immensely important benefit – their application in disaster prevention, mitigation and management. The use of the Internet for rescue, relief and rehabilitation in a natural calamity was most strikingly seen when Japan was rocked by the triple calamity of an earthquake, a tsunami and a nuclear emergency at Fukushima in March 2011, and also when Haiti was struck by a massive earthquake in January 2010. Social media communities including Twitter, Facebook and YouTube played a significant role in the rescue and relief effort. Google has launched highly useful applications such as 'Crisis Response' and 'Person Finder' to disseminate real-time information that can help rescue and relief efforts in disaster situations.

All this, truly, is digital democracy in action.

Democratiser of Education

Gandhi's views on education are profoundly different from what passes for education in the institutionalised learning in most of our schools, colleges and universities today. By education he meant 'an all-round drawing out of the best in the child and man – body, mind and spirit'. Ethical conduct was, for him, the beginning and the end of education. 'An education which does not teach us to discriminate between good and bad, to assimilate the one and eschew the other, is a misnomer,' he wrote.[8]

Contrary to the prevailing myth that guides the government's policy and parental thinking on primary education, he held that 'literacy is not the end of education, nor even the beginning'. 'Literacy education', he wrote, 'should follow the education of the hand – the one gift that visibly distinguishes man from beast. In my scheme of things the hand will handle tools before it draws or traces the writing'. Learning by doing, producing and serving the surrounding community was his methodology of education. Therefore, he said: 'The method adopted in the institutions of India I do not call education, i.e., drawing out the best in man, but a debauchery of the mind.'[9]

We have briefly described in Chapter 12 how Gandhi sought to introduce his radically different philosophy of education by conducting practical experiments in what he called Nayi Talim – New Education.

We cannot claim that the Internet has so far made a major contribution to realising Gandhi's enlightened vision of education. However, it is definitely serving a few important elements of that vision – especially, his insistence that good-quality education that is available to the rich should also become available to the poor. It has created many powerful educational tools that are rapidly democratising access to knowledge, across geographical and economic barriers. IT-enabled open and distance learning, if backed by useful and creative content, can expand not only access but also advance the other important criteria of education – namely, quality, affordability and equity.

Indeed, the biggest impact of the Internet-enabled culture of content-sharing can be seen in an area where it is most needed – education. The Internet offers a cornucopia of high-quality pedagogical content in the form of educational videos, e-tutorials, encyclopedias, etc., that can, in the hands of a trained teacher, make learning any subject exciting and joyful in rural as well as urban schools. For example,

Google Earth has made geography fascinating to learn. Google Sky has done the same to learning astronomy, a subject that immensely fascinated Gandhi. He wanted music to be made an integral part of the syllabus of primary education. The Internet has made the best and the most varied treasure of world music available to students as well as connoisseurs.

The UNESCO-sponsored Open Educational Resources (OER) movement has given a big fillip to universal access to high-quality education. Under OER, more and more prestigious universities around the world have been sharing their online courses, course materials, modules, textbooks, streaming videos, tests, software, and any other tools or techniques that can enrich the experience of teaching and learning. Indeed, OER is making printing and purchase of textbooks almost redundant by allowing teachers to share and modify course materials freely, anywhere in the world.

For example, two successful Silicon Valley entrepreneurs of Indian origin, Vinod Khosla and his wife Neeru Khosla, have established the nonprofit CK-12 Foundation, which provides free and high-quality digital textbooks to teachers and students in USA and around the world. Says Neeru Khosla, its chairperson: 'Today's textbooks represent a system of learning and knowledge transfer that is centuries old and has not kept pace with modern technologies. The consequence is that traditional textbooks are often expensive, rigid and difficult to update. Today's children are so tuned into technology and up-to-the-minute news and information that I think that children see a "cool" factor in having the most current, updated textbooks, in the most technologically advanced format.'[10]

If the US is having a problem with expensive, outdated and difficult-to-update textbooks for school and college students, the situation is far more serious in India. Thanks to the government's apathetic, inefficient and corruption-ridden approach to this issue, most textbooks in India are of dismal quality. Also, they are hardly synchronised with the rich multimedia content available on the Net. Hence, there is an urgent need to empower both teachers and students to benefit from digitally enhanced methods of teaching and learning. Also, as mentioned earlier, the imperative need to produce high-quality and frequently updated pedagogic content in non-English Indian languages must not be lost sight of.

Innovative and IT-enabled enterprises in education will not only replace traditional textbooks but also make knowledge-acquisition and knowledge-creation a collaborative activity. Khan Academy, a US-based nonprofit educational organisation, is one of the most inspiring initiatives in using the Internet to offer high-quality pedagogical content to students globally. Its motto is to 'change education for the better by providing a free world-class education to anyone anywhere'. Founded by Salman Khan, an idealistic computer professional of Bangladeshi origin, this hugely popular and widely acclaimed academy has so far delivered over forty million video-assisted lessons online on a wide range of subjects. Similar online educational initiatives have been sprouting in many countries.

Many of these online initiatives address the issue of self-learning and lifelong learning, which is another key ideal in Gandhi's philosophy of education. Never an enthusiast of exclusive classroom learning, much less of rote learning, he believed that living and learning should be inseparable, a belief he best expressed by saying: 'Live as if you were to die tomorrow. Learn as if you were to live forever'.[11] This Gandhian aphorism prefigures modern management concepts such as 'lifelong learning' and 'the learning organisation' that have been developed by Peter Senge and other renowned thinkers. Learning from others, and learning from the world we live in, must continue ceaselessly throughout our lives. The Internet makes this possible like no other tool in history has done.

Wisdom of the Crowd

Even though the Internet is still in its infancy, its impact on knowledge creation has already been revolutionary. By effecting the 'death of distance', it has enabled people across countries, continents and cultural barriers to connect and collaborate with each other in numerous creative pursuits, and to form altogether new 'virtual communities'. It has brought the ocean of knowledge in diverse fields and from around the world within the reach of netizens anywhere and anytime – and their numbers are growing by leaps and bounds. We have already referred to blogs, on which people from anywhere can post comments. The Internet is populated with countless websites of organisations and individuals that make their activities and expertise known to the entire world. Similarly, free-to-use social information sites such as Wikipedia, to which scholar-volunteers around the world can contribute in terms of content creation and editorial work, are demonstrating the power and potential of what is called 'the knowledge of the crowd' or 'the wisdom of the crowd'.

When Wikipedia's founder Jimmy Wales says that 'access to information, basic information in particular, is a fundamental human right', or when Wikimedia Foundation's Sue Gardner says that Wikipedia aims to provide 'the sum-total of all human knowledge', they are essentially endorsing the Gandhian approach to knowledge – that is, knowledge is a universal human value and must belong to the entire humanity. Further, it should be used for the wellbeing of our planet and all the living beings on it. By supporting invaluable knowledge-dissemination resources such as Wikipedia, the Internet is certainly increasing the weight of universal values and facilitating cooperation among diverse cultures across the world.

Before the advent of the Internet, it was not possible for the huge wealth of the cultural and intellectual heritage residing within museums, galleries, libraries, educational institutions and archives to be made widely available. Even after their resources were digitised, a major obstacle in making them universally accessible was the obsolete nature of copyright and intellectual property rules. These are now being radically rewritten by netizens to promote creative collaboration globally on a common digital platform. Nonprofit organisations like Creative Commons have made it possible for the people worldwide to share, remix, reuse and repurpose Internet resources – legally. By providing a free, public, and standardised infrastructure and licensing protocols, Creative Commons has given a big boost to universal access to digital creativity, innovation and R&D. As Lawrence Lessig, a founding member of Creative Commons and a strong proponent of reduced legal restrictions on copyrights, says: 'If the Internet teaches us anything, it is that great value comes from leaving core resources in a commons, where they're free for people to build upon as they see fit'. Such indeed was the practice in traditional workshops and guilds in India. Gandhi sought to promote a similar ethos of resource-sharing in the various cooperative institutions that he founded.

If the 'Wisdom of the Crowd' concept has been rapidly gaining ground, a major catalyst behind it is the growing global backing for Open-Source Software (OSS). It is a collaborative, transparent and low-cost method of software development which has posed a big challenge to vendors of commercial software, who often resort to predatory practices. The word that best captures the spirit of OSS is 'Ubuntu', the South African philosophy of showing humanitarian care and consideration towards others. Says Nobel laureate Bishop Desmond Tutu, South Africa's widely respected anti-apartheid activist who was deeply influenced by Gandhi's life and teachings: 'A person with ubuntu is open and available to others, affirming of others, does not feel threatened that others are able and good, for he or she has a proper self-assurance that comes from knowing that he or she belongs in a greater whole and is diminished when others are humiliated, or diminished when others are tortured or oppressed'.

Ubuntu is also the name of a computer operating system based on Linux and, in the true spirit of open source, it is absolutely free to download, use, share and improve however and whenever one likes. In Chapter 32, we present the Gandhian-sounding views of Richard Stallman, the chief propagator of the movement for Free and Open-Source Software (FOSS).

Inclusive Research and Innovation by 'Citizen Scientists'

We have seen in Chapters 7 and 13 how Gandhi envisioned collaborative scientific research to take place in the institutions that he founded for the promotion of spinning, village industries, sanitation, public health and for the eradication of leprosy. He told the volunteers working in these institutions: 'I expect something unique from you', some 'truly original work instead of mere imitation.' He urged scientists and workers in the constructive movement to give the highest priority to finding solutions to the problems faced by the poor.

Gandhi's vision of collaborative research for the collective good of humanity has now found a powerful ally in the Internet. Knowledge creation and technological innovation in the twenty-first century has become unthinkable without Internet-enabled collaboration. In today's age of 'Science Without Borders', almost all major research projects, (except those in the area of national defence) involve alliances among nations and international institutions. A growing volume of research papers in high-energy physics, nanotechnology, space science, oceanography and other cutting-edge sciences are co-authored by researchers across borders. This new culture of globalism in science and technology is perhaps best showcased by the prestigious TED (Technology, Entertainment and Design) conferences and projects, which provide a digital platform for all the 'Ideas Worth Spreading'.

The most heartening example of such collaborative research in India is the the Open Source Drug Discovery (OSDD), a consortium conceived and led by Dr Samir Brahmachari, director general of the CSIR, which is India's largest R&D organisation. It is inspired by the success of open-source models in IT and biotechnology. OSDD aims at contributing to the goal of 'affordable healthcare for all' by leveraging the power of the Internet. It enables scientists, doctors, technocrats, students and others from diverse domains to collaboratively discover low-cost but effective therapies for tropical diseases like malaria, tuberculosis, etc., which are neglected by the giant Western multinational companies in the pharmaceutical sector. Tuberculosis, for example, kills 1.7 million people every year globally, mostly in Asia, and India accounts for one-fifth of those deaths. In a novel initiative, OSDD engaged 400 college students in mapping the genome of the bacterium that causes tuberculosis. This was facilitated by Twitter-based communication within the group. This shows how the massive data provided by the ambitious Human Genome Project can now be mined by the global scientific community to produce precious knowledge that can promote health and happiness.

The Internet is supporting not only sophisticated research projects like OSDD, but also grassroots innovations that are critical for alleviating poverty and improving the quality of life in rural India. This vision is being realised through the National Innovation Foundation (NIF), a laudable initiative of the Indian government's Department of Science and Technology (DST). A brainchild of Dr R.A. Mashelkar, former director general of CSIR and president of Global Research Alliance (GRA), and Professor Anil K. Gupta of the Indian Institute of Management Ahmedabad (IIM-A), it provides institutional support in searching, spreading, sustaining and scaling up eco-friendly and pro-people grassroots innovations. Following Gandhi's footsteps, NIF has begun the first nationwide movement to rediscover and rejuvenate the traditional knowledge systems, talent pool and skill sets of our farmers, artisans and craftspersons, fishing communities, slum dwellers, workshop mechanics and other productive communities in the vast informal sector of India's economy. NIF has so far scouted and popularised more than 10,000 innovations in machines or processes that have improved the efficiency in rural transportation and energy conservation; boosted farm productivity; helped in the protection of biodiversity and reduction of the drudgery of humans and animals; and created new livelihoods of sustainable kind. It has also created a large digital database of medicinal plants that can promote affordable healthcare using the knowledge of traditional village-based doctors.

The concept of establishing NIF originated in a novel campaign launched by Prof. Gupta in the late 1980s through what he called the Honeybee Network. Like honey bees, he and his students travelled from village to village in Gujarat in search of innovations by local communities, which they documented and catalogued. They were astounded by how rural people, using mostly naturally available or locally producible resources and tapping their traditional knowledge systems, had found remarkably efficient and self-reliant solutions to the challenges they encountered in their own social and economic life.

ICTs have become an indispensable tool for realising the objectives of NIF. Without ICTs, it would have been impossible to build a national register of innovations, manage the ever-expanding multilingual and multimedia database, disseminate its applications, and create a large network of creative people who are keen to learn from one another's knowledge and experience. Thanks to the Internet, every Indian village can potentially benefit from, and contribute to, this grassroots innovation movement. It has also enabled bright school and college students to participate in this movement.

Participants in, and beneficiaries of, grassroots innovation movements are often seen by the global academic and media circles as belonging to 'the bottom of the pyramid'. Prof. Gupta disagrees. A khadi-wearing guru at India's most prestigious management institute, he counters this notion by making a pertinent point: 'I don't like the term "bottom of the pyramid" because it assumes that poor people are at the bottom of *all* pyramids. They may be at the bottom of the economic pyramid, but they're not necessarily at the bottom of the ethical pyramid. They are more generous quite often than rich people. They tend to be more open. They are community-oriented and they also have very many times, more creativity and innovative spirit, so in innovation they may be at the top. In the ethical pyramid, they will be at the top, so we must be very careful when using language because language shapes the habit of thought.'[12] The Mahatma would have been pleased to hear this rebuttal.

The Internet is promoting inclusive research and innovation in another heartening way. Just like 'citizen journalists', it is also assisting the emergence of a new type of scientists and innovators, who may be called 'citizen scientists' and 'citizen innovators'. Today a lot of ordinary netizens, with no PhD in science and engineering, no formal institutional linkages and no dependence on funding agencies, have been contributing to the progress of scientific knowledge and its application, simply by studying available online information and applying their creative minds. Their work may not meet the rigorous standards of leading scientific journals. They may not even have patents in their names. Nevertheless, these 'citizen scientists' and 'citizen innovators' are slowly breaking the myth that advancement of science and technological innovation can only happen in mainstream R&D institutions or universities.

This is because the best among them approach their subject with what Zen masters call a 'beginner's mind', which is characterised by openness, curiosity and lack of rigid preconceptions when grappling with a problem. 'In the beginner's mind there are many possibilities, in the expert's mind there are few,' writes Shunryu Suzuki (1904-71), a great exponent of Zen Buddhism and author of *Zen Mind, Beginner's Mind.* Incidentally, one of the 'citizen innovators' who was a college dropout but went on to create some of the most adored, and also successful, products in the Internet age by approaching every innovation with a 'beginner's mind' was Steve Jobs. *Zen Mind, Beginner's Mind* was one of Jobs's favourite books.[13]

Time-saver, Efficiency-enhancer

The Internet is the greatest time-saving technology ever invented by mankind. Gandhi valued time so much that he called it 'true wealth'. Quoting the *Bhagavad Gita*, he said: 'The Great Annihilator annihilates those who waste time'. He was a believer in the power of innovation to improve the efficiency of machines that helped mankind. In the Internet, he would have found a matchless promoter of time-saving innovation and efficiency.

In this context, it is worth recalling an important observation made by Gandhi in response to criticism that his opposition to machines and his insistence on the universal use of the spinning wheel showed him to be indifferent to the proven power of modern machines to save time and labour. As we have noted earlier, he had written in *Young India* on 13 November 1924: 'What I object to is the craze for machinery, not machinery as such. The craze is for what they call labour-saving money. Men go on "saving labour" till thousands are without work and thrown on the open streets to die of starvation. I want to save time and labour, not for a fraction of mankind, but for all'.

The Internet has already saved time and labour for more people in the world than any other machine has done so far without causing loss of jobs. And it has the potential to do so for the entire mankind, thus fulfilling Gandhi's dream.

In the same article in *Young India*, Gandhi had further stated: 'The saving of labour of the individual should be the object, and not human greed the motive. Thus, for instance, I would welcome any day a machine to straighten crooked spindles. Not that blacksmiths will cease to make spindles; they will continue to provide spindles, but when the spindle goes wrong, every spinner will have a machine to get it straight. Therefore, replace greed by love and everything will be all right'.

We see here how Gandhi was enthusiastic about machines helping machines in a production system aligned to creation of mass employment and promotion of people's welfare. IT is realising this objective. It is already being widely used in amazing ways to 'straighten crooked spindles' – namely, to conduct remote repair of computer systems and troubleshoot utilities, services and manufacturing units located in different parts of the world. Furthermore, with the help of advanced robots, glitches in satellites in orbit are being repaired by human operators from Earth, a task that is either impossible or too dangerous for an astronaut to perform. Thus, the Internet has become a provider of help anytime, anywhere and for almost everybody.

Although the tools of IT hold the attractive promise of increasing efficiency and augmenting time for the human race, the moot question is: How well do we use our time? Time offers to us infinite possibilities to enrich our lives. However, just as we waste much of the huge potential of our brain power, we also squander away a lot of possibilities of putting the limited time at our disposal to meaningful, creative and joyful uses. We allow our mind to be enslaved by dissipative thoughts, emotions and deeds. This is because we have not cultivated the art of mental concentration. Thus, even when we spend time with our family members, colleagues or strangers, usually we neither gain much from them nor they from us. Here again we have much to learn from Gandhi's life. This is what B.R. Nanda, one of his best biographers, tells us:

Gandhi's punctuality was proverbial; it was said that he was a slave only to his watch. He rigorously rationed his time, but as Amiya Chakravarty, who was Tagore's secretary for some years, recalls, 'even if Gandhi gave you only five minutes, he gave you *all of himself*...He was just as deeply interested in you as your own family'.[14] *(Emphasis added)*

This Gandhian ability to give all of oneself to whatever one has chosen to do at a particular moment, is a far greater augmenter of time than what the best of time-saving technologies can offer to us.

Reviver of the Wealth of Arts and Cultures

Like so many other fine things in human life whose meanings have been distorted by the pervasive ethos of commercialism, wealth in modern times has come to mean only material assets and possessions measured in money terms. What is true wealth? The Sanskrit term for it, *samriddhi*, means material, cultural and spiritual prosperity for all. In Indian philosophy, *riddhi* or material success is incomplete without *siddhi*, which means spiritual success. Thus, the importance of an ethical and egalitatian orientation to achieving material success has been in-built in the very etymology of the Indian words for wealth.

According to Gandhi, 'A man's true wealth hereafter is the good he has done to his fellowmen'.[15] This begets a question: Is it man's duty to do good only to fellowmen of his own generation, or also to the generations that lived before him and to the ones that will come in the future? Is it not our duty to take care – caring being one of the highest forms of 'doing good' – of the invaluable wealth of mankind's tangible and intangible heritage? This wealth which cannot have any price tag, has been created with immense care, love and ingenuity by countless women and men in the past. Therefore, isn't it our duty to preserve, both for today's and future generations, the magnificent or historically significant monuments and sites?

A few years ago I visited Shekhawati havelis in Rajasthan, a land blessed with tangible and intangible heritage of incalculable value and indescribable beauty. These havelis – traditional houses built in yester-centuries – are so splendid that they look like exhibits in what may be called a vast 'open air art gallery'. Sadly, a large part of this fairy-tale heritage today stands in various stages of dilapidation, decay, disfigurement – even impending death.

Then, like a thirsty and troubled man who finds a small water body while wandering in a desert, I stepped into one haveli, in a small town called Fatehpur, which has been restored with meticulous care and passion by Nadine Le Prince, a French artist. The Haveli Cultural Centre established by her is housed in a 200-year-old building, which was once in a decrepit condition. Using the tools offered by the Internet, she has carried out extensive restoration and recreated its old grandeur inch by inch. She has also set up in its premises a beautiful art gallery and a studio that trains young French and Indian students of art. 'In the beauty of these havelis one feels the omnipresence of God,' said Nadine. But she also added, in a voice filled with foreboding: 'If rapid action is not taken, the entire Shekhawati heritage will be destroyed within ten years.'

I had gone to Rajasthan to participate in the inauguration of the state government's mid-day meal scheme for school children. The scheme is run by the Akshaya Patra Foundation, the world's largest mid-day provider to school children, feeding 1.3 million children daily. In my speech, I recited a famous poem 'His Name is Today' by Gabriela Mistral, a Nobel laureate poetess from Chile. The poem is about our urgent humanitarian and moral duty to end hunger and malnutrition among children – nearly eight million children die of malnutrition in the world each year, of which slightly less than a million are from India alone. Here is the poem.

> *We are guilty of many errors and many faults,*
> *But our worst crime is abandoning the children,*
> *Neglecting the fountain of life.*
> *Many of the things we need can wait,*
> *The child cannot.*
> *Right now is the time his bones are being formed,*
> *His blood is being made,*

And his senses are being developed.
To him we cannot answer 'Tomorrow'.
His name is 'Today'.

The poem has an equally urgent message about the endangered Shekhawati havelis, and similar close-to-extinction heritage sites and resources around the world. With due apologies to Gabriela Mistral, it can be said:

To them we cannot answer 'TOMORROW'.
Their name is 'TODAY'.

How do we end our collective callousness towards our architectural, artistic, cultural and spiritual inheritance? No doubt, enormous political will, societal commitment and sound legal safeguards are needed. However, in the context of this book, it is useful to know that ICTs have proven power to preserve and enhance this wealth. They have revolutionised the art of heritage conservation. The Internet and other digital tools offer a wide variety of opportunities for identifying, collecting, recording, analysing, processing and popularising information about every kind of heritage resources. Some of these tools are 3D data capture; on-site and remotely sensed data collection; radiographic dating; computer animation; virtual reality in archaeology and historical research; multimedia and multi-lingual data management and archiving; e-museums, e-exhibitions and e-learning in heritage conservation; and ICT assistance in fund-raising, monitoring and restoration.

Successful restoration of Angkor Wat in Cambodia, which is one of the greatest wonders of the world, is a fine example of both the power of digital tools and the efficacy of UNESCO-led international cooperation. This magnificent 1,000-year-old architectural complex, site of the world's largest Hindu-Buddhist temple, was in such an endangered state, especially after the genocidal war in Cambodia in the 1970s, that UNESCO decided to take up the responsibility of safeguarding and restoring it. Several countries, including India, participated in the restoration project. Happily, its successful completion, using the latest digital technologies, led to UNESCO removing Angkor Wat from the List of World Heritage in Danger in 2004.

Numerous minority languages, cultures, artistic traditions and manuscripts, which today face the threat of extinction, may survive and thrive, thanks to the growth of voice recognition, character recognition, image processing and sophisticated translation technologies. These will erode the traditional limits on interaction between linguistic communities. The UNESCO World Heritage Centre has joined hands with Fotopedia, a collaborative photo encyclopedia, to celebrate the beauty of all the outstanding cultural and natural heritage sites around the world. The collaboration brings together thousands of photographers and hundreds of curators from all over the globe to offer to netizens a treasure trove of images and information about these places, thus helping their better protection and preservation.

Most of the rich intellectual heritage of ancient civilisations is stored in old manuscripts. Pandit Jawaharlal Nehru, India's first prime minister, had recognised the need to preserve them. In his widely acclaimed book *The Discovery of India*, which he wrote during his imprisonment during 1942-46 at Ahmednagar Fort (now a heritage site), he had remarked: 'One of our major misfortunes is that we have lost so much of the world's ancient literature – in Greece, in India and elsewhere... Probably an organised search for old manuscripts in the libraries of religious institutions, monasteries and private persons would yield rich results. That, and the critical examination of these manuscripts and, where considered desirable, their publication and translation, are among the many things we have to do in India when we succeed in breaking through our shackles and can function for ourselves'.

Sadly, our country has already lost a large treasure of manuscripts due to neglect, theft and natural decay. Nevertheless, it still possesses about five million manuscripts in various media and languages, which makes it, probably, the largest collection in the world. Many of these are in the homes of individual scholars, a majority of whom are too poor, or their children are too ignorant, to maintain them. One of the many proud initiatives of Atal Bihari Vajpayee's government (1998-2004), with which I was associated, was to launch the National Mission for Manuscripts in 2003. This first-of-its-kind mission in India aims to unearth our vast manuscript wealth, preserve and catalogue it on digital formats and make it available for research to scholars around the world. The mission has set up a National Digital Manuscripts Library, with easy-to-search contents.

The Convention for the Safeguarding of the Intangible Cultural Heritage, adopted by UNESCO in 2003, calls for safeguarding traditional indigenous knowledge and skills that are transmitted from generation to generation. Traditional knowledge in India and other ancient civilisations has richly contributed to holistic healthcare, environmental protection and sustainable livelihoods. However, massive dislocation of indigenous communities due to urbanisation, globalisation and exploitation of their natural resources is leading to steady annihilation of this knowledge. This has become a matter of particular concern in India because our traditional knowledge and resources face the threat of bio-piracy in the form of patents by foreign entities. There is, therefore, an urgent need for the government to take effective steps to preserve, protect and promote the traditional cultures and knowledge of the indigenous people.

Here again, digital technologies have come to our aid. The CSIR and the Department of Ayurveda, Yoga & Naturopathy, Unani, Siddha and Homoeopathy (AYUSH) have collaboratively established a Traditional Knowledge Digital Library (TKDL). This effort, the brainchild of CSIR's former head, Dr R.A. Mashelkar, helped India successfully fight for the revocation of turmeric and basmati patents granted by the United States Patent and Trademark Office and neem patent granted by the European Patent Office. TKDL has created a database of hundreds of Ayurvedic, Unani and Siddha formulations for treating various diseases.

By facilitating these and many more previously unimaginable developments, digital technologies are undoubtedly proving themselves to be an elixir to mankind's imperilled heritage, in which are hidden the grandest visions, deepest aspirations and mesmerising creative energies of our common ancestors.

Nicholas Roerich (1874-1947), a Russian artist, is highly revered by art lovers around the world. One of the twentieth century's greatest painters, he made the Himalayas his home in the last two decades of his life, which overflowed with creativity. He was also a tireless campaigner for the protection of the world's cultural and artistic heritage. 'There, where Culture is, is Peace,' he proclaimed:

> The concept of Culture must arouse in us the consonant concept of Unity. We are tired of destruction and of common misunderstanding. Only Culture, only the all-unifying conception of Beauty and Knowledge, can restore the pan-human language to us.

After seeing the destruction caused by the First World War, he launched a global mission to safeguard the artistic and cultural heritage of mankind by mobilising artists, scientists, intellectuals and political leaders. The Roerich-designed 'Banner of Peace' is a white flag with a red circle with three simple red dots, signifying the 'Past, Present and Future enclosed in the ring of Eternity', or 'Religion, Science and Art held together in the circle of Culture'. About this mystical symbol, which appears in numerous spiritual treasures around the world, Roerich wrote: 'This sign, unfurled over all treasures of human genius, will say: Here are guarded the treasures of all mankind; here above all petty divisions, above illusory frontiers of enmity and hatred, is towering the fiery stronghold of love, labour and all-moving creation'.

In the Internet, mankind has found a revolutionary new tool to safeguard and revive all such priceless treasures, and make them accessible to the entire global population. For example, Roerich's own spiritually eloquent paintings – indeed, the paintings of all the great artists around the world – can be seen online by all.

Friend of Freedom, Foe of Dictatorship

The Internet is proving to be a great promoter of two other ideals very dear to Gandhi's heart: freedom and democracy. Just look at what it is doing in communist-ruled China, where the blogosphere is humming with the most interesting and insistent young voices for change. Zhan Wen, a prominent Chinese blogger, was asked by a French documentary filmmaker: 'Do you think that the Internet will help to promote democracy in China?' His answer: 'Definitely. I have said many times before that I thank God for bringing the Internet to China.[16] The Internet allows information to flow more freely. It has increased the cost of controlling information flow, even making it impossible in same cases. There may be mixed messages on the Internet, including large amounts of false information. But at the very least, it has broken the monopoly of communication channels. People can listen to different voices. There is no longer an absolute authority. Every person can make his own judgment based upon the various types of information in his hands. What I called the age of solo singing has arrived. Individuals, not groups; diverse, not monolithic. This is the pre-condition as well as the essential characteristic of a democratic society.'[17]

In late 2010, massive street protests in Tunisia pulled down the twenty-four-year-old dictatorial rule of Zine El Abidine Ben Ali, who thereupon fled the country. Soon thereafter, a sustained and nonviolent mass protest action in Egypt ended the three-decade long autocratic regime of Hosni Mubarak. The heroes of these democratic revolutions were young people whose anger at the soaring unemployment rate, rising food prices, rampant high-level corruption and lack of freedoms had reached a boiling point. However, these heroes had a powerful new ally: the Internet and satellite television. These new digital media played a major role in sensitising the people on the value of democracy and freedom, organising their protests and in disseminating news and pictures of their revolution to the world. Facebook was extensively used to send vidoes and photographs of the protests, accounts of police repression and stories of the illicit wealth amassed by the president's family and his coterie. Bloggers and Twitter users reported the daily events with first-hand accounts. Autocratic Arab governments blocked thousands of sites, but to no avail.

The Internet's democracy-promoting potential is apparent not only in a communist party-ruled country like China or in countries where information flow is controlled. It is equally manifest in countries where democracy, with varying degrees of imperfection, already prevails. The Internet has made it possible for citizens and civil society organisations to air their views on a wide range of issues that they think are socially important. This has vastly strengthened the voice of the public, which cannot be ignored in a democracy.

In 2005, the Congress-led United Progressive Alliance (UPA) government, headed by Prime Minister Dr Manmohan Singh, got the Indian Parliament to enact a revolutionary law, the Right to Information (RTI) Act, which has empowered citizens to seek official information covering a wide range of governmental activities. This has cast the sunshine of transparency on the functioning of government departments, often forcing them to alter or abandon their indefensible decisions. The Internet has been powerful tool in the hands of ordinary citizens to ensure the enforcement of RTI.

Some government bodies proactively seek the views of the public using the Internet. In recent times, leaders such Barack Obama and Wen Jiabao have used the Internet to connect to the people and listen to their opinions. In India, the leader who has used the Internet most ardently and effectively is L.K. Advani, the eighty-four-year-old BJP veteran and India's former deputy prime minister. His weekly blogs, which have been published in a full-length book[18], have enriched public debate in the country on a wide range of issues.

Thus, one of the greatest contributions of the Internet to the promotion of democratic culture is its capacity to bring a wide diversity of views and suggestions on a common platform that is accessible to all. 'Evolution of democracy,' Gandhi remarked, 'is not possible if we are not prepared to hear the other side'.[19] He also said: 'My notion of democracy is that under it the weakest should have the same opportunity as the strongest'.[20] It is easy to see how the Internet is aiding the realisation of these Gandhian goals.

Nevertheless, a lot needs to be done to harness the full potential of Internet-based systems to promote democracy, indeed to help countries move towards the ideal of direct democracy. As far as India is concerned, this would need (a) provision of Indian language based content in respect of every subject of relevance to the common people; (b) transforming citizens' RTI into government's duty to inform (DTI), whereby all public information is proactively made available on the Web; (c) making available all policy documents and all legislative material (bills introduced in Parliament and state legislatures, etc.) on the Web; (d) creating web-based discussion portals where all these bills and policies can be freely discussed and the legislators influenced; (e) introducing a system of Internet-enabled referendums on issues of local and national importance; (f) people's audit of governments' budgets and schemes; (g) people's periodic evaluation of the performance of their elected representatives and civil servants; (h) empowered participation of professional groups in the running of the diverse affairs of society; and (i) constant education of the people not only about their rights but also about their duties and responsibilities.

According to Gandhi, 'That government is the best which governs the least'.[21] This was his ideal of swaraj or enlightened self-governance. In the Internet, we have a revolutionary tool to help the world move towards this ideal.

  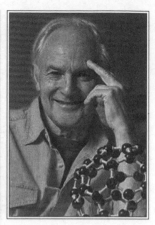

Pioneers of Nanotechnology: *Richard Feynman (left), delivered in 1959 a prophetic lecture titled 'There's Plenty of Room at the Bottom: An Invitation to Enter a New Field of Physics'; Eric Drexler (centre) popularised the term 'nanotechnology'; Dr Harold Kroto (right) won the 1996 Nobel Prize in Chemistry for co-discovering Buckminsterfullerene (C_{60}), also called buckyball, a new form of carbon structure.*

Photo: Anurag Sharma, Observer Research Foundation Mumbai

'Science to the People, Science for the People, Science by the People': *Dr Harold Kroto watching with amazement a scientific experiment demonstrated by the students and teachers from a tribal school in Yamgarwadi village in Maharashtra. At the invitation of the Observer Research Foundation (ORF), he delivered on this occasion a public lecture on 'Nanotechnology for Peace and Development' to a slum community in Mumbai in 2011. Also seen, at extreme left, is Sudheendra Kulkarni.*

27

THE NANOTECH REVOLUTION
Small will not only be Beautiful,
but also Bountiful

⊷⊶◈◇◈⊷⊶

The most striking thing about modern industry is that it requires so much and accomplishes so little. Modern industry seems to be inefficient to a degree that surpasses one's ordinary powers of imagination. Its inefficiency therefore remains unnoticed...Wisdom demands a new orientation of science and technology towards the organic, the gentle, the non-violent, the elegant and beautiful.

— E.F. Schumacher (1911–77) in *Small is Beautiful: Economics as if People Mattered.*

Trees, though, are not crude: To make wood and leaves, they don't cut, grind, stir, bake, spray, etch, or grind. Instead, they gather solar energy using molecular electronic devices, the photosynthetic reaction centers of chloroplasts. They use that energy to drive molecular machines – active devices with moving parts of precise, molecular structure – which process carbon dioxide and water into oxygen and molecular building blocks. They use other molecular machines to join these molecular building blocks to form roots, trunks, branches, twigs, solar collectors, and more molecular machinery. Every tree makes leaves, and each leaf is more sophisticated than a spacecraft, more finely patterned than the latest chip from Silicon Valley. They do all this without noise, heat, toxic fumes, or human labour, and they consume pollutants as they go.

— Eric Drexler, a pioneer in Nanotechnology.

NOT JUST INFORMATION TECHNOLOGY, BUT EVEN OTHER breathtaking advances in science and technology in the twenty-first century – genetics, nanotechnology, robotics, *et al.* which have been powered by IT – have the potential to produce benefits for humanity that would have warmed Gandhi's heart. We examine here how nanotechnology can promote several Gandhian ideals.

Necessity, it is said, is the mother of invention. True. But it can also be said that daring insight is the midwife of all scientific discoveries. The birth of nanotechnology owes to one such adventurous insight. On 29 December 1959, forty-one-year-old Richard Feynman, who had already earned the reputation of being one of the leading theoretical physicists in the world, delivered a keynote address at the annual meeting of the American Physical Society at the California Institute of Technology (Caltech). The title of his address was tantalising: 'There's Plenty of Room at the Bottom: An Invitation to Enter a New Field of Physics'.

In his talk, Feynman (1918-88), who won the Nobel Prize in 1965, asked a few bold questions that must have seemed products of pure fantasy then. 'Why cannot we write the entire twenty-four volumes of the Encyclopaedia *Britannica* on the head of a pin?' 'Can the power of a microscope be enhanced a hundred times so that it should be possible to see the individual atoms distinctly?' 'Today's computing machines are very large; they fill rooms. Can we miniaturise the computer?' Feynman's answer to these and similar questions was simple and straight: 'There's Plenty of Room at the Bottom'. The entire edifice of nanoscience and nanotechnology rests on this insight.

All the objects around us – the computer screen on which I am writing these lines, the water that I am drinking and the glass holding the water – are made of molecules. These molecules are made of atoms, which in turn are composed of subatomic particles. Atoms of different types joined together in different chemical structures create a wide variety of molecules. As Feynman put it: *'It is a staggeringly small world that is below'*. A water molecule, for example, is a bit less than 10^{-9} or one-billionth of a metre long. However, there is plenty of room – 'empty space' – between one molecule and another, and one atom and another. If this space can be manipulated, and if 'we could arrange the atoms one by one the way we want them' in different and denser configurations, the resultant objects will have vastly enhanced capabilities or altogether new properties.

Like most undergraduate students of physics around the world, I first came to know of Feynman through his famous *Feynman Lectures on Physics* when I was studying at IIT Bombay in the late 1970s. Few scientists have described the romance of physics as engagingly as Feynman has. ('Our imagination is stretched to the utmost, not, as in fiction, to imagine things which are not really there, but just to comprehend those things which are there.') But even he did not have full foreknowledge of how breathtaking would be the growth of the plant that he had seeded with his 'Plenty of Room at the Bottom' concept.

It took another visionary scientist, Eric Drexler of MIT, to sketch the larger canvas of possibilities arising out of Feynman's insight in his 1986 book *Engines of Creation: The Coming Era of Nanotechnology*. Drexler, who first popularised the term 'nanotechnology', affirmed that it would develop 'new modes of science and technology in harmony with nature and human society, a new technology for the twenty-first century. It appears destined to replace most of technology as we know it today.'

Drexler, an admirer of Mahatma Gandhi, received a lot of scornful criticism for his championing of nanotechnology in the 1980s and 1990s. His claims were dubbed as fanciful and unworkable. He countered his critics by quoting Gandhi:

> *First they ignore you.*
> *Then they laugh at you.*
> *Then they attack.*
> *Then you win.*

Nanotechnology is the science of the unbelievably tiny. It means refinement of manufacturing to nano levels – that is, involving particles as small as molecules measuring a few nanometres. A nanometre is 10^{-9} m and spans approximately ten atomic diametres. To know how small nano-scale actually is, consider the following comparison: If the world were scaled down so that people averaged one hundred nanometres tall, the Moon (3,475 km in diametre) would be about eight inches (20.5 cm) across – about the size of a basketball. The Earth (12,750 km in diametre) would be roughly thirty inches (seventy-six cm) across – about the size of a large globe in a classroom.[1] Scientists have now found that even the nano-scale is not really the bottom and there is plenty more room below to explore! Thus, picotechnology seeks to manipulate matter – or, rather, fundamental particles – on a scale of trillionths of a metre or 10^{-12} m, and femtotechnology does it on a still tinier scale of 10^{-15} m.

Nature arranges atoms and molecules of different elements in myriad different ways, but all at nano, pico, femto and even smaller scales, to produce things of infinite diversity that we see around us. Thus, if the carbon atoms in coal are rearranged, we get diamonds. However, when the carbon and other atoms in soil, water and air get rearranged in a different way in the course of the growth of a plant, we get a flower. This just goes to show how hi-tech Mother Nature is in producing trees, leaves and flowers, and how backward, gross and low-tech modern man is even in his most sophisticated systems of manufacturing.

Man, ever an eager imitator of Nature, is now applying this understanding in producing nano-scale computer chips through rearrangement of the atoms in silicon, along with the atoms of some other materials. One of man's first nanotech creations is the carbon nanotube, which is the strongest and stiffest material yet invented. It is thirty times stronger than steel, yet is one sixth the weight. It has a cylindrical structure and is constructed by rearranging carbon atoms to achieve length-to-diametre ratio of up to 13,20,00,000:1, which is larger than any other cylindrical material. By combining carbon nanotubes in a particular configuration, it is possible to manufacture a synthetic diamond-like material in a laboratory.

Dilip Kumar Ray,[2] a renowned musician and writer who closely interacted with Gandhi invokes a famous Sanskrit metaphor to describe him: *Vajradapi kathorani mruduni kusumadapi* (As strong as a diamond, but also as soft as a flower). This description made me think of the incredible promises of nanotechnology. Nature uses nanotechnology to grow carbon atoms into something as soft as flowers on a tree. On the other hand, man is using nanotechnology to synthetically reconfigure carbon atoms to 'grow' the world's hardest known material, diamond. It seems to me that both the soft-as-petal and hard-as-diamond aspects of Gandhi's character were the result of a conscious, persistent and nano-scale internal reconfiguration of his own body, mind and soul.

How is nanotechnology linked to Gandhian ideals and concerns? The answer lies in its bouquet of promises, which address many critical challenges facing humanity. In agriculture, nanotechnology's potential uses span the entire spectrum from production to processing, packaging, transportation, waste reduction and food safety. It promises supply of clear water globally through large-scale water purification and conservation solutions. Nanotech water-filters can save tens of thousands of lives in poor countries, where water-borne diseases are rampant. For example, Tata Group's low-cost Swach water filter uses silver nano-particles. Nanotechnology assures renewable clean energy and material saving, which can have a big impact on heavy industry and construction. Carbon nanotubes are being used to make vehicle frames lighter and stronger, so that vehicles can become safer and more fuel-efficient. Nano-engineered solar panels are lighter and more durable, but produce more energy. New kitchenware use nanoscale silver that are antimicrobial, capable of ensuring food safety.

In healthcare, nanotechnology provides solutions in improved diagnostics and in treating difficult-to-cure blood disorders. Doctors can conduct nanomachine-assisted surgery in hard-to-operate-on areas of the body, and provide precision treatment for Parkinson's disease, cardiovascular disease and cancers (with vastly improved efficiency and safety). Nanotechnology can create artificial tissues for replacing diseased kidneys and other body parts. It addresses environmental hazards by offering new products such as recyclable batteries and biodegradable plastics. It also offers new ways of recycling garbage thereby eliminating the need for landfills, which is a gargantuan problem in all big cities. Carbon nanotubes can hugely enhance the capabilities of ICT devices. Microchips and nanoscale batteries can open the door to supercomputers that would be a million times smaller, and more powerful, than the ones we have now. It is no longer a fantasy to think of a day when all the knowledge of the world would be available in, or accessed from, a pocket-sized supercomputer. With its promise of creating new materials with extraordinary properties, nanotechnology also offers game-changing possibilities in space research and exploration. This will enable mankind to gain deeper knowledge of the mysteries of the universe, a subject very dear to Gandhi's heart.

Among nanotechnology's most benevolent applications is that it can be used to reverse the horrifying destruction of the environment – by regenerating our polluted rivers, denuded forests, degraded lands and the threatened world of non-human species – and thus bring about a new harmony between mankind and Mother Nature.

Drexler tells us[3]:

Technology-as-we-know-it is a product of industry, of manufacturing and chemical engineering. Industry as we know it takes things from nature – ore from mountains, trees from forests – and coerces them into forms that someone considers useful. Trees become lumber, then houses. Mountains become rubble, then molten form, then steel, then cars. Sand becomes a purified gas, then silicon, then chips. And so it goes. Each process is crude, based on cutting, stirring, baking, spraying, etching, grinding, and the like.

Trees, though, are not crude: To make wood and leaves, they don't cut, grind, stir, bake, spray, etch, or grind. Instead, they gather solar energy using molecular electronic devices, the photosynthetic reaction centers of chloroplasts. They use that energy to drive molecular machines – active devices with moving parts of precise, molecular structure – which process carbon dioxide and water into oxygen and molecular building blocks. They use other molecular machines to join these molecular building blocks to form roots, trunks, branches, twigs, solar collectors, and more molecular machinery. Every tree makes leaves, and each leaf is more sophisticated than a spacecraft, more finely patterned than the latest chip from Silicon Valley. They do all this without noise, heat, toxic fumes, or human labour, and they consume pollutants as they go.

In words that would have provoked Gandhi to listen to with rapt attention, Drexler further writes:

> Nanotechnology promises to bring new capabilities, giving us new ways to make things, fulfil the needs of the planetary population, heal our bodies, and care for the environment. In the process, it turns upside down most of today's common assumptions, such as 'Industrial development is the only alternative to poverty'; 'Many people must work in factories'; 'Greater wealth means greater resource consumption'; 'Logging, mining, and fossil-fuel burning must continue'; 'Manufacturing means pollution'; 'Development land will never be returned to wilderness'; 'Third World development would doom the environment'. Nanotechnology questions the basic assumption that 'Industry as we know it cannot be replaced'.

Nanotechnology is indeed winning the minds and hearts of both people and policy-makers around the world. Its promise of more production from less resources for the benefit of more people – what Dr R.A. Mashelkar and the late Dr C.K. Prahalad called 'Gandhian Engineering' – looks indeed realisable. It is now possible to visualise a post-industrial economy in which the real needs of the entire planetary population can be met while, at the same time, conserving precious natural resources.

Nanotechnology reminds me of the widely acclaimed book that I had read in my student days – *Small is Beautiful: Economics as if People Mattered* by E.F. Schumacher, who was much influenced by Gandhi. Schumacher would have probably said that nanotechnology provides compelling proof that small is not only beautiful, but can also be bountiful.

Mention must be made here of the many ethical concerns that are being voiced in the global debate over nanotechnology. The gravest concern is about the possibility of it being used for building lethal nano-weapons and explosives. Concerns have also been raised about its likely use for electronic surveillance in ways that infringe upon citizens' privacy and dignity. The possibility of its misuse in the hands of unscrupulous drug manufacturers and medical professionals has been pointed out. These ethical concerns are indeed genuine, and render the case for effective monitoring and regulation of nanotechnology strong. But stronger still is the case for harnessing the broad-spectrum beneficial uses of nanotechnology for healing the wounds that man has inflicted on Mother Nature by pursuing misconceived development so far, and for building a healthier future for himself and other creatures on our planet.

Nanotechnology, it must be admitted, is still a science in its infancy. There is, admittedly, a big gap between the promise envisioned by its greatest champions such as Drexler, and the current state of its practical development. Dr Harold Kroto, a Nobel laureate and British scientist who is regarded as one of the pioneers of nanotechnology, says that it is very hard to foresee how rapidly the truly revolutionary promises of this new science will come to fruition. 'It might take between 20 and 40 years.' But he also indicates the possibility of unexpected breakthroughs. 'People didn't foresee the Internet, people didn't foresee the application of the laser for eye surgery.'

About the likely harmful effects of nanotechnology, what Dr Kroto says has a strong ring of wisdom: 'All powerful technologies have tremendous potential to be of benefit to society – or to cause harm. Nanotechnology per se may or may not have the capacity to do more harm than other technologies such as nuclear weapons. But if people say they don't want technology, then we will go back to the time when a quarter of children died at the age of five and people worked in the fields twelve hours a day just to survive. The technologies are here and society has to decide how it wants to use them. The problem is that although our technologies have developed rapidly, our social behaviour has remained pretty much the same since the Stone Age.'[4]

When a Nobel Laureate Scientist
Encountered Gandhi's Nayi Talim

I met Dr Harold Kroto, who won the 1996 Nobel Prize for Chemistry, in a memorable circumstance. He had come to India in early 2011 to deliver a lecture at the Mahatma Gandhi University at Kottayam in Kerala. On his way back to the Florida State University, where he researches and teaches, he was to give a talk to the students and faculty of the prestigious IIT Bombay, my alma mater. I, who head a public policy think tank, the Observer Research Foundation (ORF) in Mumbai, requested him to deliver another talk on nanotechnology in the city, but to an altogether different audience: to the students in a slum community. Dr Kroto readily agreed. He has a passionate interest in popularising advanced scientific knowledge among the common people – the Vega Science Trust set up by him gives top-notch scientists a broadcasting platform to inform students, teachers and the general public directly about scientific matters that are exciting and also are of concern. More recently he has set up the Global Educational Outreach for Science Engineering and Technology (GEOSET) programme which is pioneering the Internet's capability to revolutionise education on a global scale.

The talk was organised in a small playground in a slum in Santacruz, where a local non-governmental organisation (NGO) called Triratna Prerana Mandal has been doing incredible work for all-round development of the community with people's participation. This organisation has won national and internatonal recognition for its work in the areas of slum sanitation, recycling of solid waste, environmental hygiene, mid-day meal for pre-primary school children, women's education and empowerment through self-help groups, education for school dropouts, youth development through sports and cultural activities, leadership training for slum activists – and all this through the Gandhian spirit of voluntarism and cooperation. Dr Kroto was so pleased to interact with the volunteers of this organisation that his spontaneous comment was: 'Such selfless work is desperately needed around the world'.

Dr Kroto's talk, which was translated into Marathi, was a huge success. It was the first time that a Mumbai slum was hosting a talk by a Nobel laureate scientist. It was also the first time that Dr Kroto, who has delivered hundreds of talks on nanotechnology before traditional audiences around the world, was explaining the subject to a slum audience. An inspiring and exhilarating illustration it was of turning the slogan of the people's science movement – 'Science *for* the People, Science *to* the People, and Science *by* the People' – into action.

But what drew the biggest applause, and what gave Dr Kroto the greatest satisfaction, was when a group of secondary school students from Yamgarwadi, a remote and poverty-stricken village near Solapur, in Maharashtra, interacted with him. These children, who study in a boarding school that runs on the principles of Gandhi's Nayi Talim *(see Chapter 12)*, showed him several scientific experiments, using simple and low-cost gadgets that they had themselves made with local materials. For example, a seventh-grade student innovatively explained the concept of convex and concave lenses using the sole of a worn-out rubber slipper, which had five-six equidistant holes punched in lengthwise, with a soft drink straw in each of them. 'Imagine the sole to be a lens and the straws to be sun rays,' he explained in Marathi. 'I bend the sole to make the straws point inwards. This is how a convex lens works. When I bend it the other way to make the straws point outwards, it becomes a concave lens.'

I had specially invited these students, along with their teachers, to attend Dr Kroto's lecture. They were children of nomadic tribes, many of which the British had branded 'criminal tribes' because they were the most militant in the anti-colonial struggle. Even today, people belonging to these tribes suffer from extreme poverty and social exclusion, and rank lowest in formal school education. A poignant poem describes the plight of these stigmatised tribes, known as Pardhis, in the following words:

Open sky over the head,
And scorched earth their bed,
For ages they wander for a cooling shed,
And in search of a caring friend.

The 'friend' in this case is the Bhatke Vimukta Vikas Pratishthan, a socially committed NGO inspired by the RSS, which has been running the school at Yamgarwadi since 1993. It was established by my friend Girish Prabhune, a social activist and writer, whose lifelong work for the social liberation and educational uplift of Pardhis has been widely acclaimed. In the words of Dr Mohanrao Bhagwat, the RSS chief who recently inaugurated a new school building, the Yamgarwadi project 'has become a centre of pilgrimage for social reformers'.

Even though many Pardhis are still unlettered, it would be naïve to think that their minds are uneducated. As I had discovered during my earlier visit to Yamgarwadi, their children have amazing knowledge of the environment around them. They know the medicinal properties of the locally grown 'weeds'. They can identify different birds from their chirping and other sounds. Being used to sleeping in ramshackle tents in the open, they can name the stars in the night sky. In a little room that served as the 'science laboratory' in the school, all the various types of snakes, crabs and scorpions kept in specimen jars had been caught by the children themselves. And how incredibly talented they all were in singing, dancing, playing local sports and using their magical hands to create things of beauty in wood, mud and grass! A perfect example of the soundness of Gandhi's Nayi Talim system of education, in which students learn by doing, playing, praying, working and serving. *(See Chapter 12.)*

Dr Kroto's public lecture was focussed not merely on the technical aspects of nanotechnology. Of course, he explained the discovery that won him and two others the Nobel Prize – Buckminsterfullerene (C_{60}), also called buckyball, a new form of carbon structure shaped like a tiny soccer ball, which has amazing applications in producing futuristic materials. But the bulk of his talk was devoted to explaining three overarching themes, which also form the thesis of this book.

Firstly, Dr Kroto believes that science, engineering and technology, which have revolutionised the world we live in, are capable of immeasurably improving the quality of life of the entire planetary population. However, for this promise to be realised, people must change their social behaviour to limit their unnecessary wants, which are exhausting the planet's resources. Sustainability must be taken seriously and must be reflected in our actions.

Secondly, Dr Kroto has deep faith that the Internet has emerged as a revolutionary new tool of communication, connectivity, education and empowerment on a global scale. He demonstrated how he, now seventy-two years old, still derives immense pleasure in networking with bright students in their teens and twenties, and studying in different parts of the world, for collaborative research projects pursued on the Internet. This theme made me wonder: 'There are hundreds of thousands of bright, but opportunity-deprived, kids in Indian villages like Yamgarwadi and in Indian slums like the one where Dr Kroto is giving this talk. When will all these children be empowered to participate in the co-creation of new scientific knowledge? When will the incredible promises of new technologies be realised in a way that ends the poverty, deprivation and drudgery of these communities? And, when this happens, what an unimaginably transformed future for India it will be!'

Dr Kroto's third theme was the urgent need to transform global politics, and the politics in individual countries, to realise the ideal of a world without wars and violence. He made an impassioned appeal for the elimination of all nuclear weapons, and also other weapons of mass destruction, by all countries that possess them. He expressed disappointment and anguish that India – 'the land of the Buddha and Mahatma Gandhi' – had joined the club of nuclear weapons nations, thereby losing the moral authority to champion the cause of universal nuclear disarmament. Science and technology, he affirmed, must be used exclusively and extensively for peaceful purposes, for improving the conditions of the people, for enhancing the joy of life and for saving our planet.

Here was nanotechnology speaking the language of nonviolence!

Man's Destiny: 'Outmeasuring Space, Outlasting Time'

It is true that nanotechnology evokes an immense sense of awe in us. As has been stated in this chapter, and also in some other chapters in this book, nanotechnology has the potential to realise Gandhi's dream of sustainable development based on a decentralised economy.

It convinces us that small can be not only beautiful but also bountiful. However, it's necessary not to make a fetish of the small. For small alone is not beautiful, nor is small alone bountiful. Both in Nature and in human life, Small has its place and so does Big have its place. It's given to man to experience the mysterious fungibility of the two, as William Blake tells us in his beautiful poem: *To see a world in a grain of sand, And a heaven in a wild flower, Hold infinity in the palm of your hand, And eternity in an hour.*

Maharshi Aurobindo captures the same sense of awe and mystery in a poem that reminds us that man, the Infinitesimal, is capable of becoming a part of the Infinite.

The Infinitesimal Infinite

Out of a still Immensity we came!
These million years were to it
The poor light-bubbles of a trivial game,
A fragile glimmer in the Infinite.

It could not find its soul in all that vast:
It drew itself into a little speck
Infinitesimal, ignobly cast
Out of the earth's mud and slime strangely awake,

A tiny plasm upon a causal globe
In the small system of a dwarflike sun,
A little life wearing the flesh for robe,
A little mind winged through wide space to run!
It lived, it knew, it saw its self sublime,
Deathless, outmeasuring Space, outlasting Time.

How can man outmeasure Space and outlast Time? Gandhi sought to answer this by using a concept closely related to nanoscience – 'zero', which represents the lowest point in nano measurement. As he said in his dialogue with Romain Rolland in 1931 *(see Chapter 16)*, man can swim in the bosom of the infinite Ocean of Truth – which contains, and is a creator of, both Space and Time. However, to succeed in this, man must reduce his ego to 'zero'.

Gandhian Benefits of a Local Currency

Spending Local Currency	Spending US Currency

The Local Economy

Spending Local Currency	Spending US Currency
• Promotes buying from local stores and from neighbors, keeping jobs here.	• Promotes buying from distant locations, catalogues, and chain stores.
• Fosters the local production of a greater variety of goods and services to meet local demands.	• Forces local production of only those things that are competitive in a global market.
• Makes our economy more dependent upon ourselves. We have greater control.	• Makes our economy more dependent on people and events outside of our control.
• Keeps money within the local economy.	• Lets money quickly leave the local economy.

The Environment

Spending Local Currency	Spending US Currency
• Encourages use of local resources and local production.	• Encourages use of global resources and distant production.
• Results in less pollution and less energy used for shipping.	• Results in more pollution and more energy used for shipping.
• Ensures that materials will be used in line with local laws and values.	• Allows use of materials from places with unknown practices and values.
• Favors disposing of waste in environmentally sound ways.	• Favors disposing of waste by cheapest means possible.
• Makes consumers aware of the impact of their consumption.	• Keeps consumers unaware of the impact of their consumption.

Fair Wages

Spending Local Currency	Spending US Currency
• Provides support for local labor.	• Forces labor to compete globally.
• Distributes wealth more evenly.	• Concentrates wealth.
• Makes small-scale production viable.	• Encourages industry-scaled production.
• Creates new jobs at home.	• Demands a mobile labor force.

Courtesy: PLENTY (Piedmont Local EcoNomy Tender)

28

THE FUTURE OF MONEY
How the Internet will Promote Gandhian Economics

→❖◇◆◇❖←

A century from now social analysts will look back with angry astonishment at the extent our generation accepted the economists' fantasy – happiness requires perpetual economic growth. This may have been true once; definitely now it is false. Indeed, the exponentially expanding use of energy and resources brought by pursuit of growth now erodes the foundations for the happiness, even threatens the survival, of our species. The growing number of people who recognise this tend to seek technological changes…These are helpful. However, none of these efforts will succeed without…profound changes in our systems of money.

— Dennis Meadows, in preface to *Creating Wealth: Growing Local Economies with Local Currencies* by Gwendolyn Hallsmith and Bernard Lietaer.

NOWHERE WILL THE CHANGE-INDUCING POWER OF THE INTERNET be more visible in the twenty-first century than in the realm of economics. One of the most far-reaching impacts of the Internet will be on the nature and the role of money in the world of tomorrow. And this impact will be of a kind that advances the Gandhian ideals of decentralised, sustainable and equitable development with the empowerment of the people worldwide. Basic human values such as trust, cooperation and mutual care will be gradually mainstreamed in economic activities. Concomitantly, the operational terrain for impersonal and despotic economic forces, unhealthy competition and lack of concern for the human factor will gradually diminish.

Like every expression of hope, this too is rooted in an experience of deep despair. The world has experienced the inherent instability and inequities of the US-dominated financial system, which have prompted leading thinkers of the world to conclude that this system cannot possibly last long. The financial meltdown in the West in 2008, which sent the American and European economies into a series of interconnected crises from which they haven't yet fully recovered, was an early alert about a much bigger collapse that may come sooner or later. It has made more and more people around the world suspect that at the core of the ecological and economic crises in our times is the reigning financial architecture itself, made up of giant banks and financial institutions that have more wealth than the combined GDPs of all the poor countries in the world; private equity funds whose operations are largely non-transparent; and regulatory bodies that have often been found to be weak or complicit. All these organisations are at the service of a giant economic beast whose interests are at odds with the needs of both the common people and the planetary ecology, but which is accountable to none.

Gandhi had censured 'commerce without morality' as one of the seven deadly sins that are the roots of violence in the world. He was referring not only to individual morality but also to institutional and systemic morality. The system of high finance, as it has evolved in the West, has banished morality – by which we mean the overall welfare of the world – from its considerations and operations. Money creating more and more money for huge corporations through clever financial engineering, with little correlation to actual wealth creation in society, and by luring individuals and nations to spend recklessly on borrowed money, has become the norm for many leading economies, most notably the US economy. This is not normal commerce as civilisations around the world have known and practiced for thousands of years. This is commerce converted into a global casino. For example, less than five percent of all the foreign exchange transactions among giant financial institutions relate to the 'real' economy corresponding to the exchange of real goods and services – the remaining are entirely speculative. This bubble of artificial wealth has to burst every now and then. And whenever it bursts, it leaves a trail of deaths (including suicides), destruction, misery and instability in countless families and communities near and far in today's globalised world.

Gandhi had warned about this consequence as early as in 1937:

> True economics never militates against the highest ethical standard, just as all true ethics to be worth its name must at the same time be also good economics. An economics that inculcates Mammon worship, and enables the strong to amass wealth at the expense of the weak, is a false and dismal science. It spells death. True economics, on the other hand, stands for social justice, it promotes the good of all equally, including the weakest, and is indispensable for decent life.[1]

Gandhi had made the following bold affirmation in an illuminating lecture, titled 'Economic vs. Moral Progress', which he delivered at a meeting of the Muir Central College Economic Society in Allahabad on 22 December 1916:

> I venture to think that the scriptures of the world are far safer and sounder treatises on laws of economics than many of the modern text books....(in) so far as we have made the modern materialistic craze our goal, so far we are going downhill in the path of progress...Let us seek first the Kingdom of God and His righteousness, and the irrevocable promise is that everything will be added unto us.[2]

Expressing the same thought in his foreword to the book *The Economy of Permanence* by Dr J.C. Kumarappa, his lieutenant in the promotion of village industries, Gandhi wrote: 'Shall the body triumph over and stifle the soul or shall the latter triumph over and express itself through a perishable body which, with its few wants healthily satisfied, will be free to subserve the end of the imperishable soul? This is "Plain living and high thinking"'.[3]

Sadly, neglect of the basic Gandhian principles of the Economy of Permanence has made today's world economic order permanently crisis-prone. More and more thinkers around the world are recognising the devastation caused by the reigning global financial system in rich and poor countries alike in the form of unemployment, environmental degradation and community breakdown. One of them is Hazel Henderson, a renowned thinker on sustainable development who is influenced by the Gandhian philosophy. An author of several acclaimed books, she remarks:

> Economics is now widely seen as the faulty sourcecode deep in societies' hard drives...replicating unsustainability: booms, busts, bubbles, recessions, poverty, trade wars, pollution, disruption of communities, loss of cultural diversity and bio-diversity. Citizens all over the world are rejecting this malfunctioning economic sourcecode and its operating systems: the World Bank, the IMF, the WTO and imperious central banks...The word is out that economics, never a science, has always been politics in disguise. Economics and economists view reality through the lens of money. Happily, all this focus on money is leading to the widespread awareness of ways money is designed, created and manipulated. This politics of money is at last unraveling centuries of mystification.[4]

Ellen Brown, whose book *Web of Debt: The Shocking Truth About Our Money System and How We Can Break Free* x-rays the inner workings of the US-dominated global financial system, writes: 'The modern banking system manufactures money out of nothing. The process is perhaps the most astounding piece of sleight of hand that was ever invented. Banking was conceived in inequity and born in sin.... Bankers own the earth'.[5]

'A cruel hoax,' is how Henry C.K. Liu, a New York-based investment adviser to developing countries, describes America's prevailing financial system. Liu, a radical economics philosopher who writes for the *Asia Times* website, explains that the hoax is that there is very little 'real' money in the US system, only debts. 'Except for coins, which are issued by the government and make up only about one-thousandth of the money supply, the entire U.S. money supply now consists of debt to private banks, for money they created with accounting entries on their books. It is all done by sleight of hand; and like a magician's trick, we have to see it many times before we realise what is going on. But when we do, it changes everything. All of history has to be rewritten'.[6]

Manipulation is not limited to the financial sector alone. It also extends to the production, marketing and advertising sectors of the modern capitalist system, which survives and thrives mainly by playing on human desires. Liu hits the nail on the head by observing that 'corporations routinely and effectively manipulate consumer preference and market acceptance often through if not false, at least misleading advertising, not for the benefit of consumers, but to maximise return on faceless capital raised from global capital markets. The subliminal emphasis by the corporate culture on addictive acquisition of material things, coupled with a structural deprivation of adequate income to satisfy the manipulated desires, has made consumers less satisfied than in previous times of less material abundance. Corporations have been allowed to embed consumption-urging messages into every aspect of modern life. The result is a disposable culture with packaged waste, an obesity crisis for all age groups, skyrocketing consumer debt, the privatisation of public utility that demand the same fee for basic services from rich and poor alike, causing sharp disparity in affordability'.[7]

Reform of the Global Financial Architecture

Gandhi had serious doubts about privately owned banks and insurance companies working for the benefit of the ordinary people. In this he was influenced by the writings of Richard Gregg, the American pacifist who spent four years in India, including seven months at Gandhi's ashram. in the late 1920s. The book that Gregg penned upon his return, *The Power of Nonviolence,* had a big impact on Martin Luther King Jr, who wrote to him: 'I don't know when I have read anything that has given the idea of nonviolence a more realistic and depthful interpretation. I assure you that it will be a lasting influence in my life'.[8]

Writing in *Young India* on 15 April 1926, Gandhi had approvingly quoted Gregg's following observation on the banking and industrial institutions in the West that had put enormous concentration of material power and wealth in the hands of a few. 'Such tremendous power is a temptation which human nature cannot withstand. It involves tyranny, vanity, pride, greed, selfishness, ruthless competition on the one side; loss of liberty, insecurity, fears, loss of self-reliance and of independence, degradation, poverty, loss of dignity and self-respect, on the other'.

Gandhi's skepticism about the global financial institutions of his time has been more than vindicated by their subsequent track record. The system of abusive issuance of credit money, combined with the greedy operations of privately held banks, insurance companies, equity funds and other such institutions that seek to multiply money through financial instruments and practices of dubious merit, has created havoc. Even a billionaire investor like Warren Buffet has likened such 'unregulated financial innovations' to 'financial weapons of mass destruction'.[9]

Mary Mellor, author of *The Future of Money: From Financial Crisis to Public Resource*, says:

> Privatised control of money issue creates the impression that it is the private market that is creating wealth. Certainly it is making money, quite literally, largely through issuing it to itself as leverage to swell speculative trading. Private ownership and control of money issue has created huge differences of wealth. The mass of the people can only hope for a trickle down of economic activity through the consumption of the champagne-swigging traders and increasing numbers of billionaires. On the illusion that the manipulators of money have actually generated the wealth they gamble with, those playing the money markets demand a huge percentage of the product. The levels of pay and bonuses have become so obscenely bloated that they have become an economic 'gated community' set apart from ordinary mortals by their wealth.

In fact, they have stolen what should be a public resource and harnessed it for private benefit.

Recently bank lending has contributed to the vast use of 'leverage' to enable the investments of the rich to go even further. Hedge funds, private equity investments and the investment arms of banks use borrowed money to inflate their speculative gambles. Some of these may even be gambles against the banks themselves or the national currency. As more money is issued it floods into the financial system and becomes part of the waves of money looking for a profitable home. As it is impossible to separate the interests of bank depositors or pension holders from financial speculators, in a crisis the whole system must be secured.[10]

When the global financial system suffered an inevitable crisis in 2008, many governments, including our own, had to introduce rescue and stimulus packages worth billions of dollars to secure the system. In USA and other Western countries where failing private banks and financial institutions had to be bailed out using public money, the solution highlighted a peculiar nature of the problem. If ordinary people, through their democratically elected governments, are required to save the privatised financial system when it fails, why shouldn't they have a say over the allocation of finance in the first place?

Indeed, the situation poses an even more fundamental question. If the pain and hardships, social dislocation and environmental destruction, caused by global finance are of a global scale, why shouldn't the global community, through democratically run multilateral institutions, have a say in its working and in its restructuring?

Democratisation of the global financial architecture has, therefore, become one of the pressing tasks before the international community. How to accomplish this task in a manner consistent with Gandhi's ideals? And what role can the Internet play in this process? Here are a few ideas.

Firstly, the current anomaly between global trade and global finance must be removed. It is strange that global finance is subject to hardly any multilateral regulation, even though a rules-based multilateral framework for the regulation of global trade in goods and services already exists. The World Trade Organisation (WTO), however imperfect it may still be in its functioning, came into effect in 1995 and now has 153 members. With all the asymmetry in the power structure that operates in the WTO, it is nevertheless a democratic body in which every member nation nominally has a say. It also has a dispute settlement mechanism that is becoming more effective with the passage of time. Hence, there must be a WTO equivalent for reforming and democratising the global financial architecture. Both the World Bank and the International Monetary Fund (IMF), the two institutions which underpin the post-Second World War architecture created by the Bretton Woods treaty are completely unsuited to this task. They both are relics of the West-dominated global financial system. Being a part of the problem, they cannot become a part of the solution.

The Bretton Woods system collapsed in 1971 when the United States unilaterally terminated the linkage of its dollar, the key currency of the system, to gold reserves and made it a fiat currency. This has had far-reaching consequences both on the global economy and society and also on the US itself. Its dollar being the main currency for international trade, the US became disproportionately more prosperous without really working hard to earn its wealth. The US now prints dollars at will and consumes much of the goods and services the world produces. In contrast, the rest of the world 'consumes' US dollars by competitively selling its products in the US market cheaply. Even when other countries trade among themselves, their competitiveness depends on the exchange value of their national currencies vis-à-vis the US dollar. Thus, they are forced to keep the dollar strong. Also, in the absence of any non-national global currency, they are forced to build their dollar reserves both to buy what they need – above all, ever-more expensive oil, which is traded mostly in dollars – and also to sustain the exchange value of their domestic currencies. This requires them to export more and more. As dollar reserves cannot be kept idle, they are used to buy US treasury bonds. And since interest rates on these bonds are low, poorer countries like India, in effect, end up lending money cheap to the US!

This type of globalisation has made the US society hyper-consumerist and the US economy unbelievably debt-ridden. Its effect on other countries can be seen in the imbalances and distortions in the growth of their domestic economies. Competition in the export market has compelled wages at the lower end of the work force to be depressed. Also, labour-saving technologies are being preferred over those that can, in a more domestic-oriented economic growth, create greater employment opportunities, which is a key Gandhian concern. Aggressive competition has also meant disregard for the environment and dislocation of families and disempowerment of communities.

Therefore, the second most important element in the reform of the global financial system is ending of the hegemony of dollar as the principal denominator of global trade and investment, and replacing it with a suitable alternative. In the interim, as many progressive economists suggest, major exporting nations could begin by unilaterally deciding that all their exports would be payable only in their national currencies. Eventually, a universally acceptable global currency may be adopted.

Thirdly, the artificially bloated size of the financial sector must be reduced to bring it in reasonable alignment with the real economies of the world, beginning with that of the US. This will need a kind of democratic revolution in the US, driven by the ideal of global egalitarianism. This, however, is strongly resisted by the religiously-inspired forces of right-wing extremism, which are on the rise in many parts of the West. At present, the global financial sector is at least ten times bigger than world GDP. Downsizing the financial sector and, simultaneously, re-prioritising its goals would also lead to reforms of the real economy itself. In other words, real economy should be aligned to the real needs of the people and to the generation of sustainable livelihood opportunities for every person. It should not be driven by endless multiplication of wants spurred by seductive advertising, predatory marketing, routine product obsolescence and easy availability of credit.

Fourthly, reform of the financial sector and the real economy should aim at moderating trade among nations and also within large nations. Even a liberal British economist like John Maynard Keynes (1883-1946), who was once a proponent of free trade, had this to say after the Great Depression of 1933 in the United States:

> I sympathise, therefore, with those who would minimise, rather than with those who would maximise, economic entanglement among nations. Ideas, knowledge, science, hospitality, travel – these are the things which should of their nature be international. But let goods be homespun whenever it is reasonably and conveniently possible, and, above all, let finance be primarily national.

This is nothing but a Keynesian endorsement of Gandhi's enlightened concept of swadeshi, which harmonises global interdependence in knowledge, culture and humanitarian needs with national and local self-sufficiency in basic goods. *(See Chapter 30 on swadeshi. It explains how digital technologies can facilitate successful adoption of this Keynesian-Gandhian prescription.)*

Fifthly, the United Nations is the most appropriate platform for spearheading a globally participative and cooperative effort to discuss the design, rules and priorities of a new multilateral body for regulating global finance. It must attach the highest priority to elimination of poverty, hunger, disease and deprivation, and also to the regeneration of the environment, worldwide. The principle of 'affirmative action', which many governments have accepted under the force of domestic democratic opinion, must be applied in the working of the reformed global financial bodies. In other words, the least developed countries, and also of the less developed communities within rich or emerging economies, should benefit from 'positive discrimination' in credit supply, interest rates, investment portfolios, etc.

What this means is that no institutional finance and governmental support should be extended to the creation of golf courses, luxury mansions, private leisure resorts, etc. On the contrary, cheaper credit should be made available to projects involving mass housing, sanitation, water supply, waste management and recycling, public hospitals, renewable energy generation, etc.

Information and education are critical to widening the participation of the global civil society in the reform of the prevailing global financial system. The workings of this system are hardly transparent. Therefore, the United Nations, along with national governments, should make it mandatory for all international and national financial institutions to abide by comprehensive and transparent disclosure norms covering their structures, finances, policies, procedures, decision-making processes and activities in various countries and sectors. On the lines of the RTI Act in India, which empowers citizens to seek governmental information, there should be provisions that enable civil society organisations to procure information about ethically challenged international and national banks and financial institutions. This will, among other things, also throw a flashlight of transparency on the billions of dollars of illicit wealth that is stashed away by the global rich in secret overseas bank accounts in tax havens.

Digital Money as a Democratiser

Thus, we see that today there is growing consensus worldwide – not so much among governments but among thinking people – that the problem of global finance has to be tackled at its roots: in the nature of money, as it has evolved under Western capitalism in the past few centuries. This is precisely what the Internet has begun doing. It is proving itself to be the greatest disruptive agent in the history of money. It is changing not just the way people earn, spend, exchange, manage and invest. It is also expanding the economic freedom of ordinary citizens and simultaneously reducing the control of big banks, financial institutions and even governments.

It is true that, in its initial stage of development, ICTs have helped the reigning West-dominated financial system grow bigger and bigger. ICTs are also being used by speculators who transfer trillions of dollars daily around the world simply by clicking the computer mouse. However, the spread of the Internet and smart mobile phones across the world at a blinding speed is effecting radical changes in the global financial system. It is also changing the way money is stored, exchanged and used.

In their book *The March of Mobile Money*, Sam Pitroda, who was the chairman of India's National Knowledge Commission and is currently adviser to the Indian prime minister on public information infrastructure and innovations, and his co-author Mehul Desai, write: 'In the near future, we will begin to see a whole new revolution around mobile phones – with respect to technology and commerce, with significant socio-economic impact – which will ultimately change the very concept of money. It will begin first in Asia, especially in India and China, where there are more mobile phone users than Internet users or bank account holders...Future banks with focus on mobile banking will be borderless and will require less brick-and-mortar infrastructure. At stake is nothing less than the very future of money as we have understood it for centuries'.

Pitroda and Desai also predict: 'As mobile money proliferates with multiple currencies, financial services will be significantly deregulated worldwide over the next decade, significantly changing the role of central banks'.[11]

The consequences of money becoming digital and mobile in the hands of potentially the entire global population are mind-boggling. One of the most important consequences is that it is going to empower the poor and help them come out of the trap of poverty. Take banking services, for example. Until now, mainstream banking and financial institutions have had little incentive to serve the poor. This is less because of the difficulty to physically reach out to where the rural poor live and more due to the belief that provision of banking services to the poor, rural or urban, is not profitable. Now, instead of the poor having to go to the doorsteps of banks, mobile banking will come to the doorsteps of the poor. Mobile money, made secure by encryption-based technology, will lead to a boom in micro-loans and micro-payments between individuals, local community organisations and small or tiny-scale businesses in the informal sector, which today receive little credit from the formal banking and financial institutions. This can greatly benefit small and marginal farmers, for whom availability of timely, adequate and affordable credit is nearly as important as timely, adequate and affordable availability of water for their crops. Mobile banking will also enable governments to directly transfer monies into the accounts of targeted beneficiaries of various welfare and development schemes, such as the Mahatma Gandhi National Rural Employment Guarantee Scheme (MNREGS) in India, and thereby plug leakage of funds all along the delivery system.

A major potential benefit of the Internet mobile banking in the hands of farmers, artisans, and micro, small and medium enterprises (MSMEs) is that they can, on a commonly shared global digital platform, have access to credit information, market information and information about the availability of resources and labour necessary for their economic activities. They can also have information about science, technology and training inputs that can enhance their productivity. This can bring much-needed vibrancy to the informal sector of the economy which, in countries like India, employs nearly ninety percent of the work force. Hence, creative use of ICTs, in conjunction with the introduction of pro-people policies, can significantly increase employment, self-employment and entrepreneurship opportunities for the common people, a key goal in Gandhian economics.

Compassionate Currencies of Local Communities

There are also other ways in which Gandhian ideals are going to be promoted by the Internet in the economic sphere. Some of these trends are already visible in different parts of the world. In a likely revival of the barter system of sorts, the Internet is facilitating currency-less direct exchange and redistribution of resources. It is also introducing new flexibilities in the way people work and the way their work is valued. This has led to a well-grounded hypothesis that innovative future businesses could develop alternative or complementary forms of money – community money, for example – as a way of considerably reducing the unnecessary transaction costs of the traditional banking system. Community money, based on trust within local communities, is being seen as a way of creating broadly shared local wealth. It can also enhance social capital and promote cooperation within communities facilitated by informal pacts.

Happily, this is already happening in many parts of the world. And these innovations are being introduced largely by small entrepreneurs for the benefit of small people. Alternative currencies have become a means of empowerment for those who have been pushed to the margins of fiscal life, helping the elderly, the disabled and the underemployed. For example, in some systems of alternative currencies, one can 'bank' Time Dollars for jobs such as childcare and tending of local parks. 'Each person has "value" that is "exchangeable" on the basis of time spent on a given task'.[12]

One of the compelling examples of a 'compassionate currency' is Hureai Kippu, which the Japanese have introduced as a new type of Healthcare Currency. It means, literally, 'caring relationship tickets'. This is people's own proactive, creative and empathetic response to the major problem of healthcare for Japan's ageing population. In this system, the hours that a volunteer spends helping older or handicapped persons are credited to his or her Time Account. This is managed along the lines of a savings account in a bank, the difference being that the unit of account is hours of service instead of yen. The Healthcare Credits can be availed by the volunteers themselves, or assigned to someone else of their choice, within or outside of their families. The system is managed by a nation-wide Internet-based clearing network. Close to 1,00,000 retired people needing periodic help and another one million handicapped people are benefitting from this system. It is so successful that the elderly people prefer to receive care from a volunteer who is paid with 'care relationship tickets' rather than someone who is paid in yen in the formal system of healthcare. This alternative Internet-enabled currency is fostering the spirit of volunteerism in Japanese society – an increasing number of volunteers, especially young volunteers, see in it an opportunity to be happy by doing community service.

Isn't this future trend of decentralised production and consumption, using compassion-based and trust-based local currencies and contracts, in conformity with Gandhi's economic philosophy? Explaining his concept of swadeshi, Gandhi had written: 'A man's first duty is to his neighbour. This does not mean hatred for the foreigner or partiality for the fellow-countryman. One who serves his neighbour serves the world'.[13]

Gandhi's supportive thoughts on barter and, specifically, on voluntary exchange of labour as a means of payment in a decentralised economy, had prefigured the concepts of time banks and local compassionate currencies that are now becoming very popular in many countries in the world. According to him:

> Coins are but a measure of labour performed. They have no other value. If I buy a rupee worth of flour, I have paid for the labour of cultivation, carrying and grinding. Therefore... it is the same thing whether I pay the State one rupee or its equivalent of labour as tax. Often it will be found that payment in labour invigorates the nation. [And indeed,] where people perform labour voluntarily for the service of society, exchange of money becomes unnecessary; the labour of collecting the taxes and keeping accounts is saved and the results are equally good.[14]

Jean-François Noubel of France is one of the visionaries who are driving the agenda of promoting 'free currencies' as the bedrock of the 'next global monetary system'. Founder and president of TheTransitioner.org and a researcher in Collective Intelligence, Wisdom and Consciousness, Noubel makes a profound prediction:

> What no one anticipates is that money is about to follow the same path the media followed during the past years; from controlled ownership of media with one-way top down broadcast systems, to peer-to-peer, participatory, open publishing. Millions of free currencies will soon circulate on the Net and through our cell phones. They will not be controlled by states or central banks, they will be issued and used by millions of marketplaces willing to free themselves from conventional debt-based, interest-based money (85-90 percent of currencies circulating

today). Everyone will use these free currencies simply because they will be ubiquitous, easy to integrate into current media technologies, and because most people and organisations are undermonetised. This new paradigm is likely to turn the current monetary system into a completely obsolete system.

According to Noubel, the Free Currencies Project (also called the Metacurrency Project) 'is aimed at becoming the next planetary tool for accounting, transacting and storing wealth. It will belong to the common people. It's open source. It will be easy to use via computers and cell phones, making it accessible to the most part of humanity.'

'Conventional money,' says Noubel, 'self-aggregates in the hands of the few. It leaves other economic areas empty. We call this phenomenon "undermonetisation", it creates artificial pauperisation. The consequences are: concentration of power (which violates the ideal of democracy); poverty, violence, harsh competition, predatory behaviors; natural resources unnaturally drawn from undermonetised places to places of concentrated money; secrecy (don't share what has value, make it scarce); and artificial rarefaction of what is not scarce (so it can have higher market value).'

Noubel, who envisions making his social networking site one of the 'global wisdom-driven organisations', believes that a future of Free Currencies will benefit the entire humanity. 'Developing countries will realise that they don't need conventional money ($ or €) to exist on the international scene.' Human relationships will benefit because, with unhealthy competition and predatory behaviours curbed, they will shift to 'higher consciousness'. The economy will benefit worldwide due to 'optimised flows of wealth across the planet at local and global levels because of the right supply of money'. The planet will benefit because 'the incentive to hunt or hoard scarce money by producing useless products sold through illusionary marketing (ninety percent of consumerist market) is deactivated'. Less junk production and consumption will mean that the people will have 'an incentive to focus on higher meaningful activities'.[15]

Bernard Lietaer, a Belgian, is another prominent thinker who believes that the Internet has become an 'ideal space for economic symbiosis'. In his book *The Future of Money: Creating New Wealth, Work, and a Wiser World,* Lietaer writes:

> Because Internet offers unlimited "space" and transcends natural and cultural boundaries, the electronic marketplace need not be limited to one exclusive currency system; indeed, a "free market" of different kinds of currency systems may benefit all of them. Virtual space provides indeed an ideal space for the coexistence and integration of different economic paradigms, because of its flexibility and non-exclusiveness. In physical space, if Big Business buys up Fifth Avenue in New York, there is no room for alternative systems to even be present, not to speak of flourishing. The Net in contrast always can expand to accept another parallel system without detracting anything from each other. Internet itself would be enriched by such a variety. Furthermore, new synergies between virtual communities and local communities would become possible, improving the quality of life of the participating Netizens.[16]

Does the proliferation of local currencies mean that national currencies will become irrelevant? Will there be no need for harmonisation between the financial operations at the local, national and global levels? The answer is clearly in the negative. If we accept the logic of Glocalisation, the synergistic coexistence of Globalisation and Localisation, both driven by the enormous power of the Internet, it is obvious that local currencies will become 'complementary currencies'. This point is persuasively explained by the Schumacher Society in London, one of the many institutions around the world promoting alternative solutions to today's crisis-ridden economic system. Founded to honour the legacy of the great Gandhian thinker, it is a strong proponent of Internet-enabled local currencies. 'To create a local currency is not a form of local isolationism; it is not cutting oneself off from the rest of the world; it is simply a movement of citizens taking responsibility for the well being of their own community. Local and community currencies do not seek to replace national currencies, but to supplement them, hence the increasingly popular term "complementary currencies".'

Thus, the future eco(nomic) system in the Internet age promises to bring back the diversity of currencies and customs, ending the 'monoculture' of today. Global economy is indeed moving in that direction. The likely end of the US dollar as the dominant global currency, to be replaced by a basket of international currencies, is only an initial pointer to the shape of things to come. Other changes in the world of finance and business, catalysed by the Internet, are going to be far more revolutionary. Many business and financial institutions that seem invincible today will be swept away by the power of the Internet in the coming decades. Premises and parametres that are widely used today as markers of commercial success will be radically redefined. The purpose of economics and its practices will be realigned to foster sustainable development – which in its deepest sense is simply another word for nonviolent development. Even something as basic to any economic activity as money will be transformed beyond imagination by the Internet. Most importantly, future generations will have the real opportunity to reduce the power of money itself in human affairs. New yardsticks of success, status, prestige, power and personal satisfaction, rooted in culture, ethics and the innate qualities of individuals, will assert themselves in the society of tomorrow.

In short, the twenty-first century is certain to witness democratisation of the economic order, at the global, national and local levels. The power of technology, combined with the power of democracy, will produce a multiplier effect in propelling human history in the direction of nonviolence, cooperation and caring – just the values that the Mahatma had made his meek spinning wheel a mighty symbol of. [17]

What will be the place and role of capital and labour in tomorrow's just economic order? Gandhi does not provide elaborate views on this issue, but the main direction of his thinking, and its relevance for any progressive action for change now and in the future, are evident from the following interview he granted to French journalist Charles Petrasch and some others while in London in 1931.

Question: You speak of stopping the exploitation of the masses, which implies the abolition of capitalism. Do you intend to suppress capitalism, and if so, are you ready to deprive the capitalist of his surplus wealth so as to prevent him from restarting a new capitalism?

Gandhi: If I come to power, I shall certainly abolish capitalism but I shall not abolish capital, and it follows that I shall not abolish the capitalists. I am convinced that the coordination of capital and labour is perfectly possible. ...I do not consider capital in itself as an evil, *no more than I consider the machine system in itself as an evil.*[18] *(Emphasis added)*

The nature of capital and labour has changed significantly with the advent of the age of the Internet. The two have also become fungible to some extent insofar as knowledge, a product of intellectual and innovative labour, has now become a form of capital. There is growing debate worldwide on the ethical and ecologically sustainable uses of capital. Similarly, there is increasing affirmation of dignity of labour, although drudgery and degrading conditions of work continue to be the lot of workers in many parts of the world. Much of this will change as the age of digital technologies advances. However, it will not change in the right direction on its own. Conscious and sustained efforts will have to be made to marry the revolutionary power of new technologies with the eternal human values that Gandhi and other sages have propounded.

In particular, as discussed in this chapter, the role of money in the life of men and nations has to be fundamentally changed. Money, like machines, cannot be dispensed with. The two have been in existence throughout human civilisation, and will continue to exist in future too. However, freed from enslavement to Mammon worship, money and machines – the latter, in the age of the Internet, includes the entire cornucopia of digital devices and applications – will have to be put in the exclusive service of Man and Mother Nature.

INTERNET FOR PEACE

www.
internet
for peace
nobel 2010
candidate

Courtesy: N.K. Ranga's family

'Technology really can change the world. People want peace, and when given a voice, they'll work tirelessly for it. In the short term, a Twitter account may be no match for an AK-47, but in the long term the keyboard is mightier than the sword.'
– **Chris Anderson,** editor-in-chief *of WIRED* magazine

29

A MESSENGER OF GLOBAL HOPE
The Internet is Born for Promoting Peace

✦

We have finally realised that the Internet is much more than a network of computers. It is an endless web of people. Men and women from every corner of the globe are connecting to one another, thanks to the biggest social interface ever known to humanity. Digital culture has laid the foundations for a new kind of society.

And this society is advancing dialogue, debate and consensus through communication. Because democracy has always flourished where there is openness, acceptance, discussion and participation. And contact with others has always been the most effective antidote against hatred and conflict. That's why the Internet is a tool for peace. That's why anyone who uses it can sow the seeds of nonviolence. And that's why the next Nobel Peace Prize should go to the Net. A NOBEL FOR EACH AND EVERY ONE OF US.

— Appeal sent to the Nobel Committee in Oslo in 2010 from an international campaign that nominated the Internet for the Nobel Peace Prize. It was launched by *WIRED*, a reputed magazine that covers the Digital Revolution.

IS THE INTERNET THE LATTER-DAY AVATAR OF THE SPINNING WHEEL? The proposition may seem absurd to many people – to Gandhians and also to geeks. I know I run the risk of being ridiculed for seeing a correlation between the two that are, outwardly, as dissimilar as a bullock cart and a spaceship. Nevertheless, the more I study the two tools, the greater becomes my conviction that the Internet, like the spinning wheel of Gandhi's conception, has the potential to advance his cherished ideal: nonviolence. He had said: 'Just as there are signs by which you can recognise violence with the naked eye, so is the spinning wheel to me a decisive sign of nonviolence.'[1] It won't take much effort to see that the Internet has also become a servant of nonviolence. Indeed, it can act as a promoter of peace and brotherhood on a much larger, global, scale than the spinning wheel could in Gandhi's time. It has already begun playing that role, albeit to a limited extent so far.

Thinking of the Internet as an avatar of the spinning wheel prompts me to borrow a helpful concept from James Cameron's widely acclaimed 2009 Hollywood blockbuster *Avatar*. This epic sci-fi film, which carries a distinct imprint of Hindu philosophy and mythology, explores modern man's troubled relationship with Nature by metaphorically depicting the encounter between humans and a virtuous humanoid species, called Na'vi, inhabiting a moon full of flora and fauna in outer space. When the Na'vi meet, they greet each other by saying: 'I see you'. Incidentally, 'I see you' is also the title of a beautiful, and profoundly meaningful, song in the movie. Like many other Hindu symbolisms in the film, 'I see you' is nothing but namaste, the common greeting among Indians. However, namaste connotes a lot more than ordinary 'Hello'. Consistent with the Hindu belief that divinity pervades all beings and all things, namaste means 'I see myself in you', 'I see me through your eyes', or 'I honour the Spirit in you which is also in me'.

Now if, hypothetically speaking, Gandhi's spinning wheel were to meet the Internet, how would it greet the new technological marvel? It would, with great enthusiasm, say: '*Namaste* – I see myself in you and I see me through your eyes'.

Avatar, a Sanskrit word, is often loosely used in English to connote incarnation or embodiment of a concept. However, it is much more than that. In Hindu philosophy, an avatar fulfills a highly spiritual task mandated by God. As I have written earlier in this book (*see Chapters 6 and 14*), Gandhi saw the spinning wheel carry out a spiritual mandate, which subsumed its economic and national-liberation mandates. Likewise, the Internet is also called upon to serve a lofty spiritual agenda of helping humanity move closer towards the goal of a world without wars and violence. And it's already on the job.

Joseph Rotblat and the Russell–Einstein Manifesto

The Internet's potential to contribute to realisation of the ideal of world peace is being recognised by many leading scientists and information technology professionals around the world. One of the early spotters of this potential was Joseph Rotblat (1908–2005), a Polish-born British nuclear physicist who won the Nobel Peace Prize in 1995. He had great respect for Gandhi's message of peace. He was once a member of the team of senior scientists who worked during the Second World War on the Manhattan Project in the United States that produced the first atomic bomb. In his deeply moving Nobel acceptance speech[2], which became famous for its appeal 'Remember Your Humanity, and Forget the Rest', he paid this tribute to the Internet, when it was still in its infancy.

> Now, at age eighty-eight, I am one of the few remaining such senior persons (associated with the Manhattan Project) alive. Looking back at the half century since that time, I feel the most intense relief that these weapons have not been used since World War II, mixed with the horror that tens of thousands of such weapons have been built since that time... Notwithstanding the fragmentation that has occurred since the end of the Cold War, and the many wars for recognition of national or ethnic identities, I believe that the prospects for the acceptance of this new loyalty (to humanity) are now better than at the time of the Russell-Einstein Manifesto.[3] This is so largely because of the enormous progress made by science and technology during these 40 years.
>
> The fantastic advances in communication and transportation have shrunk our globe. All nations of the world have become

'**Remember your humanity, and forget the rest**': *Joseph Rotblat, a renowned physicist and pacifist, won the 1995 Nobel Peace Prize jointly with the Pugwash Conferences for their efforts towards universal nuclear disarmament.*

close neighbors. Modern information techniques enable us to learn instantly about every event in every part of the globe. We can talk to each other via the various networks. This facility will improve enormously with time, because the achievements so far have only scratched the surface. Technology is driving us together. In many ways we are becoming like one family.

Rotblat returned to the theme of a world without wars, and explicitly praised the Internet as a peacemaking force, in yet another celebrated speech given at the 54th Pugwash Conference on Science and World Affairs in Seoul, South Korea, in October 2004.

The prospects for developing a loyalty to humankind are becoming brighter due to the growing interdependence between nations, an interdependence not only in the realm of economics, but also in social and cultural matters; an interdependence brought about by the advances in science and technology, in particular, the progress in communications technology; the fantastic advances in transportation, communication and information, that have occurred in the twentieth century, and which I have witnessed in my own long life. Of particular importance is the progress in information technology, in its various forms. The Internet technology enables us to chat with people wherever they are. It provides access to an infinite source of information, and the means to contribute our own knowledge or ideas. Information Technology has truly begun to convert the world into a global village: we know one another; we do business with one another; we depend on one another; we try to help one another. We are perforce becoming world citizens. I welcome the fantastic advances in communication and information as a powerful factor against strife and war, because they provide new means for people to get to know one another and develop a sense of belonging to the whole of the world community. In the course of time, this will also reduce the economic gap between rich and poor nations.'[4]

Nobel Peace Prize for the Internet

In 2010, the Nobel Committee in Oslo received an unusual appeal – the Internet was nominated for the Nobel Peace Prize. The appeal was initiated by the 'Internet for Peace' campaign, launched by *WIRED*, a reputed and widely read magazine that covers the developments and debates in the world of information technology. The manifesto of this campaign, reproduced in full at the beginning of this chapter, made out a highly persuasive case. It states that 'digital culture has laid the foundations for a new kind of society'. It pithily described how the Internet is promoting democracy and peace around the world. Finally, it emphasised that a Nobel for the Internet will be 'a Nobel for each and every one of us'.[5]

Chris Anderson, editor-in-chief of *WIRED*, remarked: 'Technology really can change the world. People want peace, and when given a voice, they'll work tirelessly for it. In the short term, a Twitter account may be no match for an AK-47, but in the long term the keyboard is mightier than the sword... The Internet can become a weapon of global hope.' Riccardo Luna, editor of the magazine's Italian edition, wrote: 'Internet can be considered the first weapon of mass construction, which we can deploy to destroy hate and conflict and to propagate peace and democracy...Internet was born for peace'.[6]

The campaign quickly received support and endorsements from people around the world – both ordinary netizens and celebrities alike. One of them was Nicholas Negroponte, a renowned computer scientist, founder of the MIT's Media Lab and also initiator of the worldwide 'One Laptop Per Child' campaign. 'Internet has provided the ingredients for peace,' he said. 'Peace comes from understanding. Understanding comes from education and also from a window that offers multiple points of view. The Internet supports education and also provides that window. The 'One Laptop Per Child' campaign has taught me that the end of isolation is the key to education. The Internet is ending the isolation of millions of children around the world by causing the Death of Distance'.[7]

Umberto Veronesi, an Italian surgeon globally renowned for his contribution to control and treatment of breast cancer, said: 'I'm fully aware how unusual and bizarre it may appear when I advocate the Nobel Peace Prize to a means of mass communication instead of the traditional individual or a group of people. ...The Nobel Peace Prize awarded to the Web would convey a dual meaning to future generations: firstly, how we had grasped the extent of the global revolution that the Internet has brought into our daily lives; secondly, how determined we were to put the Web to better use in the interest of mankind.'[8]

The Internet is a Mind-Machine: Its Positive Uses Outweigh Negative Ones

Shirin Ebadi, a well-known democracy activist in Iran who won the Nobel Peace Prize in 2003, also supported the campaign, but with some important reservations. She pointed out that the Internet can also be used for violent purposes. 'Taliban and some other terrorist groups have used the Internet to attract many fans. It should not be ignored that in some cases Internet has been used as a tool to spread information about making small bombs.' She reminded that the Internet can create friendships only if it is used for peace.[9]

Ebadi's reservations were shared by many people who took part in the vigorous worldwide debate on the Web. 'Isn't the Internet used for pornography? Aren't there many voices of hatred and bigotry on the Net? What about piracy, identity theft, financial scams and virus attacks?' they pointed out. One critic ascerbically asked: 'Would we ever give the Nobel award to the machine gun just because it could be used by UN peacekeepers?'

Whether the Internet will ever win the Nobel Peace Prize is really secondary to my main argument in this chapter – namely, that the Internet is a promoter of peace and nonviolence, the same goal that Gandhi sought to advance by choosing a very different kind of tool, the charkha. I know that this argument would have no credibility if I failed to address the points of criticism, hurled at the Internet such as those mentioned above. As the Mahatma used to say, 'Healthy, well-informed, balanced criticism is the ozone of public life'.[10]

Who can deny that the Internet is widely misused for several illegal, unethical and undesirable activities? In this respect, the Internet is crucially different from the spinning wheel, a device that cannot conceivably be used for any wrongful ends. However, in defence of my argument, I would like to reiterate a point that I have made earlier. There cannot be complete similarity or equivalence between the Internet and the spinning wheel. Indeed, no two tools or technologies in human history are ever exactly identical. I have also emphasised earlier that the Internet has the *potential* to serve Gandhian ideals, but the extent to which this potential is realised depends on many other factors.

For the most persuasive understanding of the negative uses of the Internet, one has to turn to an important but least-recognised truth about the uniqueness of this technological creation. The Internet differs from all other tools or machines invented by man in the past insofar as it is not really a tool or a machine in the conventional sense. It is less like a machine, and more like mankind itself. The Internet is indeed a de-materialised machine – it has less to do with matter and more to do with the human mind. In this sense, it is truly a mental machine supported by a material infrastructure

Machines and tools in the previous eras were inert and inanimate. In traditional societies, especially in India, people were trained by their cultures to humanise and even divinise their lifeless tools of production, and thus establish an intimate and organic man-machine relationship.

Thus, the farmer in India saw the divine in the plough he used, as did the weaver in his loom. In contrast, the industrial revolution in the West, based as it was on exploitation and violence, saw nothing divine or human in the machines it invented. Its devices were devoid of any moral content, lofty social purpose or ennobling spiritual message. As a result, the man-machine relationship became purely functional at best, and soul-killing at worst. Indeed, this explains why Gandhi largely rejected modern machines, and was attracted towards the humble charkha for his mission in service of truth and nonviolence.

The Internet is the first technological invention in the modern era that has started restoring the man-machine relationship to its proper harmonious level. By no means has it succeeded fully in this endeavour, but the main direction of its effort is unmistakable. Its success lies in the fact that it differs from all the machines of the previous eras, including those used in traditional societies, in a fundamental way – it is a strange kind of machine that is blurring the man-machine duality. This is because man is no longer an external user of this machine, as was the case in the past, but an integral and inseparable part of it. Man is *inside* the Internet, and the latter is not only a network of computers but also a network of people. Moreover, unlike any other machine in human history, it is a technology that can be simultaneously accessed and used by millions of people across the world. *(See Chapter 35 for a more elaborate examination of the Internet as mankind's 'Species Machine'.)*

Therefore, naturally, all the problems, shortcomings and negative traits of human beings naturally get displayed on the Internet. Our deviant sexual behaviours, our dishonesty, our proneness to crime and violence, our ignorance and prejudices, our bigotry in religious matters, our multiple insecurities and inadequacies – they are all out there on the Web because they are all in there in the present human reality. If there is something ugly about a man's face, the mirror cannot be blamed for showing it.

But does this mirror called the Internet show only man's negative side? Certainly not. There is also a positive and reassuring side to the human story, and it far outweighs his negative and disappointing aspects.

Accordingly, the Internet, reflecting the inherent regenerative impulse of mankind, exuberantly projects all that is good and beautiful in the aspirations, activities and achievements of people all over the world. There are hundreds of thousands of different ways in which the Internet is making people living in every corner of the planet responsible Global Citizens, daily conducting their normal – that is, peaceful – interactions and conversations on the Web. The overall, and ever-increasing, volume of human inter-connectivities that ICTs have fostered all across the planet constitute a constructive force of unprecedented proportions and of a kind that was previously unimaginable.

There are also more striking ways in which the Internet is breaking barriers and building bridges. The abundant resources on the Net for inter-faith dialogue have helped religious and national communities battle ignorance and promote mutual understanding and harmony. Conflict-weary Israelis and Palestinians connect with each other on Facebook and befriend each other. Indians and Pakistanis make new discoveries about their mutual cultures and realise how much they share in common. Speaking for myself, the Net has helped me shed many of my own previous misconceptions about China. It has educated me on the richness of the Chinese civilisation and also on the strong undercurrents for change in contemporary China. If China became a democracy, its rise on the world stage could greatly strengthen global peace. The Internet would have contributed immensely to this positive transformation.

Mahatma Gandhi is one of the highest searched names on search engines, demonstrating the growing interest in his life and philosophy that people around the world have been showing. Significantly, this has led people in different countries to discover the common ground between Gandhi and the great peace-promoting personalities in their own cultures – Martin Luther King Jr. in USA; Nelson Mandela and Archbishop Desmond Tutu in South Africa; the Dalai Lama; Aung San Suu Kyi in Myanmar; Mario Rodrigues Cobos, also known as Silo, who founded the Humanist Movement in Argentina; Gustavo Gutierrez, who is regarded as the 'Father of Liberation Theology' in Latin America; George Grant, an influential Canadian philosopher;

Tanaka Shozo, a nineteenth century environmental conservationist from Japan who said: 'True civilisations do not devastate mountains nor kill humans'; Syrian-born philosopher Jawdat Said, who has been propagating for the past forty years a vision of Islam free of violence; Khalid Kishtainy, an Iraqi writer who argues for nonviolent 'jihad' as an effective strategy for change in the Arab world; and many others like them around the globe.

Tawakkul Karman, a journalist and human rights activist from Yemen who became the youngest Nobel Peace Laureate (2011) and also the first woman from the Arab world to receive the honour, has said: 'India has given us our biggest source of inspiration – Mahatma Gandhi. We are following his path of nonviolence.'[11]

Video technology has been revolutionalised by the Internet. And although there are lots of offensive videos to be found on the Web, the ones that strengthen human bonding are by far more numerous, creative and effective. Every minute people upload forty-eight hours of video content on YouTube. Some of this content is indeed silly, but most clips on YouTube and other free video-sharing sites simply reveal ordinary people's natural instinct to share with the entire world whatever brings happiness and meaning to their lives. Sharing music has become one of the most popular uses of YouTube, where one can find the best in world music. For example, 'Imagine', John Lennon's famous song about a world without wars has been watched by tens of millions of people – a vindication of the line in the song where Lennon says: 'You may say I'm a dreamer/But I'm not the only one'.

And then there are happy and proud mothers who have uploaded video recordings of their babies taking their first tiny steps in life. It may not mean much to a stranger watching such a video in some other part of the world. Or, it might actually mean a lot. It might just rekindle the thought in her or him that all children in the world have a God-given right to grow up in a safer and better world. Indeed, there are numerous websites on the Internet that tell stories of the incredibly valiant efforts being made to ensure a better future for children in unsafe and vulnerable situations.

The Internet is catalysing multiple peacemaking initiatives across the world – diplomatic, political, social, economic, cultural, philanthropic and even in the field of sports. For example, post-apartheid South Africa is now brimming with hope and self-confidence, and the Internet's contribution to transmitting this message has been significant. Nothing illustrated this better than the enthusiasm with which the worldwide community of netizens applauded South Africa for its spectacular hosting of the 2010 FIFA World Cup.

Although more than a billion people watched the football tournament live on television, it is the Internet (which now subsumes television) that really highlighted the peace-promoting power of this greatest sporting event on the planet. Besides enabling millions of people to watch the best moments of the World Cup again and again, it provided a platform for countless conversations on the historic transformations taking place not only in South Africa but also in many other African countries. The inspiring official anthem of the FIFA World Cup – 'Waka Waka ...This Time for Africa', sung by Colombia's superstar Shakira – became so popular around the world that it has been viewed nearly 450 million times on YouTube so far. Never before had the African continent become so connected within itself, and with the rest of the world. It was a moment of pride for Africa, and the Internet played a big role in making it possible.

One of Africa's proud achievements is how deaths due to malaria are being rapidly reduced. Here, too, the Internet has played a role, promoting a major anti-malaria campaign to save lives in Africa, where a child dies every forty-five seconds due to a lethal mosquito bite. In the lead up to the World Cup, football teams, celebrities, governments, philanthropic foundations, corporations, and thousands of ordinary people joined forces with the United Nations Foundation in the 'Nothing But Nets' campaign to raise awareness about malaria. The ongoing online campaign has helped bed nets to be procured and distributed free to millions of needy Africans. The Bill and Melinda Gates Foundation, the world's largest philanthropic organisation that is powered by the billions of dollars that Bill Gates earned in the IT business, has made a stellar contribution to this humanitarian effort.

In many African countries, deaths due to malaria have been

reduced by half. Lives of more than a million children have been saved from malaria since 2000. This has strengthened the hope that one of the key UN Millennium Development Goals – ending malaria deaths globally by 2015 – can indeed be achieved.

The point I am trying to make here, with the help of all the above examples, is simply this: Those who associate the Internet only with pornography, hate speech and cyber crime either haven't bothered to see much else on it, or are too cynical to admit to the Internet's – and mankind's – brighter side. In particular, the Internet's promotion of peace is becoming so pronounced with each passing year that it is impossible not to agree with *WIRED's* editor Chris Anderson when he exclaims: 'The Internet can become a weapon of global hope'.

The Slow, but Sure, End to Institutionalised Wars

'We are probably living in the most peaceful time of our species' existence, and it will only get more peaceful.' This startling conclusion comes from Steven Pinker, a reputed Harvard professor, who conducted a study of the history of violence around the world. 'Global violence has fallen steadily since the middle of the twentieth century. According to the Human Security Brief 2006, the number of battle deaths in inter-state wars has declined from more than 65,000 per year in the 1950s to less than 2,000 per year in this decade. In Western Europe and the Americas, the second half of the century saw a steep decline in the number of wars, military coups, and deadly ethnic riots.'[12] Since Pinker published his article on the subject in 2007, it has evoked a spirited debate on the Internet, with many people disbelieving his conclusion but unable to disprove it.

Why does it seem difficult for us to believe that many parts of the world have enjoyed remarkable peace in the era after the Second World War and, especially, in the past two decades? Fareed Zakaria, the renowned Indian-American journalist and writer, deals with this issue in his book *The Post-American World: And the Rise of the Rest.* 'Part of the problem is that as violence has been ebbing, information has been exploding. The last 20 years have produced an information revolution that brings us news and, most crucially, images from around the world all the time. The immediacy of the images and the intensity of the 24-hour news cycle combine to produce constant hype. Every weather disturbance is the "storm of the decade". Every bomb that explodes is BREAKING NEWS. Because the information revolution is so new, we – reporters, writers, readers, viewers – are all just now figuring out how to put everything in context. We didn't watch daily footage of the two million people who died in Indochina in the 1970s, or the million who perished in the sands of the Iran-Iraq war ten years later. We saw little of the civil war in the Congo in the 1990s, where millions died. But today any bomb that goes off, any rocket that is fired, any death that results, is documented by someone, somewhere and ricochets instantly across the world.'[13]

The curious thing about the information explosion is that, even though it makes us think that we are living in very violent times, it is actually contributing to the reduction of violence in the world. And this is where we can see the amazing impact that information and communication technologies are making on geo-politics of our times. Inter-state wars have actually become a lot less likely in recent decades. The probability of a Third World War breaking out has become near-zero, especially after the end of the Cold War between USA and the now-extinct Soviet Union two decades ago. And even though an accidental nuclear catastrophe can never be ruled out so long as there are nuclear weapons anywhere in the world, there is now a reasonably large global consensus about an inter-state nuclear warfare being completely unthinkable. The idea that 'a nuclear war can never be won and must never be fought' – most passionately propounded by Mikhail Gorbachev, the last president of the erstwhile Soviet Union and one of the real heroes of the movement for world peace – has now become axiomatic. The theory of Mutually Assured Destruction (MAD), which propelled the nuclear arms race during the Cold War, is now universally accepted to be a mad and bad concept.

It is not that the world has not witnessed any wars or violent conflicts in the past few decades. But whenever a war of aggression has been waged, such as America's wars in Iraq and Afghanistan, the

Internet has played a big role in discrediting the aggressor, both in the home country and abroad, thereby strengthening anti-war forces around the world. At the same time, the Internet has also cast a powerful spotlight on the forces of terrorism and religious extremism. It has vastly expanded the debate within the Muslim world on the true teachings of Islam and the real meaning of jihad. It has also deepened a similar soul-searching debate among people belonging to other faiths.

What has brought about this remarkable change? A large part of the answer to this question lies in the fact that the information explosion caused by the mass media, and especially by the Internet in the past ten-fifteen years, has immensely enhanced humankind's interconnectedness and boosted our self-awareness as a species. People all over the world want peace. They have always wanted peace. However, now for the first time in human history, the limitless constructive and nonviolent interactions are helping realise that what unites them is a lot more real than what separates them. Thus, while being conscious and even proud of their national, cultural, religious, racial or linguistic identities, every netizen has consciously or subconsciously begun to feel that he or she is now also, simultaneously, a World Citizen.

This new global consciousness, which is still at a formative stage, is both influencing, and is being strengthened by, the rapidly growing Internet-enabled dialogues and interactions among the people. It is causing a big shift in the relative weight of ordinary people's views vis-à-vis those of politicians and governments. Most countries in the world have embraced democracy in one form or the other in the post-Second World War era. Even the few remaining non-democratic countries are today not as authoritarian and closed as they were in the past. This, combined with the fact that more and more members of the global society are beginning to think like World Citizens, is creating an ever-expanding global constituency for peace.

Another factor is also aiding this process: the phenomenal level of transparency that the Internet is forcing upon governments, including the most autocratic among them. Governments, which are habitually inclined to keep information secret and away from the common people, are finding it increasingly difficult to do so. This became starkly evident when WikiLeaks, a nonprofit media organisation, put out massive troves of classified governmental information into the public domain in 2010. Most of the leaked information was of a kind that greatly embarrassed governments, politicians and diplomats in many countries, including in India. In what has come to be known as the 'Cash-for-Votes' scandal, WikiLeaks made a shocking disclosure in March 2011 that huge bribes were paid to some Opposition Members of Parliament (MPs) in order to secure their support for the survival of the government. In a flash, the Internet showed what a powerful tool for global communication it had become, one capable of demolishing the walls of secrecy imposed by governments.

The power of the Internet to combat secrecy and enlarge transparency in the functioning of governments and security establishments is particularly relevant in minimising wartime atrocities. To illustrate this point, I can do no better than to visit a scene from *Judgment at Nuremberg*, one of the most thoughtful movies ever made on the theme of war. This award-winning 1961 film by Stanley Kramer is about the trial of Nazi generals for the war crimes they committed during the Second World War, especially against Jews in the concentration camps. An American judge at the Nuremberg war trials is faced with a peculiar dilemma: to what extent is a morally upright public official guilty of atrocities, which are committed by the State but are condoned by him in the interest of the Nation? There is a powerful courtroom scene in the film in which the defence counsel states that although there was no justification for what happened, it was the Nazi extremists, and not the defendant or ordinary people of Germany, who were responsible for the atrocities. The truth of the matter, he says, is that '*very few Germans knew the full extent of what was going on*'.

It is indeed debatable as to whether many Germans in Hitler's time knew, and how much they knew, about the Holocaust in which nearly six million Jews were killed. What is certain, however, is that the people in any modern country today with ubiquitous access to camera phones and high-speed Internet would not be in the dark if such a colossal state-sponsored crime were to take place in their country. We have known how, in recent years, the online media exposed American military's torture of prisoners in the Abu Ghraib prison in Iraq and in the Guantanamo Bay detention centre of the United States located in Cuba. This generated intense public outrage worldwide and ultimately forced the US administration to put plans in motion to close the torture camps.

Perhaps the most potent factor that is serving as a deterrent to warmongers is globalisation – the relentlessly growing interconnectivity and interdependence between national and sub-national economies. This is an altogether new phenomenon in human history, made possible and daily accelerated by the revolutionary power of information and communication technologies. John Naisbitt, a leading futurist in USA, says that one of the megatrends in the twenty-first century is the 'shift from nation-states to networks'. As far back as in 1995, he had insightfully predicted that the global economy would look like the Internet. The bigger the globalised economic system, the more interconnected, efficient, synergistic and autonomous would its parts become. Many businesses would be more closely interlinked to their counterparts overseas than in their own home country. As a result, the nation-states would lose their unfettered powers to take decisions hurtful to businesses.

Naisbitt's forecast – 'The bigger the world economy, the more powerful its smallest players' – has important implications for the politics of war. The millions of small and autonomous players have no inclination for war or conflict. And since they operate in a networked economy, the instinct for peace and stability is shared by all across the small and big networks. Thus, interconnected businesses have come to exert the greatest pressure on governments to resolve disputes and differences in nonviolent ways.

Wars to occupy and colonise territories will become a near-impossibility in the twenty-first century. Similarly, the world is not going to be divided on ideological grounds into rival blocks, headed by mutually hostile superpowers, as happened during the Cold War in the latter half of the twentieth century. Indeed, even the sole surviving superpower, USA, is becoming weaker with every passing year and losing its relative economic superiority over other emerging global powers such as China and India. As the current trend towards multipolarity already shows, the world in the twenty-first century will witness the play of multiple centres of mutually competing, but also mutually cooperative, powers. A good example of this is how both USA and China, despite having serious differences on several issues, have been building their bilateral relations on essentially cooperative lines.

If the international community – especially, its leading members – can succeed in making mutual synergy and cooperation the signature tune of global affairs, and if it can evolve effective multilateral institutions of conflict-resolution, the twenty-first century will witness an epochal change: nation-states will gradually see the futility of maintaining large standing armies and spending huge resources on armaments that are rarely going to be used. Neither of these two 'ifs' is impossible to address. The Internet can effectively address both. For it is the most potent weapon ever invented by humankind, one that can make all the ultra-costly and utterly repulsive mass-killing weapons amassed by nation-states – nuclear warheads, Inter-Continental Ballistic Missiles (ICBMs), stockpiles of chemical and biological weapons, and all other weapons of mass destruction – redundant. It will make them relics of a dark epoch of world wars, inter-state wars and an arms race that is bound to come to an end in this very century. Finally, thanks to the Internet, Isaiah's dream, powerfully depicted in a sculpture at the UN headquarters in New York of converting 'swords into ploughshares, will come true!

What the Internet hasn't Been Able to Achieve

In this discussion on the potential of the Internet to promote world peace, it is necessary to add an important caveat. What we have seen in the period after the Second World War is the diminishing occurrence of institutionalised wars between nation-states, and the near-impossibility of nuclear weapons states precipitating a new world war. This trend has become particularly pronounced in the past two decades, after the end of the Cold War. This is also the period when information and communication technologies have knit the world together in the fabric of globalisation. As discussed earlier, the unifying power of ICTs has made our world largely secure from institutionalised inter-state wars.

However, this does not mean that the world has become similarly secure from other manifestations of violence – terrorism, inter-faith or inter-ethnic conflicts, armed insurgencies, civil wars, systematic state-sponsored violence against citizens, or structural violence or 'indirect violence' in the form of widespread poverty and socio-economic injustice in many parts of the world, much of it exacerbated by the flawed process of globalisation itself. Although ICTs have made some contribution to reducing these other forms of violence, it is obvious that their full potential in this regard has not yet been realised.

Out of these diverse forms of violence, removal of structural violence by way of eradication of poverty is relatively easy. It is eminently possible to make a big dent in global poverty, starvation, homelessness, illiteracy and communicable diseases within the next couple of decades. What is needed is radical reorientation of globalisation to serve the needs of poor countries and communities, sound domestic policies, good governance at national and local levels, empowerment of communities and families and, above all, huge cuts in the military budgets of big and small countries alike, so that the resources so saved can be diverted to development and people's welfare. However, none of these necessary measures is possible without the harnessing of strong political will and cooperative action at every level, especially in national governments and multilateral institutions. As we have discussed earlier in this book, both ICTs and other technologies can play a big supportive role in this task of promoting 'structural nonviolence'.

Where technology has really a limited, and very tough, role to play is in combating forms of violence that have deep-rooted social, religious and ideological roots. All violence is committed first in human minds before it manifests itself in the spilling of human blood. Mental prejudices and exclusivist identities on the grounds of race, ethnicity, caste, creed and nationality often have long antiquity. When bitter memories and narratives of the past conflicts continue to remain a part of the present consciousness of communities, it sometimes becomes very difficult to make people think in new, reconciliatory, ways. The same is true about widely held religious or racial dogmas, which make people react in violent ways whenever their inflexible beliefs and their notions of superiority are questioned.

Even though globalisation and technological advancement have given birth to a new consciousness of global citizenship, they have not yet significantly diminished the potency of the above-mentioned sources of violence. These can be countered only through a strong and sustained revival of enlightened spiritual, cultural and moral traditions around the world.

Gandhi's khadi and charkha campaign, which was an integral part of his campaign for India's independence, was one such inspiring and intrepid attempt at reviving the spiritual traditions in India to lay the foundation of a nonviolent society. However, his message through this campaign was as much global as it was national. 'History is a record of perpetual wars, but we are now trying to make new history'.[14] Gandhi wrote this in 1937. With an audacity that only he was capable of, he tried to make new history with the help of his simple spinning wheel. The Internet is not yet invested with the all-embracing spiritual and moral purpose that his spinning wheel carried. This – to be guided by an overarching spiritual and moral purpose – is the most important challenge before the Internet and all its users. One thing is certain: Even a partial success in this endeavour can change history on a far bigger scale than the spinning wheel could.

When that happens, the Internet will have more emphatically proved that it is a worthy new avatar of Gandhi's charkha.

'For my material needs, the village is my world. For my spiritual needs, the world is my village.' *Gandhi, a philosopher of glocalisation, also stated: 'Interdependence is and ought be as much the ideal of man as self-sufficiency'. These Gandhian concepts create a harmonious relationship between Village and the Global Village, and between swadeshi and globalisation. The Internet Age has the potential to translate these concepts into reality.*

Illustration: Saurabh Singh

30

VILLAGE AND THE GLOBAL VILLAGE
How the Internet Harmonises
Swadeshi and Globalisation

→⊱⊱◈◈◈⊰⊰←

Carmaker Henry Ford had told an American friend of Gandhi that mass production was necessary to raise the people's standard of living. 'What do you feel, Gandhiji?' the friend asked. 'I do not believe in it at all,' replied Gandhiji... 'The mania for mass production is responsible for the world crises. Granting for the moment that the machinery may supply all the needs of humanity, still it would concentrate production in particular areas, so that you would have to go in a round-about way to regulate distribution; whereas, if there is production and distribution in the respective areas where things are required, it is automatically regulated, and there is less chance for fraud, none for speculation.' Gandhiji believed that the answer to the world's needs lies in 'production by the masses', and not in 'mass production'.

— Gandhi for 21st century: Man Vs. Machine,
Gandhi Smriti, New Delhi, and Mani Bhavan, Mumbai.

The factory of the future will focus on mass customisation and may look more like those weavers' cottages than Ford's assembly line.

— *The Economist* (21 April 2012). Special Report on 'The Third Industrial Revolution'. Vindicating Gandhi's vision of Swadeshi and 'production by the masses', it affirms that that the digitisation of manufacturing — through 3D printing, versatile robots and new materials — will transform and decentralise the way goods are made.

ANDHI SMRITI IN NEW DELHI, WHERE THE MAHATMA SPENT HIS last days, is a haven of serenity and solemnity. It is located on Tees January Marg, a road named after the day – 30 January 1948 – when he fell to the assassin's bullets. The house, surrounded by tall trees, has since become a national museum, untouched by the kind of modern construction that is rapidly changing the landscape of this part of the national capital. The most moving sight in the museum is the narrow pathway showing Gandhi's last slow steps leading to the lawn on which he was to address his customary prayer meeting that fateful evening. The saint indeed ended his earthly journey as he wanted – with a prayer, '*Hey* Ram', on his lips.

Prophets, saints and mahatmas don't really die. They remain alive in their works and in their words. I have felt this about Gandhi whenever I have visited his samadhi at Raj Ghat, the place on the banks of River Yamuna where he was cremated; or his ancestral house in Porbandar in Gujarat, where he was born; or his ashrams in India and South Africa; or the dozens of other places associated with the intense drama of his life. Through every aphorism that is displayed at these places, Gandhi speaks directly to those who are interested in conversing with him. Sometimes a single sentence of his can cast a flashlight of startling understanding on a complex contemporary issue,

It happened to me on a cloudy and quiet afternoon, when I visited Gandhi Smriti. For a long time, my mind had been grappling with a question: how to reconcile the seeming contradiction between Gandhi's concept of swadeshi and today's reality of globalisation? I then came across this Gandhian thought, inscribed on one of the plaques along the pathway bearing his last footprints: 'For my material needs, the village is my world. For my spiritual needs, the world is my village'.

This aphorism instantly established, at the conceptual level, a harmonious relationship between swadeshi and globalisation, between Village and the Global Village. It also helped me understand how the Internet age has the potential to translate this Gandhian thought into reality.

Geography determines history. Who can deny this truth? In mankind's long evolution, the specific characteristics and constraints of geography have considerably influenced the economic life, social development and cultural progress of every society. Geographical location has indeed been the basis of the identity of nations and sub-national communities. However, in the future evolution of the human race, the impact of geography on history will be relatively less. This is due to the advent of a new agent of change: information and communication technologies that conquer geographical separation, save time and connect peoples around the globe. The ICT revolution, which has been the driving force of globalisation, has inaugurated an altogether new era in the individual and collective histories of nations.

The phenomenon of globalisation has posed a peculiar problem before the students and followers of Gandhian philosophy. The specific source of the problem is the concept of swadeshi – Home Economy or National Economy, as Gandhi called it – which is an important and inseparable part of his vision of a nonviolent world. Swadeshi has been widely misunderstood, and routinely misused to show that his economic philosophy is both outmoded and obscurantist. This is because his critics, and many of his admirers too, understand swadeshi to mean just this: 'Buy Indian, Boycott Foreign'. Accordingly, the critics' most charitable judgment is that his campaign for swadeshi was perhaps necessary in the context of India's struggle for freedom from British rule, but has no relevance in today's era of global interdependence.

If the votaries of globalisation try to junk swadeshi as outdated, many ardent supporters of swadeshi flay globalisation as the source of most of the ills afflicting the common people in the world. There is no dearth of Gandhians who, though well-meaning and fully dedicated to the ideals dear to the Mahatma, think that the ills created by globalisation can be overcome only by going back to self-sufficient village republics or local-national economies. What they do not realise, or are reluctant to acknowledge, is that societies can never go back in time.

Thus, we see a peculiar stalemate in the debate over a major principle in Gandhi's economic philosophy. The supporters of globalisation oppose swadeshi, and the supporters of swadeshi oppose globalisation. Can the stalemate be broken? Is it possible to show that globalisation and swadeshi can become mutually compatible? Yes. The implication of believing the two to be incompatible is that Gandhi was horribly wrong in his economic thinking or, alternatively, that globalisation is an absolute curse for mankind. Both inferences would be wrong.

This is where we see the Internet as the new game-changing techno-social development capable of harmonising Gandhi's swadeshi with globalisation. The beauty of the Internet is that it is driving both globalisation and localisation at the same time. A *globally* interconnected and interdependent world is simultaneously becoming *locally* more interconnected and interdependent, a prospect that Gandhi would have surely loved. With more and more transnational as well as neighbourhood interactions and initiatives being facilitated by the Internet, the future of globalisation will be GLOCALISATION.

For example, in the highly organised and widely spread super-market culture of America, thousands of small and tiny enterprises have mushroomed, powered by the Internet, specialising in locally produced farm-products, crafts and clothes, and a variety of home goods.

Thus, mankind for the first time has an opportunity to give effect to a new principle that may be called: 'THINK GLOCAL, ACT GLOCAL.' This has enormous potential to foster nonviolence.

Like much else in the Gandhian vision, swadeshi was a concept that was both rooted in its own time and also ahead of its time. Some of its conceptual elements are no longer relevant, and have to be either discarded or modified in the light of today's realities. Others, however, are of universal and timeless relevance. Therefore, it is necessary to sift the enduring from the outmoded in the message of swadeshi.

Swadeshi became the code word for Gandhi's economic philosophy when it was associated with his call for the boycott of British-made clothes in the early 1920s, and with his campaign for the revival of khadi and village industries. It was a protest against the subordination of the Indian economy to the interests of a colonial power. It was a part of his strategy to instil national pride by boosting indigenous, especially village-based, capabilities. Unfortunately, even today swadeshi continues to carry the 'anti-foreign' connotations, although the economic circumstances in India and the world have changed radically. This has distorted our understanding of the basic underpinnings of Gandhi's economic philosophy.

Gandhi's critique of the Western model of industrialisation had convinced him that subjugation of distant lands for raw materials and domination of external markets for the sale of manufactured goods was intrinsically exploitative, unsustainable and violence breeding. As colonial India's experience with England showed, admirals and generals followed the trader. That model inflicted violence both on human beings and on nature. It treated both labour and natural resources with disrespect, fair game to be exploited for maximising profits for the small class of owners. It frequently led to overproduction and scarcities. This continues to be true even today. Therefore, Gandhi's search was for a model of economic activity that honoured the natural law and was in accordance with the moral code of religions. The outcome of this search was swadeshi, which, according to him, 'is the only doctrine consistent with the law of humanity and love'.[1]

Swadeshi: The Science of Home Economics

Gandhi's swadeshi rested on three principles. Firstly, welfare of man and his immediate community or neighbourhood should be the primary concern of all economic activity. Hence, whatever is made or produced in the local community should be for the use, first and foremost, of members of the local community. Surplus should be shared with those who are in need. Maximum local self-sufficiency through decentralised and cooperative production using local resources, with full employment for all able-bodied members of the community, was the cornerstone of swadeshi. As we shall soon see, this principle needs some modification to reflect today's changed circumstances.

Secondly, goods that cannot be made and services that cannot be provided within the local community can be purchased from elsewhere. However, trading between communities should be minimal in order to avoid wasteful and harmful transportation. Moreover, such import and export between communities should be on a non-exploitative basis and guided by the principles of mutual care and accommodation.

Although the first and second principles may seem mutually contradictory, Gandhi himself reconciled them beautifully in his economic and social philosophy. Never a xenophobe, and one who always subordinated nationalism to his vision of globalism, he had explicitly said: 'Interdependence is and ought be as much the ideal of man as self-sufficiency'.[2] He did not draw any rigid and unbreakable lines between the 'local' and the 'global'. For example, he wrote in *Young India* in 1925:

> My definition of swadeshi is well known. I must not serve my distant neighbour at the expense of the nearest. It is never vindictive or punitive. It is in no sense narrow, for I buy from every part of the world what is needed for my growth. I refuse to buy from anybody anything, however nice or beautiful, if it interferes with my growth or injures those whom Nature has made my first care. I buy useful healthy literature from every part of the world. I buy surgical instruments from England, pins and pencils from Austria and watches from Switzerland. But I will not buy an inch of the finest cotton fabric from England or Japan or any other part of the world because it has injured and increasingly injures the million of the inhabitants of India. I hold it to be sinful for me to refuse to buy the cloth spun and woven by the needy million of India's paupers and to buy foreign cloth although it may be superior in quality to the Indian hand-spun.[3]

For Gandhi, village was the most basic local economic unit. But it was integrally linked, through the principle of interdependence, to larger local communities extending right up to the nation and the world. In other words, the interdependent relationship between the village and the Global Village that modern information and communication technologies have established is not at all incompatible with the Gandhian vision of economics or society. As Gandhi wrote in 'The Law of Swadeshi' in 1931:

Swadeshi in its purest form is the acme of universal service...
To reject foreign manufactures merely because they are foreign
and to go on wasting national time and money to promote
manufactures in one's country for which it is not suited
would be criminal folly and a negation of the swadeshi spirit.
A true votary of swadeshi will never harbour ill-will towards
the foreigner, he will not be moved by antagonism towards
anybody on the earth. Swadeshism is not a cult of hatred. It
is a doctrine of selfless service that has its roots in the purest
Ahimsa, i.e. love.[4]

Gandhi's conception of an ideal Global Village is one which embodies
the spirit of the family – an extension of home in which members
imbibe the values of mutual love, caring and sharing, and, when
needed, readiness to sacrifice for the larger wellbeing of the family.
Which is why, he himself translated swadeshi as 'Home Economics'.
By insisting that one local unit's relationship with another, and also
with larger units such as community, nation and the world, should be
guided by the principles of care and cooperation, Gandhi's swadeshi
lays the basis of a nonviolent economic ecosystem right from the
village to the Global Village.

The third principle of swadeshi is that, although economic
activities are unavoidable as they ensure the survival and sustenance of
communities, economics should not dominate society. Economics is a
means to an end, and not an end in itself, as it has now unfortunately
become. Individuals and communities should learn to limit their
material wants and, hence, to moderate economic growth only to satisfy
their genuine needs. Beyond a certain reasonable limit, economic
growth in pursuit of endless prosperity becomes detrimental to human
wellbeing and also to the environment. As has been noted by Kenneth
Boulding (1910–93), a famous educator, peace activist, and poet who
was influenced by Mahatma Gandhi, 'Anyone who thinks exponential
growth can go on forever in a finite world is either a madman or an
economist'!

Dharampal (1922–2006), a profound Gandhian thinker who re-
appraised India's cultural, scientific and technological history from a

non-colonial perspective, has succinctly summarised swadeshi's above-mentioned three principles in the following words:

> A major aspect of the *ahimsak* (nonviolent) way of life is to minimise one's needs and to fulfill these as far as possible from within one's immediate neighborhood. His (Gandhi's) practice of relying on local availability is as important a part of the principle of ahimsa as the doctrine of non-killing. Thus for Gandhi, ahimsa and swadeshi (of one's own locality) were not two different principles.[5]

Village Self-Sufficiency: An Outmoded Idea

Has the age of information and communication technologies altered the meaning of swadeshi? Also, has it altered its meaning as much as to render it meaningless today? The answer to the first question is 'yes'; to the second, it is 'no'.

Undoubtedly, the principle of absolute village self-sufficiency has become irrelevant today. Many Gandhians, however, have continued to project swadeshi through the broken prism of village self-sufficiency. For example, Satish Kumar, a highly respected Gandhian scholar and activist, writes in his otherwise insightful article *Gandhi's Swadeshi: The Economics of Permanence*: 'Every village community of free India should have its own carpenters, shoemakers, potters, builders, mechanics, farmers, engineers, weavers, teachers, bankers, merchants, traders, musicians, artists, and priests. In other words, each village should be a microcosm of India – a web of loosely inter-connected communities. Gandhi considered these villages so important that he thought they should be given the status of "village republics"'.

Similarly, Kumar also writes: 'Gandhi's vision of a free India was not a nation-state but a confederation of self-governing, self-reliant, self-employed people living in village communities, deriving their right livelihood from the products of their homesteads. Maximum economic and political power – including the power to decide what could be imported into or exported from the village – would remain in the hands of the village assemblies'.[6]

The trouble with presenting swadeshi exclusively through the idea of village self-sufficiency and village republics is that the above portrait of India is not ever going to become a reality, for obvious reasons. Today's India, and today's world, are vastly different. Urbanisation has become the defining trend all over the world. In 1947, India had only four cities with a population of one million and more; in 2011, it has over fifty of them. India was a predominantly rural society in 1947, but no longer so. The 1951 census classed about seventeen percent of the population as living in urban areas. The urban population, 27.8 percent of the total population in 2011, is projected to reach 50 percent within the next two decades.

Moreover, India's villages and rural communities are no longer as isolated as they were in Gandhi's time, their isolation having been hugely reduced by physical connectivity in the form of better roads, transportation facilities, market linkages and social mobility. Indian villages now constitute a sizeable market for bicycles and fuel-driven two-wheelers. Bullock carts have actually become a rarity in many Indian villages! The spread of satellite and cable television, combined with the incredible expansion in digital connectivity, in India's villages has minimised their isolation even more dramatically. Therefore, if we do not reinterpret swadeshi by contextualising it in the reality as it exists today, and as it is likely to evolve in the time to come, a very important Gandhian ideal faces the danger of being seen only as a relic of history.

However, my proposition is that there is another defining trend in the contemporary reality in India and the world which has put life back into the concept of swadeshi. The earlier notions of the 'local' and 'non-local' in the geographical space have become fungible in the digital space, thanks to the unbelievable distance-reduction and time-compression power of information and communication technologies. New virtual localities, neighbourhoods and communities, which are often international in character, have been created. Therefore, no geographically defined local community, small or large, can hope to be fully self-sufficient on its own. Global or universal self-sufficiency is the only realistic ideal in the age of the Internet.

Slowly but surely, the Internet is changing the nature of globalisation itself. In its infancy, flawed globalisation produced centralisation of economic activities and concentration of economic power in the hands of the industrialised nations of the West. However, in its mature adulthood, its effect will be quite to the contrary. Globalisation, aided by the Internet, will lead the world towards universal self-sufficiency by facilitating three cardinal tenets of swadeshi – decentralisation, cooperation and conservation. It will even aid and abet the revival of villages in a way approximating Gandhi's dream. Nowhere is it more starkly evident than in the field of manufacturing, an important driver of urbanisation until now. Tomorrow's IT-driven paradigm of manufacturing will change the nature of urbanisation into something resembling 'rurbanisation', a mutually sustainable co-existence of rural and urban spaces.

Glocalisation of Manufacturing

A study titled 'Manufacturing in 2020', by Capgemini, a global consulting and outsourcing firm, reveals that manufacturing is getting increasingly decentralised around the globe and this trend is certain to become more pronounced in the decade ahead. Accelerated competition at home and the growing sophistication of developing economies are driving manufacturers to source components from multiple locations internationally, assemble final products in multiple locations and sell them in local markets through local partners. The earlier model of manufacturing in one country and exporting from there to global markets is giving way to a new reality of many inter-connected localised activities. The Capgemini study states: 'Ten years from now manufacturing will have become more collaborative in nature, with companies involving suppliers and customers to a greater degree at all stages of the manufacturing process and the product lifecycle – from R&D to end-of-life disposal'.[7]

The migration of manufacturing from the West to the Rest can be clearly seen not only in China, which has already become the 'factory of the world', and in India, where the manufacturing sector has seen a big turnaround in the first decade of this century, but also in Africa, Latin America and in those countries in South-East Asia that have so far remained poor, such as Cambodia. In the years ahead, manufacturing and related economic activities are going to be further dispersed geographically even within these countries. This will reverse the production paradigm of the last two centuries when it was concentrated in a few areas.

What is making this process of decentralisation and localisation possible? Clearly, it is the digital technologies in manufacturing, simulation and system integration that seamlessly link the production process from a company's headquarters to multiple shop floors and from design studios to quality monitoring units. Computer-Aided Design (CAD); Computerised Numerical Control (CNC); Enterprise Resource Planning (ERP); Product Lifecycle Management (PLM); Robotics-Enabled Production processes for high-precision handling and positioning of parts; 3-D printing of design files that can be sent over the Internet and used both for creating prototypes and for actual manufacturing; and Radio Frequency Identification (RFID) technology for managing complex supply chains – all these and many other digital tools have transformed manufacturing into a collaborative activity that is at once global and local in nature. Armed with these new technologies, manufacturers are adopting best practices like Just-in-Time, which minimises inventory costs, and Total Quality Management (TQM), which empowers workers to detect and correct errors wherever they find them.

Telecommuting and flexible work options are the other impact-making changes that information and communication technologies will introduce in both manufacturing and services. With the cost of mobile video conferencing of HD quality drastically falling, more and more companies will adopt a 'work wherever you want, whenever you want' policy for their workers and managers. This has several benefits. Companies will spend less on office and factory space. Employees can work from home, thus being able to spend more time with their families. Cities can get de-congested and become more eco-friendly. IT-enabled flexible work will also mean that talented and skilled people can offer their services globally. This will create a new culture of workplace globalism. Thus, the gains accruing from the economies of *scaling up* in the previous paradigm of concentration of production in a few places will be replaced by the greater gains from the eco-friendly technologies of *scaling down*.

Gandhi would have surely applauded all these technological advancements.

Greening of Manufacturing

Until now, the main reason behind manufacturers embracing decentralisation and localisation was cheaper labour in non-Western countries. Labour wage differentials will continue to be a factor for many years to come, although they are now slowly eroding. However, a new factor has now come into being: the desire of manufacturers to be closer to their customers in the new markets that are emerging in different parts of the world, and also to be closer to the sources of raw materials and component suppliers. With energy costs going up, manufacturers want to save on transportation. This is also necessitated by the stiff emission reduction targets that businesses are now required to adhere to, in order to help countries move towards the goal of a low-carbon economy. This goal has come to occupy the centre stage of the global debate on climate change.

With environmental consciousness rapidly rising all over the world, businesses are constantly looking for ways to save resources and to reduce and recycle waste. This has encouraged large-scale technological innovations for environmental protection. For example, several carbon sequestration techniques are being developed for capturing and removing carbon dioxide. One such technique is the planting of 'artificial trees' along highly polluted roads; these can trap CO_2 far more efficiently than live trees.

Conservation of resources, a principle very dear to the Mahatma's heart *(see Mirabehn's vivid description of his anti-waste attitude in Chapter 23)*, is now also at the very heart of the IT-enabled manufacturing practices of several leading companies in India and the world. To the 3-R principle of environment-friendly business practice – Reduce-Recycle-Reuse – they are adding a new R: Recover. They are thereby faithfully trying to follow the appeal of the Global Earth Charter (1992): 'Pursue production activities that do not generate waste'.

Panasonic, one of the major manufacturers of electrical and electronic equipment, has embarked on an ambitious plan to employ, by 2020, nearly one-fifth of recycled resources from its own products as a proportion of total resources used in making new products. In other words, components of appliances such as television sets, air-conditioning units, refrigerators, washing machines, etc., will be recovered, recycled and used in the manufacturing process, instead of being consigned to the hazardous heaps of e-waste.

In 2007, five major Japanese companies producing electronic goods – Panasonic, Sharp, Toshiba, Mitsubishi and Sanyo – came together to set up the Electronic Manufacturers Recycling Management Company (MRM), which operates a large number of recycling collection and processing facilities not only in Japan but also in the United States. MRM embraces the Japanese concept of *junkan gata monozkuri*, which means 'recycling-oriented manufacturing'. It assists consumers and also other manufacturers to ensure electronic products are diverted from the waste stream and recycled in an environmentally responsible and sustainable manner. This proactive green manufacturing initiative is also in response to an acute realisation that some of the critical component materials, such as rare earths, have a finite global supply and are expected to become scarce in the near future.

A similar initiative, called the 'Green Bag Campaign', has been started by HCL Infosystems, a leading manufacturer of IT hardware in India. It invites customers to bring their e-waste to HCL outlets for disposal – and subsequent recover and recycle by the company. India's software companies, led by Tata Consultancy Services (TCS), Infosys and Wipro, are also setting exemplary standards in sustainability, by considerably reducing not only their own carbon and ecological footprints, but also those of their business associates and partners.

I saw a zero-waste manufacturing marvel when I visited Reliance's refinery and petrochemical complex at Jamnagar in the Saurashtra region of Gujarat, not far from Porbandar, the birthplace of Gandhi. This coastal refinery, the world's largest at a single location, uses enormous quantities of sea-water, purified in its own desalination plant, for all its operations and also for supplying drinking water to the large industrial township. Nevertheless, it ejects not a single drop of water polluted in the refining process back into the sea. Its computerised treatment facilities purify the waste water again and use it for various industrial and non-industrial purposes. The recycled water sustains, through drip-irrigation, an artificially created forest area covering thousands of acres within the refinery complex! The refinery also has Asia's largest mango orchard. Thus, what was a vast expanse of barren and treeless land until the late 1990s in one of the most drought-prone areas in India, has today become a haven of greenery and a sanctuary for birds, butterflies, wildlife and marine life.

Driving this process of conservation of resources in manufacturing will be the rapid technological advances in renewable sources of energy. Economic growth until now has been propelled by fossil fuels, the days of which are certainly numbered. We are probably living in the few decades of the environment-degrading usage of hydrocarbons extracted out of the womb of earth. With a severe energy crisis looming over the world, research and development into eco-friendly alternative energy sources, solar energy in particular, is going on at a furious pace. This too has generated a tremendous quantum of international collaboration, which is assisted by the Internet.

What is peculiar about most of the renewable sources of energy is that, unlike oil, petroleum, natural gas and coal, they lend themselves to decentralised generation and local consumption. This is especially true about solar, wind, small-hydro and biomass-based energy sources. This, too, will have a big impact on geographic dispersal of economic activities away from cities.

We thus see how the new mantra of manufacturing in the era of glocalisation will address several key concerns of swadeshi economics.

When I saw Gandhian Ideals in a Toyota Factory

Modern manufacturing facilities that are supported by digital technologies and managed by enlightened leaders are no longer the sweatshops of England of the Victorian era, when child workers were 'chained, belted, harnessed like dogs...black, saturated with wet, and more than half-naked, crawling upon their hands and knees, and dragging their heavy loads behind them'.[8] Nor do employees in them resemble the lifeless cogs in a great dehumanising machine, as was portrayed brilliantly by Charlie Chaplin in his 1936 silent film *Modern Times*. It is true that working conditions are still wretched for millions of factory workers around the world, especially in the informal sector. Nevertheless, in the 'Factories of the Future', a new harmonious man-machine relationship is emerging, which will become more pronounced as the Internet era advances.

I saw one such 'Factory of the Future' when I visited Toyota's main manufacturing plant in Nagoya, Japan, in 2006. What triggered my desire to visit the plant was Jeffrey Liker's celebrated book *The Toyota Way: 14 Management Principles from the World's Greatest Manufacturer*. One evening, while looking for second-hand books on the pavements near my home at Matunga in Mumbai, the title of this book caught my attention. 'Toyota is as much a state of mind as it is a car company,' said a blurb on the bookcover. I finished reading it overnight, and said to myself: 'This is mind-expanding stuff. The ideas in this book go well beyond car manufacturing. The best minds in politics and governance in India must read this treatise to get insights into nation-building.' This conviction was reinforced when I spent a day at Toyota's sprawling headquarters.

'Respect for Humanity' is at the foundation of the Toyota Way, also known as the Toyota Production System (TPS), which is now studied globally by students of manufacturing management. The company's chairman Fujio Cho says: 'Since Toyota's founding we have adhered to the core principle of contributing to society through the practice of manufacturing high-quality products and services. Our business practices based on this core principle created values, beliefs and business methods that over the years have become a source of competitive advantage. These are known collectively as the Toyota Way.'

The fourteen Toyota Way principles, each of which strongly echoes Gandhian principles, can be briefly summarised as follows:

1. Base your management decisions on a long-term philosophy, even at the expense of short-term financial gains. Have a philosophical sense of purpose and mission that supersedes any short-term decision-making. Work, grow, and align the whole organisation towards a common purpose that is bigger than making money.

2. The Right Process will produce the Right Results. Don't hide problems within the organisation, but create a continuous process flow to bring them to the surface.

3. Avoid overproduction by following the principle of just-in-time – namely, customers should get what they want, when they want it, and in the amount or numbers they want.

4. Eliminate *muda* (Japanese for waste) – any expenditure of time, money, material, effort, or other resource that does not generate perceptible value for the customer. Also, strive to cut back to zero the amount of time that any work project is sitting idle or waiting for someone to work on it.

5. Build a culture of stopping operations to fix problems. This will help in getting quality right the first time.

6. Standardised tasks are the foundation for continuous improvement and employee empowerment. Capture the accumulated learning about a process by institutionalising today's best practices and allow employees to improve the standard through creative self-expression.

7. Use visual and manual control so that no problems are hidden.

8. Use technology to support people, not to replace people. Reject or modify technologies that conflict with your work culture. Nevertheless, encourage your people to consider new technologies when looking into new approaches to work.

9. Develop such leaders in your organisation who thoroughly understand the work, live the philosophy, and teach it to others.

Do not view the leader's job as simply accomplishing tasks. Leaders must be role models of the company's philosophy and way of doing business.

10. Develop exceptional people and teams who follow your company's philosophy. Make an ongoing effort to teach individuals to work together as teams towards common goals.

11. Have respect for your business partners and suppliers and treat them as an extension of your business.

12. Continuously solving root problems improves organisational learning. Even high-level managers should go and see things for themselves, so that they will have more than a superficial understanding of the situation.

13. Make decisions slowly by consensus, thoroughly considering all options; but implement decisions rapidly.

14. Become a learning organisation through relentless reflection (*hansei*) and continuous improvement (*kaizen*). Protect the organisation's knowledge and cultural base by developing stable personnel, careful promotion, and well thought-out succession systems.

The fourteen principles show that the Toyota Way is also, in many ways, the Gandhian Way. In the manufacturing paradigm of Toyota (founded in 1937), every employee is made to feel important, honoured, empowered and responsible to achieve the company's objectives of zero-defect, zero-waste and complete customer satisfaction. The company's multiple car-making facilities send zero waste to the landfill. 'We have no waste management concept in our company,' a Toyota executive told me. 'We only know, and practice, resource management.' The so-called 'waste' from one production unit becomes resource, through intelligent recycling for another production unit. Liker's book presents amazing case-studies of how Toyota doubled or tripled the speed of every business process, reduced production cost through constant innovation, and made quality control a company-wide obsession. This is what helped Toyota beat American auto giants Ford and General Motors in most markets globally.

My discussions with Toyota executives and my study of other innovation-driven companies in Japan convinced me that, for the

Japanese, manufacturing and other business activities are not only about making money. They are about seeking, preserving and promoting *Wa* or 'harmony', a quintessentially Japanese principle, which they practice within their own companies, in product design, in art, in society, and in their relationship with customers. Adherence to this principle sometimes poses difficult choices for a business enterprise: short-term gains vs. long-term reputation. Japanese companies have often had to make this choice, and many have always made the right choice.

In late 2009 and early 2010, Toyota faced one of the worst crises in its history. It had to recall nearly eight million cars and trucks worldwide due to quality and safety problems. The loss it incurred on account of this ran into several billion dollars. The crisis revealed that, in its bid to grow fast and capture a bigger share of the global car market, the company had failed to ensure that all its far-flung suppliers adhered to its own strict quality standards. 'Toyota has become too big and distant from its customers,' Toyota's president, Akio Toyoda, admitted. The company's policy had always been to 'seek quality, and volume will follow'. However, the temptation of capturing a higher and higher share in foreign markets led some of its managers to replace the company's Quality First mantra with a 'plan for volume and achieve volume' approach. The company paid a heavy price for this deviation. However, it rectified the mistake by following, once again, the Toyota Way, and has returned to good profitability.

On a sunny afternoon in early 2009, in the sprawling and verdant campus of the Godrej factory in Powai, a Mumbai suburb, my friend Dr Kavi Arya and I met Prof. Shoji Shiba, a Japanese guru of TQM in manufacturing and a great admirer of Mahatma Gandhi. Kavi, a professor of computer science at IIT Mumbai, has developed small robots which can be effectively used in engineering education. Shiba has been helping several Indian companies, including Godrej, with his pioneering concept of 'breakthrough management' as part of the 'Visionary Leaders for Manufacturing' (VLFM) programme launched by the Confederation of Indian Industries (CII). He told us that the key ingredients to success in manufacturing are maximising efficiencies and minimising waste (of time, resources and human energy) all across the value chain in a production system. 'Knowledge and application of technology is no doubt a critical necessity in achieving this. But no less important is transformation of the human factor – how motivated the workers are, how good is the cross-functional relationship within a production unit, how holistic are the qualities of team leaders at various levels, and how clean and pleasant is the working environment.' This is indeed the TQM philosophy that Gandhi followed in his own work and also in the work of the khadi and village industries that he promoted.

Shiba explained to us the concept of 'breakthrough management'. According to him, every organisation or system goes through a lifecycle, in which inception, evolution and extinction are inherent. However, in the course of the evolution there comes a tipping point when the system starts showing signs of decline. If a business or an organisation reinvents itself at this disruptive point, it achieves a breakthrough and places itself on a new evolutionary path.

Shiba admires Gandhi for many reasons, one of them being that he sees him as a management guru. He says: 'One day I went to the government-run Cottage Emporium near Connaught Place in New Delhi. At the cashier's counter, I noticed a big board bearing a quotation from the Mahatma – "A customer is the most important visitor on our premises. He is not dependent on us. We are dependent on him. He is not an interruption in our work – he is the purpose of it. We are not doing him a favor by serving him. He is doing us a favor by giving us the opportunity to serve him." How visionary, I thought. This customer-centric approach to business is precisely what led Japan to develop quality-focused management practices in the 1960s. This was the key factor behind the success of Japanese companies. It is time for us to learn again from Mahatma Gandhi, especially with regard to the challenge of sustainable development.'

The Internet has Changed the Concept of Neighbourhood

'The Customer is King' is an idea found in most books on marketing. However, there is more to it than marketing. It reveals the moral principle of mutuality between every manufacturer, trader, service provider and customer. After all, each is both a customer of certain goods and services, and also a producer or a provider of the same or other goods and services for others. Therefore, everyone has to follow Christ's dictum, which Gandhi often invoked: 'Do unto others as you would have them do unto you'. Since all businesses in the age of globalisation, unlike in the previous eras, are interconnected parts of a single worldwide economic ecosystem, reciprocity is no longer an option limited to one's immediate neighbours; it has become a necessity extendable to the entire global community.

In the past, the ethic of reciprocity was conjured in the context of one's geographical neighbours – hence the biblical maxim: 'Love thy neighbour as thyself'. This finds resonance in all the ancient philosophies around the world. The *Mahabharata* says: 'One should never do that to another which one regards as injurious to one's own self. This, in brief, is the rule of dharma. Other behaviour is due to selfish desires.' A disciple once asked Confucius: 'Is there one word which may serve as a rule of practice for all one's life?' The Master said: 'Is not RECIPROCITY such a word?' Prophet Mohammed, in his Farewell sermon, exhorts: 'Hurt no one so that no one may hurt you.' The ancient Greek philosopher Pittacus says: 'Do not to your neighbour what you would take ill from him.'

The concept of neighbourhood has changed in the era of globalisation and the Internet. Therefore, the moral of reciprocity in business as also in other aspects of life must perforce embrace the entire global community. In his time, Gandhi's concept of serving the neighbour – the first principle of swadeshi that we have referred to above – was circumscribed by the limitations of extant technologies. In other words, although his vision was global, its fructification was not supported by the pre-globalisation technologies. Hence, he relied essentially on good conduct by human beings, as is clear from the following remarkable passage from what he wrote in *Harijan* in 1947:

I believe in the truth implicitly that a man can serve his neighbours and humanity at the same time, the condition being that the service of the neighbours is in no way selfish or exclusive, i.e., does not in any way involve the exploitation of any other human being. The neighbours will then understand the spirit in which such service is given. They will also know that they will be expected to give their services to their neighbours. Thus considered, it will spread like the proverbial snow-ball gathering strength in geometrical progression, encircling the whole earth. It follows that swadeshi is that spirit which dictates man to serve his next-door neighbour to the exclusion of any other. The condition that I have already mentioned is that the neighbour, thus served, has, in his turn, to serve his own neighbour. In this sense, swadeshi is never exclusive. *It recognises the scientific limitation of human capacity for service.*[9] *(Emphasis added)*

Gandhi's lament of 'scientific limitation of human capacity for service' in 1947 was only natural. There was no Internet those days. Today, science itself has converted limitation into augmentation of human capacity for service. Thanks to the revolutionary power of digital technologies, the truth that Gandhi had implicitly understood in his time – 'that a man can serve his neighbours and humanity at the same time' – has become an explicit mandate for implementation. Of course, this cannot be implemented by technology alone. Enlightened human conduct – serving one's neighbours (both in the real and digital worlds) and they in turn serving their neighbours ...and so on – will be as necessary as ever. What is new today is that technology has come as a scientific boon to achieve an ethical imperative worldwide.

Technology is now married to morality.

The Future of Cities and Villages

Technology in future will be married to another important theme in Gandhi's vision and mission – all-round development of villages. Uncontrolled and seemingly unstoppable urbanisation, at the cost of the natural vitality of villages, is now a worriesome global trend. 'The blood of the villages is the cement with which the edifice of cities is built,' is how Gandhi had bemoaned this trend way back in 1946. It has become far more pronounced and widespread now, with a disastrous impact on the human and natural environment.

The roots of urbanisation, of the kind the world has seen in the past two centuries, are in the specific nature of the economy shaped by the industrial revolution in Europe. However, since the Internet and digital technologies will radically change the nature of the economy, both nationally and globally, in the coming decades of the twenty-first century, it is safe to predict that they will also fundamentally transform the city-village relationship in the future. Vividly describing his own dream of the ideal relationship between cities and villages, Gandhi had said: 'I want the blood that is today inflating the arteries of the cities to run once again in the blood vessels of the villages.'[10] The Internet Age can indeed make this dream a reality.

Digital technologies, and the new human-centric and environment-friendly manufacturing paradigm, have provided that all-important breakthrough to the world economy, without which it would have certainly stagnated. Now, this paradigm finds itself on a new evolutionary path. We shall see below how, within the realm of manufacturing, digital technologies are about to create a new disruptive breakthrough which has the potential to enable the modern economy to promote the ideals of reinterpreted swadeshi in even more decisive ways.

In explaining his swadeshi philosophy, Gandhi said that economic activities should be of a 'human scale'. Huge factories, in which workers are overwhelmed by impersonal machines, create a sense of alienation and devalue human life. His critique of big cities was also based on the same reason. Besides the conditions of congestion and squalor in which the urban poor are condemned to live in many cities around the world, the sheer impersonality of giant-scale urban habitats, combined with the domination of money in all social interactions, weakens the human core of almost all relationships. The rich feel as alienated as the poor in such dehumanised urban milieu.

Our habitats can be rehumanised if our economic activities, in particular the manufacturing activities, become as natural and as creative as the work of traditional artisans and craftspeople. This ideal, which seemed impossible earlier, is now within the reach of the revolutionary hands of digital technologies. Let us look at the new trend of micro-factories, which can help reduce the consumption of energy and materials, require less space, provide flexibility of production and, at the same time, boost productivity.

3-D Printing and the 'Third Industrial Revolution': How They will Prove Gandhian Swadeshi Right

In April 2012, *The Economist*, one of the world's most influential magazines, carried a special report titled 'The Third Industrial Revolution'. In terms of impact and recall value, this report, by Paul Markillie, is certain to be in the same league as another memorable special report in *The Economist* – 'The Death of Distance' (1995) by Frances Cairncross, which predicted that distance would not be a limiting factor in people's ability to communicate, instantaneously, in the Internet age through voice, data and video. The third industrial revolution, which refers to the currently unfolding phenomenon of digital manufacturing, extends the death-of-distance promise of the Internet further: It is all set to create a future when distance will not be a limiting factor even in the making of products of one's choice – practically anything, anywhere and anytime.

The first industrial revolution began in Britain in the late eighteenth century with the mechanisation of the textile industry, pioneered by the likes of Samuel Crompton and James Hargreaves, about which Gandhi himself has commented extensively *(see Chapter 12)*. It gave birth to the town-based factory by sounding the death knell for the weavers' cottages in villages.

The second industrial revolution arrived in America in the early twentieth century, when carmaker Henry Ford pioneered the modern model of mass production based on moving assembly lines. It entailed standardisation of tools and implements, the use of various time-saving devices, detailed instructions for workmen on what, when and how they should carry out their tasks, etc. Workers thus became inseparable, unfree and soulless parts of the assembly line, a predicament that was memorably portrayed in *Modern Times* (1934), one of the most popular films by Charlie Chaplin. However, this process of dehumanising mass production in a factory setting was turned into a 'science' by researchers like Frederick Taylor, whose *Principles of Scientific Management* (1911) – also known as 'Taylorism' – soon became a gospel for manufacturers worldwide. Taylorism lays down that productivity and efficiency in manfacturing can be maximised by division of tasks and time, minutely specified by management, in such a way that the workers' labour – and wages – would be based solely on the dictates of the assembly line.

The 'Third Industrial Revolution' turns upside down the central paradigms of both its first and second editions. Thanks to the revolutionary power of the high-speed, large-bandwidth and ubiquitously accessible Internet, it has engendered completely new manufacturing processes such as three-dimensional or 3D printing, easy-to-use robots and a wide range of collaborative manufacturing services that are available online – such as creation of both standard and customised designs and manuals, provision of information regarding materials and parts, remotely controlled repair services, etc.

In 3D printing, the digital machine 'prints' – rather, manufactures – an object based on a design file fed to the computer and using a software that enables it to add, layer after layer, material needed to make the object three-dimensionally. The materials can be plastics, metals, ceramics, rubber-like substances and also combinations of these. This process is also called 'additive manufacturing' since, unlike traditional machining – which is a subtractive manufacturing methodology – it involves spraying of ultra-thin layers of materials and adding more such layers as per the design. The range of objects that can be 3D-printed is incredibly large – from footwear to dental products, and from automotive and critical aerospace components to self-cleaning glass in buildings. Specialised 3D printers, called bio-printers, can also be used to repair or replace human tissues, including blood vessels.

In January 2010, Chris Anderson, editor-in-chief of *WIRED* magazine wrote a similar and widely discussed cover feature titled 'In the Next

Industrial Revolution, Atoms Are the New Bits'. Its blurb said: 'In an age of open source, custom-fabricated, do-it-yourself product design, all you need to conquer the world is a brilliant idea'. He gave several examples, the most striking being that of a car manufactured by an American company called Local Motors. Its design is crowdsourced – meaning that it is outsourced to the worldwide community of designers who share their designs under a Creative Commons license. The components are mostly off-the-shelf. The final assembly is the job of the customers themselves in local assembly centres.

Another example is the Jawbone, a Bluetooth mobile phone headset, which removes environmental noise and produces high-definition sound to the user. Aliph, the company that has designed it, sells millions of headsets each year, but has no factory. It has only eighty employees, who create the software for its products, and outsources all of its production to thousands of partners around the world. Writes Anderson: 'It's the ultimate virtual manufacturing company – Aliph makes bits and its partners make atoms, and together they can take on Sony. Welcome to the next Industrial Revolution'.

'The tools of factory production, from electronics assembly to 3-D printing, are now available to individuals, in batches as small as a single unit,' writes Anderson. 'Anybody with an idea and a little expertise can set assembly lines in China into motion with nothing more than some keystrokes on their laptop. A few days later, a prototype will be at their door, and once it all checks out, they can push a few more buttons and be in full production, making hundreds, thousands, or more. They can become a virtual micro-factory, able to design and sell goods without any infrastructure or even inventory; products can be assembled and drop-shipped by contractors who serve hundreds of such customers simultaneously... Three guys with laptops used to describe a Web startup. Now it describes a hardware company, too.'

It is difficult to disagree with Anderson when he says: 'Transformative change happens when industries democratise, when they're ripped from the sole domain of companies, governments, and other institutions and handed over to regular folks. The Internet democratised publishing, broadcasting, and communications, and the consequence was a massive increase in the range of both participation and participants in everything digital – the long tail of bits. Now the same is happening to manufacturing – the long tail of things.'

How does digital manufacturing paradigmatically differ from the previous two industrial revolutions? And how does it validate the Gandhian paradigm, especially his concept of swadeshi? Firstly, it allows things to be made in much smaller numbers and when they are needed – not only 'just in time' but also 'just in quantities required' by the user or for sale in the nearby markets. 'The wheel is almost coming full circle,' *The Economist* remarks, 'turning away from mass manufacturing and towards much more individualised production'. In other words, 'economies of scale', which was a systemic necessity both in the first and second industrial revolutions, is thus replaced by 'economies of scaling down'. Therefore, huge factories with assembly lines that dominated and dwarfed the human being will become things of the past. Factories of the future will have a 'human scale', just as Gandhi had desired.

Secondly, overproduction, the bane of both the first and the second industrial revolutions, will no longer remain a systemic necessity. Gandhi had repeatedly spoken about the ills of overproduction, as can be seen from his interview to the Associated Press of India in December 1931. 'There must be a return to simplicity and proper proportions,' he said. 'The flesh has taken precedence over the spirit. The machine age is ruining the Western civilisation. Overproduction and lack of means of proper distribution may finally spell the doom of capitalistic society. The only solution I see is a return to hand industry and the emancipation of the individual from factory slavery.'[11] Digital manufacturing is finally going to bring economics to its 'proper proportions', facilitate 'a return to hand industry' and the 'emancipation of the individual from factory slavery'.

Thirdly, if overproduction in the economy is reduced, over-consumption, which is the twin ill of capitalist economies, will also come down significantly. This is because overproduction, which is often driven by the desire to maximise profits, necessitates maximisation of consumption even if the people do not really need to consume a product – or do not need to consume a product in large quantities. This is a need of the economic machine, not of the people. The machine then engages the seductive profession of advertising to induce over-consumption in society. As Will Rogers (1879–1935), an American humourist and social commentator memorably put it: 'Advertising is the art of convincing people to spend money they don't have on something they don't need'. Of course, the flip side of the capitalist economies is that the poor people in society remain deprived of even their real needs.

Fourthly, digital manufacturing will also allow things to be made in a decentralised setting, which has the promise of accomplishing something revolutionary. As *The Economist* puts it: 'The factory of the future will focus on mass customisation and may look more like those weavers' cottages than Ford's assembly line'. Isn't it the kind of rural re-industrialisation that the Mahatma had dreamt of?

Precisely because manufacturing in the digital age promotes – rather, necessitates – decentralisation, it will also require manufactured products to be sold mostly in local markets. Both the compulsion and the opportunity to export to far-off markets will be significantly reduced since almost anything can be made economically, more flexibly and with much lower input of labour and material resources, thanks partly to the invention of amazingly versatile new materials – such as nano-manufactured graphene and carbon tubes. Explaining his concept of swadeshi, Gandhi had stated that the first responsibility of an individual is towards his or her neighbours. Universal welfare or 'sarvodaya' is automatically guaranteed when all the people in the world care for their neighbours. Which is why, Gandhi described swadeshi as 'care economics' or 'home economics', in which one's home has an organic relationship with one's neighbours in the community. Digital manufacturing will thus help make economics compatible with ethics. As we have noted earlier *(see Chapter 3)*, this is a truth that Gandhi had internalised after reading Ruskin's *Unto This Last* in South Africa, and which he had paraphrased in a booklet titled *Sarvodaya*.

Decentralised, localised, customised and smaller-scale digital manufacturing will create new kinds of economic activities and relationships in which production and consumption will be more or less evenly balanced. Often the producer and the consumer will be the same – individual, family or the neighbourhood community. Therefore, there will no need for unrealistic advertising. Similarly, besides wasteful consumption, waste in production will also be substantially reduced. Hence, tomorrow's digital economy will create such producers and consumers who will be responsible towards themselves, towards society as a whole and also towards the environment.

Digital manufacturing will bring another transformative benefit to the environment. Since much of physical manufacturing will become decentralised and localised – albeit with the borderless participation of the entire global population in terms of providing online digital services necessary for making things – today's systemic need for centralised generation, transmission and distribution of power will also be considerably lessened. The demand for decentralised production and provision of energy will grow. This will give a big boost to renewable and non-polluting sources of energy such as solar power. It is absolutely certain that the future will belong mainly to solar power, and not to the perishable and highly polluting hydrocarbon-based energy sources, which necessitated centralised production and long-distance transportation or transmission of energy.

The age of the third industrial revolution will make yet another Gandhian dream come true. As *The Economist* has noted in its special report, decentralised digital manufacturing will re-skill workers, unlike the previous two industrial revolutions that required workers to be largely de-skilled. This means that the workers even in the village-based factories of the future will have to be intelligent and proficient in the use of software and new technologies. They also should have an aesthetic sense and artistic talents, since digital manufacturing makes it possible to customise products to suit the cultural tastes of the producers and customers.

Gandhi had a similar vision about the ideal Indian village. He had written in *Harijan* on 4 August 1946:

When our villages are fully developed, there will be no dearth
in them of men with a high degree of skill and artistic talent.
There will be village poets, village artists, village architects,
linguists and research workers. In short, there will be nothing
in life worth having which will not be had in the villages.

Today the villages are dung heaps. Tomorrow they will be
like tiny gardens of Eden where dwell highly intelligent folk
whom no one can deceive or exploit. The reconstruction of
the villages along these lines should begin right now....not on
a temporary but permanent basis.

The Internet has indeed begun the reconstruction of life on Gandhian
lines all over the Global Village.

All this will of course take a long time. However, one thing is
certain. Factories of the future will be very different from the ones
of today. They will be human-scale centres of sustainable, intelligent,
high-performance, knowledge-intensive and high-skill manufacturing.
Many will have manufacturing platforms and equipment for handling
micro- and nano-scale components. They will be agile, self-reconfigurable,
scalable and multi-functional. Machines with self-learning, self-repairing
and auto-calibrating capabilities will be common. They will ensure
utmost energy efficiency, resource recycling and waste elimination.
Above all, these decentralised production systems will greatly minimise
the need for long-distance transportation.

To summarise, four breakthrough developments, each aided and
accelerated by digital technologies, will transform global and national
economies in the twenty-first century in ways that advance the ideals
of re-interpreted swadeshi: Future Media (social media resources as
instruments of democratic empowerment); Future Money (local or
community currencies, and new trust-based economic activities); Future
Manufacturing (empowerment of local producers and restoration of the
dignity of labour); and Future Energy (ubiquitous use of renewables).

It is possible to imagine that these four developments will decisively impact the Future of Cities as well as the Future of Villages.

Cities of the kind that grew chaotically all over the world with the advent of industrialisation were creations of an economic order that demanded, and thrived on, centralisation. Centralisation in turn required spatial concentration of populations and organisations of production, service-provision and administration by the state machinary. The functioning of these organisations has become increasingly complex with the passage of time. The demands of these organisations are met by people having diverse specialisations and job functions. These people need to closely work together, and be in efficient and reliable communication, without which they can neither fulfill their own specific mandates nor ensure survival of the economic and governance order. The Internet has begun to meet this mission-critical necessity.

However, the very system that created the Internet, and is sustained by it today, is going to be radically restructured by it tomorrow. The new economic order, which is being engendered by technologies of the digital era, works on the logic of decentralisation. Globalisation is becoming glocalisation. Big is becoming small, but this 'new small' has more capabilities than the 'old big', without having the latter's complexities. This logic of the digital era will inexorably change the size and nature of today's cities, apart from rejuvenating today's villages into economically viable, socially livable and spiritually supportive units.

It is important to note here that decentralisation does not mean a throwback to the past. This is because digitally-empowered decentralisation is fundamentally different from non-centralisation or lack of centralisation, which was the norm of the pre-industrialisation era. Centralisation of the economy was impossible in that era, when even physical mobility was severely limited. Hence, villages remained largely isolated entities, self-sufficient and self-managed. Tomorrow's villages will be totally different. Taking off on Schumacher's 'small is beautiful' concept, Dr James Martin, a futurist at Oxford, has written: 'Small is beautiful if the parts are in communication'. The Internet has already enabled instantaneous communication between Village and the Global Village. Going forward, digital technologies will impart the pure blood and strong muscles of sustainability to tomorrow's interconnected villages.

By facilitating the economic revival and social revitalisation of rural areas and smaller towns, by making these habitats more vibrant, healthy and livable, and by generating plentiful and fulfilling employment opportunities for all, these breakthrough developments could indeed achieve something that now seems unthinkable in India: reverse migration of people from mega-cities to rurban areas – sustainably urbanised rural areas, offering the best of both.

Thus, what we can plausibly envision is not just the Digital Future of Cities, but also the Digital Future of Villages. Unlike at present, tomorrow's villages in India and in other countries will be proud and prosperous addresses in the Global Village – just as Gandhi had wanted.

Gandhi's Gurus: *The Mahatma used to keep the small statues of these three monkeys always with him. They were among his very few personal possessions. Their message – 'Speak no evil, See no evil, Hear no evil' – was his credo.*

31

THE ILLS OF THE INTERNET
Gandhian Swaraj Provides the Antidote

⇢⋰⋱∘⋰⋱⇠

We are being propelled into this new century with no plan, no control, no brakes... The only realistic alternative I see is relinquishment: to limit development of the technologies that are too dangerous, by limiting our pursuit of certain kinds of knowledge... As Thoreau said, 'We do not ride on the railroad; it rides upon us'; and this is what we must fight, in our time. The question is, indeed, Which is to be master? Will we survive our technologies?

— Bill Joy, Co-founder of Sun Microsystems,
in his essay 'Why the Future Doesn't Need Us'.

Will robots inherit the earth? Yes, but they will be our children.

— Mervin Minsky, a pioneer of artificial intelligence
and co-founder of MIT's AI lab.

AFTER DESCRIBING THE INTERNET'S ONE BENEVOLENT contribution after another, this book, I realise, is in danger of being slammed by critics on two counts. Firstly, it could be faulted for downplaying the ills of the Internet. Secondly, it could be pointed out that my comparison between Gandhi's spinning wheel and the Internet would sound ludicrously naïve if I did not acknowledge several fundamental differences between the two. It is necessary to respond to this anticipated criticism.

The spinning wheel, by its very nature, is a harmless tool. Even if its users were not people as spiritually evolved as Gandhi, they would not be able to use it to inflict harm on anyone or on themselves. And because of its association with the Mahatma, it has now become a messenger of love and nonviolence. This, certainly, cannot be said about the Internet, which can be misused – indeed, it is being misused every minute – in a hundred different ways.

The most dangerous misuse of IT is in the area of warfare. After land, sea, air and space, cyber space has become the newest, or the fifth, frontier of warfare for nation-states to fight a fearsome new genre of warfare: cyber warfare. More and more governments around the world have recognised their information and communication infrastructure as 'strategic national assets'. Since almost all vital installations, utilities and infrastructure facilities are linked these days to the digital infrastructure, cyber attacks by hostile nation-states as well as by non-state actors have the potential to cause extensive harm.

As has been acknowledged in Chapter 28, the Internet has also spawned an altogether new term in wrongdoing and law-breaking: cyber crime. It is used for hacking others' websites, for virus attacks, bank fraud, theft of information, espionage, plagiarism, cyber blackmail, cyber terrorism and other criminal activities. Bigots and extremists find it useful to spread hatred and prejudice among people belonging to different faiths and communities. It is awash with pornographic content that degrades human sexuality and assaults the dignity of women. Many conversations on the Net use offensive, vulgar and demeaning language, hiding behind the anonymity that cyber space offers.

Internet-addiction can make people aloof and indifferent to the real world. It also can distort our understanding of culture and even the nature of human thinking, giving primacy to information over knowledge and wisdom. In his book *The Shallows: What the Internet is Doing to Our Brains*, Nicholas Carr writes: 'Culture is more than the aggregate of what Google describes as "the world's information". It's more than what can be reduced to binary code and uploaded onto the Net. To remain vital, culture must be renewed in the minds of the members of every generation. Outsource memory, and culture withers'.[1]

Carr further writes: 'In the 1950s, Martin Heidegger observed that the looming "tide of technological revolution" could "so captivate, bewitch, dazzle, and beguile man that *calculative thinking* may someday come to be accepted and practiced as the only way of thinking." Our ability to engage in "*meditative thinking,*" which he saw as the very essence of our humanity, might become a victim of headlong progress. The tumultuous advance of technology could...drown out the refined perceptions, thoughts, and emotions that arise only through contemplation and reflection'.[2] Heidegger's warning has been echoed by Dr Oliver Sacks, the renowned professor of neurology and psychiatry at the Columbia University Medical Centre, who says: 'Humanise technology before it dehumanises us.'[3]

It is by no means my case that every change that the Internet has caused so far, and is going to cause in the future, is positive and helpful for mankind. However, as has been sought to be explained in Chapter 28, the right way to understand the negative uses of the cyber space is to recognise that the Internet is a Human Machine. Unlike all the previous inanimate machines or devices invented in history, the Internet is animated by human intentions, aspirations and qualities such as cooperation and confrontation, generosity and greed, compassion and cruelty, sharing and stealing, love and apathy, creation and destruction – in short, by all that is both good and bad about human beings and their institutions. As Gandhi himself had noted: 'In our present state we are, according to the Hindu doctrine, only partly human; the lower part of us is still animal; only the conquest of our lower instincts by love can slay the animal in us'.[4]

It was Gandhi's belief, however, that the human prevails over the animal in us. The good and beautiful in human nature far outweighs the evil and ugly. Therefore, this preponderance of the positive over the negative in the real world of human beings can also be seen in the world of the Internet.

This poses an important question: How can we combat ills in the world of the Internet? The answer to this question begets, and is actually contained in the answer to, a related question: How can we combat ills in the world of human beings? That answer is obvious: through morally guided self-governed behaviour.

The potential of the Internet to deliver its loftier promises depends purely on the morally illumined self-restraint exercised by its users, be they individuals, institutions or nation-states. Without morality in the conduct of individuals, institutions and national governments, the Internet – and other futuristic technologies like genetics and artificial intelligence – can become a nightmare rather than the harbinger of a new civilisational dawn for mankind. Of course, the same can be said about human conduct in the non-cyberspace. As human history has shown in countless instances, individuals, communities, commercial and non-commercial institutions, and governments can inflict immense harm upon themselves and others when they abandon moral self-restraint.

Swaraj as Morally Guided Self-Governance

What can serve as a source of moral self-regulation? What can reliably ensure that individuals and institutions have an understanding of 'right' and 'wrong', and act according to that understanding?

This is where we see the profound significance of the Gandhian concept of swaraj. As we have noted earlier, swaraj for Gandhi meant much more than political freedom for a country from foreign rule. 'The word swaraj is a sacred word, a Vedic word, meaning self-rule and self-restraint, and not freedom from all restraint which "independence" often means,' he says. 'Swaraj,' he explains, 'really means self-control. Only he is capable of self-control who observes the rules of morality.' He further clarifies: 'My swaraj is to keep intact the genius of our civilisation[5]... If swaraj was not meant to civilise us, and to purify and stabilise our civilisation, it would be nothing worth. The very essence of our civilisation is that we give a paramount place to morality in our affairs, public or private.'[6]

To understand what swaraj means, it is necessary to know what it does *not* mean. It is not a synonym for the Western concepts of freedom, independence and liberty, which fundamentally carry negative connotations – for example, freedom from something outside oneself. According to Bipin Chandra Pal (1858–1932), a great leader of the Indian national movement, these Western concepts 'indicate absence of restraint, regulation and subjection. Consequently, Europe has not yet discovered any really rational test by which to distinguish what is freedom from what is license. ...The cause of orderly progress in different countries, or of peace between different nations, will never be really secured or advanced without a radical change in the present European conception of freedom.'

Pal explains the meaning of swaraj by invoking a synonymous word '*swadheenata*'. In his masterly work *Nationality and Empire: A Running Study of Some Current Indian Problems,* he writes:

Our own concept corresponding to that which is called freedom or independence or liberty in Europe, is different. For, unlike that of the European, the Hindu's conception of freedom is not negative but a positive something. The corresponding term in our language is not *anadheenata* or not-subjection, which would be a literal rendering of the English word 'independence', but *swadheenata* or self-subjugation, which is a positive concept. It does not mean absence of restraint or regulation or subjugation or dependence, but self-restraint, self-regulation and self-dependence. In fact, our *swadheenata* means a good deal more than what even the terms self-restraint, self-regulation and self-dependence would convey in English. For the self in Hindu thought, even in the individual, is a synonym for the Universal. *Swadheenata* means therefore in our thought, really and truly, subjection to the Universal. The complete identification of the individual with the Universal, in every conscious relation of his life, is thus with us an absolute condition precedent of the attainment of *swadheenata* or freedom as it would be called in English.

Pal elucidates further:

The conscious identification of the individual with the Universal is both the form and the norm of the Hindu Gospel of *swadheenata* or swaraj. This word 'swaraj'...belongs really to our ancient philosophical and theological literature. It occurs in the Upanishads, where it indicates the highest spiritual state, wherein the individual self stands in conscious union with the Universal or Supreme-Self. When the self sees and knows whatever is as its own self, it attains swaraj – so says the Chandogya Upanishad. [7]

In Vedic and Upanishadic wisdom, the root word *'swa'* for swaraj and *swadheenata* has a multi-layered meaning. It means 'self', but 'self' can mean 'self' of the individual, or of the family, village, community, tribe, nation and the universe. Beyond the farthest of these concentric circles that define man's individual and collective identities and inter-relationships, lies the Supreme Self or God Almighty. He encircles every entity in the world, every human being and every human collective, but is not encircled by anything. He is a Circle without a circumference and having a point everywhere in the infinite universe, which is His own creation.

Adheen in Sanskrit means 'being under the control of'. The word *'raj'* means 'being governed by'. Therefore, *swadheenata* and swaraj mean, in the ultimate sense, consciously choosing to be controlled and governed by the Supreme Self. The concept is valid for individuals, nations as well as for the human race.

This expanded meaning of swaraj or *swadheenata* has another unique beauty, and Pal explains it compellingly.

The family, the tribe, the race, the nation – these form the ascending series of social evolution. In this series, each succeeding term is larger and more complex than each and all the preceding terms. Each succeeding stage is reached also by simultaneously restricting and expanding the freedom enjoyed by the social units in the preceding stage. The individual sacrifices his individual freedom in gaining the larger freedom of the family. The family sacrifices, similarly, its older and narrower freedom in entering into the large and more regulated freedom of the tribal life. ...Man has, thus, both individually and collectively, to always lay down his freedom to gain it. Every human association encroaches upon our freedom, and even by encroaching upon it, it enlarges its bounds and increases its quality and strength...Every new human association, thus, actually expands our self.

Hence, Pal explains to us that *swadheenata* or swaraj prepares the path for individuals and nations to advance 'towards that Universal Humanity, which is the Ideal-End of all Social Evolution'.

This conceptual framework of swaraj enables us to understand how Gandhi's own advocacy of it encompassed the entire universe.

> My patriotism is not an exclusive thing. It is all embracing. The conception of my patriotism is nothing if it is not always, in every case without exception, consistent with the broadest good of humanity at large. Not only that, but my religion and my patriotism derived from my religion embrace all life. I want to realise brotherhood or identity not merely with the beings called human, but I want to realise identity with all life, even with such things as crawl upon earth...because we claim descent from the same God, and that being so, all life in whatever form it appears must be essentially one.[8]

In other words, man, by identifying himself with all other beings on earth, takes upon himself the duty of ensuring their protection. His freedom, thus, casts a responsibility on him to act wisely.

A serious study of Gandhi's concept of swaraj tells us that neither the Internet nor nanotechnology, artificial intelligence, robotics and other advances in S&T can, by themselves, be harbingers of a non-exploitative society and a nonviolent new world order. Technology is beneficial only if its deployment is backed by wisdom. Without wisdom, the best of technologies can be put to the worst conceivable use. Which is why, there is merit in the caution expressed by some scientists that research in potentially dangerous areas like artificial intelligence should be well-regulated by society. Dr M.A. Valerie Gremillion, a neuroscientist at the University of New Mexico, USA, with whom I discussed this subject, made the following observation by giving a telling analogy: 'We are careful in deciding what kind of things children should touch or play with, aren't we? The same logic is valid for artificial intelligence. Mankind is still a "child" in its evolutionary journey. And it has proved to be a wayward child at that. It needs to grow up, become mature and learn to conduct itself with responsibility.'

Since digital technologies are certain to become an integral part of our lives, including our bodies, in the coming times, Gandhi's philosophical concept of swaraj as morally guided self-governance is the only antidote to the ills inherent in them.

Future of the Internet: Waiting for a New Thought Revolution

For the world to accept and practice swaraj in the Gandhian sense, a new Thought Revolution – as Gandhi put it when he launched the Non-Cooperation Movement *(see Chapter 6)* – has to take a firm hold on the collective mind of mankind. This morally guided Thought Revolution has to begin with the individual. The light of social change becomes brighter only when more and more individuals become torchbearers of New Thinking. Happily, the Internet itself is prodding people to think and act in new and morally defensible ways. This phenomenon has by no means become very pronounced as yet. Nevertheless, its gradual progress in the twenty-first century can be clearly seen.

Two different factors are at work here. One works on the conscience of the individual and the other plays on his sense of shame.

It is not generally recognised that one of the biggest potential benefits of the Internet comes from its power to make its users look inwards. This power is greater in the Internet than in any other machine known to man. Whenever a person uses it for an undesirable or forbidden purpose – such as visiting a pornographic website – he has to make a conscious choice: 'Should I or shouldn't I?' The depth, intensity and longevity of this 'look within' experience of course vary from user to user. But the very experience of intimacy with oneself, of having to make moral choices in using the Internet, is something that would have pleased Gandhi. After all, he always emphasised the desirability of people making a conscious choice in accepting the right and rejecting the wrong.

The second factor that deters people against the negative uses of the Internet is that it is relatively more difficult to erase the footprints and fingerprints of cyber crime. Today's digital technologies provide very powerful tools to discover the evidence of crime and identify its perpetrators. Thus, far from providing the safety of anonymity, cyber space has actually enhanced the possibility of the wrong-doer being caught. And there is always a sense of shame attached to getting caught in committing a crime.

Recognition of these two factors does not in the least mean that the ills of the Internet are going to be eliminated any time soon. The point I am making is that the Internet has provided human beings a new domain for self-correction, mediated by individual conscience and societal action. In other words, digital technologies are aiding swaraj or enlightened self-governance at the lowest, individual, manifestation of Self; as well as at the numerous higher, institutional levels, of Self. To repeat what has been stated earlier in this chapter, Self with capital 'S' refers to the highest Creative Power or the all-loving Supreme Self, the divine source of all human morality.

Although God as Truth is the source of all human morality, human beings are not duty-bound to accept and blindly follow a certain given moral code, even if it has the sanction of some interpreter of religion or the other. As Gandhi states: 'True morality consists, not in following the beaten track, but in finding out the true path for ourselves and in fearlessly following it.'[9] One's own honest quest for the right path, one's refusal to be afraid of treading the path one has found, willingness to learn from others, and sacrificing one's own interests for the larger good of society – these are the four cornerstones of self-governance.

Sorokin's Thoughts on the 'Sane Sex Order': Its Relevance for the Internet Age

The greater the number of self-governed individuals, institutions and communities in our world, the more successful will our collective efforts be in steering the Internet age in the right direction. Well-considered laws and regulations that seek to prevent or minimise the misuse of the Internet and other digital technologies no doubt deserve our support. However, when such restrictions are devised and enforced by the state machinery in our imperfect democracies, there is always the danger of their being misused to curtail people's legitimate freedoms or to persecute the innocent and inconvenient persons in society. The scope for such misuse is far greater in authoritarian societies.

Therefore, the Gandhian method of nonviolently resisting injustice by the state, while at the same time constantly improving and expanding the terrain of swaraj or self-governance by individuals and institutions, is the best way of countering the ills of the Internet. In the specific context of the epidemic of pornography on the Internet, what the renowned Harvard sociologist Pitirim A. Sorokin (1889–1968) wrote about this phenomenon in the pre-Internet age in his book *Sane Sex Order* is quite relevant. (Incidentally, he lavishes high praise in his book on Gandhi's experiments in brahmacharya.)

'If one is a parent', Sorokin writes, 'his irreproachable sexual behavior influences the children and others much more effectively than spasmodic crusades. If the ordinary citizen refuses to buy and read the contaminating publications, to attend erotic shows...he can greatly contribute to the task of desexualising the whole cultural and social life. If one is a businessman, one can undercut many roots of sexual poison ivy by refusing to participate in business enterprises which commercially exploit sexual dregs, by not sponsoring unsuitable programmes of radio, television, movies....If a person is graced by a spark of creativity, he can tangibly ennoble the socio-cultural world by using his talent for creation of real values, and by refusing to misuse it for accretion of sham-values generally and of sexual muck specially.'

Sorokin continues: 'If a considerable and ever-increasing part of our women and men follow this path in their thoughts, words and deeds, the infection discussed (of sex anarchy in society) will rapidly diminish until its ugly scales, rashes and sores disappear from the cultural and social world in which we live. ...Cleansed from the sexual poisons, our women and men will regain not only their vital, mental and moral sanity, but also the full integrity of the total person, enjoying the grace of total love at its happiest, noblest and best. These total persons can hardly fail to develop and release a vast stream of creative forces for rejuvenating and recreating our cultural and social life. The renaissance of our culture and social institutions in its turn will retroactively exert an ennobling and creative influence upon the total personalities. Through this mutual invigoration of the personal, the cultural and the social creative forces, the whole human universe will be improving and progressing from the initial kingdom of the human animal through the more and more ennobled kingdom of man, to the magnificent kingdom of the semi-divine Man-Creator'.[10]

It is not difficult to see that Sorokin's thoughts on sexual sanity are far more relevant to the era of cyber sex.

The Internet is steadily increasing the number of such self-governing individuals and institutions – swarajists, if we may call them – across the world. They are steering the Internet in a progressive direction.

The Internet has no doubt enlarged the choices for its users in unprecedented and unimaginable ways. However, the swarajists on the Internet – and they are far more numerous than is generally believed – are constantly asking themselves: 'What is the best use that we can put this great gift of science to? How can I benefit the most from it? And how can society benefit the most from it?'

Gandhi asked himself the same questions in respect of the spinning wheel. Of course, this truth-seeking swarajist brought an immeasurably greater resolve, self-discipline and higher purpose to bear on his use of the charkha than most of us do in using the Internet. He had found his answer in Karma Yoga, the philosophy of self-realisation through action, which he had learnt from the *Bhagavad Gita*. His numerous discourses on the *Gita* at his prayer meetings fill a book. 'Karma Yoga of our age is service through the spinning wheel,' he had declared. We can turn this thought around and say, without the fear of being proved wrong, that the motto for a growing number of netizens on this planet is: 'Karma Yoga of our age is service through the Internet'.

And herein lies our hope for the future of mankind.

A future *sans* man-man or man-machine conflict: *In 1946, Gandhi envisioned mankind as an 'Oceanic Circle' with an ever-widening family of concentric circles – inter-connected identities – with the individual at the centre. No longer will any 'outer circumference' wield power to 'crush the inner circle'. Rather, 'it will give strength to all within and derive its own strength from it'. In this symbiosis, each cares for all, and all care for each. In Gandhi's vision, 'There is no room for machines that would displace human labour and concentrate power in a few hands. Every machine that helps every individual has a place. But I must confess that I have never sat down to think about what that machine can be.'*

We now know what that machine, which can help eliminate both man-man and man-machine conflict, is. It is the INTERNET.

Illustration: Saurabh Singh

32

HOW GANDHI AWAITED THE ARRIVAL
OF A UNIVERSALLY USEFUL MACHINE

The Web evolved into a powerful, ubiquitous tool because it was built on egalitarian principles. However, (it) is being threatened in different ways. Some of its most successful inhabitants have begun to chip away at its principles...Web developers, companies, governments and citizens should work together openly and cooperatively, as we have done thus far, to preserve the Web's fundamental principles, as well as those of the Internet, ensuring that the technological protocols and social conventions we set up respect basic human values. The goal of the Web is to serve humanity. We build it now so that those who come to it later will be able to create things that we cannot ourselves imagine.

— Tim Berners-Lee, inventor of the World Wide Web, in 'Long Live the Web: A Call for Continued Open Standards and Neutrality', *Scientific American* (November 2010).

VISIONARIES OF EVERY PERIOD IN HISTORY HAVE SERVED AS LINKS between the past, the present and the future of mankind. They derive inspiration from the past, act with the full force of their life's energies in the present, and leave behind ideas and legacies that light up the path for future generations. However, they come in varying degrees of greatness. Most are visionaries in their limited domains of knowledge or activity, and the light they emit illumines a few decades or a few centuries. In contrast, some others, though few and far between, belong to humankind's past, present and future *simultaneously.* Even though they live, like other mortals, in the present, they do so as if a good deal of the best of the past of human race were alive in them, and a good deal of the best of the future, too. Despite their mission in life being limited by the coordinates of time, space and society, their vision has an abiding significance for the world for all time. In other words, although their birth, death and the life in between are located in history, they outlive history.

It is not that everything they say is true for all times. They too are imperfect, though more perfect than other mortals. Truth is always greater than any human being, and Truth as God alone is ever perfect. Nevertheless, through the prism of their extraordinarily radiant lives, humanity gets the clearest glimpse of the collective wisdom and achievements of its own past and the still greater possibilities waiting to be actualised in the future.

Gandhi belonged to this rare category of visionaries.

As he himself said with characteristic humility, he had 'nothing new to teach the world', because 'Truth and Nonviolence are as old as the hills'.[1] However, what was breathtakingly new about him was that he fully embodied these timeless ideals. ('My life is my message'.[2]) Also, he was the first apostle of peace in the modern era who boldly said: 'We have to make Truth and Nonviolence, not matters for mere individual practice but for practice by groups and communities and nations. That at any rate is my dream. I shall live and die in trying to realise it.'[3] Studying his life is like going on a pilgrimage to a sacred hill-top shrine that never fails to be spiritually uplifting and never fails to offer breathtaking sights.

The title of this chapter is bound to invite curiosity and scepticism in equal measure. To put it in a proper perspective, I need to briefly summarise the exploration in the previous pages of two seminal and inter-related Gandhian thoughts – science of nonviolence and the philosophy of swaraj – which in my view will lay the foundation for a peaceful, harmonious and upwardly evolutionary new global civilisation.

The first Big Gandhian Idea, with multiple layers of meaning, is swaraj. Gandhi first explained it a hundred years ago in *Hind Swaraj* (1909) and reiterated it on numerous occasions later. It was valid not only for the India of his time. Its validity is broader and more enduring. In Gandhian philosophy, swaraj is a faith-based and values-driven concept of self-governance that means a lot more than the narrowly and conventionally understood conception of political independence for India from the British rule. It connotes a network of inter-dependent sovereignties – lesser forms of self, beginning with the individual, who is linked to many concentric collectivities. All of these sovereignties are subordinate to Self or God, which represents the Highest Sovereignty. In this comprehensive sense, swaraj was, is, and will always be relevant for India, for all the other nations of the world, and for every individual too.

India attaining political freedom in 1947 was only a partial fulfillment of the Gandhian ideal of swaraj. However, today's India is far from having attained this ideal, as anyone can see by looking at the deepening corruption in politics, shocking socio-economic disparities, entrenched divisions in our society, and the erosion of ethical values in our ruling political, business, bureaucratic, judicial and civil society elite. There isn't much evidence of morally guided self-governance in India's democratic institutions. Indeed, no country in the world has attained swaraj as envisioned by Gandhi.

Although many Gandhians would disagree, I believe that swaraj in the Gandhian conception has found a new ally in globalisation, in which independence and interdependence increasingly go together. Enlightened self-governance and cooperative management of the affairs of the world are no longer an option in the era of globalisation – they have become an imperative.

The second Big Gandhian Idea is the science of nonviolence, of which the Internet is a child. Like any child, it is still learning to walk and feel its way around. It sometimes fumbles and falls. It commits mistakes. But it also exhibits the instinct of self-rectification. In small but unmistakably promising early steps, it is showing that its raison d'être is to promote peace and harmony in the world. And this is something that many scientists, professionals, entrepreneurs and policy makers in ICT have not yet sufficiently realised. The Internet has not only made the world more connected than ever before, but also more cooperative than ever before. Indeed, it is already radically reforming globalisation itself. Not only in form, but also in content and intent, it is beginning to harmonise the global and the local.

Based on its early promise and performance, it is possible to hypothesise that the Internet has the potential to become the most potent promoter of nonviolence. For this potential to be realised, the Internet and all other sunrise sciences and technologies of the digital era have to come closer to the ethical canons of Truth. Their development and application has to be guided by the Gandhian philosophy of swaraj. If this happens – and it certainly will happen – the Internet can become the iconic new avatar of Gandhi's spinning wheel. If the charkha, as Gandhi used to state as repetitiously as he turned its wheel, was a tool of nonviolence and universal love, so too can the Internet be.

Is it wishful thinking? Is it too fanciful to be taken seriously? Well, only if we disregard the salutary saying of the great German philosopher Arthur Schopenhauer (1788–1860), who was greatly influenced by the wisdom of Hinduism and Buddhism:

> *Everyone takes the limits of his own vision for the limits of the world.*

The limits of today's world are already enormously greater than those of the world of yesterday. And those of tomorrow's world will be immeasurably greater still.

Society: An Oceanic Circle with the Individual at the Centre

To appreciate the above point – and, indeed, to know what IT is and what it can be – we need to revisit the supremely optimistic prophesy about the future of science that Gandhi made in 1940:

> In this age of wonders no one will say that a thing or idea is worthless because it is new. To say it is impossible because it is difficult, is again not in consonance with the spirit of the age.

Things undreamt of are daily being seen, the impossible is ever becoming possible. We are constantly being astonished these days at the amazing discoveries in the field of violence. *But I maintain that far more undreamt of and seemingly impossible discoveries will be made in the field of nonviolence. (Emphasis added)*

He also affirmed, in 1946: 'Science has yet much to learn. It has so far touched *only the hem of the garment*.[4] *(Emphasis added)*

As we have noted earlier, Gandhi wrote these lines about the future of science at a time when the outbreak of the Second World War had spread darkness all around. We do not know what 'undreamt of and seemingly impossible discoveries in the field of nonviolence' he visualised in the womb of the future. He certainly couldn't have been thinking of IT, since it was not visible to him on the horizon. Even the first primitive computer was invented only several years later. What then was he anticipating?

A faint glimmer of the answer to this question comes into view when we visit the final stage of India's freedom struggle. The year was 1946. India's independence was just a year away. And so also was the catastrophe of India's Partition. The flames of communal riots between Hindus and Muslims had started to consume many innocent lives. Gandhi, though experiencing enormous agony in his heart, had still not given up hopes of preventing the tragedy of partition, and was doing his best to achieve this end. However, even in the midst of earth-shaking political developments, his mind was fixed on the kind of swaraj India should have after the departure of the British. On 15 July 1946, he wrote an article in *Harijan* under the title 'The Real Danger', which expressed concern that most Congressmen did not know the kind of independence they wanted. The article caused more than a flutter in Congress circles, and deepened people's suspicion that he and even his closest colleagues were not on the same wavelength. On 21 July 1946, he granted a detailed interview on the subject, in which the interviewer asked him: 'Would you kindly give them (Congressmen) a broad but comprehensive picture of an Independent India of your own conception?'

The political parts of Gandhi's answer are not relevant to our purpose here. What is of utmost relevance to us is his precise and exquisite elucidation of the concept of swaraj. It vividly portrays man's relationship with his immediate neighbourhood and also with his cosmic neighbourhood. Interestingly, this elucidation presents not only Gandhi's conception of an Ideal Society, but also his speculation about an Ideal Machine.

Since this is one of the most important thoughts of the Mahatma, it needs to be quoted *in extenso*. Swaraj, he stresses, must begin with the individual.

> Ultimately, it is the individual who is the unit. This does not exclude dependence on and willing help from neighbours or from the world. It will be a free and voluntary play of mutual forces. Such a society is necessarily highly cultured in which every man and woman knows what he or she wants and, what is more, knows that no one should want anything that others cannot have with equal labour.
>
> This society must naturally be based on Truth and Nonviolence which, in my opinion, are not possible without a living belief in God, meaning a self-existent, all-knowing living Force which inheres in every other force known to the world and which depends on none and which will live when all other forces may conceivably perish or cease to act. I am unable to account for my life without belief in this all-embracing living Light.
>
> In this structure composed of innumerable villages, there will be ever-widening, never-ascending circles. Life will not be a pyramid with the apex sustained by the bottom. But it will be an oceanic circle whose centre will be the individual always ready to perish for the village, the latter ready to perish for the circle of villages, till at last the whole becomes one life composed of individuals, never aggressive in their arrogance but ever humble, sharing the majesty of the oceanic circle of which they are integral units.

Therefore, the outermost circumference will not wield power to crush the inner circle but will give strength to all within and derive its own strength from it. I may be taunted with the retort that this is all Utopian and, therefore, not worth a single thought. If Euclid's point, though incapable of being drawn by human agency, has an imperishable value, my picture has its own for mankind to live. Let India live for this true picture, though never realisable in its completeness. We must have a proper picture of what we want, before we can have something approaching it. If there ever is to be a republic of every village in India, then I claim verity for my picture in which the last is equal to the first or, in other words, no one is to be the first and none the last.

In this picture, every religion has its full and equal place. We are all leaves of a majestic tree whose trunk cannot be shaken off its roots which are deep down in the bowels of the earth. The mightiest wind cannot move it.

In this there is no room for machines that would displace human labour and that would concentrate power in a few hands. Labour has its unique place in a cultured human family. *Every machine that helps every individual has a place. But I must confess that I have never sat down to think about what that machine can be.*[5] *(Emphasis added)*

The above portrait of Utopia is remarkable for many reasons. Firstly, his conception of mankind as an oceanic circle with numerous concentric identities and interconnectivities, with the individual at the centre, provides an immensely more profound philosophical understanding of man's place in the universe than the currently popular phrase 'Bottom of the Pyramid'. Indeed, Gandhi specifically mentions that pyramid as an analogy for the structure of human society is unsatisfactory.

Secondly, Gandhi underscores that swaraj or self-rule must begin with the individual self. He confirms, yet again, the primacy of the individual in the architecture of the universe. However, primacy of the individual does not mean individualism, which is the bane of the modern materialistic civilisation. It does not connote a supreme right; rather, it casts a supreme responsibility, as is evident from the most famous Gandhian aphorism: 'Be the change you want to see in the world'.

Specifically, the responsibility that the individual has to discharge is to be humble, non-aggressive, nonviolent, truthful and highly cultured. He has to be free-thinking (he should 'know what he wants'), but he also has to accept and respect the dignity and equality of others. And what is the reward for the individual for discharging this responsibility? The reward, as described by Gandhi, radiates with spiritual brilliance: the individual, a mortal creature of clay, will 'share the majesty of the oceanic circle'. What monetary reward, and what worldly fame or power, can match the prospect of man sharing the splendour of the universe?

Thirdly, Gandhi's Utopia also shows that swaraj or self-rule is consistent with internationalism and universalism. This is because, Self is an ever-widening family of concentric circles. And in this 'ocean of circles', no longer will the 'outer circumference' wield power to 'crush the inner circle'. Rather, 'it will give strength to all within and derive its own strength from it'. In this progressive philosophy of symbiosis, each cares for all, and all care for each.

Fourthly, Gandhi's Utopia prefigured globalisation. However, it is not the imperfect globalisation that we see today, but the more perfected and harmoniously interdependent world of tomorrow. It envisages 'dependence on and willing help from neighbours or from the world', in which all relationships 'will be a free and voluntary play of mutual forces'.

Fifthly, the use of the word 'forces' has profound significance in our discussion. Notice that Gandhi, in the above excerpt, describes God as 'a self-existent, all-knowing living *Force*'. Moreover, this living Force, he says, 'inheres in every other force known to the world'. This prompts us to think that Gandhi had indeed been contemplating about the similarity between forces in physical nature and forces operating in human nature. For, earlier in Chapter 19, we have come across his bold assertion: 'All society is held together by nonviolence even as the earth is held in her position by the force of gravitation'.

How well he anticipated the findings of modern scientists! We have already encountered mathematical cosmologist Brian Swimme's statement: 'Gravity is love.' Swimme, author of *The Hidden Heart of the Cosmos,* further says: 'I think that gravitational attraction is an early form of compassion or care. If there weren't that kind of care at the foundation of the universe, there would be no formation of galaxies... When we use words like compassion, we tend to limit them to the human world... And we think of the rest of the universe as being *stuff,* and we don't use words that are spiritual or warm or emotional concerning them. I talk about compassion as a multilevel reality. It's not just something that's true of humans.'[6]

This prompts us to hypothesise about Self and Force – both of which connote God – and their diverse manifestations, individual 'self's and forces. Conventional science studies only such 'forces' as operate in physical nature. It does not recognise the divine Force or Self, nor does it bother to study how forces such as love and compassion operate in society – which is nothing but a collective of ever-widening 'self's. This only goes to show the limitations of conventional science to understand the physical and human realities comprehensively and in their inter-connectedness. Gandhi's life and ideas provide several helpful pointers to the evolution of a unified and holistic science of forces.

Lastly, the most remarkable thought in the excerpt cited above comes in its last paragraph in which Gandhi presents his views, very briefly, about the role of machines in his ideal swaraj. 'In this', he says, 'there is no room for machines that would displace human labour and that would concentrate power in a few hands'. Yet, he also describes the kind of machine he would welcome. *'Every machine that helps every individual has a place'.* Then comes the curious confession: *'But I must confess that I have never sat down to think about what that machine can be'.* *(Emphasis added)*

What this paragraph unmistakably points out is that Gandhi was indeed seized by the thought of a future machine that would be universally useful. However, he was candid enough to confess that he had not given himself time to think about 'what that machine can be'.

We now know what that machine, which 'helps every individual' and which had made an abstract appearance in the Mahatma's probing mind, is.

It is the INTERNET.

It is not at all my case that Gandhi had any actual idea of the Internet. Given the state-of-the-art of the extant S&T, nobody could have visualised it in the 1940s. Nevertheless, it is my case that he had a faint idea of the truth or the essence that later came to be embodied, in a limited way, by the Internet. The spiritual aspect of that truth had been revealed to him in much greater fullness in the spinning wheel. But he was well aware of the practical limitations of the charkha to fulfill the economic and social needs of the people in a changing India and the world. Therefore, he was himself looking for a suitable substitute to the spinning wheel in a machine or a technology that would help, in a holistic sense, all of mankind. He was mentally searching for an idea of a new machine that would be universally useful and also eliminate the man-machine and man-man conflict. That substitute has now made its presence in the form of the Internet and other digital technologies. These technologies do not displace the human being. Rather, they have the potential to extend, augment and become integrated into the various human faculties.

An Insight from Heidegger's Thoughts on Technology

I have based my conceptual extrapolation of the spinning wheel to the Internet partly on the basis of an insight on technology coming from a widely different source – a seminal work *The Question Concerning Technology* by German philosopher Martin Heidegger (1889-1976).[7]

Technology is generally understood as the mode of application of scientific knowledge that results in modernisation. Since modernisation is accepted as an unquestioned value, technology as a means to achieve it has also acquired universal acceptability. Thus, it has become commonsense to believe that more technology means more progress and greater modernity. Technology is not only seen as value-neutral – that is, free from being judged as good or bad – but as positively good. Indeed, such is the modern-day superstition in technology that anything old (even in the field of technology itself) is regarded as backward and worth discarding.

A questioning of technology became necessary for Heidegger because, like Gandhi, he saw that modern technology did not necessarily contribute to human welfare or to genuine modernity. In some ways, it has limited man's real growth and his authentic sense of being human. Heidegger adverts to a situation in which the more technology advances the more it 'threatens to slip from human control'. He writes: 'Everywhere we remain unfree and chained to technology, whether we passionately affirm or deny it. But we are delivered over to it in the worst possible way when we regard it as something neutral; for this conception of it, to which today we particularly like to pay homage, makes us utterly blind to the essence of technology'.

According to Heidegger, 'the essence of technology is by no means anything technological'. Metaphysically speaking, its essence lies in 'unconcealing' or 'bringing forth' man's rootedness to Being – of 'that which precedes all: the earliest'. Being is in many ways a philosophical synonym for Satya (truth) as Gandhi understood it: one without beginning or end. In other words, technology is much more than a particular way of producing a certain useful product or service, employing devices that work on the application of certain scientific knowledge. The true usefulness of technology lies in the extent to which it 'reveals' his connectedness to Nature, universe, and to Being, which is the source of *veritas* (truth).

To understand this point, it is useful to know that the word 'technology' stems from the Greek word *techné*, which designates 'skill', 'art', 'craft', and a mode of doing or making. It also refers to that which is performed, produced, or fabricated. The fundamental way in which technological production differs from production in Nature is in terms of causality. Natural production is organic or self-developing.

Technological production, on the other hand, implies the work of an external agent – human reason and creativity, using Nature's resources and knowledge of Nature's laws. Therefore, the intention with which, or the purpose for which, human reason is applied in technological production becomes a crucial determinant of whether, or to what extent, it 'reveals' man's relation with Being.

In the evolution of the human race, there came a time – with the advent of the Industrial Revolution – when technology sought to achieve control and domination of Nature. Those who sought to do so, also employed technology to achieve domination of other men and other nations. This is when technology became a source of 'unfreedom', a rupturing of man's essential relationship with Being. This also is the reason for Gandhi's opposition to technology of the kind that contributed, in the name of 'progress' and 'modernity', to exploitation, colonial subjugation, militarism, wars and destruction of the environment.

But, as Heidegger points out, *techné* is also closely related to another Greek word '*poiesis*', from which is derived the word 'poetry', and it refers to artistic creation in general. Artist or artisan, both create, bring forth something new into presence, or actualise the potential of the not-yet-present. Thus, *techné* is the name not only for the skills of the hand but also for the arts of the mind. What is peculiar to an artisan is that before he produces a thing, he projects its image and purpose in his own mind. Thus, the product is 'unconcealed' or 'brought forth' in his mind before the mental construct is artistically worked upon in reality to embody the idea and the intention. In doing so, he reveals some aspect of the Being or Truth, *poetically*, to other men.

Thus, technological production in all the traditional cultures in the past sought to bring forth various attributes of Being or Truth in its works – scientific knowledge, utility, beauty and visual poetry, and, not the least, care for human beings. Respect for humanity and a reverential attitude towards Nature was integral to technological production in the past. It is not surprising, therefore, that the work of craftspersons, artisans and architects was invariably accompanied by ritualistic prayers to the divine, the source of all original beauty, creativity and energy.

Sadly, the application of much of modern technology is un-poetic. Man has no respect for Nature – or for his own true nature. Heidegger bemoans, for example, that under conditions of modern technology, 'the earth reveals itself as [only] a coal mining district, [its] soil as a mineral deposit'.

How to make technology *poetic* again? How to reform the man-machine relationship in such a way that the machine benefits and frees all human beings, and at the same time restores man's gratitude and reverence towards nature? This is the question that Gandhi attempted to answer.

For Heidegger, the answer lies in modern technology rediscovering its essence – namely, to 'unconceal' man's rootedness in Being through poetry or production, through artist's works or artisan's magic. Here he provides an interesting insight. We have seen earlier, in trying to understand the meaning of *techné*, that artisans, who are traditional technologists, bring forth the image as well as the purpose of a product in their own minds before they produce it. Scientists in traditional cultures also followed the same principle. They knew the purpose for which they were seeking knowledge, and that purpose, more often then not was linked to the commands of Being. Knowledge was not separable from universal values such as justice, love, nonviolence, and human welfare.

In other words, the essence of technology is to serve as a means for sourcing good and beneficial ideas that exist in the human mind before their manifestation in the form of concrete machines. Heidegger writes: 'It is as revealing, and not as manufacturing, that *techné* is a bringing-forth … Technology comes to presence in the realm where revealing and unconcealment take place, where *aletheia*, truth, happens'.

In short, the essence of modern technology precedes and determines its actual development.

Another Insight from Turing and Shannon

The validity of the above proposition – namely, that the essential truth of a technology reveals itself to the human mind much before the development of the specific tools on which that technology rests – is evident from the way the computer itself was born. A fascinating description of the birth of the computer can be found in James Gleick's acclaimed book *The Information: A History, a Theory, a Flood.*

No single scientist or inventor is credited with the invention of the computer. Nevertheless, the names of Alan Turing and Claude Shannon (along with that of John von Neumann[8]) figure high among the pioneers of information theories that led to its creation. At the height of the Second World War, these two like-minded scientists, the former a Britisher and the latter an American, interacted closely on some important cryptography projects at the Bell Labs in USA. One day in early 1943, Turing and Shannon talked about a subject close to their hearts – the possibility of machines learning to think. Shannon visualised an 'electronic brain' to which 'cultural things' such as music could be fed. Turing's response was less ambitious. 'No, I'm not interested in developing a powerful brain. All I'm after is just a mundane brain.'

Gleick writes: 'It bordered on impudence to talk about thinking machines in 1943, when both the transistor and the electronic computer had yet to be born. The vision Shannon and Turing shared had nothing to do with electronics; it was about logic'.[9]

In other words, the computer as an intelligent machine, when it was born, existed *only as a thought.* It was only a thought experiment, a construct of pure logic. The machine did not exist in a physical form at the time of its birth, although it now exists everywhere! Every student of the history of computer science knows that the famous Turing Machine, a universal computing machine envisioned by the tormented genius (Alan Turing committed suicide following shock therapy administered to him to cure his homosexuality) was just an idealised computer. It can be created using any available material. Turing himself had affirmed: 'The essence of a computer is not its material substance but its architecture of ideas'.[10]

Incidentally, the title of a widely acclaimed recent book (2011), by Jon Gertner, on the history of the unique research institution where Turing and Shannon laid the foundation of information theory is *The Idea Factory: Bell Labs and the Great Age of American Innovation.* The transistor, UNIX, the C programming language, the modern photovoltaic cell, the first global communications satellites are just some of the many amazing 'idea' products of the computer age that were invented at Bell Labs.

Similarly, neither the computer nor the Internet existed when Gandhi wrote that he was thinking about a 'machine that helps every individual'. What he had was only an abstract idea of a universally useful machine, rooted in an architecture of his own ideals. However, that idea and the ideals associated with it had the seed of truth, which a succession of scientists and engineers have 'unconcealed' or 'brought forth', to use Heidegger's terms, in the form of a cornucopia of discoveries, inventions and innovations that have created today's ubiquitous Internet.

The cornerstone of Gandhi's economic and social philosophy was to remove the dichotomy and disharmony between man and machine, on the one hand, and between man and man, on the other. This is the idea and the ideal that he sought to promote through his spinning wheel. However, as we have seen, he was also, towards the end of his life, awaiting a new machine that would embody this idea and the ideal – of becoming a reliable aid to labour which 'has its unique place in a cultured human family' – all over the world. This is the basis of my thesis that the Internet has become the conceptual incarnation of Gandhi's spinning wheel.

Indeed, as we shall see in the next chapter, Gandhi and Gandhian ideals have influenced many widely respected inventors and innovators who have contributed to the evolution of the Internet.

Wizards of the Internet

(Left to right, first row) **Norbert Wiener** *(1894–1964): Regarded as the Father of Cybernetics, he made a strong case for morality in the use of Information Technology.*

Alan Turing *(1912–54): His vision of future computers was that they would not only be intelligent but also have human qualities – 'Be kind, friendly, tell right from wrong'.*

Vannever Bush *(1890–1974): He prophesied in 1945 that the* Encyclopaedia Britannica *could be reduced to the size of a matchbox. He envisioned the computer as a democratiser and a peace-promoter.*

(Second row) **J.C.R. Licklider** *(1915–90): He established ARPANet in 1969. 'If ICTs were owned and controlled by all, instead of remaining the monopoly of the rich, the boon to humankind would be beyond measure'.*

Doug Engelbart *(1925-): He invented the computer mouse (1963). His motto, from the beginning of his scientific career: 'How a person could invest their professional career to maximise their return to mankind'.*

Tim Berners-Lee *(1955-): He invented the World Wide Web. 'Basic Internet access to every human being on earth should be treated as a universal human right'.*

<h1 align="center">33</h1>

<h1 align="center">1869: BIRTH OF MAHATMA GANDHI
1969: BIRTH OF THE INTERNET</h1>

<h2 align="center">How, and Why, the Internet was Born</h2>

⤙⟡⟡⟡⤚

Once the machine thinking method has started, it would not take long to outstrip our feeble powers. ... At some stage therefore we should have to expect the machines to take control, in the way that is mentioned in Samuel Butler's Erewhon.

— Alan Turing (1912-1954), a visionary of computer science.

I set the date for the Singularity – representing a profound and disruptive transformation in human capability – as 2045. The nonbiological intelligence created in that year will be one billion times more powerful than all human intelligence today.

— Ray Kurzweil, in *The Singularity is Near — When Humans Transcend Biology.*

THE PREVIOUS CHAPTER HAS SHOWN THAT GANDHI, IN 1946, HAD a mystical realisation that a revolutionary new machine capable of helping 'every individual' in the world was coming. The context in which he prefigured the arrival of this new machine was the same in which he also, equally presciently, presented his philosophical portrait of life in a future globalised, inter-connected, egalitarian and harmonious world. That structure, he said, will not be a 'pyramid with the apex sustained by the bottom'. Rather, it will be an 'oceanic circle' consisting of 'ever-widening, never-ascending circles' with the individual at the centre and extending to the family, the neighbourhood, the village and all the way up to the whole world and the universe. 'The outermost circumference', he averred, 'will not wield power to crush the inner circle but will give strength to all within and derive its own strength from it'. The picture he sketched was one in which 'the last is equal to the first or, in other words, no one is to be the first and none the last'. Further, with boldness of belief that was characteristic of him, Gandhi stated: 'If Euclid's point, though incapable of being drawn by human agency, has an imperishable value, my picture has its own for mankind to live'.

Cooperation and Truthfulness: How a Gandhian Code was Written into the Internet's Software

Let us try and draw a picture, mentally, of many concentric circles, each centre-point connoting a unique individual on our planet. What will we see? Each individual, who has multiple identities, will be seen to be connected to the other by one or the other intersecting circle. None of these individuals can be seen as the first or the last. All are equal. And all are working for each, and each is working for all, in a large human family. Now, isn't this also how one can visualise the Internet? It has millions of computers connected to tens of thousands of networks. Once any network is connected to the Internet, as per the universally accepted protocol of Transmission Control Protocol and Internet Protocol (TCP/IP), every node on it has equal value with every other node. Any computer can communicate with any other no matter where it is, with no consideration given to colour, race, religion, nationality, geography, gender, age, income and educational status of the user. This openness and inclusiveness of the Internet's architecture is the secret of the success of its growth to a global scale.

Indeed, the principle of 'all for each, and each for all' is also inherent in every single piece of the Internet architecture. All data communicated over the Net is broken up into discrete packets, which are sent over thousands of kilometres of telephone lines, satellite signals and microwaves. Remarkably, all the packets pertaining to a particular message do not travel along the same path, much less are carried by a single network. They get fragmented and take countless different routes. Yet, once all the packets arrive at their destination, they are digitally stitched back together to recreate the original message. Coherent reassembly of the message takes place due to the fact that each packet contains not only data but also the addresses of the sender and the receiver. It is as if a letter that is torn into bits and pieces, and scattered to the winds, still manages to reach the recipient in its original shape almost instantaneously!

This miracle happens because the Internet is built on the Gandhian principle of cooperation. No network refuses a particular packet, or plays favourites. When one route is busy, the packet hops on another with the least traffic. Thus, no network chooses to remain idle for a long time and all work with near-perfect harmony to accomplish a common goal. Similarly, no router blocks any message because discrimination is alien to the ethos of the inner working of the Internet. When a certain message does not reach the destination, networks automatically activate repeater devices that patiently remove the noise, regenerate the signal and retransmit it.

The ethic of cooperation is the life breath of the information age because the Internet is quintessentially a Grand Integrator. The platform of digital technology, on which the Internet works, integrates both machines and humans. This is the moral purpose for which it was born. To know this is to know where both the Internet and the human race are headed.

Before the advent of digital technologies, machines led more or less independent existences. They performed their own individual functions but in a rather isolated manner. For example, printing, calculation, communication, storage, manufacturing, image reproduction, etc., were done on different devices using different technologies that had low capability and, moreover, did not converge. Vacuum tubes and mechanical switches, having extremely limited capacity, were used for calculations. Similarly, machine-enabled communication was made possible by wire-based telephone lines carrying electrical signals or by radio and television that used air waves. Both suffered from constraints. Telephone and telegraph usage was restricted due to access and cost factors. Besides, it was good only for voice communication, and not for sending or receiving text, image and moving images. Radio and television were one-way communication devices. Printing of books happened in its own separate domain, manually for a long time. Photographic reproduction, using chemical processes, was a standalone technology, and so was audio reproduction in the form of long-playing (LP) records or magnetic tapes going around plastic spools.

Undoubtedly, all these devices, and the technologies that supported them, benefitted humanity and aided its evolution. But there was something vital missing. Metaphorically speaking, these mutually unconnected machines were mirror images of the divisions in human society caused by the industrial age. True, humankind did not lack grand ideas and ethical ideals that sought to unite and integrate races, communities, countries and creeds. After all, every religion and spiritual philosophy of antiquity proclaimed the essential unity of the human race and of all animate and inanimate creations, governed by a single Supreme Power. Nevertheless, the awareness of this unity was considerably weakened by the disunity and discord created by the economic, social and political developments in human history, especially after the advent of the era of colonialism. Science and technology were used to promote what Gandhi refers to as industrialism of the West.

A paradigm shift in science took place in the latter half of the last century with the birth of the Internet. It promised to integrate, potentially, all disparate machines and devices and also all the diverse people using them. This science was premised on the principle that (a) all quantifiable information pertaining to anything in the world can be digitised into bits and bytes of data – sequences of 0's and 1's; (b) the data can be processed on silicon chips housing an ever-increasing population of transistors occupying an ever-decreasing space; (c) the information contained in the data can be communicated through carriers of ever-expanding bandwidth provided by the twin media of waves (wireless) and light particles (optic fibre); and (d) the information as data can be reconfigured and enriched for countless different integrated applications.

This science progressed in two broad stages. In the first stage, micro-processing of information gave birth to the idea of a digital computer in 1946. In the second stage, digital communication of information between computers, connected through both the wired and wireless media, gave birth to the Internet. At the heart of both computation and communication, however, is one simple philosophical truth: Everything in the material world can be dematerialised into the abstraction of 0's and 1's, and thereafter re-integrated, reproduced and enriched in value. Everything can be digitised, and everything digital can be transformed into Information, Knowledge and Wisdom.

This is how the Internet has become a single planet-wide platform on which people can send letters and talk to each other; students can study every subject under the sun; book lovers can access, read, write and publish books; producers and consumers can sell and buy goods and services; professionals can provide remote services in diverse areas ranging from healthcare to environment care; friends and families can make, store and share photographs and videos; scientists from different countries can do collaborative research; innovators can improve agriculture, manufacturing and services globally; citizens can monitor the functioning of corporates and governments to enforce transparency and accountability; votaries of justice, democracy and freedom can conduct campaigns and mobilise people to participate in them...and dreamers of a better world can dream, and be reassured of the power of their own individual selves to make a difference in our big and chaotic world. The Internet provides a plethora of resources for inspiration and education – among them, the *Collected Works of Mahatma Gandhi* on the Net, all the ninety-eight volumes of them, each consisting of about five hundred pages.

If 'cooperative connectivity' is one internal operative code of the Internet, the other is 'truthfulness'. Unlike other inanimate machines of the past, the Internet simply cannot function without being aligned to Truth, the Mahatma's most cherished ideal. 'The network is like a truth serum', writes Douglas Rushkoff in his book *Program or Be Programmed: Ten Commands for a Digital Age*. 'Put something false online and it will eventually be revealed as a lie. Digital technology is biased against fiction and toward facts, against story and toward reality. This means the only option for those communicating in these spaces is to tell the truth'.[1]

Coincidentally or otherwise, the Internet was born in 1969, a hundred years after the birth of Mohandas Karamchand Gandhi. Both events took place in October.

History was made on the night of 29 October 1969 in the University of California, Los Angeles, when Professor Leonard Kleinrock and his graduate student Charley Klein tried to send a message – the first ever computer-to-computer message – with the word 'login' to a terminal at the Stanford Research Institute's Augmentation Research Center 400 miles away. The carrier of the message was the US Department of Defense's Advanced Research Projects Agency Network (ARPANet), the world's first packet-switching network. Kleinrock and his student typed the first letter 'L', and it was received at the other end. They typed the second letter 'O', which too was eagerly received. But before the next letter 'G' could be typed, the Stanford computer crashed. Thus, by design or by accident, the very first message that the Internet carried at the moment of its birth was, lo and behold, 'LO'. 'As a result, history now records how clever we were to send such a prophetic first message, namely "LO",' said Kleinrock. It aptly captured the sense of awe and magic that all of us who use the Net continue to experience even now. It was truly a spiritual moment.

'Gandhian' Voices from the Internet History

It is not without significance that both the computer and the Internet were born after the Second World War, which was a 'gift' of the industrial age to humankind. The bloodiest of all the wars fought on this planet was in some ways the logical outcome of the exploitation-based and violence-breeding economics and politics of the industrial age, which brought out the worst in the human race. However, the end of the Second World War not only marked the beginning of the

Thought leaders of the Internet Age

(Clockwise) **Bill Joy** *(1954-), cofounder of Sun Microsystems and co-author of the Java language. His landmark essay (2000) 'Why the future doesn't need us' set off a big debate on the unwise uses of technology. 'Today scientists, technologists, businessmen, engineers don't have any personal responsibility for the consequences of their actions.'*

George Gilder *(1939-), an influential Internet evangelist and forecaster. 'It is the working together of the "definite" (particles) and "infinite" (waves and energy fields) which constitutes the beauty of the Information Technology.'*

Lawrence Lessig *(1961-), a founding member of Creative Commons. He is a strong proponent of Net neutrality and reduced restrictions on copyright in socially useful technology applications. 'Monopoly controls have been the exception in free societies; they have been the rule in closed societies.'*

Michio Kaku *(1947-), a celebrated physicist, futurist and science populariser. He concludes his bestselling book,* Physics of the Future: How Science Will Shape Human Destiny and Our Daily Lives by the Year 2100, *by quoting Mahatma Gandhi's aphorism on 'The Roots of Violence'.*

end of the industrial age, but also the birth of the information age, with its lofty mandate of promoting global sharing and solidarity. If the industrial age dehumanised economic growth and social development, the information age was born to re-humanise them.

Indeed, some of the great scientists and inventors who have contributed to the birth and blossoming of the information age were driven by the same noble ideals and ethical concerns that Gandhi had so powerfully articulated in his time. Among them are Norbert Wiener, Alan Turing, Vannever Bush, J.C.R. Licklider, Jon Postel, Doug Engelbart, Tim Berners-Lee, Richard Stallman, K. Eric Drexler, Ray Kurzweil, Lawrence Lessig, Bill Joy and Jaron Lanier.

Norbert Wiener (1894–1964), an American mathematician, is regarded as the Father of Cybernetics, which is the study of control and communication in the animal and the machine. His concepts have inspired scientists to understand the similarities between mechanical technologies, biological organisms and social systems, and to think of computer technology as a means to extend human capabilities. But Wiener – he had great regard for Gandhi and advised the Indian government during the 1950s – was more than a scientist. Having witnessed the horrors of the Second World War, he made a strong plea against the use of technology for destructive ends. In their paper 'Thoughts of Wiener and Gandhi', academicians Manju Dhariwal, Ramesh Pradhan and Raghubir Sharan write:

> Norbert Wiener makes a strong case for a moral reasoning in the use of technology, especially of information technology. He is aware that the enormous advance in communication technology has its adverse impact on the human beings and on their moral and spiritual well-being. He writes: 'Thus the new industrial revolution is a two-edged sword. It may be used for the benefit of humanity, but only if humanity survives long enough to enter a period in which such a benefit is possible. It may also be used to destroy humanity, and if it is not used intelligently it can go very far in that direction'.[2]

Wiener's moral vision was deeply rooted in the four principles of justice: the Principle of Freedom, the Principle of Equality, the Principle of Benevolence, and the Principle of Minimum Infringement of Freedom by the State and other powerful agencies. Like Gandhi, Wiener too believed that human nature cannot be defined merely in terms of the mechanical forces which constitute the human body, nor can man be satisfied by material possessions alone. His book *The Human Use of Human Beings: Cybernetics and Society* (1950) intoned that IT cannot be divorced from human values and moral responsibilities. Earlier, in his courageous article 'A Scientist Rebels' (1947), he had expressed his disillusionment with the unethical behaviour of the American war administration and urged scientists to consider the ethical implications of their work, clarifying that by ethics he meant the human good as well as the good of the whole universe.

Another influential name in the early development of computer science, whom we have encountered in the last chapter, was Alan Turing (1912–54). A brilliant English mathematician – the prestigious science journal *Nature* hails him as one of the top scientific minds of all time – his father served in India as an officer of the British civil service. From pure mathematical logic, he imagined an abstract machine, which later came to be known as the Turing Machine, capable of mimicking human thinking. His landmark scientific paper in 1950, titled 'Computing Machinery and Intelligence', begins with an audacious sentence: 'I propose to consider the question – Can machines think?' He answered the question with a prophesy: 'Machines will eventually compete with men in all purely intellectual fields... by the turn of the (twentieth) century'. He had once said: 'I want to build a brain'.

Turing's vision of future computers was that they would not only be intelligent but also have human qualities – that is, *'Be kind*, resourceful, beautiful, friendly, have initiative, have a sense of humour, *tell right from wrong*, make mistakes, fall in love, enjoy strawberries and cream, make someone fall in love with it, learn from experience, use words properly, be the subject of its own thought, have as much diversity of behaviour as a man, do something really new'.[3]

Notice the words: 'Be kind'. 'Be beautiful'. Be moral – that is, 'tell right from wrong'. We see here how one of the greatest pioneers of the information age had a vision of re-humanised technology that Gandhi would have warmly applauded.

The principle of local and global cooperation, which is central to Gandhian philosophy, also finds a strong echo in Turing. He did not attach much importance to the intelligence of a single human being, however brainy that person may be. He put a far greater value on the collective and cooperative intelligence of humanity. He wrote: 'The isolated man does not develop any intellectual power. It is necessary for him to be immersed in an environment of other men, whose techniques he absorbs...He may then perhaps do a little research of his own... From this point of view, the search for new techniques must be regarded as carried out by the human community as a whole, rather than by individuals'.[4]

Turing attached no importance to money-making as the main motivation for doing scientific research. His mother often asked him what use his mathematics had, and he told her as early as in 1936 that he had discovered a possible application: 'a lot of particular and interesting codes'. He added: 'I expected I could sell them to His Majesty's Government for quite a substantial sum, but am rather doubtful about the morality of such things'.[5]

The computer was born to fulfil a need, more acutely felt towards the end of the Second World War, for a device that could help preserve, retrieve and analyse the ever-growing load of information. The first man to conceive that a machine could store and process information better than people do was Vannever Bush (1890-1974), an American engineer who developed his concept in the form of an analog computer. He called the concept *memex* or memory extension. In his prophetic article 'As We May Think' (1945), he wrote: 'The world has arrived at an age of cheap and complex devices of great reliability; and something is bound to come out of it'.[6] He predicted that the *Encyclopaedia Britannica* could be reduced to the volume of a matchbox and a library of a million volumes could be compressed into one end of a desk. (Indeed, the *Encyclopaedia Britannica* ceased the publication of its print edition in March 2012 and has now moved solely into the digital age.)

Bush's path-breaking contribution was his idea that a computer should not be just a device for information storage but function like the human mind that operates by association. It was a brilliant insight, which he expressed in these words: 'With one item in its grasp, it (the human mind) snaps instantly to the next that is suggested by the association of thoughts, in accordance with intricate web of trails carried by the cells of the brain. It has other characteristics, of course; trails that are not frequently followed are prone to fade, items are not fully permanent, memory is transitory. Yet the speed of action, the intricacy of trails, the detail of mental pictures, is awe-inspiring beyond all else in nature'.[7] Bush's insight helped later IT inventors, such as Doug Engelbart and Tim Berners-Lee to come up with breakthroughs such as *hypertext* trails and the World Wide Web.

Like Gandhi, Bush also envisioned a machine that would 'help everybody'. His vision of the computer was that of a democratiser. He figured that a memex could be made affordable enough to be purchased by libraries, laboratories, educational institutions and business enterprises. This would liberate information ownership and management from both totalitarian communist governments and bureaucracies in capitalist countries.

Bush also contributed to another Gandhian ideal: peace. Although he had worked on the Manhattan Project that developed the atom bomb, Bush advised President Harry Truman that mutual exchange of scientific information between USA and the Soviet Union would promote international collaboration and assist in effective control of nuclear weapons, thereby reducing the threatening prospect of an arms race. 'The applications of science', he wrote, 'have built man a well-supplied house, and are teaching him to live healthily therein'. At the same time, he warned that other applications of science 'have enabled him to throw masses of people against one another with cruel weapons'. He hoped for the elevation of man's spirit so that 'we can better review his shady past and analyse more completely and objectively his present problems'.[8]

Bush's belief that computers could free human beings from the drudgery of routine, repetitive and low-skilled work influenced the work of J.C.R. Licklider (1915–90), whose creative spirit led to the establishment of ARPANet, which in turn hastened the birth of today's Internet. In his seminal work *Man-Computer Symbiosis* (1960), Licklider prophesied: 'In not too many years, human brains and computing machines will be coupled together very tightly, and that the resulting partnership will think as no human brain has ever thought'.[9] Licklider and his colleagues shared Wiener's conviction that ICTs should be owned and controlled by all, and not remain a monopoly of the rich and the powerful minority. Would the impact of ICTs on the society be good or bad? Licklider wrote that the answer depended mainly on the question: 'Will "to be online" be a privilege or a right? If only a segment of the population gets a chance to enjoy the advantage of "intelligence amplification", the network may exaggerate the discontinuity in the spectrum of intellectual opportunity'. He further said that if ICTs were used by the entire society, 'the boon to humankind would be beyond measure'.[10]

It is worth mentioning here that a recent report of the United Nations (2011) strongly endorses Licklider's – and most netizens' – view that 'to be online' is a right and not a privilege. The report, by the UN Special Rapporteur on the Promotion and Protection of the Right to Freedom of Opinion and Expression, says 'that disconnecting people from the Internet is a human rights violation and against international law'.[11]

Another voice of Gandhian idealism among the pioneers of the Internet is Doug Engelbart, best known for inventing the mouse (1963), which is used by every computer user in the world. He could have been a billionaire had he chosen to commercialise his inventions, which also include display editing and hyperlinking. 'It's very different if your goal had been to get patents and be the first,' he says. But, from the very beginning of his scientific career, he had been thinking about 'how a person could invest their professional career to maximise their return to mankind'.

According to Engelbart, now eighty-seven, our world is a complex place facing urgent problems of a global scale. The rate, scale, and nature of change is unprecedented and beyond the capability of any one organisation or even nation to comprehend and respond to. 'How can we collectively develop an energy plan for the world? What about the inevitable depletion of fossil fuels? Or clean water worldwide? How to bridge the gap between rich and poor?' To address these and similar global challenges, Engelbart emphasises the need for what he calls 'co-evolution' of technologies which will help organisations, communities, institutions and nations develop their collective IQ. In his 1962 manifesto titled 'Augmenting Human Intellect: A Conceptual Framework', he had prophetically described the computer as the means by which people can augment their personal and collective intellect.

Engelbart believes that 'the digital revolution is far more significant than the invention of writing or even of printing'. However, he reminds us that we have only just scratched the surface. 'The tools we use to share information – video, blogs, e-mail, instant messaging – are ubiquitous, but primitive. We have yet to really apply our considerable talents to co-evolving tools that will help us address real issues'. What the world needs to create, he says, is the 'innovation superhighway', and not just the 'information superhighway'.

One of the foremost idealists in the history of the Internet is Tim Berners-Lee, a renowned British computer scientist who invented the Hypertext Markup Language (HTML)-driven World Wide Web in 1990. His philosophy echoes the Gandhian ideal that public good, and not private greed, should guide all applications of scientific knowledge. He could have made billions of dollars by patenting his invention, but he decided to share it freely with netizens all over the world. He did so because of his conviction that the Web would take off only if it were free. There was another noble reason for forsaking proprietary ownership of his invention. He believed that the future development of the World Wide Web would be truly a worldwide collaborative activity involving the participation of tens of thousands of scientists and software engineers. In his book *Weaving the Web* (1999), he calls proprietary licensing 'an act of treason in the academic community and the Internet community'.[12]

Further, Berners-Lee believes that basic Internet access to every human being on earth should be treated as a 'universal human right'. His is a strong voice in defence of the universal ownership of the World Wide Web, which he fears is threatened by powerful business interests, including industry leaders.

'The principles of an egalitarian society where all are equal immaterial of race, colour, class, wealth or nation is embodied in the Web today. It has become the beacon of democracy and is more vital to free speech than any other medium, because it is perhaps the least censored, most used, and universally connected resource in the world. ...The web is critical not merely to the digital revolution, but also to our continued prosperity – even our liberty. Like democracy itself, it needs defending'.[13]

Why is Berners-Lee so obsessed with safeguarding the Internet from greedy corporates trying to fragment it and gobble up its pieces? Because, as he vividly puts it, 'Democracy is flying today with wings borrowed from the Internet'.[14] If the Internet gets divided into gated communities of the elite, entry to which is barred for the rest, democracy itself would be debilitated.

Berners-Lee's next Big Idea is called the Semantic Web, which connotes the next phase of the Internet's development and involves making the Web more intelligent and communicative. Billed as the 'Google of the future', it aims to build more meaningful and comprehensive association between tiny bits of information, thereby creating 'applications that are much more powerful than anything on the regular web'. He believes that the advanced Internet of tomorrow can arrange information like neurons in the brain. In other words, the Internet can bring the 'workings of society closer to the workings of our minds'.[15] There is a profound truth hidden in this insight. We know that the workings of the individual human mind can be streamlined and brought in alignment with the higher purposes of life with the help of mind-sharpening and capacity-enhancing practices like yoga, better education, spiritual seeking, enlightened work ethic, voluntary service of humanity, etc. Tomorrow's Internet can help us pursue this ideal of yoga on a societal scale.

Berners-Lee's soaring idealism is evident from the following lines from his book *Weaving the Web*:

> If we end up producing a structure in hyperspace that allows us to work together harmoniously, that would be a metamorphosis. Though it would, I hope, happen incrementally, it would result in a huge restructuring of society. A society that would advance in interactivity and group intuition rather than conflict as a basic mechanism would be a major change. [16]

Jon Postel (1943–98), another key figure in the development of the Internet, was also, like Berners-Lee, a practitioner of science for the people and not for profit. Jon was a founding member of the Internet Architecture Board (IAB). He is remembered for his major and selfless contribution in setting technical standards and domain names. He was responsible for assigning all the numbers that go with Internet names, through the Internet Assigned Numbers Authority (IANA) which he formed. He always maintained that decisions on domain naming 'have to be made fairly and with the long-term benefit of the Internet community in mind'.

Vinton Cerf, who, along with his fellow American Robert Kahn, invented TCP/IP, swears by the mantra of cooperation in technology development. TCP/IP signify the two most important and internationally accepted protocols that have powered the explosive growth of the Internet. Cerf says: 'It is vital for all of us to recognise that the Internet has reached the point where it is today because of a great deal of cooperative labour among great many individuals and organisations on an international scale. The energy of the Internet comes from the creative ideas of hundreds of millions of people around the world. But it also comes from the culture of cooperation and collaboration among all the stakeholders who make policy for the development of the Internet – users, civil society organisations, private entrepreneurs, governments and the technical sector.' [17]

Richard Stallman, father of the free software movement, is another Gandhian – rather, a Gandhian radical – who is shaping the discourse in the Internet world. In 1985, he launched the GNU[18] manifesto which proclaimed that the campaign for free software, far from being a technical issue, was for a universal social, political and moral cause. It is well known that the license agreements of most software companies are written in such a way that they keep users tied to those companies. Licenses, copyrights and other such proprietary instruments are not only used to earn unfair profits, but they also restrict socially useful software to be used widely. 'My work on free software', Stallman declares, 'is motivated by an idealistic goal: spreading freedom and cooperation. I want to encourage free software to spread, replacing proprietary software that forbids cooperation, and thus make our society better'.[19]

Linux, which is used by millions of people and organisations worldwide, is one of the many examples of Free and Open-Source Software (FOSS) systems engendered by Stallman's GNU movement. The GNU General Public License enables Linux users to freely modify and redistribute it to anyone for commercial or non-commercial applications.

According to Stallman, 'the desire to be rewarded for one's creativity does not justify depriving the world in general of all or part of that creativity'. Hence, he has popularised the term 'Copyleft – all rights reversed', a brilliant pun on the standard phrase 'Copyright – all rights reserved'. The idea of copyright, he reminds us, did not exist in ancient times, 'when authors frequently copied other authors at length in works of non-fiction'.[20] This is how scientific and technological knowledge developed and spread in pre-capitalist times.

Stallman is not opposed to the market economy per se. But few can contradict him when he points out the critical flaw in its functioning. 'The paradigm of competition is a race: by rewarding the winner, we encourage everyone to run faster. When capitalism really works this way, it does a good job; but its defenders are wrong in assuming it always works this way.'[21] The truth of this remark is borne out by the unfair and anti-competitive practices that private businesses, both in IT and non-IT sectors, frequently indulge in.

Unhealthy competition among IT companies has another deleterious effect: it prevents the growth of healthy relationships among software programmers. Proprietary software development encourages programmers to hoard ideas and discourages the culture of sharing, co-creating and working together, which is so essential for fostering friendship and innovation. As the GNU Manifesto says:

> The fundamental act of friendship among programmers is the sharing of programs; marketing arrangements now typically used essentially forbid programmers to treat others as friends.[22]

An admirer of Gandhi, Stallman views his own campaign for free software as a kind of satyagraha, as is evident from his favourite

Gandhian quote: 'You assist an evil system most effectively by obeying its orders and decrees. An evil system never deserves such allegiance. Allegiance to it means partaking of the evil. A good person will resist an evil system with his or her whole soul'.

Stallman lives a simple life with minimal materialistic possessions. He says: 'I've always lived cheaply ... like a student, basically. And I like that, because it means that money is not telling me what to do.' He could have made a lot of money writing commercial software. Had he chosen that course, he says, 'I knew that at the end of my career, I would look back on years of building walls to divide people, and feel I had spent my life making the world a worse place'.

Michio Kaku is not a pioneer of the digital era, but he is certainly one of its optimistic futurists, a Jules Verne of the twenty-first century. A celebrated theoretical physicist – he is a co-founder of the string field theory, he is also one of the best-known science popularisers of our times. He has authored several bestselling books that capture the mystery as well as the promise of cutting-edge sciences and technologies. What caught my attention was his latest book *Physics of the Future: How Science Will Shape Human Destiny and Our Daily Lives by the Year 2100* (2011), which reveals the Gandhian influence on him. Based on his interviews with hundreds of leading scientists in the world, the book makes several astonishing predictions of 'near term' (present to 2030), 'midcentury' (2030-70) and 'far future' (2070-2100) nature in areas as diverse as artificial intelligence, medicine, nanotechnology, energy, space travel and wealth creation. (The Internet will be our contact lens; nanobots will scan our DNA and cells for signs of danger; extinct life forms can be resurrected; replicators can assemble molecules to create anything; space travel will become cheaper and commonplace; and so on.)

However, Kaku is not oblivious to the harmful potential of technology. He writes: 'We saw the raw, destructive side of science during World Wars I and II. The world witnessed in horror how science could bring on ruin and devastation on a scale never seen before, with the introduction of poison gas, the machine gun, firebombings of entire cities, and the atomic bomb. The savagery of the first part of the twentieth century unleashed violence almost beyond comprehension'.

The key, therefore, 'is to find the wisdom necessary to wield the sword of science', he says in a note of caution. 'As the philosopher Immanuel Kant said, "Science is organised knowledge. Wisdom is organised life." Unlike information, it cannot be dispensed via blogs and Internet chatter. Since we are drowning in an ocean of information, the most precious commodity in modern science is wisdom. Without wisdom and insight, we are left to drift aimlessly and without purpose, with an empty and hollow feeling after the novelty of unlimited information wears off...Let us hope that the people of this century will use the sword of science wisely and with compassion'.

But where does wisdom come from? Kaku answers this question, and also concludes his fascinating book, by reproducing a famous aphorism by Mahatma Gandhi. We have read it before (in Chapter 18), but it merits re-reading: *'THE ROOTS OF VIOLENCE – Wealth without work; Pleasure without conscience; Knowledge without character; Commerce without morality; Science without humanity; Worship without sacrifice; Politics without principles'.*

I discussed the relevance of Gandhian philosophy in the information age with my Bengaluru-based friend and IT entrepreneur Mohan Tambe, whose passion for doing original inventions in digital technologies is matched by his deep social commitment. He invented Graphics and Indian Scripts Terminal (GIST) technology, which has become a standard software package for Indian languages, and Language Independent Programme Subtitles/Dubbing (LIPS) technology, which is used by TV channels. He played a vital role in the making of Indian Script Code for Information Interchange (ISCII) standards for Indian language computing. He has recently developed a cable TV-based multi-lingual interactive service that provides users the best fare in education and entertainment from around the world. Like other true inventors around the world, Tambe is motivated not by money but by the desire to serve humanity in uniquely creative ways.

Tambe said to me: 'Once we recognise the Internet to be essentially a network of mutually cooperative computers, it becomes apparent that the Digital Revolution is actually following Nature's Law of Evolution.

Steve Jobs featured Gandhi, along with his other personal heroes, in Apple's highly acclaimed 'THINK DIFFERENT' advertising campaign in the late 1990s. The photograph of Gandhi that Jobs personally selected for the ad campaign was the one taken by another legendary American – Margaret Bourke-White. (See Annexure IV)

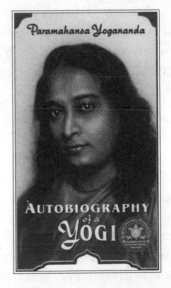

Steve Jobs (1955-2011), iconic inventor who co-founded Apple. He was greatly influenced by Paramahansa Yogananda, whose Autobiography of a Yogi *was the only book that he had downloaded on his iPad 2. He had first read it as a teenager, 'then re-read in India and had read once a year ever since'.*

In Nature, life evolves not through conflict and confrontation, but through mutual cooperation. Gandhi articulated this powerfully in his vision of human progress.' Tambe, however, cautioned that the Internet can betray its promise and harm human progress if it is allowed to be controlled by narrow commercial and political interests. 'Just as the human mind can go haywire if it is not properly guided by an enlightened value system, the Internet can cause damage on a much larger scale if conscious efforts are not made. It can be used either to resurrect and spread the wisdom of the ages to take humanity to a higher level of evolution or to purvey mediocrity and muck. Gandhi helps us make the right choice.'

How Gandhi Inspired Steve Jobs to 'Think Different'

Steve Jobs (1955–2011), the iconic inventor who co-founded Apple, regarded Mahatma Gandhi as one of his personal heroes. Hinduism, Buddhism and Eastern spirituality cast a spell on him during his self-exploratory journeys in India in his youth, especially in the Himalayas and in Banares. He was fascinated by the concept of *prajna* or experiential wisdom which a seeker can intuitively experience through concentration of the mind. Walter Isaacson's riveting biography provides an account, in Jobs's own words, of how India left a lasting influence on him:

> Coming back to America was, for me, much more of a cultural shock than going to India. The people in the Indian countryside don't use their intellect like we do, they use their intuition instead, and their intuition is far more developed than in the rest of the world. Intuition is a very powerful thing, more powerful than intellect, in my opinion. That's had a big impact on my work.
>
> Western rational thought is not an innate human characteristic; it is learned and is the great achievement of Western civilisation. In the villages of India, they never learned it. They learned something else, which is in some ways just as valuable but in

other ways is not. That's the power of intuition and experiential wisdom.

Coming back after seven months in Indian villages, I saw the craziness of the Western world as well as its capacity for rational thought. If you just sit and observe, you will see how restless your mind is. If you try to calm it, it only makes it worse, but over time it does calm, and when it does, there's room to hear more subtle things – that's when your intuition starts to blossom and you start to see things more clearly and be in the present more. Your mind just slows down, and you see a tremendous expanse in the moment. You see so much more than you could see before. It's a discipline; you have to practice it.[23]

Jobs's observation resonates with what Gandhi has said on numerous occasions about the need to discipline the working of the human mind. In *Hind Swaraj*, he writes: 'The mind is a restless bird; the more it gets the more it wants, and still remains unsatisfied'.[24] Regular prayers, fasting, keeping a weekly day of silence and daily spinning were his ways of 'calming' his mind and listening to 'more subtle things' from one's inner being – such as the 'music of the spinning wheel'.

Jobs tried his own unorthodox, and quite un-Gandhian, ways of achieving this – such as using, at some time in his life, psychedelic drugs for making him more enlightened. But he also sought to achieve this by immersing himself in designing and creating technology products that have wowed the world with their functional and aesthetic value.

Jobs's observation also echoes Gandhi's sayings about the intuitive knowledge of Indian villagers. In a speech at a meeting of intellectuals in Madras (now Chennai) on 8 April 1921, Gandhi said: 'Throughout my long travels, I have noticed that the masses and the women of India … are neither so unintelligent nor so uncultured as we often consider them to be. They see far more truly through their intuition than we educated Indians do with our intellect clouded by multiplicity of ideas.'[25] He was especially laudatory about Indian women's experiential wisdom, saying: 'A woman's intuition has often proved truer than man's arrogant assumption of superior knowledge. There is method in putting Sita before Rama and Radha before Krishna.'[26]

Incidentally, Jobs was greatly influenced by the teachings of Paramahansa Yogananda, who, as we have seen in Chapter 24, shared a relationship of deep mutual respect with Gandhi. *Autobiography of a Yogi*, Yogananda's international bestseller, was the only book that Jobs had downloaded on his iPad 2. It was a 'guide to meditation and spirituality that he had first read as a teenager', his biographer Walter Isaacson writes, 'then re-read in India and had read once a year ever since'.[27]

Jobs showed his admiration for Gandhi by featuring him, along with his other personal heroes, in a widely praised advertising campaign for Apple in the late 1990s. He had returned to his own company after a gap of eleven stormy years, and the ad campaign, which was mostly his own creation from concept to commissioning, did wonders in restoring Apple's reputation as a maker of dream products in the computer space. The campaign was titled 'THINK DIFFERENT', and its manifesto-like message read:

> Here's to the crazy ones. The misfits. The rebels. The troublemakers. The round pegs in the square holes. The ones who see things differently. They're not fond of rules. And they have no respect for the status quo. You can quote them, disagree with them, glorify or vilify them. About the only thing you can't do is ignore them. Because they change things. They push the human race forward. And while some may see them as the crazy ones, we see genius. Because the people who are crazy enough to think they can change the world, are the ones who do.

The photograph of Gandhi that Jobs personally selected for the ad campaign was the one taken by another legendary American – Margaret Bourke-White (1904-71), the first female photo-correspondent of *LIFE* magazine. There is a fascinating story about how Bourke-White, who has left behind some of the most stunning photographs of the evolution of the machine age in America, took this iconic photo of the Mahatma with his humble machine. She has herself recounted that story, and also the story of her subsequent interactions with Gandhi, in her autobiography *Portrait of Myself*. My essay on the photograph, and my tribute to this intrepid photographer, appears as an annexure to this book.

Internet's Inventors and Developers were 'Satyagrahi Scientists'

A question often asked is: Who invented the Internet? The truth is: no single individual or organisation invented it. As computer scientist Jaron Lanier, who coined the phrase 'Virtual Reality', puts it:

> The web was built by billions of people simply because they wanted it, without need, greed, fear, hierarchy, authority figures, ethnic identification, advertising, or any form of manipulation. Nothing like this ever happened before in history. We can be blasé about it now, but it is what we will be remembered for. *We have been made aware of a new dimension in human potential.*[28] *(Emphasis added)*

How true! Nothing like this has ever happened before. Never before was a machine built with the cooperative and collaborative efforts of countless people around the world. Nevertheless, at the core of these efforts have been those visionaries, some of whom have been mentioned in this book, in whose lives brilliant ideas and boundless idealism marched together. Each of them has improved the Internet by building on others' labour of love. Many of them were inspired by Gandhi's life and moral philosophy.

This reminds me of Gandhi's innovative and participative concept of improving the spinning wheel. Writing in *Young India* on 27 May 1926, he said: 'All the improvements that have been made in the mechanism of the spinning wheel and the speed of the spinning wheel up till now are solely due to the efforts of those devoted workers who spin for sacrifice'.

Gandhi called such devoted workers 'satyagrahi scientists'. It is apt to use the same epithet to describe all those who have selflessly toiled for the birth and evolution of the Internet, and also for the augmentation of its revolutionary potential.

Courtesy: Gandhi Smriti

Twentieth century's Jesus Christ on a mission to restore Hindu-Muslim amity: *Gandhi in Noakhali, 1946. For two months, he, now seventy-seven years old, walked from village to village, armed with nothing but his walking stick, a set of holy books, and his favourite Bengali song,* Ekla Chalo Re *(Walk Alone), composed by Rabindranath Tagore.*

Illustration: Saurabh Singh

34

'UNDREAMT OF DISCOVERIES IN NONVIOLENCE'
Where the Internet is, and Ought to be, Headed

→§◇◈◇§←

Man is a rope, fastened between animal and Overman – a rope over an abyss.
A dangerous going-across, a dangerous wayfaring, a dangerous looking-back, a dangerous shuddering and staying-still.
What is great in man is that he is a bridge and not a goal; what can be loved in man is that he is a going-across and a down-going.

— Friedrich Nietzsche (1844-1900), German philosopher.

Modernity sees humanity as having ascended from what is inferior to it – life begins in slime and ends in intelligence – whereas traditional cultures see it as descended from its superiors.

— Huston Smith, a renowned scholar on comparative religions.

GANDHI WAS A ROMANTIC AT HEART. HE BELIEVED, AS WE HAVE described in Chapter 10, that 'everything can be turned into a science or a romance' with the right attitude of the mind, heart and soul. He experienced the romance of the spinning wheel and village industries. He felt the romance of the microscope when he used it for treating leprosy patients, and also the romance of the telescope when he used it to watch the infinite mysteries of the starry night. We have earlier tried to explain why he would have felt similar romance in using the Internet, as it has evolved so far. He would have eulogised it for its unmatched service to humankind, but also expressed his concern about its misuse. I am sure that the Mahatma would be similarly enraptured by the future promises of the Internet, which will contribute far more to peace and human progress in the coming decades than it has done so far.

To know why, it is necessary to recall a record of his earliest awestruck experience of one of the greatest marvels of technology in the late nineteenth century. It can be found in Gandhi's gushing description of the Suez Canal during his first voyage from Bombay to London, where the nineteen-year-old was going to study law. The Suez Canal had been built in 1869, the year in which Gandhi was born, as an artificial waterway of 164 kilometres connecting the Mediterranean Sea and the Red Sea. It enabled water transportation between Asia and Europe without the ships having to circumnavigate Africa. Within days of reaching his destination in November 1988, Gandhi wrote in his *London Diary:*

> The construction of the Suez Canal I am not able to understand. It is indeed marvellous. I cannot think of the genius of a man who invented it. I don't know how he would have done it. It is quite right to say that he competed with nature. It is not an easy task to join two seas... The beauty of the scene it is beyond my power to describe. You cannot enjoy it unless you see it.[1]

Man competing with Nature. The indescribable beauty of engineering as a work of art. Connecting continents and connecting people. Isn't this what the Internet is all about? It has digitally connected the entire planet, from anywhere to anywhere, across seas and oceans, across deserts, mountains and forests, and across the man-made barriers of country, culture, race, religion and language.

Digital-age technologies could do something even more incredible tomorrow. So far they have only connected points in space. Some day, they might succeed in connecting points in time. They certainly will become more intelligent and proactive in ways that mimic the powers of the human brain. There are even predictions that machine intelligence would surpass human intelligence within the next three to four decades. Is this desirable? What would be the consequences of the future Internet on the future of mankind? Would an artificial intelligence system create its own updates without human intermediation – AI 1.0, giving rise to AI 2.0, which in turn engenders AI 3.0 and so on? Might one of these powerful versions of AI turn malevolent and destroy the human species itself? Alter it? Or replace it? And does Gandhi's philosophy provide any useful insights for the coming generations to harmonise unabated scientific and technological progress with human beings' eternal aspirations for peace, justice and all-round development? We shall now examine these questions.

Four Drivers of the Internet

Until now, three inter-related drivers have been propelling the explosive growth in the power of the Internet – power of the microprocessor; speed, capacity and content of the Internet; and the number of people using it. Now, a fourth driver is being added in the form of an incredibly large family of intelligent devices or 'things' that will 'talk to each other' through the Internet. It is called Internet 3.0 or the Internet of Things – also called the 'Internet of Everything'. Each of these four drivers is accelerating the creative power of 0's and 1's, which are the basic Yin and Yang, or Purusha and Prakriti, of the digital world, and activating a tsunami of bits and bytes.

The explosive growth in the power of microprocessors has been made possible by Moore's law, which is named after Gordon Moore, co-founder of Intel Corporation. It states that the number of transistors on an integrated circuit (IC) gets doubled approximately every two years. The first transistor in 1947 measured 1.3 cm. Today, Intel produces microprocessors with transistors measuring only 22 nanometres (less than one-billionth of a metre) wide. Intel's smallest microprocessor, called the Atom and used in mobile devices like smartphones, measures 26 square millimetres and has 47 million transistors.

Keeping pace with the growing processing capacity of individual computer devices is the data carrying capacity of the Internet. The best dial-up modems available in the early 1990's were 56 kbps. Today, in early 2012, the highest Internet speed has increased by over 3,000 times. The first website was created in 1991. In 2000, there were just over 7 million websites on the Internet. The number has crossed 150 million within a decade. Significantly, every country in the world is adding to the web content, unlike in the past when most of the content was generated in the West.

Dramatic has been the fall in the price of computers. In 1970, IBM introduced a new mainframe computer model with the highest ever memory – one full megabyte. It occupied a room and cost US $46,74,160. In 1982, Prime Computer sold a megabyte of memory on a single circuit board for $36,000. In 2011, a terabyte (10,48,576 megabytes) disc drive could be purchased for a hundred dollars, and it could be held in the palm of one hand.

No less remarkable is the steep rise in the number of Internet users worldwide, from 25 million in 2000 to 2.5 billion in 2012. By 2020, the number is expected to reach five billion. With global population expected to reach eight billion then, it means that five out of eight people in the world will be using the Internet by the end of 2020. A decade later, the life of every person in the world will be linked to the Internet in multiple ways.

Extension of the connectivity revolution to the world of objects will be the most impact-making development in the Internet. Until now, it is the people who have been connected to the Internet via computers and, lately, mobile phones. Now the Internet will connect a wide array of chip-embedded communication devices, sensors, actuators and databases. Sensors are ultra-small tools for measurement and detection that send relevant information to the devices connected to the Internet. These devices will 'speak' with each other in inter-connected networks, collecting and sharing data which, in turn, can be used by many of them to carry out pre-programmed commands without human intervention. In other words, these devices will act intelligently. The greater the number of such connected objects, and the more they 'speak' amongst themselves, the more exponential will be the growth of their collective 'intelligence' which humans can tap.

There will soon be more Internet-enabled devices than people in the world. One company, Hewlett Packard (HP), alone is planning to install 1 trillion advanced sensor nodes worldwide and interconnect them into an immense environment network under its ambitious Central Nervous System for the Earth (CeNSE) Project. Under this project, use of nanomaterials can boost the detection power of sensor devices by over one hundred million times the sensitivity rates of existing technologies. The 'Internet of Things' has wide-ranging applications – such as detection of several types of cancer based on a single breath; identification of structural damage on buildings and bridges before they fall; advance warning about cracks or snags that may have developed on railway tracks or engines; minimising fatalities on roads by equipping vehicles with safety sensors that can help prevent collisions in split-seconds; monitoring weather patterns for farmers; broadcast of early warnings about cyclones and earthquakes; and so on. HP Labs describes CeNSE as benefiting human lives by 'hearing the heartbeat of the Earth'.

Digital technologies of tomorrow have many other promises. Voice recognition technology will have become so advanced that search engines can respond to voice commands. On-person devices will be able to do instant translation of speech or text from any of the world's 8,000 languages. Future Internet will make HD-quality video services available practically everywhere and at affordable rates. This is thanks to the massive increase in the speed of both mobile Internet (close to 1 Gbits/sec) and wired Internet (10 Gbits/sec) by 2020, up from the current (2012) highest speed of about 15 mbps. (The average Internet speed is less then 1 mbps in India.) Later, with Internet speeds approaching terabits per second, the web will create a multi-dimensional virtual environment in which people can have full 'immersive' experiences.

Human memory will be augmented by the intelligence of networked objects. Bionic eyes will cure many cases of blindness by restoring eyesight that surpasses the power of human vision. They will also have video recording capabilities, and hence be able to collect detailed information about their neighbourhoods. Similar wearable or implantable devices will enhance the power of other human systems. For example, deafness will become fully curable.

Supercomputers, which are used for highly calculation-intensive tasks in quantum physics, weather forecasting, molecular modelling, simulation research, etc., broke the petaflop[2] barrier (10^{15}) in 2008. They will break the exaflop barrier by 2020, by being able to do 1,000,000,000,000,000,000 (a million trillion, or a quintillion) calculations per second. By 2030, they will become zettaflop computers, a thousand times faster than an exaflop computer. This humungous computing power will help, among other things, in the accurate simulation of an entire human brain, thus giving a big boost to artificial intelligence innovations. The interaction between machine and human brain will have hitherto unbelievable applications. For example, within the next ten-fifteen years, it will be possible to send text messages on mobile phones by thought power alone.

In the pre-digital era, so much of information about the happenings in history and the activities of people was simply lost. Hundreds of thousands of manuscripts have perished. We have no record of how the master builders of the past built Egypt's pyramids, Indonesia's Borobudur Temple, Madurai's Meenakshi Temple, Agra's Taj Mahal and countless other architectural wonders around the world. Beethoven was unknown to contemporary musicians in India. Most of Bach's music was unknown to Beethoven. Similarly, the best of Indian musicians of the time were unknown to Beethoven and Bach. Almost all of this information insufficiency will become a thing of the past. The storage and computing power of tomorrow's supercomputers will be so humungous that 'everything may be recorded and preserved, at least potentially: every musical performance, every crime in a shop, elevator, or city street; every volcano or tsunami on the remotest shore...'[3]

The global community of scientists will be one of the greatest beneficiaries of this combined power of digital computation and communication. They will be able to conduct collaborative research in many ambitious and data-intensive projects such as the Large Hadron

Collider (LHC), which is the world's largest and highest-energy particle accelerator near Geneva *(see Chapter 16)*; Fusion Energy research at International Thermonuclear Experimental Reactor (ITER) in France; the Square Kilometre Array (SKA), a radio telescope development project for astronomy experiments, which will revolutionise our understanding of the origin and evolution of the universe; seismic studies for earthquake prediction; sharing of Earth Landsat imagery and atmospheric data for better weather forecasting; climate change studies, and much more. India is already a member of many of these futuristic research projects.

Nanotechnology, which enables control and assembly of matter on an atom-by-atom basis, will see tremendous progress in the coming decades. Combined with the power of tiny robots – also called nanobots – it will be used for the construction of giant structures. These will use minimal resources and yet be hundreds of times stronger than steel structures. Medical nanobots will cause the most important breakthroughs in the treatment of cancer. As predicted by Michio Kaku they will help detect cancers earlier than ever before, and also treat them with unprecedented precision. Even terminally ill patients, in some cases, can be saved. Medical nanobots will also help in early-stage alerts on heart conditions and neurological disorders, boosting immune systems, regulating blood pressure and accelerating the healing of wounds. Developments in stem cell science will facilitate organ replacements grown from stem cells as well as stimulation of human cells to regrow amputated limbs.

It is also possible to visualise decentralised production centres and new decentralised, but globally connected, human habitats. Contrary to the current trend of massively expanding urban conglomerates, this could even lead to the shrinking of cities and blooming of new village communities in the future. In this sense, the Internet and other modern technologies could fulfil the wish of Einstein, who said in 1934: 'I, too, am in favour of abolishing large cities.' The local and the global will harmoniously balance each other; insofar as these human communities of the future will be increasingly self-sufficient locally in the fulfilment of their material needs, but also increasingly interdependent globally for their intellectual, artistic, aesthetic, cultural and spiritual development. Gandhi would be glad to see it happen, for, as we have noted before in Chapter 30, it is in perfect consonance with his own credo – 'For my material needs, the village is my world. For my spiritual needs, the world is my village.'

The next stage in the development of nanotechnology has the potential to make a miracle called teleportation happen. What this means is that, thanks to a major discovery in quantum physics, an object may exist simultaneously in two different places. In other words, this is like time travel or what we referred to at the beginning of this chapter, 'connecting points in time'. In 2010, scientists achieved a major milestone in quantum teleportation over a distance of sixteen kilometres. In the latter half of this century, teleportation could move macro-scale objects from one location to another, thanks to the developments in picotechnology (which manipulates matter on a scale of trillionths of a metre or 10^{-12} m), and femtotechnology (which does it on a still tinier scale of 10^{-15} m), as against nanotechnology (which does it on a scale of 10^{-9} m).

Time travel for human beings is still in the realm of speculation, but several noted scientists have averred that it is possible in the distant future. Legendary astrophysicist Stephen Hawking, author of *A Brief History of Time*, is one of them. To prove his point, he drew our attention to the audacious Large Hadron Collider (LHC) project near Geneva.

> Deep underground, in a circular tunnel 16 miles long, is a stream of trillions of tiny particles. When the power is turned on they accelerate from zero to 60,000 mph in a fraction of a second. Increase the power and the particles go faster and faster, until they're whizzing around the tunnel 11,000 times a second, which is almost the speed of light. But just like the train, they never quite reach that ultimate speed. They can only get to 99.99 per cent of the limit. When that happens, they too start to travel in time. We know this because of some extremely short-lived particles, called pi-mesons. Ordinarily, they disintegrate after just 25 billionths of a second. But when they

are accelerated to near-light speed they last 30 times longer. It really is that simple. If we want to travel into the future, we just need to go fast. Really fast.[4]

Will Digital Technologies Replace Human Species?

What the previous few pages have presented are just some illustrative examples of what the rapidly unfolding digital era has in store for us. Evidently, its possibilities are mind boggling. But what about its perils?

Peeping into the future to understand where the ongoing developments in science and technology are leading the human race has become all the more necessary because of some extremely critical philosophical questions that they have begun to throw up. These questions have been posed in two thought-provoking books by renowned futurist Ray Kurzweil – *The Age of Spiritual Machines: When Computers Exceed Human Intelligence* (1999) and *The Singularity is Near: When Humans Transcend Biology* (2005). The central theme of the first book is that since the intelligence of computers – their ability to calculate, understand abstract concepts, recognise patterns, etc. – has been progressing exponentially, human beings will no longer be the most intelligent or capable type of entity on the planet before the twenty-first century is over.

> Evolution has been seen as a billion-year drama that led inexorably to its grandest creation: human intelligence. The emergence in the early twenty-first century of a new form of intelligence on Earth that can compete with, and ultimately significantly exceed, human intelligence will be a development of greater import than any of the events that have shaped human history. It will be no less important than the creation of the intelligence that created it, and will have profound implications for all aspects of human endeavor, including the nature of work, human learning, government, warfare, the arts, and our concept of ourselves.[5]

The theme of Kurzweil's second book was an extension of that of the first book. 'By the end of this (twenty-first) century, the nonbiological portion of our intelligence will be trillions of times more powerful than unaided human intelligence.' According to him, Singularity is the 'merger of the vast knowledge embedded in our own brains with the vastly greater capacity, speed, and knowledge-sharing ability of our technology'. This merger will 'rupture the fabric of human history,' he predicts. 'The Singularity will allow us to overcome age-old human problems and vastly amplify human creativity. We will preserve and enhance the intelligence that evolution has bestowed on us while overcoming the profound limitations of biological evolution.'[6]

Kurzweil says that Singularity is driven by three overlapping revolutions – in Genetics, Nanotechnology, and Robotics (GNR).

We are in the early stages of the 'G' revolution today. By understanding the information processes underlying life, we are starting to learn to reprogram our biology to achieve the virtual elimination of disease, dramatic expansion of the human potential, and radical life extension. The 'N' revolution will enable us to redesign and rebuild – molecule by molecule – our bodies and brains and the world with which we interact, going far beyond the limitations of biology. The most powerful impending revolution is 'R': human-level robots with their intelligence derived from our own but redesigned to far exceed human capabilities. 'R' represents the most significant transformation, because intelligence is the most powerful 'force' in the universe.

Significantly, Kurzweil warns us: 'The Singularity will also amplify the ability to act on our destructive inclinations, so its full story has not yet been written.'

The destructive possibilities of the genetics, nanotechnology and robotics revolutions have prompted many scientists to warn us against being excessively effusive about the future of the Internet and Internet-enabled technologies. One of them is Bill Joy, cofounder of Sun Microsystems and coauthor of the Java programming language.

In a widely discussed essay titled 'Why the future doesn't need us', which was published in 2000, he expressed his apprehension in these words: 'With the prospect of human-level computing power in about 30 years, a new idea suggests itself – that I may be working to create tools which will enable the construction of technology that may replace our species. How do I feel about this? Very uncomfortable'.[7]

What Gandhi's Last Glorious Years tell us About the Science of Nonviolence

Does science really threaten the existence of human species? If there is even a small likelihood of the digital-age technologies amplifying man's ability to act on his 'destructive inclinations', as Ray Kurzweil cautions us, and if there is even a finite probability that these technologies may someday replace the human species itself, as Bill Joy fears, then where lies our reliable security? To know the answer – *Gandhi's answer* – let us revisit him at a very critical, yet most illuminating, period of his life.

In Chapter 24, we have acquainted ourselves with this period, which covers the months preceding and succeeding India's independence on 15 August 1947, and culminating in his assassination on 30 January 1948. This is when India and the world witnessed the Mahatma make a superhuman effort to counter the holocaust-scale communal violence raging around him with the help of the spiritual power of nonviolence harnessed from his faith in God. Although his effort was only partially successful, and earned him the reward of a heroic martyrdom, history has nevertheless recorded it as one of the most inspiring instances of the science of nonviolence in action. It has a big message about how tomorrow's world can be made just and peaceful by combining the powers of science and spirituality.

An episode during this period is of utmost importance to our discussion in this chapter. On Gandhi's seventy-eighth birthday in 1947 – the day when there was 'nothing but anguish' in his heart because of the raging flames of communal violence all around him – he had developed fever. His condition was quite serious, which prompted doctors to press him to take penicillin, but he refused.

'*Rama nama*', silent chanting of God's name, was his penicillin, he insisted. He would rather fall a martyr to his researches in the science of *Rama nama* than a casualty to theirs. The doctors argued: 'Science has definitely established that there are specific causes for specific ailments. You eradicate the cause and the disease goes. On the other hand, anyone can be given cholera by introducing cholera germs into his system. The laws of science are inviolable'.

Gandhi, however, remained unmoved. 'I call this arrogance,' he told his doctors. 'Science has yet much to learn. It has so far touched only the hem of the garment. All illness is the result of the violation of the laws of nature, in other words, the penalty of sin against Him – since He and His Law are one. Therefore, when *"Rama nama"* holds full sway, all illness vanishes. People have no idea of the full potency of *"Rama nama"*. I am out to demonstrate it. I must wish to live only to serve Him and live, therefore, through His grace alone. I have plunged into this fire to discover the science of *"Rama nama"*, just as a doctor or a scientist rushes into an area where an epidemic is raging to discover the laws of physical science. I must discover it or perish in the attempt.'[8]

Gandhi's conversation with his doctors reveals his central belief that the laws of physical science are not the only laws that operate in the universe and influence the life of individuals and society. He had articulated this belief on numerous occasions in his life. For example, in *Harijan* of 14 May 1938, he had written: 'If we have made unexpected progress in physical sciences, why may we do less in the science of the soul?' He held that even the laws of physical science are subordinate to a Higher Law, which is inseparable from the Law Giver, the Almighty God. It is the Law of Truth and Nonviolence, and it cannot be understood by reason alone. What comes to the aid of the seeker of its meaning is faith.

Gandhi's extreme inflexibility in a potentially life-and-death situation may reinforce some people's judgement of him as an unreasonable and impractical person. I for one see him as a scientist who had 'plunged into the fire' of violent social turmoil to discover the science of God, whom he understood as Truth, which for him was the same as nonviolence. He was willing to accept death but not give up his spiritual research, which involved prayerfully seeking communion with God by chanting His name.

His biographer Pyarelal tells us that 'from his reading of scriptures and his personal observation, Gandhi had come to the conclusion that when a man has attained a complete and living faith in the Unseen Power, the body undergoes internal transformation and becomes free from all ailments'.[9] Gandhi believed himself to be still imperfect in his living faith in the Unseen Power. Therefore, his research required self-suffering and constant self-purification because all illness 'is the result of the violation of the laws of nature' and should be seen as 'the penalty of sin against Him'. The illness that Gandhi was referring to was not his individual illness alone. Rather, it was allegorical about the illness afflicting Indian society as a whole, for which he believed he personally had to atone. He further believed that the purer he became, the closer he got to God and, with the help of God's power, he would be able to stop the orgy of violence that was going on around him.

This was not blind belief. Rather, for Gandhi, it had sound philosophical basis in his understanding of the triad of body, mind and soul. Like many Indian philosophers in the ancient and modern eras, he thought that, although the body and mind of an individual human being are perishable, his soul or the atman is imperishable. The atman or one's true self is identical with the transcendent self, *Paramatman* or Brahman, which is the totality of the cosmic spirit. The cosmic spirit is the source of all spiritual or divine power, which runs and sustains the universe.

Since atman is indivisible from the cosmic spirit, the individual human being can access its infinite power. To the extent that he succeeds in tapping it, the spiritual power can have extraordinary effect on his intelligence, health and wellbeing. Moreover, since it flows through his medium, it can enable him not only to overcome bodily ailments but also to exercise enormous moral influence over the people in his surroundings. This is because, as Gandhi said: 'Ahimsa is the very nature of the atman'.

However, for accessing the power of the cosmic spirit, the individual has to shed his ego, the illusion of being a separate and distinct self – Einstein described it as 'optical delusion of consciousness' – and identify himself fully and unreservedly with the all-pervasive cosmic spirit. He has to control his *manas* or mind, which is the instrument of all knowledge and action. Restlessness and unruliness is the natural tendency of the human mind. Since the mind dwells in and acts through the body in its interaction with the outer world, it develops the notion of self or ego. Self or separateness is the attribute of the body, which by its very nature is distinct and self-enclosed. The security and integrity of the body depends on protecting its separateness. Being embodied, the human mind develops ego and makes the individual to think that he is separate from other human beings and from other beings in Nature. Gandhi believed that this notion of separateness is the root cause of all the ills and violence in society. Furthermore, it disables human beings from harnessing the infinite power of the cosmic spirit.

This explains why self-purification – annihilation of ego and all the selfish desires associated with it – through prayers, fasts, brahmacharya and, of course, ceaseless service of humanity was so central to Gandhi's work in the social and political fields. Absolute identification with everything in the universe was an important formulaic practice in his 'science of nonviolence'. How apt was the title of Nobel laureate writer Romain Rolland's biography of him, published as early as in 1924 – *Mahatma Gandhi: The Man Who Became One with the Universal Being*!

This point can be further elucidated by mentioning the influence of Buddhism on Gandhi's philosophy and practice of nonviolence. Ever since he became acquainted with the teaching of the Buddha, his 'eyes were opened to the limitless possibilities of nonviolence'. He was especially struck by the Buddhist concept of Attavada. It is a Pali word derived from Sanskrit – *attan* is self or atman, and *vada* is theory. Gautama Buddha used the term to convey the unsustainability of separateness, the belief that one's self or soul is different and apart from the one universal self. Explaining it, Gandhi wrote: 'In the Buddhist tradition, *himsa* (violence) and *asatya* (untruth) alike proceed from attavada, the dire heresy of separateness. They equally constitute violence against the omnipresent Truth, the subjection of a whole to a part or the pretence of the part to be the whole.'[10]

According to Albert Schweitzer (1875–1965), a widely respected medical missionary who was a pacifist philosopher as well, 'Gandhi continues what the Buddha began. In Buddha the spirit of love set itself the task of creating different spiritual conditions in the world; in Gandhi it undertakes to transform all worldly conditions.'[11]

It is possible to imagine that, in his determined attempt to transform the prevailing 'worldly conditions' in the last turbulent years of his life, Gandhi was trying to forge himself as a 'weapon' of nonviolence, one capable of bringing to an end the inferno of violence caused by the Partition of India. All his activities those days, including the refusal of medicines and reliance on God's name-chanting, were aimed at perfecting the capabilities of that weapon. In the end, the weapon fell to the bullets of an assassin. Significantly, this happened when the Mahatma was walking towards the venue of his daily prayer meeting. And, as he had wished, he died with the name of God on his lips.

Man so Far has been 'Less Than Human'; in Future he can be 'More Than Human'

After Gandhi embraced the credo of satyagraha in South Africa in 1906, each day of his life – especially in the last glorious years of his life – had brought him new discoveries, or reinforced old ones, in the 'science of truth and nonviolence'. Everything he said, wrote or did thereafter was simply a new articulation of that science. This is how he represented that science in *Harijan* of 9 November 1947:

> All universal rules of conduct known as God's commandments
> are simple and easy to understand and carry out if the will is
> there. They only appear to be difficult because of the inertia,
> which governs mankind. Man is a progressive being. There is
> nothing at a standstill in nature. Only God is motionless for,
> He was, is and will be the same yesterday, today and tomorrow,
> and yet is ever moving. We need not, however, worry ourselves

over the attributes of God. We have to realise that we are ever
progressing. Hence, I hold that if mankind is to live, it has
to come growingly under the sway of Truth and Nonviolence.
It is in view of these two fundamental rules of conduct that I
and you have to work and live.

Gandhi makes two very important affirmations here. Firstly, notice
his statement that 'Man is a progressive being'. Therefore, man is
destined to achieve progress in science and technology – from bullock-
cart to bullet trains, from living in caves to building skyscrapers, from
Gutenberg's printing press to 3-D printing, and so on. Newer and
newer discoveries in genetics, nanotechnology, robotics, space travel,
time travel, etc., are not only inevitable but also welcome from a
Gandhian perspective.

His second affirmation is even more important than the first.
Notice those cautionary words – 'if mankind is to live, it has to come
growingly under the sway of Truth and Nonviolence'. They remind us
that man's survival depends not on the achievements he makes in his
outer world, howsoever spectacular they may be, but on the progress
of his inner being. We see the same warning echoed by two other
great personalities of the last century who were influenced by the
Mahatma. 'It has become appalingly obvious that our technology has
exceeded our humanity',[12] wrote Einstein. Martin Luther King Jr. said:
'Our scientific power has outrun our spiritual power; we have guided
missiles and misguided men...; if we are to go forward, we must go
back and rediscover those precious values: that all reality hinges on
MORAL foundations and that all reality has spiritual control...The
Moral arc of the universe bends at the elbow of justice.'[13] King also
warned in his book *Stride Towards Freedom* (1958): 'The choice is no
longer between violence and nonviolence. It is either nonviolence or
non-existence'.[14]

If man does adhere to truth and nonviolence, and to all that they
entail – love, care and justice for all, disinterested service of humanity,
responsibility towards ecology, and constant self-purification – then
the trajectory of human evolution in the future will surely be very
different from what is foreseen in Bill Joy's apprehension about the

human species being replaced by a super-intelligent machine. This is because the more mankind progresses morally and spiritually, the stronger will be its living tradition of wisdom. And the wiser man becomes, the more reliably can he distinguish between the right and the wrong uses of the machines he invents. Hence, the fear that the survival of the human species would be threatened when man's non-biological intelligence – in other words, artificial intelligence – overtakes his current unenhanced biological intelligence is misplaced. Joy has looked at man's progress in the sphere of science in the absence of his possible (and necessary) progress in the sphere of morality and spirituality.

The future direction of humanity's progress, which can stave off the fears expressed by scientists like Kurzweil and Joy, is clearly illumined in the following words of Maharshi Aurobindo:

> The most vital issue of the age is whether the future progress of humanity is to be governed by the modern economic and materialistic mind of the West or by a nobler pragmatism guided, uplifted and enlightened by spiritual culture and knowledge...We must return and seek the sources of life and strength within ourselves.... It is the spiritual revolution we foresee and the material is only its shadow and reflex. The world is in continuous evolution and there is a need to bring down a higher truth with each age.
>
> The present evolutionary crisis comes from a disparity between the limited faculties of Man – mental, ethical and spiritual – and the technical and economic means at his disposal. Without an inner change, Man can no longer cope with the gigantic development of outer life. If humanity is to survive, a radical transformation of human nature is indispensable. Only spiritual realisation and experience can achieve the change of the mental being into a spiritual being.[15]

The schism between the mental being and the spiritual being is largely due to the fact that modern societies have forgotten to distinguish between information, knowledge and wisdom. We are faced with such a deluge of information, stored, processed and disseminated by a constantly changing array of fascinating gadgets, that we often mistakenly see in this material infrastructure proof of mankind's progress. We are attracted by what Gandhi called 'toys'. In this context, what he wrote about his own experience of visiting the Eiffel Tower in Paris, when he was a student in England, is quite appropriate. 'Men flocked to see it (Eiffel Tower) and ascended it as it was a novelty and of unique dimensions. It was the toy of the exhibition. So long as we are children we are attracted by toys, and the tower was a good demonstration of the fact that we are all children attracted by trinkets'.[16]

We are bombarded with so much information, most of which is related to the omnipresent culture of consumerism, that we have become incapable of distinguishing between the essential and the inessential in life. The lament by poet T.S. Eliot (1888–1965) – *Where is the wisdom we have lost in knowledge? Where is the knowledge we have lost in information?* – seems far more meaningful today. Eliot had also expressed the same concern in another way:

> *Knowledge of speech, but not of silence;*
> *Knowledge of words, and ignorance of the Word.*
> *All our knowledge brings us nearer to our ignorance,*
> *All our ignorance brings us nearer to death,*
> *But nearness to death no nearer to GOD.*[17]

Nearness to God calls for a radical transformation of human nature through a change in man's inner life. If that happens, the phenomenal growth in his non-biological intelligence due to the advancements in Genetics-Nanotechnology-Robotics technologies will become a boon rather than a curse. For, in that eventuality, the human mind would be augmented with some of its lower functions being performed much faster and better by the newly added artificial intelligence capabilities. This, in turn, would enable the human beings to devote more of their conscious and active life to the realisation of the higher needs and promises of the human mind.

This process of self-discovery, self-realisation and self-transformation would further enhance the core powers of the human mind by making human beings more truthful and nonviolent, more intuitive and creative, more emotionally sensitive, more aesthetically refined, and more in harmony with fellow human beings and with everything else in Nature. This second type of augmentation of the human mind, however, is not an outcome of machine-augmented non-biological intelligence. Rather, it can only come with the kind of spiritual and moral quest that Gandhi and other great souls of the world were engaged in.

The future promises of this doubly augmented human mind are profoundly expressed by Aurobindo in his work *The Life Divine:*

> Man (so far) has been less than human, he can be more than human ...Our humanity is not the whole of the Reality or its best possible self-formation or self-expression – the Reality has assumed before man existed an infrahuman formation and self-creation and can assume after him or in him a superhuman formation and self-creation.

Aurobindo calls man's evolution so far as evolution in the era of Ignorance, an era in which man is still a slave of his ego. The future era will be that of Knowledge. Explaining the difference between the two, he writes:

> Our evolution in the Ignorance with its chequered pain and joy of self-discovery and world-discovery, its half-fulfillments, its constant finding and missing, is only our first state. It must lead inevitably towards an evolution in the Knowledge, a self-finding and self-unfolding of the Spirit, a self-revelation of the Divinity.

To summarise, humankind is currently undergoing an evolutionary crisis. It has reached a stage in which the human mind has achieved enormous progress – and promises to achieve still greater progress – in understanding and manipulating the outer world. However, man's moral and spiritual evolution having remained limited, his very progress in the outer world has raised the spectre of either more horrific outbreaks of violence in the future or the human species being overpowered by technologies invented by the human mind.

But the spectre can be banished. It is indeed possible to create a world without wars, weapons, and violence. It is possible to build a future with no more poverty and want, no more racism, no more religious conflicts, no more abuse of children, no more indignities on women, other vulnerable members of society and the animal kingdom, and no more destruction of the environment. And as the Internet has started showing in some rudimentary ways, it is indeed possible for technology to become mankind's partner in transforming our world into a better world. A better world for whose creation there would always be enough selfless men and women willing to make necessary sacrifices and to suffer.

In brief, divinisation of humanity and humanisation of science and technology are possible. The possibility of humanisation of technology is best captured by Isaac Asimov (1920–92), the great science fiction writer, who formulated his famous Three Laws of Robotics. These laws form the basis of Robo-Ethics:

1. A robot may not injure a human being or, through inaction, allow a human being to come to harm.
2. A robot must obey any orders given to it by human beings, except where such orders would conflict with the First Law.
3. A robot must protect its own existence as long as such protection does not conflict with the First or Second Law.

Asimov himself added a fourth law, or the Zeroeth Law, to precede the first three stating:

4. A robot may not harm humanity, or, by inaction, allow humanity to come to harm.

There is something deeply insightful in the latter part of the Zeroeth Law of Robotics. In stating that a robot may not, by inaction, allow humanity to come to harm, Asimov has cast technology in the role of man's conscience-keeper. For, barring natural calamities beyond man's control, all other manifestations of harm to humanity have occurred when man's conscience has been inactive.

But can technology become man's conscience keeper? Can machine become the torch-bearer of morality? Can it teach humanity to discriminate between right and wrong, between good and evil? These questions may baffle us, but not after we remind ourselves that Gandhi's humble machine, the spinning wheel, answered them for him in the affirmative. In the previous chapters, we have seen how the Mahatma audaciously projected the charkha as a moral machine, as a carrier of a profound cultural and spiritual message, indeed as an embodiment of the divinity in man.

Can the Internet and other digital-age machines, which are the most human-like among all the inventions of science thus far, also embody the divinity in man? Can they become the latter-day avatar of the spinning wheel?

Yes.

Yes, because, as we shall discuss in the next chapter, the Internet, which is humankind's first 'species machine', has a higher evolutionary purpose to fulfill. We must never give up this hope and belief. And we must ever be ready to do our utmost to turn this hope into reality.

Sri Aurobindo (1872–1950)

There is an ascending evolution in nature which goes from the stone to the plant, from the plant to the animal, from the animal to man. Because man is, for the moment, the last rung at the summit of the ascending evolution, he considers himself as the final stage in this ascension and believes there can be nothing on earth superior to him. In that he is mistaken. In his physical nature he is almost wholly an animal, a thinking and speaking animal, but still an animal in his material habits and instincts. Undoubtedly nature cannot be satisfied with such an imperfect result; she endeavours to bring out a being who will be to man what man is to the animal, a being who will remain a man in its external form, and yet whose consciousness will rise far above the mental and its slavery to ignorance.

Sri Aurobindo came upon earth to teach this truth to men.

*– **The Mother** (Sri Aurobindo's close spiritual collaborator)*

35

HUMANKIND'S FIRST 'SPECIES MACHINE'
The Internet has a Higher
Evolutionary Purpose to Fulfill

⊹⊱◈◈◈⊰⊹

RAY KURZWEIL: Our merger with technology has aspects of a slippery slope, but that slides up toward greater promise, not down into Nietzsche's abyss. Some observers refer to this merger as creating a new 'species'. But the whole idea of a species is a biological concept, and what we are doing is transcending biology. The transformation underlying the Singularity is not just another in a long line of steps in biological evolution. We are upending biological evolution altogether.
BILL GATES: I agree with you 99 percent. What I like about your ideas is that they are grounded in science, but your optimism is almost a religious faith. I'm optimistic also.
RAY KURZWEIL: Yes, well, we need a new religion.
BILL GATES: What would the principles of the new religion be?
RAY KURZWEIL: We'd like to keep two principles: one from traditional religion and one from secular arts and sciences – from traditional religion, the respect for human consciousness.

— From Ray Kurzweil's book *The Singularity is Near: When Humans Transcend Biology.*

THE INTERNET WAS BORN IN THE WOMB OF SCIENCE. BUT WILL its growth be nurtured in the lap of religion, in the sense in which Gandhi understood religion? Many users of the Internet, and scientists and professionals associated with its development, may dismiss this question by saying that religion has nothing to do with the world of bits and bytes, servers and sensors, and portals and protocols. However, there is little doubt that the debate over the future evolution of the Internet will be increasingly dominated by the concepts and dictates of morality, religion and God.

Some might say: 'We agree that science and technology cannot be exempt from moral scrutiny, but why bring religion and God into the picture?' The simple answer is that Gandhi regarded true religion and true morality to be inseparably bound up with each other. 'Religion is to morality what water is to the seed that is sown in the soil', he wrote.[1] 'As soon as we lose the moral basis, we cease to be religious. There is no such thing as religion overriding morality'.[2]

For him, the source of all morality was God. Nonviolence, justice and love for all without exception, which he regarded as the irreducible and universally applicable commandments of morality, were dictated by God's Law. It was an article of faith for him that 'God and His Law abide everywhere and govern everything…(N)ot a blade of grass grows or moves without His will. The free will we enjoy is less than that of a passenger on a crowded deck'.[3]

Using a scientific analogy to describe the divine basis of all morality, he wrote: 'God is in every one of us and, therefore, we have to identify ourselves with every human being without exception. This is called cohesion or attraction in scientific language. In the popular language it is called love. It binds us to one another and to God. Ahimsa and love are one and the same thing'.[4] Since he preached and practiced love for all without exception, he treated even atheists with equal respect, saying: 'In His boundless love God permits the atheist to live.'[5]

Furthermore, for Gandhi, God is the source of not only morality but also science, technology and all other activities of the human intellect. His rejection of the West's industrial civilisation was principally on account of its rejection of God. 'God gifted man with intellect that he might know his Maker. Man abused it so that he might forget his Maker.' Western civilisation's rejection of God had rendered it blind to the true needs of mankind and also to the true purpose of human life. This blindness was the cause of the many sins it committed against humanity, with the Church remaining a silent spectator and even a colluder. The blindness has to be cured for the very survival of humanity, and the cure lies in modern science surrendering itself before the spiritual wisdom of the past. Gandhi was confident of the surrender taking place sooner or later. Hence his bold prediction: 'If intellect plays a large part in the field of violence, I hold that it plays a larger part in the field of nonviolence'.

Gandhi saw himself as a servant of God in everything he did. His life's primary motivation and sole quest was to become a true saint, a *sthitaprajnya*, while remaining fully immersed in the turmoil of the mighty struggles and chaotic affairs of the world. What is remarkably unique about him is that although he was essentially a spiritual seeker and, because of his involvement in politics, a fierce critic of the colonial rule and the industrial civilisation on which it rested, he nevertheless had boundless respect for science. He respected even that science which was a product of the West's industrial civilisation and had, nevertheless, proved to be beneficial to society. He unhesitatingly upheld the sovereignty of reason vis-a-vis faith in matters which he believed belonged to the domain of reason – that is, in matters not involving any value judgements. In matters involving value judgements (that is, all matters of interaction between people), he rooted for reason that is guided by universally accepted ethical values. In higher spiritual matters, he went beyond reason – *not* because it is 'bad' to use reason (as per some priestly commandment) but because it is *impossible* to use it. Pure reason and pure faith are thus two end-points of the spectrum of Truth-seeking, and each band within this continuum is valid in its own right.

In other words, faith must not interfere in the functioning of reason in matters that reason can satisfactorily deal with. Nevertheless, since reason cannot answer all questions about life and the universe, he argued that it should surrender to the working of faith in those matters beyond its domain. Indeed, few men in modern history have transformed the fruitless 'reason *versus* faith' debate into a fruitful 'reason *and* faith' discourse as convincingly as Gandhi has done. This is precisely what makes him enduringly relevant to the worlds of both science and faith, and to everything else in life that the two are linked to.

Gandhi went a step further. He argued that the power of science – or, rather, the power of human thought that combines both reason and faith – gets immeasurably enhanced when it comes under the complete sway of God and His commandments, namely, nonviolence, love and justice. Therefore, like many leading thinkers of the world, Gandhi believed that modern science had much to learn from the nonviolent scientific discoveries of ancient seers, who had mastered the science of the human mind. In Chapter 19, we have read his following words: 'The rishis, who discovered the law of nonviolence in the midst of violence, were greater geniuses than Newton...Having themselves known the use of arms, they realised their uselessness and taught a weary world that its salvation lay not through violence but through nonviolence'.

Only dogmatic and ignorant apologists of the cult of modernity would dismiss this claim as untrue. History has recorded similar amazing mind-power discoveries made by Christian saints, Sufi mystics and Zen masters.[6] All of them showed with their personal examples that knowledge and mastery of man's inner self was a more rewarding way of knowing and interacting with the outer world. Here is an account by Paul Brunton, a widely read British philosopher and traveller. He was much influenced by Ramana Maharshi, a great Indian seer whom Gandhi referred to as 'Bhagwan'. This is what Brunton writes in his book *The Wisdom of the Overself*:

> What science has discovered with the help of cunning instruments, ancient sages discovered many thousand years ago with the help of concentrated thought alone...Modern science began by studying and describing the properties of things; it can only end by discovering their ultimate substance. But in order to attain this end, it is slowly being forced, by the revolutionary significance of its own discoveries, to turn a somersault which will land it in metaphysics.

In another book titled *A Message from Arunachala* – Ramana Maharashi lived on a hill named Arunachala in Tamil Nadu – Brunton echoes in these poetic words the prediction made by Gandhi:

> There is in the soul of every man something infinitely greater and grander than he knows, more than he ever dreamed of. We hold hard to the outer husk of body consciousness because we are ignorant of the divine kernel it contains. We have wandered the broad waters and crusted lands of this globe: it is now time to turn in our tracks and explore ourselves – the most wonderful of all globes. Here lie vast continents of the mind. Here stretch illimitable seas of the heart, hardly travelled and barely recorded in the books. The most astounding discoveries will come when our scientists turn away for a while from metal and stone and electricity to examine and explore the nature of self within the laboratory of Man.[7]

Internet: Where the 'Definite' and the 'Infinite' have an Interplay

The Laboratory of Man. What an appropriate phrase to describe the location of the current and future development of the Internet! Also, what an insightful description of the coming convergence of science and morality! Science in future will not be regarded as science unless it raises, as we have seen Gandhi insist earlier, 'the moral stature of man'. Technology in future will not be regarded as technology unless it gives an account of how it advances the nonviolent development of man.

For this to happen, science and technology have to accelerate their journey from Matter to Mind, and from man's Outer Reality to his Inner Reality. This is what the Internet is doing, and this is what it will do even more extensively in the time to come.

This may sound 'philosophical' and, worse, 'metaphysical' to those who disagree with the above argument. Generally speaking, scientists and technologists are the last ones to admit that their professions have anything to do with philosophy, much less spiritual philosophy. Nevertheless, history shows that every major advance in science and technology has sought validation at the higher reaches of knowledge – namely, philosophy. For example, the persecution of

Galileo was a defining moment in Western science. It coincided with the repudiation of the Church's authority to censor scientific research and, simultaneously, with the postulation of truths of the material world in 'secular' terms. It heralded the era of Newtonian physics in which the knowledge of the observed objective reality was believed to be totally independent of the observing subjective agent. With all its limitations, the philosophy of Newtonian physics marked an advance over the dogma of the Church, which had sanctioned faith's unacceptable interference in the working of reason.

However, the philosophical underpinnings of the Industrial Revolution, which was catalysed by Newtonian physics, led to new problems. Newton's laws were interpreted by the ruling elite in Europe in such a way as to produce a basis for social exploitation at home and conquest of foreign lands. Under this interpretation, the object has to obey the external forces. It has no independence. This deterministic approach of materialistic science led to an economic system in which not only were objects treated as inanimate, but even humans belonging to the 'less civilised' races and non-human living beings got 'objectified', fit to be exploited. 'Civilising' the people in conquered lands came to be regarded as the White Man's Burden. Science got unhinged from spirituality and morality. Industrialism, Western colonialism and forcible conversions by Christian missionaries, against which Gandhi raised a powerful voice of protest, were the consequences of this 'objectification' of nature and human beings. Obsessed with the Outer Reality, science came to negate the Inner Reality of nature and human life.

The certainties of this materialistic science collapsed with the advent of quantum physics, which came with a new philosophical approach. It showed that matter and mind – object and subject – could no longer be understood as two separate and independent entities. The scientific world began to see the two as interdependent, mutually interacting and complementary. The famous Neils Bohr Principle of Complementarity simultaneously recognises the particle and wave properties of light and all radiation. Thus, quantum mechanics gave rise to a whole new understanding of physical reality, sharply bringing into focus the limitations of conventional science.

As Max Planck, the father of quantum mechanics, who coined the term 'quanta' to describe the discrete packets of energy that comprise light, said: 'Science cannot solve the ultimate mystery of nature. And it is because, in the last analysis, we ourselves are part of the mystery we are trying to solve.'[8]

Alan Turing, one of the pioneers of computer science, said the same thing: '(W)hen we are dealing with atoms and electrons, we are quite unable to know the exact state of them, our instruments being made of atoms and electrons themselves.'[9]

Quantum physics marks the beginning of science's journey from Matter to Mind, and from man's Outer Reality to his Inner Reality.

Information technology is quintessentially a creation of the age of quantum physics. It could not have been born in the age of Newtonian physics. It is based on microelectronics, which is now moving in the direction of devices of atomic dimensions. For the first time, computer chip designers are able to manipulate matter from the inside at nano-scales – that is, to control the internal atomic structure of silicon and other elements. In the years to come, man's interaction with matter will take place at pico- and femto-scales, where matter does not even remain a structure of particles, as we conventionally understand it. It becomes waves of quantum energy. Matter ceases to be matter and resembles mind-stuff. As George Gilder, one of the foremost thinkers of the Internet age, puts it: 'It is this working together of the 'definite' (particles) and 'infinite' (waves and energy fields) which constitutes the beauty of the Information Technology.'[10]

The entry of the Infinite, which is one of the many attributes of God, into the inner working of digital technologies constitutes the greatest revolution of our times. It is therefore obvious that matter and spirit have conspired together to create the Internet to fulfil a higher evolutionary purpose of the human race.

How God has Re-entered Science through the Internet

When the computer was invented in 1950 and all through the spectacular advances in computer science since the invention of the microprocessor chip in 1971, the debate it spawned was cast in unmistakably philosophical terms. Is the computer a precursor to the development of artificial intelligence? What is intelligence? Can machines think? And is man essentially a 'thinking machine'? Now that the computer has metamorphosed into an even more intelligent machine called the Internet, which, in turn, is aiding the progress of artificial intelligence, this new phenomenon certainly demands to be understood in philosophical terms.

Philosophically speaking, the Internet can be understood as the first ever 'species machine' or 'species tool' of mankind produced by post-Newtonian scientific knowledge. The usefulness of the concept of the 'machine' or the 'tool of production' in the study of human evolution has been widely recognised. Indeed, human history is in many ways the history of the tools or devices that man has used down the ages. Marshall McLuhan, America's celebrated philosopher of the mass media who coined the term Global Village, famously said: 'We shape our tools. And then our tools shape us.' This has been true ever since the chimpanzee, our evolutionary sibling, descended from the trees to find that his upper limbs were free to discover, and interact with the surrounding environment in new ways.

Every tool created by man, including the earliest ones such as the sharpened stone or the wheel, has, in effect, meant two simultaneous things: externalisation of a certain capability inherent in man and internalisation of a certain power inherent in Nature. Thus, a moving vehicle represents externalisation of man's capability of motion, just as the powers of Nature harnessed in it (the energy contained in the fuel, the robustness of the vehicle's body, the ability of the vehicle to carry large amounts of weight, the co-ordinated and flexible working of its various parts that enable the vehicle to move faster or slower) now become internal to him. These powers become his own. The printing press externalised man's capability to write and keep a record of the written word. In turn, its power of storing huge quantities of properly recorded and categorised information became his own power.

Similarly, the calculator represents man's externalised capability to make computations with numbers. The computer does the same, with this difference that the computer additionally signifies, in an externalised form, man's ability to create, store, manipulate, process and analyse text information. A multi-media computer takes these externalised capabilities further by adding audio and video information. All these capabilities are essentially those of the human brain, but now they operate outside man in the form of an information machine, thanks to the powers of nature's products and processes now internalised by man. It is perhaps not coincidental that the word 'computer' previously referred to the human being using it! It was a job title for men and women sitting at office desks performing calculations with mechanical calculators that were precursors to the modern computer.

The Internet demonstrates the phenomenon of externalising or amplifying the human mind in an even more startling form than a standalone computer. If the individual computer is a miniature, if as yet crudely developed, virtual human mind, the Internet can be seen as a network of disembodied human minds. If the unconnected Personal Computer (PC) represents a 'brain outside the human brain' for the individual user, the Internet represents externalisation and collectivisation of key human capabilities such as information creation, information storage (memory), information processing, and communication made available to all the users. The Internet's unique beauty is that it enables communication, dialogue and cooperation among human beings on a planetary level, involving, potentially, the entire planetary population. Along with the proliferation of a large number of Intranets, the Internet is beginning to resemble the human society with its own countless communities, all of them distinct and yet integrated by an intelligent platform. In other words, it has become humankind's central nervous system.

Although the Internet, in its essential function, does what every machine tool has done so far – it has externalised and enhanced the capabilities of man – it is fundamentally different from all the earlier tools invented in human history. Machines of the industrial age processed, carried or helped store materials that were handled or used by a limited number of human hands. Internet, the machine of the information age, processes, carries and stores information that can be used *simultaneously* by the entire human race. Moreover, it is a machine to whose evolution all netizens can contribute. It has thus become the first comprehensive species tool of mankind. All the previous tools represented the externalised capabilities of individual men or, at the most, groups of men (for example, those working in a traditional factory setting). In contrast, the Internet has begun to perform those functions which can be called the functions of the 'species mind'.

World Wide Mind: Why the Internet's Future Trajectory will be Benign

'World Wide Mind' is how author Michael Chorost[11] describes 'the coming integration of humanity, machines and the Internet'. Mind-to-mind communication has existed ever since the arrival of intelligent human beings on this planet. But now, with the emergence of the Internet, a new kind of 'mind' has developed that is increasingly becoming an inseparable part of humanity itself. Chorost calls this integration 'humankind's new evolutionary step'. He writes: 'If the Internet plus humanity becomes a hyperorganism, we might see that something very strange is going on' and that 'a new form of intelligence might be at work'. He further affirms that this integration can make us 'more human than less'.

It is nothing short of a miracle in human history that a tool that was originally meant to only do faster computation has, in a very short time, evolved along the upward data-information-knowledge-wisdom spiral – as a processor and communicator of data; as a machine for storing, analysing and using information; as an intelligent device for converting information into systematised knowledge and, further, for applying the knowledge for diverse purposes; and, finally, as a universally accessible repository of the wisdom of the world.

The birth of this miraculous 'species machine' – one which a scholar and a commoner, a scientist and a craftsman, an artist and a religious preacher, and anybody from any corner of the globe can use at the same time and at any time – has a far-reaching significance for the future evolution of humanity. The trajectory of the Internet-assisted future evolution of the human species will be increasingly on benign lines. This is not merely wishful thinking; it is rooted in the following points of reason and intelligent optimism.

Firstly, when a rational individual uses a tool, it is reasonable to expect that the individual mind will use the tool for the fulfilment of some good purpose for the user concerned. Similarly, when a tool such as the Internet is used by the entire human population, we can expect the species mind to ensure that it is used for the good of the entire human family.

Secondly, we should remember that the species mind of the human race is not an independent and isolated entity. It is created by, and is a subset of, the universal mind or the cosmic consciousness in the same way as the individual mind is a subset of the species mind. The universal mind is the other name for God that is omnipresent, omniscient, and omnipotent, and about which Gandhi wrote:

> There is an indefinable mysterious Power that pervades everything. I feel it, though I do not see it. It is this unseen power which makes itself felt and yet defies all proof, because it is so unlike all that I perceive through my senses. It transcends the senses. But it is possible to reason out the existence of God to a limited extent.[12]

Individual mind, species mind and the universal mind are all inter-related. Just as the first cannot be isolated from the second, the second cannot be isolated from the third. This truth is self-evident to leading scientists and inventors in the field of the Internet and Artificial Intelligence. In Chapter 32, we have come across the following pertinent observation made by Alan Turing, the computer science pioneer: 'The isolated man does not develop any intellectual power. It is necessary for him to be immersed in an environment of other men'. Similarly, the isolated human species cannot develop any intellectual, aesthetic and creative power. It necessarily has to immerse itself in an environment of other species and also all other forms of creation in the universe. Gandhi had expressed this thought powerfully in lines that apply as much to the individual man as to the species man.

> My own experience has led me to the knowledge that the fullest life is impossible without an immovable belief in a Living Law in obedience to which the whole universe moves. A man without that faith is like a drop thrown out of the ocean bound to perish. Every drop in the ocean shares its majesty and has the honour of giving us the ozone of life.[13]

If isolation is not an option, what then are the rules of engagement between the individual mind and the species mind, and also between the species mind and the Universal Mind? These can only be in accordance with the Law of the Universal Mind, in which the Universal Mind stands for God. In Gandhi's words:

> To me God is Truth and Love; God is ethics and morality; God is fearlessness. God is the source of Light and Life and yet He is above and beyond all these. God is conscience.[14]

In other words, it is impossible to envision the birth and also the future evolution of the Internet without reference to ethics, morality and conscience of the human race. Viewed in this way, we recognise the fundamental difference between the age of the Internet as the 'species machine', working increasingly under the dictates of the Universal Mind for the overall good of the human and non-human creation, and the previous age when machines were used by dominant races and nations for their own narrow, malign and violently-pursued ends. When the West developed science and technology in the age of colonialism, from the sixteenth to the twentieth centuries, it had banished all considerations for the welfare of the human as well as non-human species because it had banished God (universal mind) from science, politics and commerce.

Sadly, even the Catholic Church, which was meant to represent the Word of God, became a handmaiden for the West's violence-driven global expansionism. To use a vivid expression from Blaise Pascal, French mathematician and philosopher (1623–62), 'a God-shaped vacuum' appeared in the very heart of Western civilisation. This is what Gandhi mourned when he said, on many occasions, that the West had cast aside the message of Jesus, who, according to him, was the greatest apostle of nonviolence in human history. Even today, when the right-wing fanatics in USA invoke Christianity, they never mention the Sermon on the Mount!

In a thoughtful essay – 'What Is Spirituality? Memetics, Quantum Mechanics, and the Spiral of Spirituality' – Dr Caleb Rosado, a sociologist and president of Rosado Consulting for Change in Human Systems, USA, says:

> (With) the emergence of scientific materialism, the focus shifted from God as the center of the cosmos to humankind as the locus of the center of meaning. Alienation took on another form as separation from ourselves, our work, and our fellow human beings. This was also a period of extreme forms of inhumanity, often supported, blessed, and led in the name of religion. Fueled by an insatiable greed and an excessive quest for materialism, this period saw the rise of European expansionism, the imposition of slavery, genocidal acts on indigenous populations and the reordering of the world into the haves, the hads, and the have-nots. But such thirst for self-aggrandisement at the core of scientism with its secular humanism already had within it the destructive seeds of the third alienation – separation from nature or ecological alienation.
>
> Beginning in the 19th century the forces of human greed have marched steadily forward in an endless wave of environmental destruction, with little thought for the future of our planetary home. The result is that in the latter part of the twentieth century postmodernism emerged with a new awareness of estrangement, an alienation from the natural world and from our 'ecological' selves – the interconnectedness and interdependence of humans with nature.[15]

Dr Rosado coins a profound expression to describe the civilisational impact of the God-denying Western science, commerce and politics:

Man's alienation from 'the ecological and eternal Other'. This agonising alienation can be removed only by bridging the schism created by the Western civilisation between science and religion – between data-information-knowledge produced by science, and wisdom and values that religion provides. Dr Rosado says: 'Science answers the what-questions of life in terms of causality – what happened? Religion answers them in terms of values and ultimate meaning – why did it happen? And as Friedrich Nietzsche said: "If a person has a Why to live, he can handle almost any What!"'

In my view, the emergence of the Internet as the 'species machine', dictated by the species mind, which in turn is dictated in mysterious ways by the Universal Mind, gives us the hope that the 'Why' of technology, and of human life in general, will not be forgotten in the coming decades and centuries.

The 'Why' of the spinning wheel, its ethical and spiritual purpose, was fully evident to Gandhi. Is the 'Why' of the Internet evident to us, its daily users?

My own earliest education in the raison d'être of the Internet came from reading George Gilder. In the late 1990s I was an avid reader of his regular column in *Forbes-ASAP* magazine, Although I did not subscribe to his excessive faith in the free-market economy, I was fascinated by his writings on the Internet's microcosm (the intricate and ever-shrinking microprocessor architecture inside the computer) as well as the macrocosm (the laser beams travelling inter-continentally through the tens of thousands of miles of optic fibre cables laid on the ocean floor). What wowed me especially was how his thoughts cast a sharp beam of searchlight on the lofty moral purpose of information and communication technologies. In an essay ('Civilisation Can't Afford to Forget') written in 1996, Gilder likened the Internet's spiritual agenda to that of 'a grand cathedral'.

> Human beings were made in the image of their creator, to be creative. I have compared the microchip to the Gothic cathedral. Wrought of sand and glass and air, both structures epitomise the supreme technologies of their eras. Today people still

throng to cathedrals in awe. They still respond to the moral purpose suffusing the spires and towers and iridescent glass. The people who built cathedrals were not embarrassed to make moral claims or to collect funds from churchgoers wretchedly indigent by any modern standard. They knew that these structures resonated with moral authority and significance.

Far more than most of the art and literature of our day, our science and technology resonate with moral purpose and importance. They manifest the creativity of human minds reaching beyond the material constraints that afflict their bodies, the materialist superstitions that constrict the horizons of liberty, the zero-sum limits of the economy of envy and avarice, the martial horrors of the struggle for land and natural resources.[16]

The coming together of reason and faith was expressed even more presciently by Pierre Teihard de Chardin (1881–1955), a French scientist and Jesuit priest, in his theory of evolutionary cosmology. In this, he put forward the concept of a sphere of collective consciousness that he called the 'Noosphere'. He envisioned it as a global network and exchange of knowledge, ideas, research, trade and communication, which would ultimately connect all the people in the world in a 'sphere' of collective mind. He regarded the 'global unification of human awareness as a necessary prerequisite for any real future progress of mankind'. The arrival of the Internet, which can be seen as the 'mechanical infrastructure of the Noosphere', has fulfilled this prophesy, made more than fifty years ago.[17]

Incidentally, after reading Aurobindo's magnum opus *The Life Divine*, Chardin is reported to have said: 'This is comparable to my own work, but for the Indian tradition.' (*Teilhard de Chardin: A Hindu Viewpoint* by Dr Karan Singh; UNESCO seminar on the occasion of Chardin's birth centenary; Paris, 1981.)

Being a theologian, Chardin also said: 'Some day, after mastering the winds, the waves, the tides and gravity, we shall harness for God the energies of love, and then, for a second time in the history of the world, man will have discovered fire.'

Harnessing of fire was, perhaps, the earliest scientific baby-step in the journey of human civilisation. By re-discovering God, the Internet age will have helped man rediscover one of God's most beautiful attributes, love, the Gandhian synonym for nonviolence.

This offers the strongest basis for hope that tomorrow's world will bring both prosperity and peace, as humankind advances towards a higher state of evolution on the combined strength of science and spirituality.

Mahatma's Two Jewels

*Gandhi had two erudite, devoted, competent and incredibly hard-working satyagrahi-secretaries – **Mahadev Desai** (1892–1942) and **Pyarelal** (1899–1982). They were assisted, at different points in time, by a few others in his retinue. Gandhi demanded from all of them what he displayed in his own work – Six-Sigma efficiency. It is thanks to their dedicated work, in the pre-computer era, that almost all of his speeches, articles, letters and important conversations were recorded, translated, authenticated, and preserved for posterity in the Collected Works of Mahatma Gandhi, vol. ninety-eight.*

Desai (left) was regarded by Gandhi and his wife Kasturba as their fifth son. He was with Gandhi from 1917 to 1942. He translated Gandhi's autobiography from Gujarati into English. He had endeared himself to the Mahatma because, in the latter's words, he had 'reduced himself to a zero'. After his untimely death during imprisonment in Aga Khan Palace, Poona, Gandhi remarked: 'The whole life of Mahadev was a poem of devotion...Remaining the disciple, Mahadev became my Guru.'

Pyarelal (right) worked with Gandhi from 1921 till the latter's tragic death in 1948. (His sister Dr Sushila Nayyar was Gandhi's personal physician.) After Desai's departure, he bore the heavy burden of providing secretarial assistance to Gandhi during his tumultous last years. Remarkably, Pyarelal continued to 'serve' Gandhi even after 1948 and right till the last day of his own life. During these thirty-four years, Pyarelal, living a life of utmost simplicity and completely aloof from power and publicity, accomplished a stupendous task – he authored one of the best and most authentic accounts of Gandhi's life in ten volumes. (Two incomplete volumes were completed by his sister.)

It is a pity that India – both society and government – has almost forgotten these two jewels of Gandhi, both of whom were immensely helpful to me in understanding the Mahatma and also in writing this book.

A scientist, a sage, and their common commitment to world peace: *'If Einstein had the courage to think about the universe in revolutionary ways, Gandhi developed the courage to act in the field of politics in a way that was completely unprecedented. If Einstein revolutionised theoretical physics by his profound intellectual brilliance, a daring venture into the field of politics armed with simple ethical principles was the distinctive feature of Gandhi'.*

Illustration: Saurabh Singh

36

WHAT EINSTEIN SAW IN THE MAHATMA

As long as the nations are not resolved to abolish war through common actions and to solve their conflicts and protect their interests by peaceful decisions on a legal basis, they feel compelled to prepare for war. They feel obliged to prepare all possible means, even the most detestable ones, so as not to be left behind in the general armament race. This road necessarily leads to war, a war which under the present conditions means universal destruction. Only the radical abolition of wars and of the threat of war can help. This is what one has to work for. One has to be resolved not to let himself be forced to actions that run counter to this goal.
Gandhi, the greatest political genius of our time, has pointed the way. He has shown of what sacrifices people are capable once they have found the right way. His work for the liberation of India is a living testimony to the fact that a will governed by firm conviction is stronger than a seemingly invincible material power.

— Albert Einstein (1879-1955).

I BEGAN THIS BOOK BY RECALLING MY SPEECH AS A SEVENTH-GRADE school student in an elocution competition in 1969 to mark the birth centenary of Mahatma Gandhi. I had argued, based merely on my rudimentary understanding of the title of his autobiography, that Gandhi was a scientist. Science is all about search for the Truth. The search for Truth requires experiments to be conducted. Therefore, if Gandhi described his life's story as his *Experiments with Truth,*

I concluded that he must have been a scientist in addition to being the leader of India's freedom movement. Forty-two years later, I am even more convinced about the merit of my argument.

My other childhood hero was Albert Einstein. The public library in my small town, Athani, in Karnataka had very little reading material about him in Kannada, my mother tongue. (I didn't know much English in my school years.) But the little that I read about the Theory of Relativity hit my intellect with the force of a punch. It was all incomprehensible to me. My mind wrestled with $E = mc^2$ without any enlightenment. However, the mystery surrounding the interconvertibility of matter and energy was enough for me to accept Einstein as my idol. After his physics became comprehensible to me, he had become my hero for another, greater, reason – I was thrilled to know that he was not only a pacifist, not only a socialist, but was also deeply influenced by Mahatma Gandhi.

Two great humanists. Two peace warriors. And two uncompromising truth-seekers, who in their own different but convergent ways contributed to the Thought Revolution in the twentieth century. Therefore, this book, which explores the relevance of Gandhi's views on science, technology and human development for building a nonviolent world, would be incomplete if it did not refer to the Mahatma–Einstein relationship.

Einstein sent a message on Gandhi's seventy-fifth birthday in 1944. The last sentence in it has since become the most quoted tribute to the Mahatma. It was used as the epigraph in Richard Attenborough's 1982 film *Gandhi*. However, the message deserves to be read in full.

> A leader of his people, unsupported by any outward authority; a politician whose success rests not upon craft nor the mastery of technical devices, but simply on the convincing power of his personality; a victorious fighter who has always scorned the use of force; a man of wisdom and humility, armed with resolve and inflexible consistency, who has devoted all his strength to the uplifting of his people and the betterment of

their lot; a man who has confronted the brutality of Europe with the dignity of the simple human being, and thus at all times risen superior.

Generations to come, it may be, will scarce believe that such a one as this ever in flesh and blood walked upon this earth.

ALBERT EINSTEIN
Princeton University
New Jersey, U.S.A.

But there is much more to the Gandhi–Einstein relationship than the above inimitably crafted compliment.[1]

A portrait of Mahatma Gandhi adorns Einstein's study in the upper room of his two-storied house at 112 Mercer Street in Princeton, near the campus of the Princeton University, where the scientist researched for the last two decades of his life. Einstein's first recorded admiration of Gandhi's nonviolent movement appeared as early as in 1929 in an interview with the *Christian Century*. He wrote his first letter of appreciation to Gandhi on 27 September 1931:

> You have shown by all that you have done that we can achieve the ideal even without resorting to violence. We can conquer those votaries of violence by the nonviolent method. Your example will inspire and help humanity to put an end to a conflict based on violence with international help and co-operation guaranteeing peace to the world.
>
> With this expression of my devotion and admiration I hope to be able to meet you face to face.

Gandhi replied to Einstein on 10 October 1931.

> DEAR FRIEND, I was delighted to have your beautiful letter sent through Sundaram. It is a great consolation to me that the work I am doing finds favour in your sight. I do indeed wish that we could meet face to face and that too in India, at my Ashram.

The two great men never met. However, Einstein never lost an opportunity to admire the political activities and the personality of Gandhi, whom he called 'the only truly great political figure of our age'. And his admiration increased with the passage of time. In 1939, at the instance of Dr S. Radhakrishnan, the then professor of Eastern Religions at Oxford, Einstein wrote in his contribution to a book to commemorate Gandhi's seventieth birthday:

> Mahatma Gandhi's life is unique in political history. He has invented an entirely new and humane technique for the liberation struggle of an oppressed people and carried it out with the greatest energy and devotion. The moral influence which he has exercised upon thinking people throughout the civilised world may be far more durable than would appear likely in our present age, with its exaggeration of brute force. For the work of statesmen is permanent only in so far as they arouse and consolidate the moral forces of their peoples through their personal example and educating influence.
>
> 'We are fortunate and should be grateful that fate has bestowed upon us so luminous a contemporary – a beacon to the generations to come.

Einstein's eulogy after Mahatma Gandhi's assassination, which he wrote for a memorial service held in Washington on 11 February 1948, was heartfelt:

> Everyone concerned with a better future for mankind must be deeply moved by the tragic death of Gandhi. He died a victim of his own principle, the principle of nonviolence. He died because, in a time of disorder and general unrest in his country, he refused any personal armed protection. It was his unshakable belief that the use of force is an evil in itself, to be shunned by those who strive for absolute justice.
>
> 'To this faith he devoted his whole life, and with this faith in his heart and mind he led a great nation to its liberation. He demonstrated that the allegiance of men can be won, not merely by the cunning game of political fraud and trickery, but

through the living example of a morally exalted way of life.

The veneration in which Gandhi has been held throughout the world rests on the recognition, for the most part unconscious, that in our age of moral decay he was the only statesman who represented that higher conception of human relations in the political sphere to which we must aspire with all our powers. We must learn the difficult lesson that the future of mankind will only be tolerable when our course, in world affairs as in all other matters, is based upon justice and law rather than the threat of naked power, as has been true so far.

On 2 November 1948, Einstein sent this message to the Indian Peace Congress:

The initiative of India, which finds such a vivid impression in this Congress, is a new and welcome proof that Gandhi's great original idea had deeply affected the thinking of his people; brutal force cannot be met successfully for any length of time with similar brutal force, but only with non-cooperation towards those who have undertaken to use brutal force. Gandhi recognised that this is the only solution of the vicious circle in which the nations of the world have been caught. Let us do whatever is within our power so that all the peoples of the world may accept Gandhi's gospel as their basic policy before it is late.

In 1949, Einstein sent the following message praising Gandhi's contribution to India's independence:

We can all be thankful to be able to experience that Mahatma Gandhi's work for the liberation of India has now come to completion. Liberation itself is already an event of world historic significance. But even more so the fact that this goal has been achieved without the use of violence. For the first time, it was shown to humanity what can be achieved through a strong will and consequential action without the force of arms. When the people of the world will succeed in grasping the full implication of this event and will adjust their behaviour accordingly, then the permanent overcoming of the current dangerous situation will not meet with great difficulties.

Expressing his views on capitalism, which Einstein believed appealed to the darker side of human nature, he wrote in his book *Ideas and Opinions*: 'I am absolutely convinced that no wealth in the world can help humanity move forward, even in the hands of the most devoted worker in this cause. The example of great and pure individuals is the only thing that can lead us to noble thoughts and deeds. Money only appeals to selfishness and irresistibly invites abuse. Can anyone imagine Moses, Jesus, or Gandhi armed with the money bags of Carnegie'?

Gandhi's critics in India were not happy with the world's most famous scientist showering encomiums on him. On 13 December 1948, a professor of physics from Ambala, in Punjab, wrote to Einstein expressing dismay as to how a rationalist like Einstein 'could have the slightest regard for an irrationalist of the type of Gandhi'. Calling the Mahatma the 'greatest enemy of scientific rationalism', the professor pointed out that his assassins, Godse and Apte, had much regard for Einstein: 'Apte continued to teach your theory of relativity to his comrade Godse'. Einstein's reply was prompt, firm and indicative of his great personality:

> I received your letter of December 13th and can well understand your attitude. But I cannot agree with it. It is true that Gandhi was to some extent anti-rationalist or at least a man who did not believe in the independent value of knowledge. But the unique greatness of Gandhi lies in his moral fervor and in his unparalleled devotion to it. What he achieved in convincing the people of India of his method of nonviolence cannot be overestimated. I believe that it is by far the greatest achievement in the political field in the last centuries – not only for India but for the whole of humanity. Gandhi's Autobiography is one of the greatest testimonies of true human greatness.
>
> Can you wonder that I am astonished about your attitude even if you have not the right understanding of Gandhi's

greatness? *Do you believe it is justified to murder anyone who has some opinion different from yours? (Emphasis added)*

On 18 July 1950, in a broadcast by the United Nations under the title, 'The Pursuit of Peace,' Einstein said:

> I believe that Gandhi held the most enlightened views of all the political men in our time. We should strive to do things in his spirit; not to use violence in fighting for our cause and to refrain from taking part in anything we believe is evil.

That Einstein was opposed to the concept of 'revolutionary violence' is clear also from a letter he wrote on 20 March 1951: 'Revolution without the use of violence was the method by which Gandhi brought about the liberation of India. It is my belief that the problem of bringing peace to the world on a supranational basis will be solved only by employing Gandhi's method on a large scale.'[2]

In a letter to the Asian Congress for World Federation, held in Hiroshima in November 1952, Einstein wrote:

> Gandhi, the greatest political genius of our time, indicated the path to be taken. He gave proof of what sacrifice man is capable of once he has discovered the right path. His work in India's liberation is living testimony to the fact that man's will, sustained by an indomitable conviction, is more powerful than material forces that seem insurmountable.

In 1954, from Phoenix in South Africa, Manilal Gandhi, the Mahatma's second son, wrote to Einstein as one of his father's 'friends and admirers of the principles for which he stood and laid down his life', asking for a message for the opening of a memorial building for Kasturba Gandhi, which occasion also coincided with the golden jubilee of the Phoenix Settlement.

Einstein replied: 'Wherever a moral genius like Gandhi has left his mark, there grows a blessed and liberating work. For, Gandhi, unlike most politicians, did not achieve results through exploitation of human weakness or even through organised force but through his convincing and irresistible example. It is very gratifying to see his son continue his noble work in his spirit and, like him, serving. In this way one serves his own people and, beyond that, humanity with deeds recorded in history books. May this work flourish and prosper.

In the same year, Einstein made his strongest ever plea that 'a new manner of thinking' is needed for humanity's survival.

> A human being is part of the whole called by us universe, a part limited in time and space. We experience ourselves, our thoughts and feelings as something separate from the rest. A kind of optical delusion of consciousness. This delusion is a kind of prison for us, restricting us to our personal desires and to affection for a few persons nearest to us. Our task must be to free ourselves from the prison by widening our circle of compassion to embrace all living creatures and the whole of nature in its beauty... The true value of a human being is determined primarily by the measure and the sense in which they have obtained liberation from the self. ... We shall require a substantially new manner of thinking if humanity is to survive.

Einstein's interview with Robert Merrill Bartlett, appearing in *Survey Graphic*, USA, August 1935, demonstrates that the great scientist did not fully agree with Gandhi's ideas on economics and his method of agitation. 'I admire Gandhi greatly but I believe there are two weaknesses in his program: while nonresistance is the most intelligent way to cope with adversity, it can be practiced only under ideal conditions. It may be feasible to practice it in India against the British but it could not be used against the Nazis in Germany today. Then, Gandhi is mistaken in trying to eliminate or minimise machine production in modern civilisation. It is here to stay and must be accepted.'

However, like Gandhi, Einstein well understood the limitations of exclusive reliance on S&T for building a better world. He said in 1951: 'Betterment of conditions the world over is not essentially dependent on scientific knowledge but on the fulfilment of human traditions and ideals. I believe, therefore, that men like Confucius, Buddha, Jesus, and Gandhi have done more for humanity with respect to the development of ethical behaviour than science could ever accomplish.'[3]

Like Gandhi, Einstein was not only a man of ideas; he was also a man of action. Although science was his main sphere of action, he showed great courage in the many public causes he espoused. When it mattered, he stood up to be counted. He attacked anti-Semetism; opposed segregation of blacks in American society; protested against McCarthyism that led to witch-hunts of those who refused to fall in line with America's Cold War mentality; criticised the military industrial complex; and condemned the suppression of freedom and democracy in communist-ruled Soviet Union. He also lent his powerful voice to the campaign for nuclear disarmament, best exemplified by the Russell-Einstein Manifesto issued in 1955. He had signed the manifesto just days before his death on 18 April 1955.

Gandhi and Einstein: Convergent Views on God

The year 2005 was observed, following a declaration by the United Nations, as 'The International Year of Physics' to mark the centenary of Einstein's famous paper on the Special Theory of Relativity. Actually, in 1905, he also made major contributions to the two other theories that revolutionised physics in the twentieth century – Quantum Mechanics and Thermodynamics. On that occasion, I had paid my own humble tribute to my favourite scientist by writing an essay in the 'Speaking Tree' column of the *Times of India* ('Unity between the Material & the Mystical', 28 March 2005). Here is an excerpt:

> As commemorations go, this one is unique. A year of physics? Why should anybody outside the limited fraternity of physicists or other scientists be interested in it? However, by bestowing this honour on physics, the UN has put the spotlight on a theory whose revolutionary meaning transcends the bounds of science. …The special theory of relativity radically altered science's understanding of the basic building blocks of our universe – matter, space, time and energy. It also catalysed a renewed debate on the relationship between science and religion.

The rudimentary truths about the Special Theory of Relativity – so named to distinguish it from the General Theory of Relativity that Einstein developed in 1915 – have by now percolated into popular consciousness. Even a lay person has heard about the equation $E=mc^2$, which states that a tiny amount of mass can convert into a colossal amount of energy. The constancy of the speed of light, as also its status as the fastest moving entity, has also become common knowledge. The theory blurred the distinction between particles and waves and, since then, quantum physics' fascination with what some scientists have termed 'Nataraja's dance' in the subatomic microcosm has not ceased.

However, Einstein did not agree with the philosophical fuzziness that some postulates in quantum physics, especially Heisenberg's famous Uncertainty Principle, had created. He refused to accept that the most basic behaviour of subatomic particles was 'probabilistic' and governed by statistics. He immortalised his position with a quote – *'Gott wurfelt nicht!'* (God does not play dice with the universe.) A new book, *God in the Equation: How Einstein Became the Prophet of a New Religious Era* by Corey Powell, describes his search for scientific truth as an 'inherently spiritual endeavour'. Einstein, whose theories won him two Nobel prizes, believed in the unity not only between matter and energy but also between the material and the mystical.

...For a scientist whose theories facilitated making of the nuclesbomb, Einstein was a crusader for world peace. A courageous champion of the ideals of socialism, he held that the salvation for humanity lay in the path shown by Mahatma Gandhi...In short, the significance of the UN Year of Physics goes beyond the magic of a famous 1905 equation. It is a call to revisit Einstein in totality.

There was unmistakable resonance between the views of Einstein and Gandhi on the science-faith relationship. Both viewed life and the universe in their totality. As Einstein affirmed: 'I maintain that the cosmic religious feeling is the strongest and noblest motive for scientific research.... A contemporary has said not unjustly that in this materialistic age of ours the serious scientific workers are the only profoundly religious people.' Further, he said: 'I want to know how God created this world. I am not interested in this or that phenomenon, in the spectrum of this or that element. I want to know His thoughts, the rest are details.'

What did Einstein mean by the term 'cosmic religious feeling'? T.S. Ananthu, in his article 'Einstein from a Holistic Perspective', explains: 'The term religion, in its original connotation, means re+legio – Latin for "that which unites with the source". So, Einstein was referring to that experience which united him with the entire cosmos... In order to move towards becoming one with the entire cosmos, one first has to become nothing, "reduce oneself to a cipher", as Mahatma Gandhi has explained in his autobiography. The result is "en+light+enment", the ability to see the Universe in a different light, from a totally self-less perspective".'[4]

Einstein was convinced that 'science without religion is lame and religion without science is blind'. He believed in God's omnipotence. 'Everyone who is seriously involved in the pursuit of science becomes convinced that a spirit is manifest in the laws of the universe – a spirit vastly superior to that of man'. Gandhi would have entirely agreed with this thought. For he too had said: 'My life is largely governed by reason and when it fails, it is governed by a superior force that is faith'.

One of the dogmas that many, though not all, practitioners of modern science have clung to is that there is no place for God or religion in their pursuit of truth. The presence of Marxism as one of the dominant ideologies in the twentieth century greatly strengthened this dogma. Belief in God, or even recognition of the existence of something called 'spirit', was anathema to Left-leaning scientists both in the West and in India. What is remarkable about Einstein is that although he never hid his anti-capitalism views – 'Why Socialism?' is the title of his most widely debated political writing, published in May 1949 in the Left-wing journal *Monthly Review* – he also didn't conceal his rather unorthodox thoughts on religion and God. In his essay 'The World As I See It' (1931), he wrote:

> The most beautiful experience we can have is the mysterious. It is the fundamental emotion which stands at the cradle of true art and true science. Whoever does not know it and can no longer wonder, no longer marvel, is as good as dead, and his eyes are dimmed. It was the experience of mystery – even if mixed with fear – that engendered religion. A knowledge of the existence of something we cannot penetrate, our perceptions of the profoundest reason and the most radiant beauty, which only in their most primitive forms are accessible to our minds – it is this knowledge and this emotion that constitute true religiosity; in this sense, and in this alone, I am a deeply religious man. I cannot conceive of a God who rewards and punishes his creatures, or has a will of the kind that we experience in ourselves. Neither can I nor would I want to conceive of an individual who survives his physical death; let feeble souls, from fear or absurd egoism, cherish such thoughts. I am satisfied with the mystery of the eternity of life and with the awareness and a glimpse of the marvelous structure of the existing world, together with the devoted striving to comprehend a portion, be it ever so tiny, of the reason that manifests itself in nature.[5]

We have encountered Gandhi's views on God at several places in this book. It isn't difficult to see the convergence of the views of these two great men on this subject.

Romain Rolland's library in his villa near Geneva displayed fine studies of the heads of his personal heroes – Gandhi, Einstein, Beethoven, Tolstoy, Garki and Tagore. This remarkable resonance between Gandhi and Einstein was highlighted by Rolland, who corresponded with both extensively. In his preface to the European edition of Gandhi's autobiography (1931), Rolland writes:

With the exactness he brings to bear on every task, Gandhi entitles this work: *A Story of My Experiments with Truth*. The word Experiment must be underlined, and one could as well say 'On' as 'With' Truth, for Truth is seen here as a cosmic element on which experiments can be carried out, just as Albert Einstein is carrying out experiments on light in the Michelson Laboratories in California. The whole book, Gandhi's whole life, is a logical chain of experiments based on facts; and this chain which, ever since his earliest childish awareness, has never ceased to grow – patiently but unceasingly, from one link to the next, broadening the thread to embrace three hundred million Indians, and soon the whole world. And it is not yet complete. He says so frankly: 'My conclusions appear to me to be absolutely correct. But far be it for me to claim any degree of perfection for these experiments. I claim for them nothing more than does a scientist who, though he conducts his experiments with the utmost accuracy, forethought and minuteness, never claims any finality about his conclusions, but keeps an open mind regarding them'.

In her luminous essay on Einstein's fascination for the Mahatma, Sarojini Henry, a Chennai-based mathematician and theological researcher, writes that a common feature in the two great men was the courage to stand alone. 'If Einstein had the courage to think about the universe in revolutionary ways, Gandhi developed the courage to act in the field of politics in a way that was completely unprecedented. If Einstein altered the way we understand the universe, Gandhi altered the course of political history, by starting the process of dismantling the structure of colonialism in the Asian context. And both had the courage in following their own truth, even to the point of ridicule or rejection. If Einstein revolutionised theoretical physics by his profound intellectual brilliance, Gandhi radicalised politics through the purity of his moral force. Whereas a bold search into the secrets of the universe was the hallmark of Einstein, a daring venture into the dubious field of politics armed with simple ethical principles was the distinctive feature of Gandhi'.

In Einstein's life, and also in the history of modern science, 1905 is regarded as *annus mirabilis* (miraculous year). It was when he published four important scientific papers in a single year, including the one on Special Theory of Relativity, which fundamentally changed physics for the rest of the century.

In Gandhi's life, there were several 'miraculous years', but if one has to be singled out for having not only decisively influenced his own life but also left an imprint on the thought process of the twentieth century and beyond, it was 1906 – the year when he launched the satyagraha movement. Einstein's Special Theory of Relativity, and his subsequent General Theory of Relativity, became the basis of an intensified effort in the global scientific community for creating what is grandly termed as a Unified Theory of Everything in Physical Sciences. Similarly, Gandhi's satyagraha, which encapsulates his philosophy and praxis of Truth and Nonviolence, has provoked, on an even larger scale, an effort to understand and reshape life in its integrality, both on the individual and global planes. No doubt, Einstein has made an important contribution in the latter endeavour, too, and that is what further enhances his greatness.

There is a tale about there being more than a close chronological proximity between the two 'miraculous years' – 1905 and 1906, one representing a landmark breakthrough in physical science and the other a similar breakthrough in socio-spiritual science. Let us hear it from B.R. Nanda, a great Gandhian scholar:

> Soon after the bombing of Hiroshima and Nagasaki in 1945, when Jawaharlal Nehru went to see him, Gandhi closely questioned him about the atom bomb; its manufacture, its capacity to kill and poison, its toll of Japanese cities. Gandhi listened to Nehru silently, and then (in Nehru's words) 'with deep human compassion loading his gentle eyes', remarked that this wanton

destruction had confirmed his faith in God and nonviolence, and that 'now he [Gandhi] realised the full significance of the holy mission for which God had created him and armed him with the mantra of nonviolence'. Nehru recalled later that, as Gandhi uttered these words, he had a 'look of revelation about his eyes', and that he resolved then and there to make it his mission to fight and outlaw the bomb.

What Nanda writes next brings Einstein into this tale:

Gandhi was not destined to launch a crusade against nuclear warfare. He was assassinated in January 1948. In the following year, when Nehru visited the United States he related his conversation with Einstein. With a twinkle in his eyes, Einstein took a pad and pencil, and wrote down a number of dates on one side, and events on the other, to show the parallel evolution of the nuclear bomb and Gandhi's satyagraha respectively – almost from decade to decade – since the beginning of the twentieth century. It turned out that, by a strange coincidence, while Einstein and his fellow scientists were engaged in researches which made the fission of the atom possible, Gandhi was embarking on his experiments in peaceful nonviolent satyagraha in South Africa; indeed, the Quit India Struggle almost coincided with the American project for the manufacture of the atom bomb.

The moral of this story is that Einstein recognised the authenticity and power of Gandhi's 'science of nonviolence', believing it to be a more salient advancement in human thought than the progress in the knowledge of physical sciences. In every era in history, some, though not all, of the applications of scientific knowledge have been for violent purposes, this phenomenon having reached its apogee in the twentieth century. In contrast, Gandhi's 'science of nonviolence', which he himself proclaimed has a longer antiquity than the 'science of violence', yields to applications that are always helpful and never hurtful, to humanity. Indeed, to the extent that the 'science of nonviolence' – which is but another phrase for truth, justice, love and cooperation – becomes the guiding principle of humanity at the international, national and local levels, it will also ensure progressive marginalisation of the 'science of violence'.

Our purpose in bringing Einstein into this book is not merely to show what the Mahatma meant to the greatest scientist in the modern era. Rather, it is also to show what the Mahatma means to the future of science and human thought. Einstein once said: 'The significant problems we face cannot be solved at the same level of thinking we were at when we created them.'[6] He also lamented that 'the unleashed power of the atom has changed everything save our modes of thinking, and thus we drift toward unparalleled catastrophe.'[7] Gandhi radically changed the 'level' and 'mode' of thinking in modern times – to use Einstein's simple but profound expressions – by reviving and putting into practice the age-old ideals of Truth and Nonviolence. Precisely for this reason, his philosophy and practice illumine the path to our troubled and struggling world as it gropes for ways to overcome the gigantic problems created by the old mindset.

Truly, Gandhi remains a Lighthouse of Hope, now and forever. In Einstein's words, he is 'a beacon to the generations to come'.

Epilogue

IT'S TIME WE BECAME
INTERNET SATYAGRAHIS

WILL DURANT (1885–1981) WAS ONE OF THE WORLD'S GREATEST historians of philosophy, best known for his eleven-volume *The Story of Civilisation*. In 1930, he wrote a remarkable book titled *The Case for India*[1]. Describing the Indian civilisation as the greatest known to man, he turned the searchlight on Gandhi, and created a peerless pen-portrait of the leader of India's freedom movement:

> Picture the ugliest, slightest, weakest man in Asia, with face and flesh of bronze, close cropped gray head, high cheek bones, kindly little brown eyes, a large and almost toothless mouth, larger ears, an enormous nose, thin arms and legs, clad in a loin-cloth, standing before an English judge in India, on trial because he has preached liberty to his countrymen. Picture him again similarly dressed, at the Viceroy's palace in Delhi, in conference on equal terms with the highest representative of England. Or picture him seated on a small carpet in a bare room at his *Satyagrahashram*, or School of Truth-Seekers, at Ahmedabad; his bony legs crossed under him in Yogi fashion, soles upward, his hands busy at a spinning-wheel, his face lined with the sufferings of his people, his mind active with ready answers to every questioner of freedom. This naked weaver

is both the spiritual and the political leader of 320,000,000 Hindus; when he appears in public, crowds gather round him to touch his clothing or to kiss his feet; not since Buddha had India so reverenced any man. He is in all probability the most important, and beyond all doubt the most interesting, figure in the world today. Centuries hence he will be remembered when of his contemporaries hardly a name will survive.

Durant ends the portrait with this observation:

Perhaps Gandhi will fail, as saints are likely to fail in this very Darwinian world. But how could we accept life if it did not, now and then, fling into the face of our successes some failure like this?

But can India, and the rest of the world, afford to see Gandhi consigned to history as a failure? More than him being proved a failure, won't it also mean the failure of India and the world to tread the path of truth and nonviolence? Complete or even substantial success in this endeavour will surely take numberless generations. Nevertheless, since the reward of all worthy human efforts, carried out with sincerity and unselfishness, lies in the effort itself, shouldn't we all keep on trying as best we can?

In the Introduction to this book, I have written: 'This is not the work of idle academic curiosity about an iconic figure of yesteryears. It is a call to action and service, based on my reflections about what Gandhi means to India and the world, today and tomorrow.' I have made an earnest attempt to make this book, in howsoever tiny a measure, an aid to the glocal movements of social, political, cultural, scientific and spiritual activists striving to create a better world. Its action-oriented appeal can be summed up thus: LET US BECOME INTERNET SATYAGRAHIS.

Naturally, this appeal is placed before those activists and readers who are already influenced, to whatever degree, by the life and philosophy of Mahatma Gandhi. It is anchored in the central theme of this book:

now that the practical or economic significance of the spinning wheel has become non-existent in the post-Gandhian era, the Internet has emerged as the tool that potentially embodies the spirit of khadi and the charkha. The underlying message of khadi and the spinning wheel has by no means become outdated. It never will, because it is the universal and eternal message of truth and nonviolence, as enfolded in the Gandhian concept of satyagraha.

Contrary to popular perception, satyagraha is not merely a specific mode of protest against injustice in the external environment. For Gandhi, it was much more than that. It was a means of internal self-improvement and self-cultivation attempted daily – self here understood both as the individual self and organisational self – so that whenever the need arises for collective action for any external cause, it can be carried out with the *right* mindset, with the *right* means and for the *right* ends.

As is well known to students of Gandhi, and as has been reiterated in this book, political freedom for India from colonial rule was not the only end for which he used the 'weapon' of satyagraha. Had he done so, Gandhi would not have become a Mahatma and his weapon would have rusted long ago. If satyagraha has retained its undiminished relevance today, it is because the end that the Mahatma had in mind, and which he served with the single-minded devotion of a Servant of God, was the birth of a new global civilisation through the total transformation of human consciousness and human conduct, both in the individual and institutional spaces. This book has argued that the Internet has created, more than any other tool in the history of humankind, an opportunity to work for the realisation of this ideal. We are indeed fortunate to have been born in an age that has given us this big opportunity. It is therefore an ideal that all of us who use the Internet can serve, in our own decidedly modest ways, if we heed the call of satyagraha.

However, this appeal to become Internet satyagrahis is also placed before the far larger community of netizens who are not social or political activists in the traditional sense of the term, but whose experience on the Internet has itself awakened an inner urge in them to 'do something to make a difference' in the world they live in. More and more people in India and elsewhere in the world are now spending more and more time surfing, communicating, learning or working on the Net. Their Internet experience generally evolves in three stages.[2] In the beginning, most Net surfers are curious about everything, there being so much to surf anyway. Curiosity, aided by anonymity, produces a certain kind of thrill that is initially irresistible. People acquire a lot of information, and even understandings, about a wide variety of subjects. However, this stage of the Net experience can also produce boredom and a sense of dissatisfaction. It is in the nature of human beings to seek self-growth, based on a desire to do something worthwhile in life. This desire is also whetted by encountering, both offline and online, positive examples of change-agents in society.

Thus, as the Internet experience of such people develops to the next stage, they begin to distinguish the trivial from the important. They consciously choose to rise to higher levels of commitment and purpose. Now, the Internet itself serves as a highly helpful resource for goal-setting and for becoming active in the public sphere, depending on the individual's interests, area of work and life experience. It is such committed netizens who are today driving tens of thousands of vibrant special-interest communities, websites and discussion groups on the Net. They are engaged in countless highly meaningful activities both in the virtual and real worlds – creating content to enrich the quality of education in schools and colleges; spreading awareness about, and promoting best practices in, environment protection and heritage conservation; trying to educate people about disease-control and healthy living; fighting battles against corruption and abuse of human rights; using the Net to conduct social, political and spiritual campaigns of various kinds; pushing forward the frontiers of knowledge and innovation through a ceaseless pursuit of truth and excellence; and so on.

Sustained activity at this second stage of the Internet experience, if it is accompanied by a willingness to evaluate one's own experience and learn from others', can lead to the third and the higher stage. Here individuals begin to demonstrate unconditional commitment to truth and justice; infinite patience and perseverance; readiness to make personal sacrifices; ability to inspire, mobilise, organise and lead others to pursue lofty goals; and determination to achieve specific objectives in their chosen cause. They, too, then become Internet satyagrahis.

Here, then, are some fifteen ways in which we all can become Internet satyagrahis.

1. BE THE CHANGE: We should use the Internet for promoting, through self-example, the Gandhian ethos of true change – 'Be the change you wish to see in the world'. All of us want to see positive change in the world we live in. We want the people we interact with to be kind, considerate, helpful, truthful and honest towards us. We want the institutions we deal with to be efficient, fair, service-oriented and non-corrupt. We want our environs to be clean and beautiful. Acts of violence and bloodshed, in our own vicinity or in far away places, fill us with anguish and concern. We, therefore, want the world to be safe and secure for ourselves and for our near and dear ones. We would like society and the state to protect our freedom, dignity and fundamental human rights. All these expectations for change are legitimate. However, do we have any right to expect the desirable change in our surroundings if we do not internalise that change in ourselves? If we, each one of us, do not contribute our fullest to that change?

Mankind's modern history has seen many economic theories and political ideologies that promised desirable change in society. But the change they pursued was largely external to the individual. They did not stress internal change in individuals, which can be effected only if people perform their own duties and social responsibilities ethically. On the other hand, many ancient as well as modern spiritual philosophies highlighted the importance of individuals' ethical conduct, but the emphasis was often limited to the latter's personal and family lives. It did not extend to the professional, institutional, social and political domains.

A distinctive strength of Gandhian praxis – theory that is practised or philosophy that is lived – is that it emphasises the need for change both in the microcosm (individual) and in the macrocosm (society), with primacy laid on the former. It affirms the centrality of the individual in society. If each individual follows his or her own personal motto of principled conduct, based on such principles as one believe in, they will have made their own unique contribution to the wealth of *lived* principles in the world. Then, irrespective of whether the entire society fully manifests the desirable change or not, the individual concerned will have given a satisfactory account to one's own conscience – hence, also to one's Maker.

This does not mean that Gandhi ignored or belittled change on a societal scale. After all, he led the world's largest nonviolent mass movement with multi-valent objectives, India's freedom from colonial rule being only one of them. However, by affirming that 'character alone will have real effect on the masses'[3], Gandhi draws our attention to a very important, and well-recorded, experience of social movements in all the eras of history. Only those movements have had an enduring impact on society, and on future generations, whose leaders and followers were persons of integrity and cultivated exemplary qualities.

Thus, by underscoring that all meaningful transformation in society must begin with oneself, and that each type of transformation must be carried out in the light of satyagraha – clinging to Truth – Gandhi has given us a mantra of change that encompasses both societal progress and individual's growth. Such change is far more robust, reliable and enduring than the one brought about either by theories and ideologies that focus solely on social transformation or by spiritual traditions that are largely concerned with man's inner transformation.

The Internet is a big helper in popularising, as well as practising, Gandhi's mantra of individual-centric social change. It is never easy to follow this mantra consistently and in all situations. The obstacles we encounter, including our own internal weaknesses, are many. But if we have the inclination, the Internet offers countless inspirational resources to seek guidance from.

2. CONSUME LESS, PURSUE PROSPERITY OF THE TRUE KIND:
We should use the Internet for service and sacrifice, and not for
indulgence and acquisitiveness. As Gandhi wrote in his autobiography,
'All other pleasures and possessions pale into nothingness before
service, which is rendered in a spirit of joy'. As per the commandment
of the *Isha Upanishad*, which he invoked frequently, wealth generated
through ethical means should be widely shared. This will strengthen
the ethos of genuine philanthropy.

Internet satyagrahis should be the last in enjoying the material fruits
of the prosperity created by new technologies. And they should be the
first in presenting, through personal example, new – rather, old but
forgotten – definitions of prosperity that enrich life culturally, aesthetically
and spiritually. Without berating the globally spreading aspirations for
'wealth' and 'good life', they should persuade people to remember that
true wealth is *samriddhi* (material, cultural and spiritual prosperity for
all) and truly good life is *sadachari jeevan* (honest and ethical living).
Today's consumerist culture has perverted the understanding of good
life by associating it with a life of overconsumption of luxuries, which
brings no happiness even to the super-rich, who alone, mostly, can
afford them. It has also restricted the meaning of wealth to material
possessions whose acquisition, without a moderating mental attitude,
can only lead to misery and disruption in human relations.

The good and prosperous life that Gandhi, and all the other
great saints of the world, envisaged is a life free of deprivation of the
basic human needs and full of uplifting human values. This alone is
the real guarantor of happiness and progress. And this is the ideal
that Internet satyagrahis should strive to place at the centre of all
development endeavours in the twenty-first century.

3. MAKE NONVIOLENCE A GLOCAL FAMILY VALUE: We should use
the Internet for spreading the culture of nonviolence, understood in
its broadest sense of ahimsa in feelings, thought, speech and conduct.
The atmosphere of aggression, hostility and dogmatism that we so

often see all around us should be sought to be changed through love. Of course, we encounter a peculiar but familiar contradiction here. 'Love' is a word that is most widely used in popular culture but least understood in its broadest and truest sense. Love is discovery of the essential unity of the human race and, indeed, of everything in the universe. It begins with attraction, affection, care, concern and respect for one's near and dear ones in one's immediate circle. But true love extends to everyone in the world and to everything in the universe – what Gandhi describes as the Oceanic Circle of relationships. Love and nonviolence are synonyms, the latter being the practical manifestation of the former.

Specifically, we must endeavour to make nonviolence the credo of not only individuals but, as Gandhi insisted, also of communities and nations. More than at any time in the past, and more than through any other technological tool in history, we have been knit together into ONE GLOBAL FAMILY in the age of the Internet. Indeed, the very word 'netizen' connotes global citizenship. Civilised members of a family never commit any act of violence to harm other members, least of all towards those who are vulnerable and need others' care. Nonviolence is thus already accepted as a family value. By extension, it should also now become a 'Global, rather, Glocal Family Value'.

In this context, male members of our immediate families as well as the Glocal Family should pay special attention to Gandhi's ringing affirmation: 'If nonviolence is the law of our being, the future is with woman'. Love, care and nurturing come naturally to women. Therefore, women's all-round empowerment must be high on the agenda of Internet satyagrahis.

4. NUCLEAR DISARMAMENT, NOW!: We should use the Internet for making the ongoing global movement for nuclear disarmament powerful enough to achieve total and irreversible elimination of nuclear weapons and all other weapons of mass destruction within the next decade or two. This is entirely achievable. Indeed, this may be regarded as a 'low-hanging fruit' for the Internet satyagrahis' movement for world peace. Further, we should use the Internet for strengthening the call for a drastic reduction in the military spending of nations, especially nations with huge military budgets. The resources so saved should be deployed for eradicating poverty, improving the quality of life, and for launching a massive campaign for ecological restoration all over the world through a cooperative global effort.

The notion, hitherto widely held, that major breakthroughs happen when science is wedded to military applications should be given a deep burial. We must believe in, and prove with our practical work, Gandhi's affirmation that there are 'undreamt of and seemingly impossible discoveries' waiting to be made in the field of nonviolence and sustainable development. This will require us to end the dangerous split between reason and faith, and to enthrone a new paradigm of knowledge-seeking that harmoniously combines science and spirituality. God, understood in the Gandhian – that is, non-sectarian – sense of Truth, will have to be accepted and re-enshrined as the source of all knowledge.

5. EDUCATION, EDUCATION, MORE EDUCATION: We should use the Internet for demanding, and achieving, a change in the purposes, priorities and uses of education and research. The principal purpose of education, in the way Gandhi understood it and in the way all great educationists have described it, is the teacher-guided and self-guided development of all the innate faculties, character and the natural personality of a person. A truly well-educated person is one who has gained both knowledge and values. They use their knowledge, talent and skills in service of society through various vocations. In so doing, they achieve self-growth and derive self-fulfilment, and also contribute to the society's wellbeing and progress.

Unfortunately, much of what goes by the name of education in our times is being determined largely by commercial considerations. This is evident in the way educational institutions are run, in the way students and parents look at the purpose of education, and also, unfortunately, in the way governments shape educational policies. This is not only stunting the growth of individual students and of society, but has also distorted the processes of knowledge-seeking, knowledge creation, knowledge integration and knowledge application.

As explained elsewhere in the book (*see Chapter 26*), the heartening thing about the Internet is that it is breaking down many barriers to true education. It is providing powerful and hitherto unimaginable tools and opportunities for seeking knowledge and also for creating new knowledge. As a result, children and youth around the world are becoming smarter and more capable. At the same time, we must realise that much more than the revolutionary tools of the Internet are needed to build the character of students, enrich their value systems, strengthen their social commitment, and raise their global consciousness, free of every kind of prejudice and sectarianism.

This is where Gandhi's educational philosophy and his practical experiments in Basic Education (Nayi Talim) show their enduring and universal relevance. He also emphasised the need for lifelong learning. (*'Live as if* you were to die tomorrow. *Learn as if* you were to live forever.') Of course, many other great educationists in different countries of the world, and belonging to both ancient and modern times, have also provided profound thoughts on education. It is now the duty of Internet satyagrahis to serve the cause of 'Education for All' by deploying the power of digitally enhanced learning in service of enlightened educational philosophies and practices. This alone can holistically meet the needs of the modern age.

6. GLOBAL DEMOCRACY, THROUGH GLOBAL CITIZENSHIP: We should use the Internet for demanding, and securing, big changes in the conduct of nation-states for strengthening friendly, cooperative and peaceful international relations. The ideal of Global Democracy, which the Internet is so spectacularly fostering, must become the overarching guiding principle of international diplomacy and politics. Going forward, we should use the Internet to press all nation-states to formally adopt a new system and structure of global governance, where all of them sign No-War pacts and accept a strengthened peacemaking and conflict-resolution role for a reformed UN. For our efforts to be effective, netizens, in addition to having pride in their respective national citizenships, should consciously develop a new identity of Global Citizenship.

7. DEMAND, AND DELIVER, GOOD GOVERNANCE: We should use the Internet for demanding, and securing, big changes in the way nation-states treat their own citizens so as to ensure that the ideals of democracy, good governance, human rights, and freedom with responsibility sink robust roots in every country. In particular, misuse of state institutions to inflict violence on ordinary citizens must be strongly resisted. The Internet is already being widely used to mobilise people's voices and actions against tyranny, corruption, official callousness and misuse of institutions of power. In recent times, it has also proved itself to be a potent agent of nonviolent political change aimed at expanding citizens' right to demand transparency and accountability in the structures of governance. The Internet offers enormous untapped potential to advance the cause of democracy, both geographically and qualitatively. It is now the task of Internet satyagrahis to evolve innovative and effective ways of tapping this potential.

8. REFORM POLITICS, TAKE RESPONSIBILITY: We should use the Internet for demanding, and achieving, big changes in the way politics is conducted today in most countries in the world. This book did not devote much attention to Mahatma Gandhi's political philosophy and activities, nor to the political issues confronting India and the world today. Nevertheless, it is crystal clear to every serious student of his that unethical, divisive, selfish and short-sighted politics is the greatest obstacle to the advancement of justice, peace, balanced development and people's welfare. Alien rule and dictatorship of various kinds are, of course, foes of freedom and human dignity, and they must be fought. But even democracies have come under the grip of many vested interests that have, to varying degrees, subverted the purpose and meaning of people's rule. Elections, even when they are largely free and fair, mask the progressive disempowerment of the people. This is because, once the people cast their votes, they have very little say either in the affairs of the nation or in the way their elected representatives work.

Far from being constantly revivified by people's active and informed participation, the political space has been monopolised by institutions that are routinely manipulated by moneybags. The governance space has been largely monopolised by bureaucracies, who have very little accountability to the people. Even the judiciary and the law-enforcing agencies have fallen prey to corruption. As far as Gandhi's goal of 'swaraj', as ethically enlightened self-govenance by individuals as well as institutions, is concerned, we are far from achieving it.

Raja kalasya karanam. (The king or the ruler of a state determines the conditions of society in his or her era.) *Yatha raja tatha praja.* (People are what the leaders make them.) These Sanskrit aphorisms tell us a lot about why and how the erosion of morality among our political leaders has weakened the moral fabric of our society as a whole. When common people see those at the top echelons of the political and economic establishment resorting to unscrupulous means to pursue their own narrow ends, they too follow the leaders' example. Thus, a growing section of the population loses sight of the lofty ideals and values that sustain the life of a nation.

Therefore, reform of politics in the true spirit of democracy and the rule of law should be regarded as one of the major responsibilities of Internet satyagrahis. Gandhian literature provides a huge wealth of wisdom on how to de-pollute politics. The irreducible condition for this is reconstruction of politics on ethical or dharmic foundations. 'Human life being an undivided whole, no line could ever be drawn between its different compartments, nor between ethics and politics,' says the Mahatma.[4]

I am aware that the use of the word 'dharma' in the context of a call to reform politics may cause some eyebrows to be raised. I would, therefore, like to emphasise here that 'dharma' is a non-sectarian and non-denominational term, not to be confused with the narrow meaning that 'religion' has acquired in the current socio-political discourse. As explained by Pandit Deendayal Upadhyaya (1916–68), the ideological guide of the Bharatiya Janata Party, to which I belong, 'Dharma is the innate law of human society. It sustains society and the whole world. The fundamental principles of Dharma are eternal and universal. However, their implementation may differ according to time, place and circumstances'. Upadhyaya's philosophical treatise, titled *Integral Humanism,* presents many profoundly inspiring and yet practical thoughts on reforming politics, economics and governance in the Indian context. It echoes Gandhi's own concerns and concepts on many issues, including 'dharma'. I strongly recommend all serious students and practitioners of politics to read *Integral Humanism,* a detailed commentary on which is beyond the scope of this book. Sadly, Upadhyaya's greatness as a political philosopher and leader has not been matched by the scholarly attention he has received either in India or abroad so far.

The other necessary condition for reforming politics is recasting of political agendas by mainstreaming into them constructive activities carried out in the spirit of service. 'Remember,' Gandhi exhorted his followers, 'that no political programme can stand without the constructive programme.'[5] To Gandhi, removal of untouchability, promotion of khadi and rural industries, improving village sanitation, research in nature cure, treating of leprosy patients, etc., were as important as leading India's struggle against the British rule. He also disfavoured giving excessive importance to politics – 'I would dance with joy if I had to give up politics'.[6]

Today, the Internet has given a potent platform to all those who are wedded to ethical and service-oriented politics to express our views individually and collectively, in India and around the world. Beyond expression of views, we can also use the Internet to network, organise, and coordinate our activities far more effectively than before. Most importantly, it is empowering the common people by giving them a voice that can, with proper organisation, be made effectively audible in the insensitive and unresponsive corridors of power. We must bring the enormous weight of democratically mobilised public opinion to bear on our elected representatives, political parties, their leaders, and functionaries in government, so that they conduct themselves as people's servants and not as their masters. The ability of the Internet to enforce transparency and accountability in our political and democratic systems must be harnessed to the utmost. In short, the vision of 'direct democracy' and 'people's power', which seemed difficult to implement in the past, has become realisable due to the Internet.

At the same time, the Internet should be used for reforming the mentality and conduct of citizens, too, so that we learn to discharge our duties and responsibilities conscientiously. Gandhi used to say: 'That government is best which governs the least.' This ideal is possible to be realised only if both institutions and individuals conduct themselves in an enlightened way. This is the ideal that should guide the Internet satyagrahis' endeavours in the domains of politics and governance.

9. GLOCALISATION, FOR GLOCALLY SUSTAINABLE DEVELOPMENT: We should use the Internet for re-orienting and reforming globalisation in order to ensure balanced and sustainable socio-economic development of every country and community in the world. Elimination of mass poverty, hunger, disease and other manifestations of underdevelopment; creation of livelihood opportunities for every family on Earth; and protection of the Earth itself from environmental destruction must become our priorities. We should never forget Gandhi's wise exhortation that man is a trustee to other living species that cohabit this beautiful and bounteous planet.

All this calls for far greater commitment and cooperative effort at all levels – international, multilateral, national and local. Of utmost and urgent importance is the need to reform the prevailing unjust global financial and economic architecture, whose interests are fiendishly at odds with the interests of the majority of the global population.

The Internet is already fostering revolutionary innovations in 'glocal' currencies, 'glocal' manufacturing, 'glocal' service delivery, and 'glocal' R&D, in which mutual trust and ecological sensitivity is having a big and expanding footprint. We therefore have an unprecedented opportunity today to make the Internet a powerful force for reorienting globalisation and accelerating glocalisation as a reliable promoter of Global Good.

10. LET US PROTECT OUR PRICELESS CULTURAL AND ARTISTIC HERITAGE: We should use the Internet for enriching the culture of cooperation and co-creation in every sphere that adds value to human life. The enormous experience that individuals and institutions around the world have already gained by collaborating in education, arts, culture, heritage conservation, scientific research, etc. should be further deepened and broadened by harnessing the power of the Internet. Art and culture are the repositories of all life-saving and life-nurturing values. Though diverse in their manifestations, art and culture never divide people; they unite and ennoble.

History has shown us that war is not the only destroyer of mankind's artistic and cultural heritage. Ignorance, neglect, theft, vandalism and ill-planned urbanisation have also been causing incalculable damage to this tangible and intangible wealth. This, too, is violence and it is directed at our ancestors, who created this heritage, and also at the generations yet to come, who have a right to receive this heritage in inheritance. Internet satyagrahis must campaign for the preservation and conservation of this priceless heritage, with the help of right policies by governments; participation of international, national and local communities; and the amazingly efficacious tools that digital technologies now provide for this purpose.

11. HARMONY IN DIVERSITY: We should use the Internet for promoting inter-faith understanding, amity and harmony, both locally and around the world. As explained in this book *(see Chapter 29)*, future global and domestic conflicts will be less on account of economic factors and more due to ignorance, prejudice and bigotry in religious and ethnic matters. Internet satyagrahis should therefore take the lead in encouraging inter-religious and intra-religious dialogues near and far to promote the ideals of tolerance, mutual respect and learning from one another's life-ennobling traditions. They should also raise their voice of protest against discriminatory practices and entrenched notions of religious superiority and exclusivism. No faith community can demand freedoms and rights that it denies to others. This has become all the more necessary in today's era of global mobility, in which almost every country in our inter-connected world is becoming increasingly multi-religious and multi-cultural.

12. PROMOTE HUMANISING SEXUAL ETHICS: We should use the Internet for evolving new sexual ethics in our societies. These ethics should be based on the values of mutual love, respect, care, sensitivity and responsibility, and also on a deeper understanding of the purpose of sex in human life. There is little doubt that cyber space has profoundly changed people's awareness, attitudes and practice of sex all over the world. It has removed many restraints, imposed by traditional societies and cultures, on visualisation, representation, articulation and experience of human sexuality. Some of the choices provided by these changes are indeed welcome, since not everything in traditional sexual mores, inhibitions and taboos was conducive to the free and joyful development of the human personality. Responsible nurturing of kaama (sensual enjoyment) is essential for human happiness.

However, it is also undeniable that much of what is being promoted in cyber space in the name of advancing sexual freedom is hurtful to the health and happiness of human beings. One of the most harmful phenomena on the Internet is the uncontrolled proliferation of pornography, propelled by crass commercial considerations. It causes the haemorrhage of human beings' psychic energies. It violates human dignity, especially the dignity of women, whose exploitation has reached unprecedented levels due to the worldwide cyber sex industry.

Therefore, in the Internet satyagrahis' attempts to evolve new sexual ethics, a major challenge they must address is how to tackle the menace of pornography and human trafficking. Since these ills feed to a large extent on the ongoing destabilisation of traditional societies and cultures, achieving a new and humane social stability is, of course, a necessity. But this will take a long time. Stricter laws and their proper enforcement are also no doubt needed. But far more important is the need to reform the personal conduct of individuals, beginning with Internet satyagrahis' self-example.

In this endeavour, creating awareness about the broader meaning of brahmacharya – purity of emotions, thoughts and action in all walks of life, combined with moderation and responsibility in sexual conduct – would prove highly useful. Needless to add, people are bound to have diverse opinions on Gandhi's brahmacharya experiments and, specifically, his veto against sex for non-reproductive purposes. This diversity of viewpoints must be respected. I myself do not agree with Gandhi's uncompromising objection to non-procreative sex, even within the relationship of marriage. However, barring this sole point of disagreement, I believe that Gandhi's brahmacharya, which was an inseparable part of his experiments in Truth and Nonviolence, is an absolutely mind-expanding philosophy whose vigilant practice can lead to amazing empowerment of the practitioner. As explained in Chapter 24, it revealed to me an altogether new and mesmerising dimension of his mahatmahood.

13. LET A MILLION THOUGHT-FLOWERS BLOOM: We should use the Internet for creating awareness about the fantabulous possibilities and promises that are taking shape in the womb of digital technologies.

Genomics, Nanotechnology, Robotics and new researches in human psychology and consciousness have the potential to transform human life far more radically than information and communication technologies have done so far. These new technologies will hugely benefit humanity, as is rather briefly described in this book. However, their misuse due to ignorance or malevolent intentions can also bring enormous harm to the human race. This book has argued that our ability to maximise the benefits of science and technology and to eliminate their likely negative consequences depends on our awareness that all knowledge – indeed, all life – has a divine origin and purpose. As affirmed by Gandhi, 'If mankind is to live, it has to come growingly under the sway of Truth and Nonviolence'. He called it a 'God's commandment'.

Not all netizens believe in God. Also, those who do believe in God have diverse understandings of what God means to them. Gandhi respected this plurality in people's belief systems and also their disbelief in God. However, he stated that none can disbelieve in Truth. Moreover, he also affirmed the validity of multiple ways of pursuing Truth. 'If we draw a circle round the goal to be reached,' he wrote, 'we shall find many ways leading to the goal, from which each one may choose according to one's needs'.[7] In other words, there are as many convergent paths to reaching a common goal as there are radii in a circle. This pluralistic concept of Truth removes the scope for sectarianism, and creates a platform for cooperation, in religion, science and also in socio-political endeavours.

Internet satyagrahis should follow this enlightened approach. Let a million different thought-flowers bloom in our collective and cooperative endeavour to build a better world.

14. NEVER LOSE FAITH IN THE IDEA OF A BETTER WORLD: We should use the Internet for strengthening our own self-belief in our ability to build a better world. We are not passive, powerless and helpless users of this most powerful technology ever invented in the history of humankind. The power of the Internet is the power that each one of us imparts to it through our intellectual and emotional participation. Therefore, we possess the capability, individually and collectively, to empower ourselves and further empower this universal machine, the spectacular Species Machine of *Homo sapiens*. We can bring about constant improvements and innovations in the way its infrastructure is developed, in the way it is regulated and, above all, in the purposes for which it is used.

Here too we have something to learn from the Mahatma. I was astounded when I read about Gandhi's innovative and participative concept of improving the charkha. Writing in *Young India* on 27 May 1926, he said: 'All the improvements that have been made in the mechanism of the spinning wheel and the speed of the spinning wheel up till now are solely due to the efforts of those devoted workers *who spin for sacrifice.*' *(Emphasis added)*

Note the words: '...*who spin for sacrifice*'.

Very few of those devoted spinners were scientists in the formal sense of the term. Yet, they ceaselessly strove to improve their technological tool to advance the larger purpose which had attracted them to Gandhi's ashrams and constructive activities. They did so because they were, in the words of their guide and leader, 'satyagrahi scientists'. Similarly, we too have a responsibility to introduce continual improvements in the way the Internet is being used today, so that it fulfills the lofty purpose for which it was born, the purpose of making the world a better place for us and for our future generations.

Is the ideal of a better world impossible to achieve? No. Let us again derive inspiration from the Mahatma, who, in an appreciative and optimistic comment about the advancements in science in his time, said: 'We are daily witnessing the phenomenon of the impossible of yesterday becoming the possible of today.'[8]

For proof of this phenomenon, just look at the birth and evolution of the Internet itself!

15. 'MAN HAS BEEN LESS THAN HUMAN, HE CAN BE MORE THAN HUMAN': Lastly, we should use the Internet for ascending at least a few of the steps that take us to the higher possibilities of human evolution. Recall the words of Aurobindo in the previous pages: 'Man has been less than human' today, but 'he can be more than human' tomorrow. What does 'being more than human' mean? What did Gandhi mean when he said that the goal of human evolution is to transform 'Man the Brute' into 'Man the God'? This inquiry takes us to the most fundamental questions about the origin and destiny of the human race. We are decidedly many millennia away from realising the full potential of the human mind and human life. Nevertheless, we should be grateful to the Internet for making it possible for us to read about the lives and thoughts of many extraordinary human beings in the past who became a good deal 'more than human' – who became Mahatmas (great souls).

For me, the Internet was enormously helpful in understanding Mahatma Gandhi's true *mahanata* (greatness). Indeed, as the principal theme of this book seeks to explain, it is the Internet itself that led me to see it as the latter-day avatar of the Mahatma's spinning wheel. Gandhi used his charkha for his karma yoga, the pathway to Godward human evolution through pure-hearted and service-oriented action. We cannot rise to Gandhi's greatness, for sure. But we can certainly use the Internet, the charkha's incarnation in our age, to spin some threads of service to humanity as a prayerful offering to our Creator.

This book is one such humble thread.

ANNEXURE I

'Mahatma Gandhi is a Prophet for the Age of the Communication Revolution'

Author's Interview with Ray Kurzweil

Courtesy: Chandradeep Kumar, India Today

R AY KURZWEIL IS ONE OF THE WORLD'S LEADING INVENTORS AND futurists in the area of digital technologies and their impact on society. He is also the author of several bestselling books, among them *The Age of Intelligent Machines* (1990), *The Age of Spiritual Machines* (1998) and *The Singularity is Near: When Humans Transcend Biology* (2005).

Singularity connotes that point in the rapid evolution of information technology when machine intelligence becomes trillions of times more powerful than unaided human intelligence, leading to the merger of our bodies and brains with our machines. What follows this event is a human-machine civilisation, whose beginning Kurzweil foresees in 2045. According to him, some of the practical effects of the acceleration of the genetics-nanotechnology-robotics (GNR) revolution are – human aging will be reversed; pollution of the environment can be effectively tackled; hunger will be eliminated from the world; and many of the limitations of biology can be overcome.

Kurzweil was a speaker at the India Today Conclave in New Delhi on 17 March 2012. I interviewed him on the sidelines of the conclave. This interview, in which he spoke for the first time about Mahatma Gandhi's influence on him, is being published here with his permission. It also appeared on the website of 'Kurzweil: Accelerating Intelligence' (www.kurzweilai.net). I sincerely thank M.J. Akbar, editorial director of *India Today*, Kaveree Bamzai, the magazine's editor, and Damayanti Datta, its deputy editor, for facilitating this interview.

Sudheendra Kulkarni: *It's an honour for me to be talking to you, Dr Kurzweil. Reading your books was a mind-expanding experience for me.*

Contrary to popular belief, Mahatma Gandhi was not opposed to science and technology. My study tells me that he had deep faith in the power of science and machines. Indeed, he held that the greatest machine ever created is the human body itself. But machine for what purpose? That is the central question he sought to answer. He was opposed to the exploitative ends to which machines were put during the Industrial Revolution. He questioned their role in the colonisation of India and other nations and in the exploitation and pauperisation of their peoples. But he was not opposed to machines per se. Now the era of the Industrial Revolution is behind us, and machine itself has undergone a fundamental change with the advent of information technology. I want to begin by trying to know your views on Mahatma Gandhi.

Ray Kurzweil: I think Mahatma Gandhi's movement is a very good early example of the power of people coming together, sharing an idea to change an oppressive reality, and achieving that purpose nonviolently. He did not have the benefit of electronic communication. His idea travelled mostly by word of mouth. But he was able to set an inspiring example. Under his leadership, people came together and showed the tremendous power of peaceful collective action. We see that happening now on a much faster scale through social networks. There are several examples in the

United States of people mobilising themselves in peaceful protest action through social networks and being able to change government decisions and laws fairly quickly, sometimes within a few days.

We've seen that happen also in the form of the Arab Spring. Of course, that story is not over yet. History never moves in a straight line. We don't know how things will finally turn out. However, we've seen how modern communication technologies have helped people overthrow some very bad dictators.

I had predicted thirty years ago that the Soviet Union would collapse on account of the power of collective action by people communicating to each other through telephone and fax machine. The old method of the communist authorities retaining complete control over newspapers and TV stations didn't work anymore.

I think Mahatma Gandhi's movement was a great example of people inspired by a noble idea organising themselves and bringing about change. He fought for social justice through constructive collective action. And that example continues to inspire the world even today. Indeed, it can be more effective today, since the world now has the tools of technology that can carry the idea far more quickly and effectively. The Internet has demonstrated the power to organise the voices of the oppressed peoples in nonviolent but effective ways. Mahatma Gandhi had done the same in his time. To me, he is a prophet for the age of the communication revolution. That is why, more people around the world are today trying to know about his life and his philosophy through the Internet than ever before.

Kulkarni: *The story of Gandhi's satyagraha movement belongs to the past. But do you think that it will be relevant in the future?*

Kurzweil: It has tremendous relevance today and tomorrow. Especially the power of peaceful collective action for bringing about a positive change. Because if you start organising yourselves violently, then it's very hard to understand the moral authority of either side. The Civil Rights Movement in the United States led by Martin Luther King, in which I participated, was directly inspired by Mahatma Gandhi. Martin Luther King made frequent references to Gandhi. So it's an example that is repeated over and over again. I cannot think of another example in human history in which ordinary people organised themselves peacefully and brought about great change.

Kulkarni: *When did you first get introduced to the name and philosophy of Mahatma Gandhi?*

Kurzweil: Gandhi is a great icon in the United States. I had read about him as a child in children's books. I continued to read about him in high school and college. He was always an inspiring figure to me because he embodied the philosophy of selfless service and nonviolent struggle to overcome oppression. I was very active in the Civil Rights Movement in the United States in the 1960s. I participated in the Civil Rights marches in the South and in Washington DC. Mahatma Gandhi was definitely a hero of that movement.

Kulkarni: *That inspiration that you as a young man felt was for a particular cause and for a particular movement. But now you are a renowned inventor and a thought leader for the digital age. Does Mahatma Gandhi continue to inspire you?*

Kurzweil: The reason I respect him even more today is that, like him, I like the experience of solving people's problems. What's exciting about coming up with technological invention is that it can overcome some limitation or suffering of human beings. The most satisfying research project that I have stayed involved in for the past thirty-five years is a reading machine for the blind. Mahatma Gandhi followed the same path. He saw suffering and he put his mind to overcoming it. This shows the ability of the human thought to overcome suffering if you are passionate about your goal. And even though Gandhi was not a technology inventor, he demonstrated that human suffering can be overcome through the devoted application of human thought.

Kulkarni: *Do you think that information technology, the way it is evolving now, will be a force to serve the cause of peace and nonviolence in the world? Gandhi had prophesied the coming of 'undreamt of scientific discoveries in non-violence'. Is information technology likely to fulfill that prophecy?*

Kurzweil: I think it does that. People talk about the wisdom of the crowd in the age of the Internet. Wisdom of the collective is always greater than the wisdom of any of the individuals. And electronic communication does harness the wisdom of the crowd. Let's say, a set of people in a country or in different parts of the world have a particular disease. They all will get insights about what to do, and they will share these insights in the group electronically. And this knowledge will be far greater than any individual or any doctor can possibly have.

On the opposite end of the spectrum, we also see the 'wisdom' of the lynch mobs. In the United States, bullying over the Internet has become a big issue. So technology can always be used for both good and bad purposes. But the chances of it being used for peace and human good are far greater.

Kulkarni: *You have argued in your books that the distinction between technology and biology will begin to blur in the decades ahead. As information technology becomes integral to our being, including our bodies, do you think that human beings will begin to be driven more and more by what is good for them – good for themselves as individuals and also good for the human race and the planet as a whole?*

Kurzweil: I believe that that's true. Technology is becoming more and more like biology. It's inspired by biology. We are beginning to learn about the limitations of human thought. What leads us to be prejudiced, for example. And these technologies – social networks etc, and the dialogue and lobbying that they facilitate – help in overcoming ignorance and prejudices.

See how information and communication technologies are making our world more democratic. Even on the level of politics, if we look back to the middle of the last century, there were very few democracies in the world. Today most countries are democracies, even though they may not be perfect. Information and communication technologies are also democratising human interactions in other ways. For example, the interaction between students and teachers. Students now have access to knowledge from many other sources, and are not dependent on teachers alone. The same is true about the interaction between patients and doctors. If a patient has a chronic disease, and if she is networked with the community having the same disease, then she knows all about it. Similarly, political activists who are part of a social network can come together, raise funds in just three minutes, and solve a problem by taking decisions collaboratively. Now groups of networked people can solve problems in ways that individuals could not do earlier, and this is being demonstrated in more and more areas.

Kulkarni: *There is another way in which the future possibilities in information technology are going to actualise Mahatma Gandhi's ideals. Take 3-D printing, for example. It is likely to completely change the current paradigm of manufacturing.*

No more physical transportation of manufactured goods. This is going to make decentralisation of manufacturing possible. And decentralisation was one of the cornerstones of Mahatma Gandhi's economic philosophy.

Kurzweil: You are right. Decentralisation is also the cornerstone of the future of technology. 3-Dimensional printing is going to decentralise manufacturing. Indeed, we are coming closer to a point when we can make all the parts of a 3-D printer using 3-D printing technology! And 3-D printers are going to become more and more inexpensive. So people will have the ability to print – that is, manufacture on their own – almost all that they need. High-quality clothing, the materials they need to build their homes, and all these at very low costs. So technology will not only decentralise manufacturing, but it will also democratise the economy.

Kulkarni: *Yes. That too was one of Gandhi's ideals. I think that 3-D printing will also lead to elimination of waste.*

Kurzweil: That's true. It will also lead to more personalisation. You can design your clothes exactly the way you want. You can design your home the way you want.

I think technologies such as 3-D printing will also help us overcome poverty. We have plenty of resources on our planet, but we are not using them efficiently. Centralised manufacturing makes very inefficient use of resources. It forces us to make large quantities of the same thing at one place, and transport them to places of consumption. But people are different, and they need different things. So, in future, they can make things that they want, the way that they want them, at the time when they want them, and in quantities in which they need. And when they don't need a thing anymore, they can simply recycle it and make something else that they need.

Kulkarni: *So personal choice will be built into the new decentralised economy.*

Kurzweil: Exactly.

Kulkarni: *Every tool or technology – be it a stick or a mobile phone – extends human capabilities. I have argued in my book that, whereas the tools or machines in the past were external to man, the tools and technologies in the digital era are becoming internal and integral to our beings. Hence, these hold the promise of extending and augmenting human capabilities in unimaginable ways.*

Kurzweil: That's right. But this distinction between external and internal is not very material. The mobile phone that I carry in my hand may seem external to me, but it is now an integral part of how I work and how I live my life. Of course, computers are getting smaller and smaller, and sometime in the future they will get implanted in our bodies and brains. It's already happening. There are different neural implants. People with Parkinson's disease can have a computer put inside their bodies and connected into their brains. For the deaf, there are computerised hearing devices. Artificial pancreas is being experimented with. And so is the artificial heart. Research is happening on artificially augmenting the capabilities of almost every organ of the body. Putting computerised devices in our bodies and brains will become quite common in a couple of decades.

Kulkarni: *Your book* The Singularity is Near *argues that well before the end of this century, machine intelligence will exceed human intelligence. But it seems to me that it's important to understand what intelligence truly means. The capability that is built into computers is one kind of intelligence. It can be called computational intelligence with a certain degree of analytical and cognitive capability. However, humans are also blessed with emotional intelligence, cultural intelligence, aesthetic intelligence and spiritual intelligence. A more commonplace way of highlighting this difference is by recognising the difference between information, knowledge, wisdom and spiritual enlightenment. What are your thoughts on this?*

Kurzweil: I regard human evolution as a spiritual process. Man's biological evolution is now being accelerated and augmented by technological evolution. After 'Singularity' is reached, the distinction between the two will disappear. Both will together expand human consciousness, which I believe has a sacred quality. Consciousness is the ultimate repository of all moral and spiritual values, such as tolerance, compassion and love. Evolution of consciousness means that man will become God-like, although humans can never become God.

Kulkarni: *One of the central thoughts in Mahatma Gandhi's philosophy is the oneness of God and respect for all religions. I heard you echo the same thought in your talk at the* India Today *Conclave. How did you arrive at this understanding?*

Kurzweil: My parents brought me up in a Unitarian Church. This is a religious organisation in the United States devoted to studying all the different religions. It does not have any dogma of its own. The religious education in this church involves learning about a particular religion for six months, and then moving on to another religion for the next six months. It meant taking part on those services, reading those books and inviting those religious leaders into our discussion. Thus, I studied Hinduism, Buddhism, Judaism, Islam and so on. The theme I learnt in all the religions was the same – namely, there are many paths leading to the same truth. Different religions tell different stories in different words, but they all talk about the same God and they all teach the same values. And I was quite active in promoting this theme. I had joined a national organisation called the Liberal Religious Youth. I went for its summer camps. This influence has remained a part of my philosophy.

Kulkarni: *You are an iconic figure in the field of technology. Are you religious?*

Kurzweil: I believe that there is wisdom in religion – in all religions. Understanding this leads to tolerance, which is very important and necessary. Of course, there are some people who believe that their truth is the only truth, and they do not appreciate others' traditions. I believe that we need more tolerance in our world.

Kulkarni: *There is a Sanskrit maxim in our tradition, which echoes your belief. It says* Ekam sat, viprah bahudha vadanti – *Truth is One, wise people interpret it differently.*

Kurzweil: That's right. Tolerance is what we learn from Gandhi.

ANNEXURE II

Gandhian Engineering

A Concept by Dr R.A. Mashelkar

THE CONCEPT OF 'GANDHIAN ENGINEERING' HAS BEEN DEVELOPED by eminent scientist Dr R.A. Mashelkar, former director general of the Council of Scientific and Industrial Research (CSIR) and current president of the Global Research Alliance. The concept presents Mahatma Gandhi as an Innovation Leader, with innovation defined as 'doing things differently, making a big difference, and making the impossible possible'. Dr Mashelkar says: 'Gandhi took on the might of the British Empire by mobilising millions of people. His strategy fulfilled all the criteria of innovation. He did things differently, made a big difference and achieved what everyone considered was impossible. His weapons: ahimsa and swadeshi!'

Dr Mashelkar views society as an iceberg, where most of society's members live below the visible surface. 'Our challenge as engineers is to lift this iceberg above the surface so that everyone can have the quality of life they deserve.' His approach to meeting this challenge: find 'extreme affordability solutions' to meet the needs of the common people. 'Gandhian Engineering is about getting more output from less resource to benefit more people,' he says.

He gives several examples of innovations that use high technology to achieve higher output and higher quality at lower cost to benefit the masses.

One such example is that of the Jaipur Foot, designed by Ram Chandra Sharma under the guidance of Dr P.K. Sethi. 'An artificial foot in the US can cost anywhere between US $12,000 to $18,000. Now there are

4 billion people in the world with income less than $2 a day. It will take them 15 years to buy one artificial foot! An Indian foot should not only be as good as an American foot, but it also has to be 10 times better in terms of performance. The stress that the Indian foot has to undergo is incredible. Now the challenge here was to make a $12,000 foot affordable at $30 and make it 10 times better in terms of performance. Indian innovators have met the challenge.'

Another example is the use of IT to address the challenge of literacy. Dr Mashelkar elaborates: 'We have 200 million illiterates. Illiteracy is reducing very slowly – at 1.3% per annum. This will take around 20 years to clear the backlog. Can we do this in five years? Can we do it in less than $2 per person? Seems insurmountable. But F.C. Kohli, founder of Tata Consultancy Services (TCS), and his team have found a workable solution. They have created a computer-enabled literacy programme, based on theories of cognition, language and communication. They emphasise on words rather than alphabets. Today an illiterate woman can start reading in 6-8 weeks. The cost is $2.5 per person. This is Gandhian Engineering.'

Dr Mashelkar mentions the work of Dr Varaprasada Reddy of Shantha Biotech, Hyderabad, who has produced affordable vaccines. 'Internationally Hepatitis vaccine costs Rs 800 per dose. Shantha Biotech has brought it down to Rs 34 per dose. As a result, 50% of global immunisation programme uses it.'

Another Gandhian engineering innovator is Ashish Gawde, a student of the late Dr C.K. Prahalad, and a leading expert in hybrid cars. 'He left his lucrative job in the US to do something for the poor people of India. His mission: bringing light into the homes of the poor in villages. The device he has developed is simple. What the user does is pedal a bicycle where an ultra capacitor is connected to an LED which generates light. Four minutes of peddling the cycle provides four hours of light. Today the ultra capacitor is expensive at $50. That has to be brought down to $5. LED prices are going down. Gawde is driven by this vision of a child in a village school being able to study because there is proper light. To me this is Gandhian Engineering. My mind went to the spinning of the charkha and the spinning of the cycle wheel!'

The idea of scientists and engineers engaged in finding 'extreme affordability' solutions to meet the basic requirements of the poor people in the world would have certainly gladdened Gandhi.

ANNEXURE III

Nonviolence in Politics:
A Tribute to Mahatma Gandhi

by Werner Heisenberg

Werner Heisenberg (1901-76), a Nobel laureate and scientist, one of the founders of Quantum Physics and the originator of the famous Uncertainty Principle wrote the following essay on the occasion of Gandhi's birth centenary in 1969. It was published in a special commemorative volume *Mahatma Gandhi: 100 Years,* brought out by the Gandhi Peace Foundation, New Delhi.

Looking back to the great work of Gandhi in the history of India, one is tempted to ask the question: Whether or to what extent Gandhi's political ideas will contribute to the future structure of our world. Such a question may not do complete justice to Gandhi's enormous effort for the independence of his own country; since in the future world, independence will be limited and will generally be replaced by some kind of inter-dependence between all nations. But the answer to this question may give a measure for the influence of Indian thought and Indian philosophy in the general way of thinking in the future state of the world. I cannot doubt that Gandhi's most important contribution in this sense was his idea of Nonviolence.

While hitherto political disputes between nations have most frequently been settled by force, i.e., by violence against those who had to be considered a hindrance, the existence of the modern technical weapons will scarcely allow a continuation of this humiliating state of affairs for a long time to come. Therefore in the future world there must be other means to pursue the interests of one group against those of another group. At this point the idea of Nonviolence may be a decisive help in two ways. First, it turns around the old and frequently disputed slogan: 'The end justifies the means'. The idea of Nonviolence states that it is the quality of the means, e.g., the intention to suffer for the good ends but not to inflict suffering upon others, which provides the justification of the ends. And thereby, secondly, it states that it is only by gaining the approval of others, of the majority of men, that we can reasonably pursue our own interests.

It has been a general tendency in our time to create international institutions or law courts, which can be invoked for settling difficult problems between nations. This is certainly a good step in the right direction. But frequently, at least in the near future, the authority of such an institution will be questioned by one of the parties, or a general lack of interest among the other nations in the problem concerned may frustrate the judgement of such an international institution. In such cases Gandhi's idea of passive resistance, or Nonviolence, could help to draw the attention of very many people to the problem under dispute and could emphasise the urgency of its solution; because the most intense personal engagement as the basis of Gandhi's idea of Nonviolence may be stronger than the somewhat impersonal idea of an international court. Hence it seems that Gandhi's way of thinking can lead directly into the political structure of the future world, in which a nation might be much better protected by not possessing atomic weapons than by having them, or might pursue its own interests much more efficiently by participating in the interests of other nations than by ignoring them. It was the unique example given by Gandhi which demonstrated that the most sincere personal engagement, combined with complete renunciation of violence, can lead to great political success.

We all are indebted to him for this example.

ANNEXURE IV

A Brief Biography of
an Iconic Gandhi Photograph

The Mahatma as Portrayed by Margaret Bourke-White

Margaret Bourke-White (1904-71), who worked for LIFE magazine,
was one of the greatest woman photo-journalists

A MACHINE IS NOT A LIFELESS OBJECT. IT IS TOUCHED AND ANIMATED by countless human hands and minds. Every machine contains its own biography, written in a hidden script, of the people who conceived it, produced it, distributed and marketed it, used it to produce other goods and services, and also of those who used these goods and services for their own needs and wants. Thus, all machines and their products tell the story of the civilisation in which they were made and consumed. No wonder, scholars attempt to understand the Harappan civilisation, for example, on the basis of the tools and structures that have survived in its ruins. Similarly, there is no doubt that scholars in AD 3000 or AD 4000 will study the history of the twentieth and twenty-first centuries, *inter alia*, by looking at the tool which Gandhi, very audaciously for his time, made the messenger of a truly humanistic civilisation.

As I have argued throughout this book, Gandhi made the spinning wheel the mascot not only of India's freedom movement but also of his broader campaign for a new world order based on truth, nonviolence, justice and universal cooperation. He animated the charkha by making it the revolutionary carrier of his triple message: economic, cultural and spiritual. Some aspects of that message, especially the charkha's role in mobilising the masses for India's freedom struggle, are no longer relevant. Indeed, Gandhi himself was never fixated about the spinning wheel as the permanent basis of a future non-exploitative economic and social order in India. In his understanding of the future man-machine relationship, he did envision the spinning wheel being replaced by a better substitute – specifically, a machine that could help the entire humanity in its pursuit of sustainable and morally guided development.

Many people in his time did not understand Gandhi's views on machines and industries; many don't understand him even now. Nevertheless, even among those were men and women who acknowledged the greatness of his personality and the nobility of his mission. One such person was Margaret Bourke-White, arguably the world's greatest woman photographer. She captured in her lens some of the finest pictures of Gandhi – including one that she took hours before he was assassinated. She has also left behind, in her autobiography *Portrait of Myself**, an equally captivating account of her several encounters with the man she came to venerate

---

*Margaret Bourke-White's autobiography *Portrait of Myself* was published in 1963 by Simon & Schuster. The full text of it is now available in the public domain at http://archive.org/stream/portraitofmyself002368mbp/portraitofmyself002368mbp_djvu.txt

after photographing him for over two years. Parts of that account are relevant to the theme of this book.

Her picture of Gandhi, which appears in Chapter 33, has become iconic. Bourke-White, who was obsessed with photographing machines, made it as much a portrait of his machine as of the man himself by dramatically making the spinning wheel in the foreground as large as Gandhi sitting meditatively behind it on a carpet. The Mahatma and his spinning wheel are thus fused into one organic and indivisible entity, just as he had always craved the relationship to be.

Bourke-White, the first female photographer of *LIFE* magazine, was in India for two years (1946–48). She writes in her autobiography: 'Photography demands a high degree of participation, but never have I participated to such an extent as I did when photographing various episodes in the life of Gandhi'. Here is an account of her first meeting with him:

'I went to see him at his camp, or ashram, in Poona where he was living in the midst of a colony of untouchables. Having thought of Mahatma Gandhi as a symbol of simplicity, I was a bit surprised to find that I had to go through several secretaries to get permission to photograph him. When I reached the last and chief secretary, an earnest man in horn-rimmed spectacles, and dressed entirely in snow-white homespun, I explained my mission. I had come to take photographs of the Mahatma spinning.

'Do you know how to spin?' asked Gandhi's secretary.

'Oh, I didn't come to spin with the Mahatma. I came to photograph the Mahatma spinning.'

'How can you possibly understand the symbolism of Gandhi at his spinning wheel? How can you comprehend the inner meaning of the wheel, the charkha, unless you first master the principles of spinning?' He inquired sharply, 'Then you are not at all familiar with the workings of the spinning wheel?'

'No. Only with the workings of a camera.'

After a while, Bourke-White agreed to learn the basics of spinning and her instructor decided she could spin well enough to be brought into the presence of the Mahatma. However, there were two injunctions she had to faithfully follow. She was not speak to him, as this was a Monday, his day of silence. And she was not to use any form of artificial light, as Gandhi disliked it. After some pleading with his secretary, she was allowed some lighting equipment – 'three peanut flashbulbs'.

> I found the inside of the hut even darker than I had anticipated. A single beam of daylight shone from a little high window directly into my lens and into my eyes as well. I could scarcely see to compose the picture, but when my eyes became accustomed to the murky shadows, there sat the Mahatma, cross-legged, a spidery figure with long, wiry legs, a bald head and spectacles. Could this be the man who was leading his people to freedom, the little old man in a loincloth who had kindled the imagination of the world? I was filled with an emotion as close to awe as a photographer can have.
>
> He sat in complete silence on the floor; the only sound was a little rustling from the pile of newspaper clippings he was reading. And beside him was that spinning wheel I had heard so much about...Gandhi pushed his clippings aside, and pulled his spinning wheel closer. He started to spin, beautifully, rhythmically and with a fine nimble hand.

This was the first of many occasions on which Bourke-White photographed the Mahatma. Gandhi soon began to joke with her, and also had his own nickname for her. 'Whenever I appeared on the scene with camera and flashbulbs, he would say, "There's the Torturer again." But it was said with affection'.

What Bourke-White writes next is highly reflective:

> As time went on, I saw this incident of the spinning wheel in a different light. Translated into the many situations a photographer must meet, the rule set up by Gandhi's secretary was a good one: if you want to photograph a man spinning, give some thought to why he spins. Understanding, for a photographer, is as important as the equipment he uses. I have always believed what goes on, unseen, in back of the lens is just as important as what goes on in front of it. In the case of Gandhi, the spinning wheel was laden with meaning. For millions of Indians, it was the symbol of the fight for freedom. Gandhi was a shrewd judge of economic

pressures as well as spiritual ones. If millions of Indians could be persuaded to make the cloth they used themselves, instead of buying manufactured textiles from the British colonial power, the boycott would be severely felt in England's textile industry. The charka was the key to victory. Nonviolence was Gandhi's creed, and the spinning wheel was the perfect weapon.

Bourke-White continues:

I was glad to turn from the decay of Europe to India, where *LIFE* next assigned me. ...My insatiable desire to be on the scene when history is being made was never more nearly fulfilled. I arrived there in 1946 when India stood shining and full of hope on the threshold of independence. I witnessed that extremely rare event in the history of nations, the birth of twins. I had a historical drama to photograph, with a full cast of characters, including villains and one of the saintliest men who ever lived. And when the saint was martyred, I was near.

Gandhi's death marked the end of an epoch...It took me two years to appreciate the greatness of Gandhi. It was only in the last act of the drama, when he stood out so bravely against the religious fanaticism and prejudice that I began to glimpse his true greatness. He was an extraordinarily complex person, with many contradictions in his nature. Some of his opinions I found difficult to reconcile. One was his opposition to industry and scientific agriculture. That an emergent nation like India needed modern industry seemed to me self-evident. This conviction of Gandhi's that machinery was intrinsically evil particularly disturbed me because of my love of the machine and my belief in what it could do for man.

Let us go to Bourke-White's meeting with Gandhi on what turned out to be the last day of his life.

I had reached my last day in India, and on this final day I had arranged a special treat for myself – an interview with Gandhi because although I had photographed him many times, and we had exchanged scraps of conversation with one another, I had never had a chance to sit down and talk with him quietly.

I found Gandhi seated on a cot in the garden, with his spinning wheel in front of him...He began to spin, as he always did during interviews. My first question seemed a rather silly one at the time; later, it seemed almost prophetic. 'Gandhiji,' I said, 'you have always stated that you would live to be a hundred and twenty-five years old. What gives you that hope?'

His answer was startling, 'I have lost the hope.'

'I asked him why. 'Because of the terrible happenings in the world. I can no longer live in darkness and madness. I cannot continue. ...' He paused, and I waited. Thoughtfully, he picked up a strand of cotton, gave it a twist and ran it into the spinning wheel. 'But if I am needed,' he went on in his careful English, 'rather, I should say, if I am commanded, then I shall live to be a hundred and twenty-five years old.'

We went on, then, to speak of other things. ...While frequently I did not agree with Gandhi's point of view, talking with him helped me understand it. He cared not at all about reshaping the structure of society. He cared a great deal about reshaping the human heart, and calling out the best in every man.

I turned to the topic which I had most wanted to discuss with Gandhiji. I began speaking of the weight with which our new and terrible nuclear knowledge hangs over us, and of our increasing fear of a war which would destroy the world. Holding in our hands the key to the ultimate in violence, we might draw some guidance, I hoped, from the apostle of nonviolence.

As we began to speak of these things, I became aware of a change in my attitude toward Gandhi. No longer was this merely an odd little man in a loincloth, with his quaint ideas about bullock-cart culture and his vague social palliatives certain of which I rejected. I felt in the presence of a new and greater Gandhi. My deepening appreciation of Gandhi began when I saw the power and courage with which he led the way in the midst of chaos.

Bourke-White asked Gandhi whether he believed America should stop manufacturing the atom bomb. 'Unhesitatingly', he replied. He went on to stress the importance of choosing righteous paths, 'whether for a nation or for a single man; for bad means could never bring about good ends'. He spoke 'thoughtfully, haltingly, always with the most profound sincerity'. As the two sat there in the thin winter sunlight, he spinning, and she jotting down his words, 'neither of us', Bourke-White wrote, 'could know that this was to be one of the last, perhaps his very last, messages to the world'.

Since that momentous day, many people have asked me whether one knew when in Gandhi's presence that this was an extraordinary man. The answer is yes. One knew. And never had I felt it more strongly than on this day, when the inconsistencies that had troubled me dropped away, and Gandhi began to probe at that dreadful problem which has overwhelmed us all.

I asked Gandhiji how he would meet the atom bomb. Would he meet it with nonviolence? 'Ah,' he said. 'How shall I answer that? I would meet it by prayerful action.'

I asked what form that action would take.

'I will not go underground. I will not go into shelters. I will go out and face the pilot so he will see I have not the face of evil against him.'

He turned back to his spinning, and I was tempted to ask, 'The pilot would see all that at his altitude?' But Gandhi sensed my silent question.

'I know the pilot will not see our faces from his great height, but that longing in our hearts that he should not come to harm would reach up to him, and his eyes would be opened...It is a question now whether the victors are really victors or victims ... of our own lust...and omission.' He was speaking very slowly, and his words had become toneless and low. 'The world is not at peace.' His voice had sunk almost to a whisper. 'It is still more dreadful than before.'

I rose to leave, and folded my hands together in the gesture of farewell which Hindus use. But Gandhiji held out his hand to me and shook hands cordially in Western fashion. We said goodbye, and I started off. Then something made me turn back. His manner had been so friendly. I stopped and looked over my shoulder, and said, 'Goodbye, and good luck.' Only a few hours later, on his way to evening prayers, this man who believed that even the atom bomb should be met with nonviolence was struck down by revolver bullets.

Here is Bourke-White's description, as everlastingly eloquent as her photographs, of the funeral on the following day:

> By dawn, the lawn and gardens of Birla House and all streets leading into it were flooded with people. By the thousands they swirled through the Birla gates until they crushed in an indivisible mass against the house. And still they came, beating against the walls of the house in surging waves of mourning humanity. I doubt if there has ever been a scene like it. Certainly there has been none in my experience. The house, with its concrete terraces, was like a rocky island, holding its precious burden high above the sea of grief. Laid out on the roof of the terrace was the figure of Gandhi, tranquil and serene.
>
> The morning sunlight lent a special radiance to the coarsely woven homespun which draped his body. He was carried down, placed on a flower-laden bier and covered with the yellow, white and green flag of the new free India. Then, that greatest of all processions began to move toward the sacred burning ground on the bank of the River Jumna. The human stream gathered to itself all the tributaries of the countryside. It grew and grew until it was a mighty river miles long, and a mile wide, draining toward the shore of the sacred river. People covered the entire visible landscape until it seemed as if the broad meadows themselves were rippling away until they reached the sacred banks. I never before had photographed or even imagined such an ocean of human beings.

Somehow I managed to get to the center of the dense, mourning throng, where the funeral pyre of sandalwood logs had been lighted. Occasionally I could catch a glimpse of the three Hindu priests kindling the fire and scattering perfumed chips on the blaze. Then a glimpse of Nehru's haggard face as he stood by the edge of the bier. Twilight was coming. The flames were rising high into the sky. All through the night, the people would watch until the flames burned down to embers.

The curtain was falling on the tragic last act. The drama I had come to India to record had run its course. I had shared some of India's greatest moments. Nothing in all my life has affected me more deeply, and the memory will never leave me. I had seen men die on the battlefield for what they believed in, but I had never seen anything like this: one Christ-like man giving his life to bring unity to his people.

In Chapter 33, I had mentioned that Steve Jobs would not settle for any other picture of Gandhi for Apple's landmark THINK DIFFERENT advertising campaign than the one by Margaret Bourke-White showing the Mahatma with his spinning wheel. It is easy to see why. A photography buff, Jobs had probably read Bourke-White's autobiography. As the above account of her encounters with Gandhi shows – and, indeed, as the account of Gandhi in all the pages of this book would show – he was, to use words from Apple's ad campaign, one of the 'crazy ones'; a 'rebel' who saw 'things differently' and had 'no respect for the status quo'. Gandhi was one of those who pushed 'the human race forward'. For only 'the people who are crazy enough to think they can change the world, are the ones who do'.

Thanks to the Internet, we can see all of Bourke-White's portraits of Gandhi. Again, thanks to the Internet, we can also read the entire text of her moving pen-portrait of the Mahatma, which is contained in her own freely downloadable *Portrait of Myself*. In a way, she too was one of those adorable 'crazy ones', an incredible reservoir of creativity, courage, zeal and idealism. Her camera recorded many historic moments and personalities in the twentieth century. She earned her own place in history for her deeply expressive, indeed mesmerising, photographs of the industrial landscape in her home country, USA. She had a romantic relationship with modern machines, which, through her lens, revealed a lofty purpose of their own. However, history remembers Bourke-White with greater admiration and gratitude for her portraits of the Mahatma – especially the one with his meek but morally powerful spinning wheel.

ANNEXURE V

A Teacher's Reflections on the Book

Prof. Deepak Phatak

Dr Deepak B. Phatak is Subrao Nilekani Chair Professor in the department of computer science and engineering at IIT Bombay. An alumnus of the same institute, he is now a legendary teacher who commands popularity and respect in equal measure from students as well fellow faculty on the campus. Since I too studied in the same institute – my initial ideological orientation in my student days appears in the narrative in the opening chapter – I was keen on getting a short comment on this book from Dr Phatak. What came from him was a long and thought-provoking letter. It is being reproduced here in full because it carries an important reflection of its own.

Dear Sudheendra,

I am sorry for responding so late. Just two days before your first mail, I had taken over from IIT Rajasthan, the dream project of procuring and deploying one lakh Aakash tablet* computers in engineering colleges. This is the first pilot, which is expected to be followed by induction of five million tablets, to benefit the larger student community in India. IIT Rajasthan had some intractable problems due to which the project has been delayed by six months. I have hardly slept in the last one month. After all, this is part of my own dream to eventually force knowledge to ride on the Internet access in every nook and corner of India. That is the reason why I could not even touch your book so far.

---

*Aakash tablet is the world's lowest cost computing/Internet device, specially designed as an educational tool for Indian students.

I spent a major part of yesterday, and the entire night, in attempting to 'peruse' your manuscript. It was impossible to skip over anything. So powerful is the grip, that one is forced to read every passage. One is further forced to think and reflect after reading every few lines.

Just the chapter on your 'Journey from Mahatma to Marx and Back' evoked memories of the nightlong debates in Hostel 1 in 1969, when I was myself a student at IIT Bombay, and I spent over one hour and four cigarettes in reminiscing the thoughts which engulfed my mind then, and which recur even today. The leftists and rightists would argue eternally on how the opponent's view was abysmally pathetic in solving problems of ignorance and poverty in India. IITians, at least a handful in numbers of each of these two ideologies, were known to spend a couple of years working in villages after their graduation. (Achyut Godbole, who later became the CEO of L&T Infotech, was one such friend.) I used to often ask both groups in the hostel debates, that when both sides are so genuinely dedicated to work for the downtrodden, why do they not work together?

It took some time for me to realise, that most dedicated people are obsessed with the thought that 'emancipation must happen, but it must happen through my religion'. (I consider every 'ism' in its dogmatic form to be not much different from any religious dogma.) The human desire to 'rule' others, manifests itself even in such sincere thoughts and serious actions for helping others.

I had written recently to a friend in the context of some administrative feud, that administrators prefer to have strong 'controls' in place, and sometimes they forget that their main job is to facilitate. This battle between control and facilitation probably is as old as the early evolution of human societies. I think it has much to do with the basic human psychology. Between any two or more people, the question that often becomes uppermost is, whether I have to do as others tell me, or whether others have to do as I tell them. I have been amazed to see the importance attached to this question, even when ALL actually want to do the same thing, as in the debating teams of Hostel 1! On a smaller scale, this happens between husband and wife, parents and children, and between family members and friends. On a larger scale, it happens between people of different organisations or sects. On a much larger scale, it happens between societies and nations. The West attributes such struggles to control of economic resources. But I think it is the human urge to 'control' anything and everything, which manifests in such behaviour. To my mind, 'freedom' and 'independence' often means that I will not accept anybody else's control over me and my actions, yet I would like to control all others!

Real situations become more complicated when personal likes and dislikes that I hold for other people start interfering in my arguments. You can guess the possible changes in stance one may take. As a human, my native desire is to control everyone else; but I may tilt on facilitating those from 'my' own group or society or nation, and try to more stringently control those from the 'other' group. As a clever and polished person, I will do that subtly and even justify my actions, but others being equally clever, they all can see these undercurrents and hate me and my group. Of course, wisdom takes a back seat, and bloody struggles often result.

You may think that I am digressing. But the point is that it is your book which has taught me the true nature of the Mahatma and his thoughts on Ahimsa and Satyagraha. That he advocated 'Truth' to reflect eternal good values, and its pursuit through strictly nonviolent means, is what I have learned more forcefully tonight. You observe that 'No leader in modern history has so categorically and courageously subordinated his love for his own nation to his love for Truth'. You have quoted the Mahatma as saying: 'If India makes violence her creed, and I have survived, I would not care to live in India'. This simple belief of the Mahatma has forced me to rethink some of my own convictions. You perhaps know that I hold India, the prosperity and honour of her people, and her flag, way above everything that is dear to me in life. That has been my God and my religion. I am religious, but follow no dogma. I genuinely respect all religions. Having chosen teaching as my calling in life, I attempt to faithfully practice the 'Dharma' of a teacher. I do have in my heart only love, affection, and concern for human beings of all nationalities. But in practice, I love Indians a little more.

I realise now that if I abhor a million Iraqis being killed by American invasion, then I must equally abhor a single innocent Assamese or Kashmiri being killed by mistake by the Indian security forces. Collateral damage cannot have a place in any civilised society. And the ultimate damage control can happen only through the discovery, realisation, and adoption of this 'Truth' as Mahatma saw it. I agree that India has the best chance to provide such thought leadership, and for that India must rediscover and re-adopt these values; and not in some isolated way, but *en masse*. And not through any coercion, but through dialogue and self-realisation. That, indeed, is the Mahatma's true notion of 'Jihad-e-Akbar' or Satyagraha. This is the true 'Music of the Spinning Wheel'.

Mahatma as a scientist, is a new look I have gained from this book. We all realise that empowerment of the underprivileged Indian villager is the need of the day. I am convinced that the Internet is the way to reach out with morsels of useful knowledge to a large number of people. This is the reason I have decided to work for ten years after retirement to create knowledge contents in Indian languages. But village as a long-time trustee of the Indian culture, and the need to rediscover the ethics and morality, the good values, and to propagate these across the globe, is the new thought this book has given me. 'Mahatma as a prophet of the communication revolution' would never have occurred to me, but for the powerful interview with Dr Ray Kurzweil which you have penned. When I embark on my post retirement journey, I will keep the exposition of these values as my main theme, not just information, not even just knowledge, but the true 'Indian' (or should I say 'human') wisdom. If I ever succeed in doing so, your book would be the root cause.

I must confess that I do not have a 'few lines' to write about the book. I do not think a 'few lines' can ever describe the power of the Mahatma Truth, which you have so beautifully brought out.

I feel privileged for your sharing the pre-print with me, and stupid, that I chose to sit on it for almost a month.

—*Deepak*

NOTES

- The *Collected Works of Mahatma Gandhi* (98 volumes), published by the Publications Division of the Government of India are referred to as CWMG. These are also availab2nline.
- *Indian Opinion, Young India, Harijan* and *Navajivan* are journals founded and edited by Gandhi.

Introduction

1. B.R. Nanda, *In Search of Gandhi: Essays and Reflections*, Oxford University Press (2002), p. 165.
2. *Collected Works of Mahatma Gandhi (CWMG)*, Vol. 75, p. 150.
3. *CWMG*, Vol. 78, p. 75.
4. From the website of Jean-François Noubel, http://www.noubel.com/wiki/tiki-index.php
5. *Antyodaya*, a Sanskrit word that means care and uplift of the last man in society, is a uniquely Indian concept of egalitarianism. It casts a responsibility both on state policy and on the wealthy sections of society to ensure a social order free of poverty and want, and full of opportunities for the progress of all. It is synonymous with Gandhi's concept of *Sarvodaya* (equitable progress of all). After Gandhi, its most passionate proponents were Vinoba Bhave (1895–1982), his spiritual heir, and Pandit Deendayal Upadhyaya (1916–68), the ideological guru of the Bharatiya Janata Party.
6. Douglas Rushkoff, *Program or Be Programmed: Ten Commands for a Digital Age*, Soft Skull Press (2011), p. 14.
7. *Hind Swaraj: A Centenary Edition* with an introduction by Prof. S.R. Mehrotra; Rajendra Prasad Academy, New Delhi (2010), p. 39.
8. *Gandhi: Hind Swaraj and Other Writings*, Anthony J. Parel; Cambridge University Press (2009).
9. *Sermon on the Sea* by Mahatma Gandhi with an introduction by John Haynes Holmes; edited by Haridas T. Mazumdar; Universal Publishing Co. (1923), p. ix. Holmes also described his meetings and interactions with the Mahatma in his book *My Gandhi* (1954).

10. Rajmohan Gandhi, *Gandhi: The Man, His People, and the Empire*, Penguin Books India (2007).
11. Dr Pranjivan Mehta's prophetic description of the personality of Gandhi is mentioned in Prof. S.R. Mehrotra's introduction to the Centenary Edition of *Hind Swaraj*. The highly illuminating introduction discusses what prompted Gandhi to write *Hind Swaraj*.
12. *Unto This Last: A Paraphrase*, M.K. Gandhi, Navajivan Trust, 1956.
13. *Harijan*, 25 August 1940.
14. Pyarelal, *Mahatma Gandhi: The Last Phase*, Vol. II, p. 455; (Navajivan Publishing House, Ahmedabad) 1956.
15. Quoted by Martin Heidegger, an influential figure in twentieth-century Western philosophy, in his seminal work *The Question Concerning Technology*.
16. *Young India*, 10 April 1930.
17. Fritjof Capra, *The Tao of Physics*; Shambhala (1991).
18. *Truth is God*, ed. R.K. Prabhu; Navajivan Publishing House, Ahmedabad (1955); p. 61.
19. *Truth is God*, ed. R.K. Prabhu; p. 60.
20. The *Times of India* 5 December 1932; *CWMG*, Vol. 58, p. 118.
21. J.C. Kumarappa, *Economy of Permanence*, Navajivan Trust, Ahmedabad.

Chapter 1

1. The Prime Minister's Task Force on IT and Telecom, set up by Atal Bihari Vajpayee in 1998, prepared a plan for the all-round development of Information Technology in India. It paved the way for a spectacular expansion and modernisation of telecom services in the country. It set an ambitious target of a ten-fold increase ($50 billion) in software and ITES exports from India by 2008. The target was indeed reached. However, there has not been much progress with regard to another important recommendation of the Task Force: promotion of IT in Indian languages. Gandhi deeply cared for the development of Indian languages.
2. *Young India*, 21 July 1920; *CWMG*, Vol. 21, p. 74.
3. *Harijan*, 4 November 1939.
4. Einstein's interview with Robert Merrill Bartlett, appearing in *Survey Graphic*, August 1935.
5. Robert Payne, *The Life and Death of Mahatma Gandhi*, Rupa & Co (1997); p. 350.
6. Bertrand Russell's article on Mahatma Gandhi was published in *Atlantic Monthly*, December 1952. It is reproduced in 'Articles on and by Gandhi' at http://www.mkgandhi.org/articles/russel.htm

7. Aldous Huxley, who criticised Gandhi's economic philosophy in his 1929 essay 'Do What You Will', later changed his views. In 'Science, Liberty and Peace' (1945), Huxley argued that Gandhi's record of achievements was not irrelevant to the industrial West, and even predicted that 'in the years ahead, it seems possible that Satyagraha may take root in the West'. Four years later, in the 'Gandhi Memorial Peace Number' of Viswa-Bharati Quarterly (October 1949), he wrote: 'Gandhi's social and economic ideas are based upon a realistic appraisal of man's nature and the nature of his position in the universe'.

8. India and the erstwhile communist-ruled Soviet Union had forged close cooperation after the First Five Year Plan in 1951. I gratefully acknowledge that I was much enlightened by reading Shambhu Prasad's highly informative essay 'Towards an Understanding of Gandhi's Views on Science' in the *Economic and Political Weekly* (29 September 2001), in which Huxley and Saha are quoted. The essay also throws light on Jawaharlal Nehru's lack of real faith in the Gandhian paradigm of development, notwithstanding the fact he had poetically described khadi as 'the *livery* of India's freedom'. Prasad rightly points out that many Congressmen, Nehru included, supported the charkha for its 'instrumental value' and 'ability' in mobilising the common people for India's freedom, but 'to be discarded later'. He also holds Nehru guilty of making 'a clear divide between himself as a science person and Gandhi as a religious man', a baseless stereotype that has survived even today. An unfortunate corollary to such stereotyping is blind acceptance. Once a person is labelled a 'person of science', everything he says automatically becomes 'scientific'!

9. *Young India*, 20 May 1926.

10. *Harijan*, 13 April 1910.

11. The British Rule in India' by Karl Marx in the *New-York Herald Tribune*, 25 June 1853; Marx-Engels Collected Works Vol. 12, p. 125; http://www.marxists.org/archive/marx/works/1853/06/25.htm

12. A riveting account of how viscerally Indian communists in the era of the freedom movement hated Gandhi can be found in the dialogue between Romain Rolland and Saumyendranath Tagore in 1933. Their hostility was understandable. After all, Gandhi, more than anyone else in India, had blunted their ideological and political appeal in every section of our society – most of all among the poor, in whose name the communists conducted their politics. Rolland was an ardent admirer of Gandhi. Saumyendranath Tagore, a young nephew of the great poet, was a staunch communist who had been living in Europe. 'Our task in

India,' he told Rolland, 'is to wage war mercilessly against Gandhism, on all sides. Gandhism must be completely crushed.' See *Romain Rolland and Gandhi: Correspondence*, a gem of a book published in 1976 by the Publications Division of the Government of India.

It must be mentioned here that Gandhi was not as critical of communism as he was of capitalism. At least a part of the reason for this was the influence of enlightened men like Rolland, who wrote that he wanted to see 'Gandhi's Revolution' and 'Lenin's Revolution' come closer. I would like to mention here that E.M.S. Namboodiripad, a renowned leader of the Communist Party of India (Marxist), presented a more balanced picture of Gandhi in his book *Mahatma and His Ism* (LeftWord Books, New Delhi).

13. *Amrita Bazar Patrika,* 5 January 1946; *CWMG,* Vol. 89, pp. 158-59.
14. Satish Kumar, 'Europe needs an amount of Eastern Wisdom', http://athens.cafebabel.com/en/post/2010/09/02/Satish-Kumar-:-Europe-needs-an-amount-of-Eastern-Wisdom3
15. *CWMG,* Vol. 79, p. 257.
16. In his foreword to Dr Bharatan Kumarappa's book *Capitalism, Socialism or Villagism?* – Poona, 24 Sept 1945, *CWMG,* Vol. 88, p. 79.
17. *CWMG,* Vol. 79, p. 257.
18. *Socialism of My Conception: A Collection of Mahatma Gandhi's Writings,* Edited by Anand T. Hingorani, Bharatiya Vidya Bhavan, Bombay (1957), p. 269.

Chapter 2

1. M.K. Gandhi, *Unto This Last: A Paraphrase*, Navajivan Trust, 1956, p. 27.
2. Britain's economic pillage of India was well documented by Dadabhai Naoroji and R.C. Dutt, both of whom Gandhi admired.
3. B.R. Nanda, *In Search of Gandhi: Essays and Reflections,* Oxford University Press (2002), p 229.
4. The 'sword of ethics' is a recurrent phrase in Gandhi's writings. According to him, India's common folk, though illiterate or semi-literate, 'saw that kings and their swords were inferior to the sword of ethics, and they, therefore, held the sovereigns of the earth to be inferior to the *Rishis* and the *Fakirs*'. Gandhi as a 'warrior' of a different type was the subject of an acclaimed psycho-biographical book, *Gandhi's Truth: On the Origins of Militant Nonviolence,* by Erik H. Erikson, a widely respected American

psychologist. Erikson showed how the Mahatma's principles could be applicable to the American civil rights movement.

5. John Dear, *Mahatma Gandhi, Apostle of Nonviolence,* www.johndear.org/ pdfs/mohandas_gandhi.pdf

6. Thomas Weber, Gandhi and the Nobel Peace Prize, http://www.mkgandhi. org/nobel/nobelpeaceprize.htm

7. *CWMG,* Vol. 15, p. 276.

8. *Hind Swaraj: A Centenary Edition* by Prof. S.R. Mehrotra; p. 209.

9. Ibid.

10. *Young India,* 1 January 1925, *CWMG,* Vol. 30, p. 35.

11. *Harijan,* 25 August 1946. Edward Carpenter (1844–1929) was an English socialist poet, with whom Gandhi corresponded.

12. *CWMG,* Vol. 22, p. 158.

13. *Hind Swaraj: A Centenary Edition* by Prof. S.R. Mehrotra; p. 218.

14. *Hind Swaraj: A Centenary Edition* by Prof. S.R. Mehrotra; pp. 160-61.

Chapter 3

1. Giriraj Kishore, *The Girmitiya Saga,* a novel on Gandhi's life in South Africa; Niyogi Books (2010).

2. Fatima Meer, *Apprenticeship of a Mahatma A Biography of M.K. Gandhi (1869-1914),* Phoenix Settlement Trust, (1970), p. 109.

3. D.G. Tendulkar, *Mahatma: Life of Mohandas Karamchand Gandhi,* Vol. 3, p. 280, 2nd Edition (1960), Publications Division, Government of India.

4. *Mind of Mahatma Gandhi,* cd. Prabhu & Rao, Navajivan Publishing House, Ahmedabad, 3rd Edition (1968), p. 92.

5. Mahatma Gandhi, *The Story of My Experiments With Truth,* Navajivan Publishing House, Ahmedabad (2011), pp. 82-83.

6. *Gandhi's Guru: An insight into the life and teachings of the Jain saint, Srimad Rajchandraji;* A monograph by Chandrika, published by the Observer Research Foundation Mumbai. Chandrika is also the author of *Atma Siddhi: In Search of the Soul,* in which she has rendered into English Rajchandraji's philosophical poem in Gujarati. Her translation of this outstanding work not only gives the reader the verses in Hindi and English but also explains the essence of each verse with the help of stories drawn from Hindu, Buddhist, Sufi, Christian and Zen sources. It is published by Vakils Feffer & Simons Pvt. Ltd. (2010).

7. M.K. Gandhi, *Ruskin's 'Unto This Last': A Paraphrase;* Navajivan Publishing House, Ahmedabad.

8. *Navajivan,* 29 December 1920.
9. T.K. Mahadevan, *Ideas and Variations,* Mittal Publications (1988).
10. It should be noted here that 'passive resistance' is an improper translation of 'satyagraha'. Gandhi's nonviolent resistance was very active. This important difference was underscored by Gandhi himself.
11. Thomas Weber, *Tolstoy and Gandhi's Law of Love,* SGI Quarterly – A Buddhist Forum for Peace, Culture and Education; http://www.sgiquarterly.org/feature2010Jan-9.html

Chapter 4

1. *Gandhi's Views on Truth*; http://www.gandhi-manibhavan.org/gandhiphilosophy/philosophy_truth_meaning.htm
2. D.G. Tendulkar, *Mahatma,* Vol. 3, p. 236; 2nd Edition (1960).
3. D.G. Tendulkar, *Mahatma,* Vol. 7, p. 132; 2nd Edition (1960).
4. D.G. Tendulkar, *Mahatma,* Vol. 3, p. 280; 2nd Edition (1960).
5. *Mind of Mahatma Gandhi*; ed. Prabhu & Rao, p. 100.
6. *Truth is God,* ed. R.K. Prabhu; Navajivan Publishing House, Ahmedabad (1955); p. 65.
7. Mahatma Gandhi, *The Story of My Experiments with Truth.*
8. Letter to Narandas Gandhi, 18-22 July 1930, *CWMG,* Vol. 49, p. 384.
9. *All About Mahatma Gandhi*; http://mkgandhimanibhavan.blogspot.com/2011/04/mkgandhis-perspective.html
10. Letter to Narandas Gandhi, 18-22 July 1930, *CWMG,* Vol. 49, p. 384.
11. *Young India,* 23 March 1921.
12. Mahatma Gandhi's audio message ('On God'), 1931, on Columbia Gramophone Company; http://www.youtube.com/watch?v=EtWr04MBGYI
13. The Poona Pact refers to an agreement between Dr B.R. Ambedkar, leader of the Depressed Classes (now known as Dalits) and Mahatma Gandhi on 24 September 1932 at Yeravada Jail in Pune (earlier called Poona) in Maharashtra. The British government had invited various Indian leaders for Round Table Conferences in 1930-32 to draft a new self-rule constitution for India. In pursuit of its 'divide and rule' policy, it had announced a 'Communal Award', which provided for separate electorates for Muslims, Christians and other 'minorities'. Ambedkar, supported by the British, raised the demand for separate electorates for the Depressed Classes. Gandhi strongly opposed this, claiming that it would split the Hindu society. In protest, he began an indefinite hunger strike inside the jail from 20 September 1932. His fast, which lasted six days, resulted in the Poona Pact, under which the two leaders agreed

upon reserved seats for the Depressed Castes (who are now referred to as the Scheduled Castes) in the central and provincial legislatures.

14. Gandhi's letter to Rajkumari Amrit Kaur on 21 October 1936, *CWMG*, Vol. 70, p. 1.

15. Jaya Jaitley, *Gandhi and Women's Empowerment*, http://www.mkgandhi.org/articles/Jaya%20Jaitly.htm

16. Physical Training and Ahimsa; *Harijan*, 13 October 1940, *CWMG* Vol. 79, p. 270-5.

17. *CWMG*, Vol. 96, p. 357.

18. *CWMG* (revised edition), Publications Division, 2000, Vol. 44, pp. 42–3 There is a good book, *The Lotus & The Spinning Wheel*, by Marie Beuzeville Byles (George Allen & Unwin Ltd., 1963) describing the personalities and philosophies of the Buddha and Mahatma Gandhi.

Chapter 5

1. Mahatma Gandhi, *Satyagraha in South Africa*; Navajivan Publishing House, Ahmedabad.

2. Ibid.

3. Gandhi regarded *Ramcharitmanas* by Goswami Tulsidas (1532–1623), a widely revered bhakti poet from north India, as one of the greatest creations of devotional literature in the world. *Ramcharitmanas*, which presents the life and deeds of Lord Rama, is widely recited in homes and religious congregations of Hindi-speaking Hindus.

4. Dr S. Radhakrishnan, *Mahatma Gandhi: His Message for Mankind*, Jaico Publishing House, Bombay.

Chapter 6

1. *Young India*, 22 September 1927.

2. *Young India*, 8 December 1927.

3. *Young India*, 10 February 1927.

4. *Young India*, 13 January 1927.

5. *Young India*, 4 September 1924.

6. *Young India*, 31 October 1924.

7. *The Hindu*, 13 July 1927, *CWMG*, Vol. 39, p. 210.

8. Nandini Joshi, *Development Without Destruction: Economics of the Spinning Wheel*, Navajivan Publishing House (1992).

9. *Young India*, 8 January 1925.

10. *Young India*, 29 June 1921.

11. See 'Adin Ballou, Tolstoy, and Gandhi', http://www.adinballou.org/BallouTolstoyGandhi.shtml
12. 'Gandhi's Views On Nonviolence', http://www.gandhi-manibhavan.org/gandhiphilosophy/philosophy_nonviolence_nonviolence.htm
13. *Young India,* 8 December 1921.
14. 'Gandhi's Human Touch', J.P. Memorial Lecture by Prof. Madhu Dandavate; http://www.mkgandhi.org/articles/humantouch.htm
15. *Harijan,* 3 May 1946, *CWMG,* Vol. 90, p. 342.
16. Geetanjali Parikh, *History of Khadi;* National Book Trust India (2010), pp. 5-6.
17. Uma Shankar Joshi, *Inspiring Stories From Gandhi's Life,* http://www.mkgandhi-sarvodaya.org/story.htm
18. Sudhir Kakar, *Mira & the Mahatma,* Penguin (2004).
19. Dr Ajai R. Singh and Dr Shakuntala A. Singh, 'The Tagore-Gandhi Controversy Revisited' *Indian Philosophical Quarterly,* Vol. XIX, No.3, July 1992.

Chapter 7

1. A good source to understand Gandhi's views on machinery is the centenary edition of *Gandhi: Hind Swaraj and Other Writings,* ed. by Anthony J. Parel and published in 2009 by the Cambridge University Press. Parel writes: 'Gandhi's thinking on machinery underwent gradual development'. He offers a helpful selection of excerpts about Gandhi's thoughts on machinery and industrialisation.
2. Shambhu Prasad, 'Towards an Understanding of Gandhi's Views on Science', http://www.mkgandhi.org/articles/views_on_sci.htm
3. *Young India,* 22 October 1931.
4. *Indian Opinion,* 21 April 1906.
5. Anthony J. Parel, *Gandhi: Hind Swaraj and Other Writings,* Cambridge University Press (2009).
6. *Young India,* 17 March 1927.
7. *Amrita Bazar Patrika,* 13 January 1946; *Harijan,* 31 March 1946; *CWMG,* Vol. 89, p. 189.
8. *CWMG,* Vol. 59, p. 127.
9. Shambhu Prasad, 'Towards An Understanding Of Gandhi's Views On Science', http://www.mkgandhi.org/articles/views_on_sci.htm
10. *CWMG,* Vol. 29, pp. 326-27.
11. From Gandhi's thoughts on God as recorded by the Columbia Gramophone Company in London on 20 October 1931; http://www.gandhiserve.org/

information/listen_to_gandhi/lec_1_on_god/augven_spiritual_message.
html

12. P.C. Ray, *Autobiography of a Bengali Chemist,* Orient, Calcutta, p. 126, 1958.

13. *Harijan,* 22 June 1935.

14. *CWMG,* Vol. 64, p. 99.

15. G. Venkataraman, 'Dr C.V. Raman: The spirit of a giant', http://ces.iisc.
ernet.in/curscinew/25nov98/articles38.htm

16. Raman Research Institute, Digital Repository, http://dspace.rri.res.in/
handle/2289/485

17. *Young India,* 22 October 1925, *CWMG,* Vol. 33, p. 139.

18. Ibid.

19. Shambhu Prasad, 'Towards an Understanding of Gandhi's Views on Science',
http://www.mkgandhi.org/articles/views_on_sci.htm, *CWMG,* Vol. 59,
p. 409.

20. Shambhu Prasad, 'Towards an Understanding of Gandhi's Views on
Science', http://www.mkgandhi.org/articles/views_on_sci.htm

21. http://www.mkgandhi.org/articles/G%20and%20the%2021st%20century.
htm

22. *Young India,* 5 January 1928.

23. 'India's Maritime Heritage', http://careerinshipping.com/indias-maritime-
heritage.htm

24. 'A Visit to Jamshedpur' in *Industrial and Agrarian Life and Relations* by
M.K. Gandhi, compiled and ed. by V.B. Kher, Navajivan Publishing House,
Ahmedabad (1984).

25. *'Sir Ratan Tata and Mahatma Gandhi'* by H. Raghunath, head of the Tata
Central Archives, Pune. He had earlier set up the Tata Steel Archives,
Jamshedpur. http://www.rediff.com/money/2004/aug/16tata.htm

26. *Young India,* 17 March 1927.

27. Although Gandhi spent his last days at Birla House in New Delhi, he did
so against his wishes. He wanted to stay in Bhangi Colony (scavengar's
quarters). Due to widespread communal tension in the capital, and also
because of fears about a threat to his life, the government persuaded
him to stay at Birla House. Gandhi agreed on one condition: he would
not have any security personnel guarding his place of stay.

28. Interview to H.N. Brailsford, *The Manchester Guardian,* 13 October 1931,
CWMG, Vol. 53, p. 384.

29. Discussion with J.F. Horrabin, Harold Laski, Kingsley Martin and others;
London, 3 December 1931; *CWMG,* Vol. 54, p. 248.

30. *CWMG,* Vol. 53, p. 422.

31. Anthony J. Parel, *Gandhi: Hind Swaraj and Other Writings*.
32. *Harijan,* 27 January 1940.
33. *CWMG,* Vol. 87, p 333. For further reference to Gandhi's praise of the Singer sewing machine, see Chapter 10.
34. *CWMG,* Vol. 85, p. 235.
35. Dr Pankaj Joshi, *Gandhi ane Vidnyan* (Gujarati), Yadnya Prakashan, Vadodara (2011), p. 14
36. Romain Rolland's letter to Stefan Zweig, 30 December 1931, *Romain Rolland and Gandhi: Correspondence,* Publications Division, Government of India (1976), pp. 458–61.
37. *Young India,* 27 September 1925.
38. *Harijan;* 13 March 1937.
39. D.G. Tendulkar, *Mahatma,* Vol. 5, p. 174, 1st Edition (1952).
40. *Harijan,* 14 October 1939; Reproduced in *Economic Thought of Mahatma Gandhi* by J.S. Mathur and A.S. Mathur, Chaitanya Publishing House, Allahabad (1962). Many admirers of Gandhi would not quite agree with what appears like his summary rejection of speed in modern life. It is possible, they would say, to reconcile technological progress (and the attendant increase in 'speed of everything') with our spiritual quest, using the methods given in the *Bhagavad Gita.*
41. *Young India,* 20 November 1924.
42. 'Talk with Manu Gandhi', 1 June 1947, *CWMG,* Vol. 88.
43. Gandhi – Ganga, http://www.mkgandhi.org/ebks/gganga.pdf
44. *CWMG,* Vol. 17, pp. 405-06.
45. B.R. Nanda, *Gandhi and His Critics,* Oxford University Press (1997); p. 158.

Chapter 8

1. Arundhati Bhanot, See 'Mahatma Gandhi: Food for the Soul', *Life Positive,* Oct.–Nov. 2002.
2. *Young India,* 13 June 1939, *CWMG,* Vol. 46, p. 106.
3. Arundhati Bhanot, 'Mahatma Gandhi: Food for the Soul', *Life Positive,* Oct.-Nov. 2002.
4. Arundhati Bhanot, 'Mahatma Gandhi: Food for the Soul', http://www. lifepositive.com/spirit/masters/mahatma-gandhi/diet.asp
5. B.R. Nanda, *In Search of Gandhi: Essays and Reflections,* Oxford University Press (2002), p. 229.
6. *Romain Rolland and Gandhi: Correspondence,* Publications Division; Government of India (1976), pp. 462 and 472–73.
7. *Young India,* 25 September 1924.

8. B.R. Nanda, a noted Gandhi scholar and former director, Nehru Memorial Museum and Library, quoted in *Life Positive*, Oct.–Dec. 2002.
9. Gandhi on Nonviolence, http://www.gandhi-manibhavan.org/gandhiphilosophy/philosophy_nonviolence_nonviolence.htm
10. *Young India*, 5 November 1931.

Chapter 9

1. *Indian Opinion*, 11 January 1913.
2. M.K. Gandhi, *Satyagraha in South Africa*, Navajivan Publishing House, Ahmedabad.
3. B.R. Nanda, *In Search of Gandhi: Essays and Reflections*; Oxford University Press (2002), p. 211.
4. B.R. Nanda, *In Search of Gandhi: Essays and Reflections*; pp. 228-29.
5. *Mahatma Gandhi Constructive Programme: Its Meaning and Place*, December 1941, *CWMG*, Vol. 81, p. 370.
6. Ramesh Menon, 'Leprosy nearly eliminated, challenges remain' India Together, http://www.indiatogether.org/2006/aug/hlt-leprosy.htm
7. www.searchgadchiroli.org
8. Gandhi's Views on Nature Cure & Holistic Treatment, http://www.gandhi-manibhavan.org/gandhiphilosophy/philosophy_environment_naturecure.htm
9. Mahatma Gandhi, *Key to Health*, Navajivan Trust, Ahmedabad.
10. Megha Bajaj, 'Mahatma Gandhi: And Gandhi Came Alive', *Life Positive*, January 2008.
11. *Young India*, 8 August 1929.
12. *CWMG*, Vol. 27, p. 344.
13. *Young India*, 17 June 1926.
14. *Harijan*, 11 August 1946.
15. *Harijan*, 7 December 1934.

Chapter 10

1. *Harijan*, 16 January 1937.
2. D.G. Tendulkar, *Mahatma*, Vol. 4, p. 191, 1st Edition (1952).
3. 'A Visit to Jamshedpur' in *Industrial and Agrarian Life and Relations* by M.K. Gandhi, Compiled and ed. by V.B. Kher, Navajivan Publishing House, Ahmedabad (1984).
4. Mahatma Gandhi's interview to *Associated Press*, 28 March 1933.

5. Rajmohan Gandhi, *Gandhi: The Man, His People, and the Empire;* Also see, *Gandhi as a Human Ecologist* by John S. Moolakkattu; *Journal of Human Ecology,* 2010, Vol. 29 (II): pp. 151-58.

6. In an interview given to Placido P D'Souza ('Hindu cosmology's time-scale for the universe is in consonance with modern science', Rediff.com, January 1997), Carl Sagan (1934–96) paid glowing tributes to Gandhi. 'What was so impressive about Gandhi was the way he was able to communicate to large numbers of people and to excite people's passion and courage. There was a great deal of courage needed to have followed him, especially in the early days of his movement. I think something along those lines is needed worldwide if we are to break out of this impasse in the nuclear arms race.' Expressing his appreciation for Attenborough's film *Gandhi,* Sagan said: 'It was splendid on many different levels. One is the idea that there are ways for the people to move governments by unconventional approaches including civil disobedience… The American Civil Rights Movement, of course, was powerfully influenced by the degree to which Martin Luther King, Jr admired Mohandas Gandhi, and I think that it is important for us, Americans, to remember that connection… The movie was beautifully filmed, and in many places, extremely moving.'

Chapter 11

1. UNICEF India, Water, environment and sanitation, http://www.unicef. org/india/wes_2924.htm

2. http://www.facenfacts.com/ColumnDetails/11/mahatma_gandhi_and_ human_security.htm

3. Mahatma Gandhi, 'Our Dirty Ways' in *Navajivan,* 13 September 1925.

4. Kumbh Mela, an ancient Hindu pilgrimage, dates back several millennia to the Vedic period. It is associated with the *Samudra Manthan* (churning of the ocean of milk) episode, which mythologises the battle between good and evil. The *Ardh* (half) Kumbh Mela is celebrated every six years at Haridwar and Prayag (Allahabad). The *Purna* (complete) Kumbh takes place every twelve years at four places – Prayag, Haridwar, Ujjain and Nashik. The *Maha* (great) Kumbh Mela, which comes after twelve '*Purna* Kumbh Melas', or 144 years, is held at Prayag. All these events attract millions of pilgrims.

5. *Young India,* 31 October 1929.

6. *Young India,* 3 February 1927.

7. *Harijan,* 11 August 1946.

8. *Navajivan,* 24 May 1925.

9. All quotations in this para are taken from the 'Sanitation' section in the book *Social Service, Work & Reform,* Vol. 1 by M.K. Gandhi, Navajivan Publishing House, Ahmedabad.

10. *Social Service, Work & Reform,* Vol. 1 by M.K. Gandhi.

11. Gandhi was a voluminous letter writer. Sometimes he wrote about fifty letters in a day in long hand. He wrote more than 1,00,000 letters in his life.

12. *Harijan;* 9 January 1937.

13. *Young India,* 19 November 1925.

Chapter 12

1. *CWMG,* Vol. 19, p. 105.

2. Samuel Crompton (1753–1827) was an English inventor and a pioneer of the spinning industry. James Hargreaves (1720–78) was a weaver, carpenter and an inventor of the Spinning Jenny.

3. Shambhu Prasad, 'Towards an Understanding of Gandhi's Views on Science' http://www.mkgandhi.org/articles/views_on_sci.htm

4. Bahuroopee Gandhi; www.mkgandhi.org/bahurupi/chap13.htm

5. The most illuminating sources for knowing how the British rule destroyed India's native industry, its science and technology traditions and also its highly evolved traditional education infrastructure are the two works of Dharampal, a noted Gandhian historian: *Indian Science and Technology in the Eighteenth Century*; and *The Beautiful Tree: Indigenous Indian Education in the Eighteenth Century,* published by Other India Press, Mapusa, Goa.

6. D.G. Tendulkar, *Mahatma,* Vol. 4, p. 186; 1st Edition (1952).

7. M.K. Gandhi, *India of My Dreams,* www.mkgandhi.org/indiadreams/chap46. htmCached

8. G. Ramachandran, *The Gandhian Contribution to Education,* published in the book *The Quest for Gandhi;* Gandhi Peace Foundation, New Delhi, and Bharatiya Vidya Bhavan, Bombay (1970), p. 334.

9. Mahatma Gandhi on Education, www.mkgandhi.org/edugandhi/basic1. htmCached

10. M.K. Gandhi, *Towards New Education,* www.mkgandhi.org/towrds_edu/ chap02.htmCached

11. *Education for Swaraj* – Articles on and by Mahatma Gandhi, www.mkgandhi.org/articles/edu_swaraj.htmCached

12. *The Hindu,* 5 December 1944; *CWMG,* Vol. 85, pp. 183-85.

13. Verrier Elwin, 'Mahatma Gandhi's Philosophy of Truth' (Studies in relation to Western mysticism), *Modern Review,* Aug–Oct. 1933.

14. *Harijan,* 31 July 1937.
15. See *Science and Domination: India Before and After Independence* by Prof. Rajesh Kochhar, a CSIR emeritus scientist at the Indian Institute of Science Education and Research, Mohali. (http://www.ias.ac.in/currsci/feb25/ articles33.htm) Prof. Kochhar writes: 'Under the Indian auspices, modern science was Brahminised during the colonial period, and Kshatriyaised after independence. The artisanisation of modern science that gave Europe its strength never took place in India'.
16. Study conducted by NASSCOM in 2009.

Chapter 13

1. The source of many of these anecdotes about Gandhi as a 'toiler', 'cook', 'teacher', 'doctor', 'shoemaker', 'farmer', etc., is a small book titled *Bahuroopee Gandhi* by Anu Bandopadhyaya ('Bahuroopee' means multi-faceted). In his foreword to this book (dated 10 March 1964), Prime Minister Jawaharlal Nehru wrote: 'It is extraordinary how in many things he (Gandhi) took interest and when he took interest, he did so thoroughly. It was not a superficial interest. It was perhaps his thoroughness in dealing with what are considered to be the small things of life which emphasised his humanism. That was the basis of his character'. Some of these anecdotes are also narrated in D.G. Tendulkar's eight-volume magnum opus *Mahatma: Life of Mohandas Karamchand Gandhi.*
2. Gandhi was jailed eleven times in his life. Once he was arrested thrice within four days. If he had to complete all his jail terms, he would have spent eleven years and nineteen days in jail. Occasionally, his punishment was reduced and altogether he spent six years and ten months in prison. At the age of thirty-nine, he first entered a jail. He came out of the prison gates for the last time when he was seventy-five.
3. *Bahuroopee Gandhi*; www.mkgandhi.org/bahurupi/chap13.htm
4. D.G. Tendulkar, *Mahatma,* Vol. 4, pp. 38-39, 1st Edition (1952).
5. www.vinaylal.com/ESSAYS(Gandhi)/eco2.pdf
6. Gandhi was a journalist par excellence. The first newspaper he founded was *Indian Opinion* in South Africa in 1903. It lasted for eleven years. The other publications he edited were *Young India, Navajivan* (in Gujarati), *Harijan* (English), *Harijan Bandhu* (Gujarati) and *Harijan Sevak* (Hindi).
7. *Mind of Mahatma Gandhi*; www.mkgandhi.org/momgandhi/chap81. htmCached – Similar
8. *Harijan,* 7 September 1934.
9. *Harijan,* 7 September 1934.

10. B.R. Nanda, *In Search of Gandhi: Essays and Reflections*, Oxford University Press (2002), p. 214.
11. *CWMG*, Vol. 73, p. 105.
12. *CWMG*, Vol. 73, p. 36.
13. Shambhu Prasad, 'Towards an Understanding of Gandhi's Views on Science' http://www.mkgandhi.org/articles/views_on_sci.htm
14. *Young India*, 26 June 1924.

Chapter 14

1. *Harijan*, 27 April 1947.
2. Dhruv, a five-year-old boy, performed extreme penance to seek God's blessings to overcome an act of injustice done to him by his stepmother, who had denied him the right to sit on his father's lap. The Lord was so pleased with Dhruv's devotion that he was transported to the highest point of heaven, where he sits on his Divine Father's lap as the Pole Star, which is also known as the North Star. The story of Dhruv becoming the Pole Star, and he being protected by *saptarshis* (seven rishis), who forever circle round him in the sky, is highly popular in the Hindu mythology.

    Prahlad is a lad who faced the wrath of his tyrant father because of his unshakeable faith in God. His father tried to frighten him with poison, sword and fire, all in vain. Each time the Lord Himself responded to the five-year-old boy's devotion and came to his rescue. Holi, the popular festival of colours, is linked to the story of Prahlad.

    Sudama was a childhood friend of Lord Krishna. He was born in a poor family, whereas Krishna belonged to the royal family. The close lifelong bond between them carries the message that difference in social status cannot come in the way of true friendship.

    Shukdev, son of Maharshi Ved Vyas, who authored the epic *Mahabharata*, was a great philosopher and administrator of justice. He was an ardent devotee of Lord Krishna.
3. *Harijan*, 27 April 1947.
4. *Young India*, 4 September 1924.
5. *Harijan*, 31 March 1946.
6. *Young India*, 27 May 1926.
7. *Young India*, 20 May 1926.
8. *Young India*, 15 April 1926.
9. Here is a pointer to Gandhi's broadminded approach to the diversity in music, transcending linguistic, religious and national barriers. Once,

after his visit to Santiniketan in 1945, he observed: 'Music in Santiniketan is charming, but has the professor there come to the conclusion that Bengali music is the last word in that direction? Has Hindustani music, i.e., music before and after the Muslim period, anything to give to the world of music? If it has, it should have its due place at Santiniketan. Indeed, I would go so far as to say that Western music, which has made immense strides, should also blend with the Indian.' Gandhi also added: 'One question about music. I have a suspicion that perhaps there is more of music than warranted by life, or I'll put the thought in another way. The music of life is in danger of being lost in the music of the voice.' – Gandhi's letter to Rathindranath Tagore, Gurudev Rabindranath Tagore's eldest son, from Khadi Pratishthan, Sodepur, Bengal, 22 December 1945. *CWMG,* Vol. 89, p. 75.

10. Will Durant, *The Case for India,* Strand Bookstall, Mumbai (2007), p. 43.

11. *Truth is God – Compilation of Gandhiji's Sayings,* ed. R. K. Prabhu, Navajivan Publishing House, Ahmedabad (1955), p. 60.

12. Hazrat Inayat Khan's son, Hidayat Inayat Khan, who too was a great exponent of Sufi music, composed a special number called the 'Gandhi Symphony' which he dedicated to Mahatma Gandhi on the occasion of his birth centenary in 1969. This symphony, which expressed the Mahatma's message of universal brotherhood, was broadcast by the United Nation's Radio in New York as well as by major broadcasting stations all over the world.

13. *Young India,* 21 February 1924.

14. Noel Salmond; 'Both Iconoclast and Idolater: Gandhi on the Worship of Images' *Studies in Religion/Sciences Religieuses, Vol.* 31 (3-4) (2002) pp. 373-390; www.wlu.ca/press/Journals/sr/issues/31_3-4/salmond.pdf

15. *Harijan,* 8 May 1937.

16. http://www.mkgandhi.org/bahurupi/chap14.htm

Chapter 15

1. Several decades later, another foreigner endeared Gandhi to the minds and hearts of people all over the world. It was Richard Attenborough, whose film *Gandhi* (1982) was widely screened and acclaimed.

2. *Romain Rolland and Gandhi Correspondence,* Publications Division, Government of India (1976).

3. Romain Rolland, *Prophets of the New India,* Cassell and Company Ltd., London.

4. Romain Rolland, *Life of Ramakrishna,* Advaita Ashrama, Almora, (1954).

5. *Romain Rolland and Gandhi Correspondence.* Rolland is also admired for his vast correspondence with other global figures such as Albert Einstein, Albert Schweitzer, Bertrand Russell and Rabindranath Tagore.

6. Carl Jung, the renowned Swiss psychologist who developed the concept of synchronicity in the 1920s, described it as the occurrence of two or more events in an apparently coincidental manner but reflecting a meaningful governing logic. He believed that life was not a series of random events but rather an expression of a deeper order.

7. *Romain Rolland and Gandhi Correspondence.*

8. Coincidentally, Leo Tolstoy also serves as a mystical link between Gandhi and Romain Rolland. Tolstoy's decisive influence on Gandhi is well known. No less decisive was Tolstoy's influence on Rolland, who, because of his courageous advocacy of peace in Europe, was described by the great Russian writer Maxim Gorky as the 'Tolstoy of France'. Rolland had written a book, *Life of Tolstoy,* which had greatly influenced Gandhi's secretary Pyarelal.

9. Mirabehn (Madeleine Slade), *The Spirit's Pilgrimage,* Longmans, London (1960), p. 66.

10. Mirabehn (Madeleine Slade), *The Spirit's Pilgrimage,* p. 170.

Chapter 16

1. We have mentioned Madeleine Slade (Mirabehn) in this essay because of her close association with both Gandhi and Romain Rolland. However, we must also show our appreciation for another Madeleine – Madeleine Rolland, the writer's sister, whom he described as 'my faithful companion in this voyage of the soul'. The two Madeleines too were companions in the same spiritual voyage, as is clear from these lines from Romain Rolland: 'The series of letters she (Madeleine Slade) wrote to my sister will one day form one of the most astonishing dossiers in religious history. Her conversations with the Mahatma, and the devout spirit with which she listens and remembers, evoke a new Gospel'.

2. Pyarelal, *Mahatma Gandhi: The Last Phase,* Navajivan Publishing House, Ahmedabad, 1956, Vol. I, p. 105.

3. Pyarelal, *Mahatma Gandhi: The Last Phase,* Vol. I, p. 105.

4. V.V. Ramana Murti, *Romain Rolland and Gandhi,* in the book *Quest for Gandhi,* ed. G. Ramachandran and T.K. Mahadevan, Gandhi Peace Foundation, New Delhi, and Bharatiya Vidya Bhavan, Bombay, 1970.

Chapter 17

1. Gandhi's thoughts on art are taken from *Truth is God – Gleanings from the Writings of Mahatma Gandhi on God, God-Realisation and the Godly Way*, compiled by R.K. Prabhu, Navajivan Publishing House, Ahmedabad.

2. Phidias was a Greek artist who lived in the fifth century BC. He is regarded as one of the greatest of all the sculptors of ancient Greece.

3. D.G. Tendulkar, *Mahatma*, Vol. 4, p. 93, 1st Edition (1952).

4. In Hinduism, the four *purusharthas* or objectives of life are: dharma (righteousness, duty), *artha* (wealth), *kaama* (desire), and *moksha* (liberation).

5. Anthony J. Parel, *Gandhi's Philosophy and the Quest for Harmony*, Cambridge University Press (2006).

6. Anand K. Coomaraswamy's answers to questions put by S. Durai Raja Singam on 15 August 1947, http://www.yabaluri.org/TRIVENI/CDWEB/lettersofanandakcoomaraswamyapr77.htm

7. Website of Dakshina Bharat Hindi Prachar Sabha, http://www.dbhpsabha.org/

8. B.R. Nanda, *In Search of Gandhi – Essays and Reflections*, p. 60.

9. Bhaswati Bandyopadhyay records this in her article *Mahatma Gandhi and His Contemporary Artists* (http://www.mkgandhisarvodaya.org/articles/art&g.htm). She also provides interesting information about Gandhi's admiration for Nandalal Bose, his favourite artist. In 1936, he called Bose to decorate the Congress pavilion at Lucknow, where the artist got an opportunity to project India's history and tradition. With his team from Santiniketan he decorated the entire exhibition hall in a very simple manner with the help of reed, bamboo and timber. In his speech at the exhibition ground, Gandhi said: 'This exhibition to my mind brings out concretely for the first time the conception of a true rural exhibition.... It is the purpose of this exhibition to show that even things which we town dwellers do not like may be used both to the villagers' and our advantage...Srijut Nandalal, the eminent artist from Santiniketan, and his co-workers who have tried to represent all the villagers' craft in simple artistic symbols, have done a great job. And when you go inside the art gallery on which Babu Nandalal has lavished his labours for weeks, you will feel, as I did, like spending there hours together. You may not find in the exhibition anything to amuse you like music or cinema shows but I assure you, you will find much to learn.' Remembering an incident from the exhibition which showed Gandhi's sharp observation of even the smallest discordant detail, Bose later wrote: 'Though everything was neatly arranged in the exhibition hall, someone

had carelessly left a bucket under a table. It escaped our eyes but not the sharp eyes of Bapuji. On entering the hall he noticed it at once and said: "Doesn't that disturb your sense of beauty?"'

Chapter 18

1. It is not that the modern economic system has only affected the health of the poor in 'developing' and 'underdeveloped' countries. Mental disorders are common in the United States of America and in other rich countries. An estimated 26.2 percent of Americans aged eighteen and older suffer from a diagnosable mental disorder. About six percent of America's population suffers from a serious mental illness, including major depressive disorders leading to suicides. Only about six percent of the country's staggering health care spending is devoted to the treatment of mental disorders. Japan, the third richest country in the world, also has the highest suicide rate in the world – one person ends his or her life every fifteen minutes. Rising prosperity, widening socio-economic disparities and growing dislocation of families and communities in China have resulted in a sharp increase in mental disorders. China now has at least 100 million people suffering from mental illness.

2. Edward Goldsmith, *Can humanity adapt to the world that science is creating?*, http://www.edwardgoldsmith.org/page30.html

3. *Young India;* 22 October 1925.

4. M.K. Gandhi, *Unto This Last – A Paraphrase*, Navajivan Trust, 1956.

5. Ibid.

6. J.S. Mathur and A.S. Mathur; *Economic Thought of Mahatma Gandhi*, Chaitanya Publishing House, Allahabad (1962), p. xlvii.

7. *Young India*, 23 February 1921.

8. M.K. *Gandhi, Towards New Education*, www.mkgandhi.org/trusteeship/chap02.htmCached – Similar

9. *The Mind of Mahatma Gandhi*, www.mkgandhi-sarvodaya.org/momgandhi/chap53.htmCached

10. *Young India*, 26 March 1931, www.mkgandhi-sarvodaya.org/momgandhi/chap53.htm

11. *The Mind of Mahatma Gandhi*, www.mkgandhi-sarvodaya.org/momgandhi/chap53.htmCached

12. Gandhiji's Philosophy on Trusteeship, www.gandhi-manibhavan.org/gandhiphilosophy/philosophy_trustees

13. Gandhiji's Philosophy on Trusteeship, www.gandhi-manibhavan.org/gandhiphilosophy/philosophy_trustees

14. Pyarelal, *Mahatma Gandhi: Last Phase,* (1958) Vol. II, p.65.
15. *Deendayal Upadhyaya's Integral Humanism: Documents, Interpretations and Comparisons,* ed. Devendra Swarup, Deendayal Research Institute, New Delhi (1992).
16. Milovan Djilas (1911–95) was a Yugoslav communist thinker and politician who became disillusioned with communism. His book *The New Class* (1957) revealed that the communist regimes in the Soviet Union and Eastern Europe were little different from capitalist societies.
17. The Gaia principle, proposed by British scientist James Lovelock, regards the Earth as a single living organism.

Chapter 19

1. *The Mind of Mahatma Gandhi;* www.mkgandhi-sarvodaya.org/momgandhi/chap53.htmCached
2. D.G. Tendulkar; *Mahatma,* Vol. 3, p. 112; 1st Edition (1952).
3. An interview with Brian Swimme by Susan Bridle; http://www.enlightennext.org/magazine/j19/swimme.asp.
4. Mahatma Gandhi – *India of My Dreams;* www.indiaofmydreams.in/mahatma-gandhi.html Cached
5. D.G. Tendulkar, *Mahatma,* (1960) Vol.5, p. 291, 2nd Editon.
6. B.R. Nanda, *Gandhi and His Critics,* p. 144.
7. B.R. Nanda, *Gandhi and His Critics,* p. 153.
8. Many critics of Gandhi refer to his letters to Hitler – in which he addressed the Nazi dictator as 'Dear friend' – as proof that he was a 'naive fool'. It is important to remember here that his motive in writing letters to Hitler was entirely to prevent the Second World War and to stop the bloodshed. In his second letter to Hitler, on the eve of Christmas in 1940, he wrote: 'That I address you as a friend is no formality. I own no foes. My business in life has been for the past 33 years to enlist the friendship of the whole of humanity by befriending mankind, irrespective of race, colour or creed.' However, he not even remotely justified or glossed over Hitler's barbaric crimes, for he wrote: '(y)our own writings and pronouncements and those of your friends and admirers leave no room for doubt that many of your acts are monstrous and unbecoming of human dignity...' For an objective analysis of Gandhi's letters to Hitler, see the essay by Koenraad Elst, a Belgian scholar, at http://koenraadelst.bharatvani.org/articles/fascism/gandhihitler.html
9. Mahatma Gandhi, *The Story of My Experiments with Truth,* p.337.

10. D.G. Tendulkar, *Mahatma*, (1960) Vol. 5, p. 180, 2nd Edition.
11. *All Men Are Brothers: Life and Thoughts of Mahatma Gandhi as Told in His Own Words,* ed. Krishna Kripalani, Navajivan Publishing House, p. 89.
12. *All Men Are Brothers: Life and Thoughts of Mahatma Gandhi as Told in His Own Words,* ed. Krishna Kripalani, Navajivan Publishing House, p. 79.
13. *All Men Are Brothers: Life and Thoughts of Mahatma Gandhi as Told in His Own Words,* p. 77.
14. Swami Ranganathananda; 'Mahatma Gandhi: The Abiding Elements in His Life and Work' published in *Mahatma Gandhi: 100 Years*, Gandhi Peace Foundation, New Delhi, 1969.
15. B.R. Nanda, *Gandhi and His Critics*; p. 156.
16. Swami Ranganathananda develops the connection between Evolutionary Biology and Gandhi's philosophy of truth and nonviolence by referring to Julian Huxley's *Evolution After Darwin*.
17. In the early phase of his life, Aurobindo Ghose was a freedom fighter espousing a revolutionary path. However, in 1910 he withdrew himself from politics completely, moved to Pondicherry and devoted his life to spiritual pursuit.
18. Sri Aurobindo, *The Hour of God*, Sahitya Akademi, New Delhi (1995) p. 83.
19. Sri Aurobindo, *The Hour of God*, p. 85.
20. Sri Aurobindo, *The Hour of God*, p. 62.
21. Sri Aurobindo, *The Hour of God*, p. 58.

Chapter 20

1. *CWMG*, Vol. 91, p. 221.
2. *Harijan*, 10 February 1946.
3. Gandhi's talk with an English journalist, *Harijan*, 29 September 1946.
4. 'Atom Bomb and Ahimsa', Poona, 1 July 1946; *Harijan*, 7 July 1946; *CWMG*, Vol. 84, p. 394.
5. *Harijan*, 23 July 1946.

Chapter 21

1. Mazhar Kibriya, *Gandhi and Indian Freedom Struggle*, APH Publishing Corporation, 1999, p. 70.
2. Upton Close, 'Gandhi – The Prophet Who Sways India', *The New York Times*, 19 January 1930. http://tv.nytimes.com/learning/general/specials/india/300119gandhi-profile.html

Chapter 22

1. *Young India,* 10 April 1930.
2. *Gandhi on Women,* Navajivan Publishing House, Ahmedabad (1988), pp. 359-60.
3. *Harijan,* 5 November 1938.
4. *Harijan,* 24 February 1940.
5. D.G. Tendulkar, *Mahatma,* (1960) Vol. 2, p. 367, 2nd Editon.
6. *Harijan,* 25 March 1933.
7. *Young India,* 8 December 1927.
8. *Gandhi on Women – A Collection of Mahatma Gandhi's Writings and Speeches on Women,* compiled by Pushpa Joshi, Navajivan Publishing House and Centre for Women's Development Studies, (1998), p. iii.
9. Eknath Easwaran, *Gandhi, the Man,* Jaico, 1997, p. 169.
10. Dr Judith L. Hand, *Women, Power, and the Biology of Peace,* http://www.jhand.com/wpbp_excerpts_intro.html
11. Dr Dacher Keltner also argues that, contrary to popular perception, Charles Darwin did not rationatise violent competition by advancing the law of 'survival of the fittest'. In Darwin's first book about humans, *The Descent of Man, and Selection In Relation to Sex* (1871), he recognised 'the greater strength of the social or maternal instincts than that of any other instinct or motive.' Dr Keltner writes: 'To be a mammal is to suffer. To be a mammal is to feel the strongest of Darwin's instincts – sympathy. ...Were he alive today, Darwin would likely have found modest delight in seeing two of his hypotheses confirmed: sympathy is indeed wired into our brains and bodies; and it spreads from one person to another through touch. Darwin, the great fact amasser that he was, would no doubt have compiled these new findings on sympathy and touch in one of his many notebooks (now a folder on a laptop). He may have titled that folder 'Survival of the Kindest'. (See http://greatergood.berkeley.edu/article/item/darwins_touch_survival_of_the_kindest/)
12. *The Daily Herald,* 28 September 1931, *CWMG,* Vol. 53, pp. 426-27.

Chapter 23

1. T.N. Khoshoo and John S. Moolakkatu, *Mahatma Gandhi and the Environment: Analysing Gandhian Environmental Thought,* published by TERI, New Delhi, 2009.
2. Mahatma Gandhi, *Truth is God,* p. 50.

3. John S. Moolakkattu, 'Gandhi as a Human Ecologist', *Journal of Human Ecology*, (2010) Vol. 29(3), pp. 151-158.

4. Press Release of the International Union for Conservation of Nature (IUCN), 27 October 2010, http://iucn.org/?6333; also see http://www.kew.org/news/one-fifth-of-plants-under-threat-of-extinction.htm

5. Suma Varughese, 'Rediscovering Mahatma Gandhi', *Life Positive*, October-December 2002. http://www.lifepositive.com/spirit/masters/mahatma-gandhi/gandhi.asp

6. John S. Moolakkattu, 'Gandhi as a Human Ecologist'.

7. *Economic Thought of Mahatma Gandhi* by J.S. Mathur and A.S. Mathur, Chaitanya Publishing House, Allahabad (1962).

8. John S. Moolakkattu, *Gandhi as a Human Ecologist*.

9. *CWMG*, Vol. 81, pp. 433-34.

10. *CWMG*, Vol. 26, p. 272.

11. Mirabchn, 'His Daily Life', The essay appears in *Incidents of Gandhi's Life*, ed. Chandrashankar Shukla, Vora & Co. Publishers Ltd., Bombay, First published on 30 January 1949, pp. 186-87.

12. http://www.mkgandhi.org/articles/g&internationalsecurity.htm

13. *Young India*, 4 December 1924.

14. *Encyclopaedia of Gandhian Thoughts*, ed. Anand T. Hingorani and Ganga A. Hingorani (1985), p. 10.

15. *Harijan*, 19 January 1937.

16. *The Ecology of Wisdom: Writings by Arne Naess*, Counterpoint Berkeley (2008), p. 295.

17. John S. Moolakkattu in *Gandhi as a Human Ecologist*.

18. I would like to make a mention here of Bhaskar Save, the legendary guru of natural farming. This ninety-year-old (in 2012) *karmayogi* embarked on his mission of natural farming about six decades ago. He grows coconuts on his fourteen-acre farmland called Kalpavruksh in south Gujarat by following the Gandhian way of farming based on five principles: 1) Harmonious coexistence for mutual benefit: Do not use artificial means to kill micro-organisms; 2) Nothing born out of Mother Earth is waste; 3) Farming is not man's *dhanda* (business), it is his *dharma* (moral duty); 4) All is Nature's will, we are mere labourers. Since our rights are limited, extract only as per your needs; 5) Do not hurry, since Nature herself does not. Land is a living being. Converse with the farm.

    At Kalpavruksh, the average yield per coconut tree is an enviable 400 coconuts, far more than the normal range of 70 to 100. In 1997, Masanobu Fukuoka, the revered father of permaculture, honoured Save as 'the Gandhi of Natural Farming'. In 2010, the International Federation of Organic

Agriculture Movements (IFOAM) honoured him with the prestigious 'One World Award for Lifetime Achievement'.

19. 'RTA-RITU – An Exhibition on Cosmic Order and Cycle of Seasons', organised by the Indira Gandhi National Centre for the Arts (IGNCA), New Delhi. http://www.ignca.nic.in/ex025017.htm

Chapter 24

1. Gerald Heard was a widely influential British historian, science commentator and philosopher. He wrote thirty-eight books, among them *Pain, Sex and Time,* which explores new vistas in human evolution. Huston Smith, one of the greatest scholars on world religions, wrote in his 2004 Foreword to *Pain, Sex and Time:* 'Overnight, the book in hand converted me from the scientific worldview to the vaster world of the mystics.' Huston was not alone in experiencing this transformation.

2. *Mind of Mahatma Gandhi,* ed. Prabhu & Rao, Navajivan Publishing House, Ahmedabad, 3rd Edition, (1968), p. 424.

3. D.G. Tendulkar, *Mahatma* 2nd Editon, (1960) Vol. 3, p. 144.

4. http://nobelprize.org/nobel_prizes/literature/laureates/1970/solzhenitsyn-lecture.html

5. D.G. Tendulkar, *Mahatma,* 2nd Edition (1960) Vol. 2, p. 159.

6. http://www.studiobrien.com/index2.php?option=com_content&do_pdf=1&id=30

7. Vinay Lal, 'Nakedness, Nonviolence, and Brahmacharya: Gandhi's Experiments in Celibate Sexuality', *Journal of the History of Sexuality,* (2000) Vol 9, (1-2), pp. 105-36. http://www.vinaylal.com/ESSAYS(Gandhi)/nak7.pdf

8. Gandhi's letter to Shankarlal Banker, 1918, *CWMG,* Vol. 19, p. 43.

9. *Harijan,* 28 March 1936.

10. Joseph Lelyveld, *Great Soul: Mahatma Gandhi and His Struggle With India,* Alfred A. Knopf (2011).

11. Pyarelal, *Mahatma Gandhi – The Last Phase,* Vol. I Book Two, pp. 217-18.

12. D.G. Tendulkar, *Mahatma,* 2nd Edition, (1960) Vol. 2, p. 237.

13. Pyarelal, *Mahatma Gandhi: The Last Phase,* Vol. 1, p. 509.

14. Manubehn Gandhi, *The End of an Epoch,* Navajivan Publishing House, Ahmedabad (1962).

15. Manubehn Gandhi, *The End of an Epoch.*

16. *CWMG,* Vol. 86, p. 368.

17. B.R. Nanda, *In Search of Gandhi: Essays and Reflections,* p. 246.

18. Gandhi writing about his twenty-one-day fast to focus attention on the

plight of the Untouchables; *Harijan,* 8 July 1933; *CWMG,* Vol. 61, p. 221.

19. A highly illuminating compilation of Gandhi's writings on brahmacharya was published in 1943 under the title *Conquest of Self.* Compiled by R.K. Prabhu and U.R. Rao, it was brought out, with the permission of Navajivan Trust, by Thacker & Co., Ltd., Bombay. In their introduction to the book, Prabhu and Rao observe: 'Even a cursory glance through any single chapter of this work will show the reader that Gandhi holds radical views on most of the subjects dealt with by him and that not infrequently some of these views constitute a direct challenge to those professed in so-called 'enlightened' and 'progressive' society. But, they are expressed in such an entire absence of dogmatism and with such compelling appeal to reason that it will be difficult to brush them aside as being obsolete or obscurantist'.

20. Gandhi's *Key to Health* is also discussed earlier in Chapters 8 and 9.

21. D.G. Tendulkar, *Mahatma,* (1952), Vol. 4, p. 59.

22. Maharashi Patanjali (2nd BCE) is the compiler of the *Yoga Sutras,* a seminal guide to the philosophy and practice of yoga.

23. *Harijan,* 13 October 1940, *CWMG,* Vol. 73, pp. 66-71.

24. *Hind Swaraj, CWMG,* Vol. 10, p. 296.

25. Mahatma Gandhi, *Key to Health;* Navajivan Publishing House, Ahmedabad, (1948), pp. 23-24.

26. Vidya Dehejia, *Yogini Cult and Temples: A Tantric Tradition,* National Museum, New Delhi, (1986), pp. 53-54.

27. Prof. P.V. Kane, *History of Dharmasastra,* Bhandarkar Research Institute, Pune, pp. 1423-24.

28. *Maharshi Aurobindo and the Mother on Physical Education,* Sri Aurobindo Ashram, Puducherry, (1967), p. 59.

29. Swami Sivananda, *Practice of Brahmacharya,* The Divine Life Society, 12th Editon (2006), p. 36. The original exposition in Sanskrit of the seven-stage formation of semen is as follows: *'Rasad raktam tato mamsam, mamsanmedah prajayate, medasosthi tatomajja, majja shukrasya sambhavah'* (From food comes juice or chyle; from chyle, blood; from blood, flesh; from flesh, fat; from fat, bones; from bones, marrow; and lastly from marrow, semen.)

30. Mahatma Gandhi, *Key to Health,* Navajivan Publishing House, Ahmedabad, (1948); p. 26.

31. Mahatma Gandhi, *Conquest of Self,* p. 27.

32. Mahatma Gandhi, *Conquest of Self,* p. 9.

33. Atal Bihari Vajpayee, *Meri Ikyavan Kavitayen* (My Fifty-One Poems), Kitabghar, New Delhi, (1995). The relevant lines in praise of Sage Dadhichi are: *'Ahuti baaki, Yagya adhura/ Apnon ke vighno ne ghera/ Antim jay ka vajra*

banaane, Nav Dadhichi haddiyan galayen/ Aao phir se diya jalaayen'. (Our sacrifices are inadequate, our *yajna* is still incomplete. We have been cornered by troubles created by our own people. Let us become New Dadhichis and make invincible weapons out of our own bones in order to achieve final victory. Come, let us light the lamp again.)

34. Paul Brunton, *Notebooks;* http://wisdomsgoldenrod.org/notebooks/para/7342

35. Paramahansa Yogananda, *Autobiography of a Yogi*, Yogoda Satsanga Math (1946), Chapter 26 of this book, 'The Science of Kriya Yoga', further explains:
    Some people have criticised Gandhi for imposing his brahmacharya on his wife Kasturba. His view at the time was that 'husband and wife do not have to obtain each other's consent for practicing brahmacharya'; 'mutual consent is essential for intercourse, but no consent is necessary for abstention.' He changed his view later. When his advice was sought by a married man who wished to observe brahmacharya in opposition to his wife's wishes, he said: 'A husband or a wife can strive for any aim which was not in the minds of both at the time of marriage, only with the consent of the other party. In other words, a husband cannot take the vow of brahmacharya without the consent of his wife.' See 'Nakedness, Nonviolence, and Brahmacharya: Gandhi's Experiments in Celibate Sexuality' by Prof. Vinay Lal, Department of History, University of California, Los Angeles; *Journal of the History of Sexuality* January/April 2000 Vol. 9 (1-2).

36. Prof. Vinay Lal, 'Nakedness, Nonviolence, and Brahmacharya: Gandhi's Experiments in Celibate Sexuality', Department of History, University of California, Los Angeles; *Journal of the History of Sexuality*, January/April 2000 Vol. 9 (1-2).

37. Mahatma Gandhi, *Key to Health*, Navajivan Publishing House, p. 43.

38. Mahatma Gandhi, *Key to Health*, p. 24.

39. Pyarelal, *Mahatma Gandhi: The Last Phase*, Vol. I, Book Two.

40. Pyarelal, *Mahatma Gandhi: The Last Phase*, Vol. I, Book Two.

41. Millie Graham Polak, *Gandhi as We Knew Him*, ed. C. Shukla, Bombay, p.47; Also quoted in *Mahatma Gandhi – The Last Phase* by Pyarelal, Navajivan Publishing House, Ahmedabad, 1956, p. 234.

42. Pyarelal, *Mahatma Gandhi: The Last Phase*, Vol. I, Book Two, Vol. I, Book Two, p. 217.

43. Mahatma Gandhi, *Ashram Observances in Action*, Navajivan Publishing House, Ahmedabad, 1955, p. 52.

44. Pyarelal, *Mahatma Gandhi: The Last Phase*, Vol. I, Book Two, p. 211.

45. Gandhi's letter to Bill Lash, 5 February 1933, *CWMG*, Vol. 53, p. 229. The woman who developed a close relationship with him was Chaudhurani

Sarladevi, an artistically and intellectually gifted niece of poet Rabindranath Tagore. That it was an intense relationship is clear from the fact that Gandhi once described her as his 'spiritual wife'. However, the many letters that they exchanged also show that their missions in life were divergent. The relationship later lost its intensity and Sarladevi became a distant figure in his life.

46. *Harijan*, 26 December 1936. Also cited in William Shirer's *Gandhi*, p. 233.
47. Gandhi's letter to Mirabehn, 3 May 1938, *CWMG*, Vol. 67, p. 61.
48. Gandhi's letter to Brijkrishna Chandiwala, 5 April 1938, *CWMG*, Vol. 67, p. 6.
49. Gandhi's letter to Premabehn Kantak, 21 May 1936, *CWMG*, Vol. 62, p. 429.
50. Mahatma Gandhi, *Conquest of Self*, p. 39.
51. *Harijan*, 23 July 1938.
52. *Harijan*, 23 July 1938.
53. Mahatma Gandhi, *Key to Health*, p. 46.
54. Pyarelal, *Mahatma Gandhi: The Last Phase*, Vol. I, Book Two.
55. Manubehn Gandhi, *Bapu: My Mother*, Navajivan Publishing House, Ahmedabad (1949), p. 3.
56. Talk with Manu Gandhi on 15 June 1947, *Bihar Pachhi Dilhi*, p. 141, *CWMG*, Vol. 95, p. 286.
57. Pyarelal, *Mahatma Gandhi: The Last Phase*, Vol. I Book Two.
58. Pyarelal, *Mahatma Gandhi: The Last Phase*, Vol. 1, Book Two, p. 235. Pyarelal quotes Dr Grey Walter, a well-known neurophysiologist and robotician, from his book *The Living Brain*.
59. Mahatma Gandhi, *Conquest of Self: Gleanings from his writings and speeches on Brahmacharya*, compiled by R.K. Prabhu and U.R. Rao, Published with the permission of Navajivan Trust by Thacker & Co., Ltd., Bombay, (1943), p. 106.
60. Mahatma Gandhi, *Conquest of Self*, *p.* 59.
61. *Ashramas* refer to the four stages of life, all of which contribute in their own different ways to an individual's self-development. In contrast, ashrams refer to spiritual hermitages of rishis, where education of different types was imparted. It is one of Gandhi's many creative innovations that he established his ashrams as communes for satyagrahis engaged in self-development and socio-political transformation.
62. *Harijan*, 17 April 1937, *Conquest of Self*, p. 30.
63. Mahatma Gandhi, *Conquest of Self*, p. 27.
64. Mahatma Gandhi, *Conquest of Self*.
65. *Young India*, 24 June 1926, *Conquest of Self*, p. 20.

66. *Young India*, 29 April 1926, *Conquest of Self*, p. 47.
67. Mahatma Gandhi, *Conquest of Self*.
68. Mahatma Gandhi, *Conquest of Self*, p. 46.
69. Pyarelal, *Mahatma Gandhi: The Last Phase*, Vol. 1, Book Two, p. 235.
70. Sri Aurobindo, *The Hour of God*, p. 311.

Chapter 25

1. *Young India*, 3 November 1921.
2. *Young India*, 27 May 1926.
3. *Young India*, 21 November 1929.
4. *Young India*, 17 September 1925.
5. *CWMG*, Vol. 53, pp. 393-94.
6. B.R. Nanda, *In Search of Gandhi: Essays and Reflections*, pp. 255-56 and 260.
7. We should remember that when Gandhi expressed in this letter to Nehru his anguish over the 'world going the wrong way', the catastrophic Second World War had just ended with America dropping atom bombs on Hiroshima and Nagasaki. Gandhi had flayed not only the use of atomic weapons, but also their development itself as a 'sinful' use of science.
8. Gandhi's letter to Jawaharlal Nehru, 5 October 1945, *CWMG*, Vol. 81, pp. 319-21.
9. Here is an example of how even those who ought to be better informed, continue to believe that Gandhi was opposed to machines and modernity. Nobel laureate Amartya Sen, speaking at a Beijing conference on 'Trade, Urbanisation and the Environment' in October 2008, said that 'Gandhi was even against railways.' Replying to a question about whether Gandhian thoughts hold the key to solving problems concerning environment degradation and climate change, Prof. Sen said that although Mahatma Gandhi 'was a great visionary who taught the world many lessons, his thoughts provide no answer to certain issues like international trade and global environment problems.' (Source: 'Gandhi did not have answer to environment problem: Amartya Sen'; Saibal Dasgupta reporting from Beijing, t*Times of India*, 28 October 2009)
Sen is entitled to believe that Gandhi has no answers to the problem of environmental degradation – a belief that will be strongly contested by many – but he is only displaying his ignorance on this issue by stating that 'Gandhi was even against railways'. True, Gandhi had castigated railways in *Hind Swaraj* in 1909. But as can be seen from his letter to

Nehru in 1945, he had revised his views on railways and welcomed them as a necessary part of the infrastructure of 'India of My Dreams'.

10. This letter of Gandhi to Nehru is of historic significance because it shows the length to which the Mahatma went to engage his political heir in a serious dialogue on the main direction of independent India's socio-economic development. 'I want that we two should understand each other fully,' Gandhi wrote. 'And this for two reasons. Our bond is not merely political. It is much deeper. I have no measure to fathom that depth. This bond can never be broken. I therefore want that we should understand each other thoroughly in politics as well. The second reason is that neither of us considers himself as worthless. We both live only for India's freedom, and will be happy to die for that freedom. We do not care for praise from any quarter. Praise or abuse are the same for us. They have no place in the mission for service. Though I aspire to live up to 125 years rendering service, I am nevertheless an old man, while you are comparatively young. That is why I have said that you are my heir. It is only proper that I should at least understand my heir and my heir in turn should understand me. I shall then be at peace.'

11. *Harijan*, 2 November 1934.

Chapter 26

1. Dr James Martin, *The Meaning of the 21st Century: The Make-or-Break Century*, Riverhead Penguin, New York (2007).

2. Gandhi quotes from Richard B. Gregg's letter to a friend on the 'Morals of Machinery', *CWMG*, Vol. 35, p. 71.

3. 'One Laptop per Child' (OLPC) is a project initiated by Prof. Nicholas Negroponte, former head of the MIT Media Lab, to provide affordable e-learning devices for use in the developing world.

4. Linguistic demography in India is as per the 2001 census http:// en.wikipedia.org/wiki/List_of_countries_by_population.

5. Neil Gershenfeld, *FAB: The Coming Revolution on Your Desktop: From Personal Computers to Personal Fabrication*, Basic Books (2005).

6. *CWMG*, Vol. I, Publications Division, Government of India.

7. *CWMG*, Vol. 26, p. 371.

8. 'Gandhi's Views on Education'; http://www.gandhi-manibhavan.org/ gandhiphilosophy/philosophy_education_gandhiview.htm

9. *Harijan*, 5 June 1937.

10. Interview with Neeru Khosla, *Education News*, 8 February 2010, http:// www.educationnews.org/michael-f-shaughnessy/47145.html

11. *CWMG*, Vol. 84, p. 283. Gandhi expresses this thought in a tribute to his secretary Mahadev Desai, who was a great scholar in his own right, on his second death anniversary in August 1944. The thought appears in a Sanskrit verse, translated as follows: 'The wise should devote themselves to learning and worldly welfare as if they were immortal and would never grow old, and follow the path of dharma as if death had seized them by the hair'.

12. Interview with Prof. Anil Gupta on *Techistan*, 25 August 2010, http://www. techistan.com/2010/08/25/mind-to-market-among-pakistan-india-and-the-world/

13. Walter Isaacson, *Steve Jobs*, Little Brown, (2011), pp. 35, 49. Also see 'The Rise of the Citizen Scientist' by Ben Goertzel.
     http://www.kurzweilai.net/h-summit-harvard-the-rise-of-the-citizen-scientist

14. B.R. Nanda, *Gandhi and His Critics*, p. 147.

15. D.G. Tendulkar, *Mahatma*, Vol. 7, 2nd Edition, p. 341.

16. Another autobiographical detour: The very first words I wrote, when I sent the first e-mail in my life, were: 'I thank God because the Internet is not man's creation. It is, and could only have been, His creation.'

17. http://chinadigitaltimes.net/2010/07/zhang-wen-blogs-democracy-and-chinas-future/

18. *As I See It: L.K. Advani's Blog Posts*, Rupa, (2011).

19. *Harijan*, 31 May 1942.

20. *Harijan*, 18 May 1940.

21. *Young India*, 2 January 1937.

Chapter 27

1. http://www.nanotechproject.org/topics/nano101/introduction_to_nanotechnology/

2. One of the best pen-portraits of Gandhi that I have come across is in the book *Among the Great: Conversations with Sri Aurobindo, Mahatma Gandhi, Rabindranath Tagore, Romain Rolland, Bertrand Russell* by Dilip Kumar Ray. A renowned Bengali musician and novelist, Ray was a mystic who tried to integrate the humanistic traditions of the East and the West. Although he was critical of some aspects of Gandhi's philosophy and political strategy, he was nevertheless strongly attracted towards the Mahatma's personality. His essay has some revealing information about Gandhi's greatness in the last years of his life.

3. Eric Drexler and Chris Peterson, with Gayle Pergamit, *Unbounding the*

Future: the Nanotechnology Revolution, William Morrow and Company, Inc., New York, (1992).

4. Interview with Dr Harold Kroto by Norbert Aschenbrenner. http://www.siemens.com/innovation/en/publikationen/publications_pof/pof_spring_2003/materials_articles/interview_with_h_kroto.htm

Chapter 28

1. *Harijan*, 9 October 1937.
2. Speeches and Writings of Mahatma Gandhi, G.A. Natesan & Co., reproduced in *'Economic Thought of Mahatma Gandhi'* by J.S. Mathur and A.S. Mathur; Chaitanya Publishing House, Allahabad, (1962), p. 524.
3. Gandhi's Foreword to *The Economy of Permanence* by J.C. Kumarapppa, 20 August 1945, *CWMG* Vol. 87, p. 383.
4. Hazel Henderson, *The Politics of Money*, in 'The Vermont Commons', http://www.hazelhenderson.com/editorials
5. Ellen Brown, *Web of Debt: The Shocking Truth About Our Money System: The Sleight of Hand That Has Trapped Us in Debt and How We Can Break Free;* Third Millennium Press, 2007.
6. http://www.webofdebt.com/excerpts/introduction.php
7. Henry C.K. Liu, 'Super Capitalism, Super Imperialism and Monetary Imperialism' Asia Times Online, 12 October 2007, http://www.henryckliu.com/page143.html
8. *Martin Luther King Jr. Papers*, Vol. 3, pp. 244-45.
9. 'Buffet warns on investment time bomb', 4 March 2003, news.bbc.co.uk/2/hi/2817995.stm
10. Mary Mellor, *The Future of Money: From Financial Crisis to Public Resource*, Pluto Press, London, 2010.
11. Sam Pitroda and and Mehul Desai, *The March of Mobile Money*, HarperCollins India, 2010.
12. 'Alternative Currencies Grow in Popularity', *TIME Magazine*, 14 December 2008.
13. Gandhi on Swadeshi, http://www.mkgandhi.org/gospel/chap44.htm
14. CWMG, Vol. 9, p. 53. Also quoted in *J.C. Kumarappa, Mahatma Gandhi's Economist* by Mark Lindley, Popular Prakashan, Mumbai (2007), p. 111.
15. From Jean-François Noubel's website www.TheTransitioner.org
16. Bernard Lietaer, *The Future of Money: Creating New Wealth, Work, and a Wiser World*, Random House, 2001.
17. In understanding the Internet's impact on money, I have benefitted much from the proceedings of the 'Future of Money & Technology Summit'. See http://futureofmoney.com/moneyconference/. See, also, the blog

by Guillaume Lebleu on 'Thoughts on the future of money' at http://lebleu.org/blog

18. Gandhi's interview to Charles Petrasch and others, London, 29 October 1931. *Young India*, 26 November 1931, *The Labour Monthly*, April 1932 Vol. 14.

Chapter 29

1. D.G. Tendulkar, *Mahatma* 2nd Edition, (1960) Vol. 5, p. 290.
2. http://nobelprize.org/nobel_prizes/peace/laureates/1995
3. The Russell–Einstein Manifesto was issued on 9 July 1955 by Bertrand Russell in the midst of the Cold War. It called for total nuclear disarmament and urged world leaders to seek non-military means to resolve international conflicts. The signatories included eleven prominent intellectuals and scientists, including Albert Einstein who had signed the manifesto just days before his death on April 18, 1955. The manifesto had called for the convening of a global conference of scientists and peace-minded public personalities. The first such conference was held in Pugwash, Canada, in 1957. The Pugwash Conferences on Science and World Affairs, founded by Russell and Joseph Rotblat, later became an influential organisation to promote the cause of world peace. Pugwash and Rotblat jointly won the Nobel Peace Prize in 1995 for their efforts on nuclear disarmament.
4. Joseph Rotblat, 'A world without war: Is it desirable? Is it feasible?' at the 54th Pugwash Conference on Science and World Affairs 'Bridging a Divided World Through International Cooperation and Disarmament', Seoul, South Korea, 8 October 2004. *Journal on Science and World Affairs* 2006, Vol. 2, No. 1, pp.1-8.
5. http://internetforpeace.org/manifesto.cfm
6. http://internetforpeace.org
7. http://internetforpeace.org
8. http://internetforpeace.org
9. http://internetforpeace.org
10. D.G. Tendulkar, *Mahatma* 2nd Edition, (1960) Vol. 4, p. 206.
11. Report by Saubhadra Chatterji, *Hindustan Times*, 4 April 2012.
12. Steven Pinker, *A History of Violence*, first published in *The New Republic*, 19 March 2007.
13. Fareed Zakaria, *The Post-American World*, W. W. Norton & Company, 2008, published in India in Viking by Penguin Books, 2008, p. 9.
14. *Harijan*, 3 July 1937.

Chapter 30

1. *Mind of Mahatma Gandhi*, ed. Prabhu & Rao, 3rd Edition, 1968, p. 412.
2. *Young India*, 12 March 1925.
3. *Young India*, 21 March 1929.
4. *Young India*, 18 June 1931.
5. Dharampal, *Essays on Tradition, Recovery and Freedom*, Other India Press, 2000.
6. Satish Kumar, *Gandhi's Swadeshi: The Economics of Permanence*, http://caravan.squat.net/ICC-en/Krrs-en/ghandi-econ-en.htm
7. *Manufacturing in 2020: Envisioning a Future Characterised by Increased Internationalisation, Collaboration and Complexity*, by Capgemini. http://www.capgemini.com/resources/thought_leadership/manufacturing_in_2020/
8. *Child Labor in Victorian England*, http://www.freeessays.cc/db/18/ehc33.shtml
9. *Harijan*, 23 July 1947.
10. *Harijan*, 23 June 1946.
11. Mahatma Gandhi's interview to the Associated Press of India on 28 December 1931; *CWMG*, Vol. 54, p. 312.

Chapter 31

1. Nicholas Carr, *The Shallows: What the Internet is Doing to Our Brains*, W.W. Norton & Company, New York, (2011), p. 197.
2. Nicholas Carr, p. 222.
3. Frank Moss, *The Sorcerers and Their Apprentices: How the Digital Magicians of the MIT Media Lab Are Creating the Innovative Technologies That Will Transform Our Lives*, Crown Business, New York, (2011), p. 240.
4. *All Men Are Brothers: Life and Thoughts of Mahatma Gandhi as Told in His Own Words*; p. vii.
5. *Young India*, 26 June 1924.
6. *Young India*, 23 January 1930.
7. Bipin Chandra Pal, *Nationality and Empire: A running study of some current Indian problems*, Thacker, Spink & Co., (1916). Pal was a member of the triumvirate of Lal (Lala Lajpat Rai), Bal (Bal Gangadhar Tilak) and Pal (Bipin Chandra Pal), which exercised a dominant influence on India's freedom movement before Gandhi's arrival on the scene. Known as the 'Father of Revolutionary Thoughts' in India, he was critical of Gandhi's leadership.
8. *Young India*, 4 April 1929.

9. *All Men Are Brothers: Life and Thoughts of Mahatma Gandhi as Told in His Own Words*; p. 221.
10. Piritim A. Sorokin, *Sane Sex Order,* Bharatiya Vidya Bhavan, Bombay, (1961), p. 151-53.

Chapter 32

1. *Harijan,* 28 March 1936.
2. Krishna Kripalani, *Gandhi's Life in His Own Words*, Navajivan Trust, 1983.
3. *Harijan,* 2 March 1940.
4. Pyarelal, *Mahatma Gandhi: The Last Phase,* Vol. II, p. 455.
5. Anthony J. Parel, *Gandhi: Hind Swaraj and Other Writings,* Cambridge University Pres, (2009); also in *Harijan,* 28 July 1946.
6. An interview with Brian Swimme by Susan Bridle; http://www.enlightennext.org/magazine/j19/swimme.asp
7. Heidegger remains a controversial figure in the world of philosophy. He was a member of the Nazi Party from May 1933 until May 1945. He made statements in support of Hitler, for which he never expressed regret nor gave a satisfactory explanation. However, I found in his work *The Question Concerning Technology* (1949) some concerns about the impact of modern technology on man and nature, which resonate with Gandhi's. I must, however, hasten to add that Gandhi's thoughts on science and technology are far more lucid, compared to the dense and complex language of Heidegger. They are also more enduring and inspirational, because Gandhi *lived* his thoughts. There was no dichotomy between his philosophy and his life. Specifically, Gandhi's Truth is a far more profound and comprehensive idea than Heidegger's conception of Being. In writing this section, I have partly benefitted from reading 'Gandhi, Heidegger and Technological Times' by Prof. R. Raj Singh, Department of Philosophy, Brock University, Canada. His essay appears in *Gandhi and Grant: Their Philosophical Affinities,* ed. Arati Barua, Academic Excellence, Delhi (2010).
8. John von Neumann (1903–57) took up Turing's ideas and is credited with the design of the first computing machine. Von Neumann's design had a central core that fetched both instructions and data from memory, performed mathematical operations, stored the results, and did this operation repeatedly. The design could also send queries to the contents of multiple locations in memory whenever necessary. This 'von Neumann architecture' is at the heart of every microprocessor and mainframe computer in the world.

9. James Gleick, *The Information: A History, a Theory, a Flood,* p. 205.
10. George Gilder, 'Evolution and Me – The Darwinian Theory has become an all-purpose obstacle to thought rather than an enabler of scientific advance', *National Review,* July 17 2006; http://www.discovery.org/a/3631

Chapter 33

1. Douglas Rushkoff, *Program or Be Programmed: Ten Commands for a Digital Age,* Soft Skull Press (2011), p. 106.
2. Dr Manju Dhariwal, 'Engaging the students of technology in an ethical discourse in the information age: Thoughts of Wiener and Gandhi', LNM Institute of Information Technology, Jaipur, Dr Ramesh Pradhan, Central University, Hyderabad; and Dr Raghubir Sharan, LNMIIT, Jaipur, Published in the *Newsletter of ACM SIGCAS Computers and Society,* Vol. 40, Issue 3, September 2010.
3. Alan Turing, *Computing Machinery and Intelligence* (1950), Mind, pp. 443-52.
4. Adam Brate, *Technomanifestos: Visions from the Information Revolutionaries;* Texere Publishing, USA (2002), p. 73.
5. James Gleick, p. 213.
6. Adam Brate, p. 37.
7. Adam Brate, p. 39.
8. Vannever Bush, 'As We May Think', from *The Atlantic Monthly,* July 1945.
9. Adam Brate, p. 91.
10. Adam Brate, p. 110.
11. http://www.wired.com/threatlevel/2011/06/internet-a-human-right/
12. Adam Brate, p. 231.
13. Tim Berners-Lee, 'Long Live the Web: A Call for Continued Open Standards and Neutrality', *Scientific American,* December 2010.
14. 'Tim Berners-Lee Identifies Threats To Democracy'; http://technorati.com/blogging/article/tim-berners-lee-identifies-threats-to/page-2/
15. Adam Brate, p. 227.
16. Adam Brate, p. 238.
17. Vint Cerf's message on the 'Future of the Internet' sent to the participants at the 1st Regional ccTLD conference in Sofia, Bulgaria, in 2008. http://oneworldgroup.org/2008/09/26/vint-cerf-on-the-future-of-the-internet-and-more
18. The name GNU is a recursive acronym for 'GNU's Not Unix.' It means, GNU would be compatible with the Unix software system, but none of

the code would come from Unix controlled by the US multinational AT&T.

19. http://en.wikiquote.org/wiki/Richard_Stallman
20. Adam Brate, p. 231.
21. http://en.wikiquote.org/wiki/Richard_Stallman
22. Transcript of Richard Stallman's speech in 2001, Free Software Foundation. http://www.gnu.org/events/rms-nyu-2001-transcript.txt.
23. Walter Isaacson, *Steve Jobs;* Little, Brown (2011), pp. 48-49.
24. *Hind Swaraj:* p. 32.
25. *CWMG,* Vol. 60, p. 16.
26. *CWMG,* Vol. 24, p. 225.
27. Walter Isaacson, *Steve Jobs,* p. 527.
28. Adam Brate, p. 214.

Chapter 34

1. Fatima Meer, *Apprenticeship of a Mahatma: A Biography of M.K. Gandhi (1869-1914),* Phoenix Settlement Trust (1970), p. 18.
2. Petaflop is a measure of a computer's processing speed and can be expressed as a thousand trillion floating point operations per second. FLOPS are floating-point operations per second. Using floating-point encoding in computers, extremely long numbers can be handled relatively easily.

The terms bit and byte are common in computer networking. Both refer to digital data transmitted over a network connection. Bits are grouped into bytes to increase the efficiency of computer hardware, including network equipment, disks and memory. A bit is a single numeric value, either '1' or '0', that encodes a single unit of digital information. A byte is a sequence of bits; usually eight bits equal one byte. The earliest computers could only send 8 bits at a time. Therefore, code was written in sets of 8 bits. A bit is represented with a lowercase 'b', whereas a byte is represented with an uppercase 'b' (B). So Kb is kilobits, and KB is kilobytes. A kilobyte (KB) is 1,024 bytes. It is eight times larger than a kilobit. Kilobits are used to express speed of transmission as well as quantity of storage.

One MB, or megabyte, is 1,024 x 1,024 bytes – that is, 10,48,576 bytes. 1,024 MB is 1 gigabyte (GB). 1,024 GB is 1 terabyte (TB). One real GB is actually 1,024 bytes x 1,024 bytes x 1,024 bytes – that is, 1,07,37,41,824 bytes. However, most people like to simplify this by saying that one GB is only 1,00,00,00,000 (one billion) bytes. One petabyte (PB) is a million

GB. One exabyte (EB) is a billion GB. One zettabyte (ZB) is equal to one billion terabytes. One yottabyte (YB) is 1,000 ZB. Internet traffic, which was about 20 exabytes per month in early 2012, is expected to quadruple and reach 80 exabytes per month by 2015.

3. James Gleick, p. 212.

4. Stephen Hawking, 'How to build a time machine', http://www.dailymail.co.uk/home/moslive/article-1269288/STEPHEN-HAWKING-How-build-time-machine.html#ixzz1DpzRJagb

5. Ray Kurzweil, *The Age of Spiritual Machines: When Computers Exceed Human Intelligence*, Penguin, 1999.

6. Ray Kurzweil, *The Singularity Is Near: When Humans Transcend Biology*, Viking Press, 2005.

7. Bill Joy; 'Why the future doesn't need us'; Published in *Wired* magazine in April 2000. http://www.wired.com/wired/archive/8.04/joy_pr.html

8. Pyarelal, *Mahatma Gandhi: The Last Phase*, Vol. II, p. 455.

9. Pyarelal, *Mahatma Gandhi: The Last Phase*, Vol. I, Book II, p. 168.

10. Dr Bharati Puri, 'Interpreting Gandhi's Nonviolence – A Study of the Influence of Buddhist Philosophy', *Journal of Peace Studies*, Vol. 16, Issue 1-2, Jan.-Jun. 2009.

11. Nicholas Gier, *The Virtue of Nonviolence: From Gautama to Gandhi*, State University of New York Press, 2004, p. 51.

12. *The History of Technology*; http://scienceray.com/technology/the-history-of-technology/

13. Martin Luther King, *Strength to Love* (1963), Chapter 7.

14. B.R. Nanda, *In search of Gandhi: Essays and Reflections*, Oxford University Press (2002), p. 251.

15. *The Hour of God* by Sri Aurobindo, Sahitya Akademi (1995).

16. Eiffel Tower was built in 1889 as the entrance arch to the first World Industrial Fair.

17. James Gleick, p. 403.

Chapter 35

1. M.K Gandhi, *Ethical Religion*, S. Ganesan, Triplicane, Madras, 1930, p. 49.

2. *Young India*, 24 November 1921.

3. *Harijan*, 23 March 1940.

4. Mahatma Gandhi, from a private letter, dated Sevagram, 1 June 1942.

5. *CWMG*, Vol. XXVI, p. 224.

6. 'A mystic is a person who is deeply aware of the powerful presence of the divine Spirit: someone who seeks, above all, the knowledge and love of God, and who experiences to an extraordinary degree the profoundly personal encounter with the energy of divine life. Mystics often perceive the presence of God throughout the world of nature and in all that is alive, leading to a transfiguration of the ordinary all around them. However, the touch of God is most strongly felt deep within their own hearts'. *The Tao of Physics* by Fritjof Capra, Shambhala (1991).

7. Paul Brunton is known among indologists for his famous work *A Search in Secret India*, an authentic record of the seemingly unbelievable mystical powers of the living yogis whom he met during his travels in India. His other books – *Hermit of the Himalayas, A Search in Secret Egypt, The Quest of the Overself, The Inner Reality* and *'The Spiritual Crisis of Man'* – also probe the same theme, namely, that man would be both happier and more powerful by choosing to be guided by his spiritual self.

8. Max Planck, *Where is Science Going?* (1932).

9. James Gleick, p. 212.

10. George Gilder, *The Materialist Superstition*, 1996; http://www.mmisi.org/ir/31_02/gilder.pdf

11. Michael Chorost, *World Wide Mind: The Coming Integration of Humanity, Machines and the Internet*; Free Press (2011), p. 191. Chorost was born with severe loss of hearing due to rubella. He has computers in his head that enable him to hear: Drawing on his personal experience, he wrote a book in 2005 titled *Rebuilt: How Becoming Part Computer Made Me More Human*. He proposes that 'our Paleolithic bodies and our Pentium chips could be physically merged'.

12. *All Men Are Brothers: Life and Thoughts of Mahatma Gandhi as Told in His Own Words,* ed. Krishna Kripalani, Navajivan Publishing House, pp. 73-74.

13. *Harijan,* 25 April 1936.

14. *All Men Are Brothers: Life and Thoughts of Mahatma Gandhi as Told in His Own Words*; ed. Krishna Kripalani, Navajivan Publishing House (1960), p. 75.

15. Dr Caleb Rosado, 'What Is Spirituality? Memetics, Quantum Mechanics, and the Spiral of Spirituality', http://www.rosado.net/articles-qumetics.html

16. George Gilder, 'Civilisation Can't Afford to Forget', *Forbes ASAP* Annual Issue 1996, also see 'Evolution and Me' by George Gilder, *National Review*, July 17 2006, http://www.discovery.org/a/3631

17. Pierre Teihard de Chardin wrote a book, *The Phenomenon of Man*, in which he postulated the existence of 'noosphere'. It was published in 1959, after his death. Sir Julian Huxley explained in his introduction to the first English translation of this book: '[Teilhard was] deeply concerned with establishing a global unification of human awareness as a necessary prerequisite for any real future progress of mankind.' See *Cyberspace and the Dream of Teilhard de Chardin* by John R. Mabry.
    http://theoblogical.org/dlature/united/ph2paper/noosph.html

Chapter 36

1. Two excellent source materials on the Gandhi-Einstein relationship are: 'Albert Einstein and Mahatma Gandhi: The Century of Physics, War, Satyagraha and Peace' by Y.P. Anand; National Gandhi Museum (2006); and 'Albert Einstein's Fascination for the Indian Mahatma' by Sarojini Henry; *Metanexus Chronos*, 2 April 2005.
2. Einstein's letter to Gerhard Nellhaus, 20 March 1951, *Einstein on Politics*, ed. David E. Rowe and Robert Schulmann, Princeton University Press (2007), p. 483.
3. *Einstein and Moral Values* by Laurence McMillin; http://news.google.com/ newspapers?nid=1144&dat=19790317&id=HIUqAAAAIBAJ&sjid=5lsEAAAA IBAJ&pg=5581,270581
4. T.S. Ananthu, 'Einstein from a Holistic Perspective' http://www. navadarshanam.org/articles/2005/06/
5. Albert Einstein, *Selected Writings*; LeftWord Books (2004), p. 27.
6. http://www.alberteinsteinsite.com
7. Albert Einstein in a letter in May 1946 published by the bulletin of the Emergency Committee of Atomic Scientists.

Epilogue

1. Will Durant, *The Case for India;* Simon and Schuster, New York (1930).
2. 'The Philosophy of the Internet' by Herbert Dreyfus, Professor of Philosophy UCLA at Berkeley. http://home.earthlink.net
3. D.G. Tendulkar, *Mahatma*, Vol. 3, p. 243, 2nd Edition (1960).
4. D.G. Tendulkar, *Mahatma*, Vol. 7, p. 350, 2nd Edition (1960).
5. D.G. Tendulkar, *Mahatma*, Vol. 4, p. 156, 2nd Edition (1960).
6. D.G. Tendulkar, *Mahatma*, Vol 5, p. 244, 2nd Edition (1960).
7. *CWMG*, Vol. 88, pp. 233-34.
8. *Young India*, 5 February 1925.

ACKNOWLEDGEMENTS

My first thanks go to eminent scientist Dr R.A. Mashelkar. The seed of the idea to write this book sprouted in my mind when I listened to his talk on 'Gandhian Engineering', organised by the Observer Research Foundation (ORF) Mumbai, which I head, in 2010. Soon came a moment of synchronicity. He requested me to contribute an essay for a special volume, which was to be edited by him, to mark the golden jubilee of the Gandhi National Memorial Society in Poona, of which he is a trustee. This organisation looks after the Aga Khan Palace in the city, where Gandhi was imprisoned for two years after he gave the historic Quit India call on 9 August 1942. The palace, now a national memorial, is a hallowed place: It is here that both Gandhi's wife Kasturba and his highly erudite secretary Mahadev Desai, who was more like a son to him, breathed their last.

My essay on the Internet as the latter-day avatar of the spinning wheel appeared in the book *Timeless Inspirator: Reliving Gandhi.* However, the subject matter had gripped my mind so strongly that I felt that I'd be able to do justice to it only by fleshing it out in a full-length book. The outcome of my labour is now in your hands.

This book has been enriched by the critical comments from my fellow IITians – Mohan Tambe, Sunil Sherlekar, Kavi Arya, Nalinaksh Vyas, Satish Agnihotri, Shailendra Mehta, Jagannath Ayyangar and Raj Kamal Jha. They combine strong knowledge of technology with equally strong social commitment. Raj, who is managing editor of *The Indian Express*, has been the reason and the motivation for my being a columnist with the newspaper, for nearly seven years now. I am indebted to them.

I have benefited much from discussing the theme of this book with Dr Uday Singh Mehta, distinguished professor of political science at the City University of New York; Dr Amrita Basu, professor of political science at Amherst College; Dr Gururaj Deshpande, a reputed Boston-based IT entrepreneur and co-chairman of President Barack Obama's Advisory Council on Innovation and Entrepreneurship; and Dr Neil Gershenfeld, director of the Centre for Bits and Atoms at MIT.

I have gained immensely from studying the available print and online literature on Gandhi's ideas – and others' views on his ideas – on diverse aspects of life. All these sources have been duly acknowledged at appropriate places in the book. I must also gratefully acknowledge here the assistance I received from the staff of the National Gandhi Museum and the Nehru Memorial Museum and Library, both in New Delhi.

Towards the end of my work on the book, a peculiar turn of events associated with a whistle-blowing operation that I had conducted, along with my colleagues in BJP, led to my imprisonment in Delhi's Tihar Jail for fifty-two days. We had exposed the 'Cash-for-Votes' scandal in the Indian Parliament in July 2008, when the incumbent government had indulged in blatant purchase of opposition MPs to ensure its own survival in a trust vote. My colleagues' and my innocence will be fully established whenever the judiciary gives its verdict in this case.

My stay in Tihar gave me an opportunity to revisit the unfinished manuscript of this book in an atmosphere of solitude and introspection. The jail library had the *Collected Works of Mahatma Gandhi*, vol. 98. Dipping into this treasure helped me make a few important additions to the manuscript, which I had to hand-write since I had no access to a laptop.

Here I gratefully acknowledge two fellow-prisoners. Librarian Raju is a twenty-three-year-old poor boy from Bihar who had come to Delhi in search of a job. Misfortune, combined with gross injustice that is endemic to our criminal justice system, brought him to jail, where he has been languishing for the past four years as an undertrial. The plight of undertrials, who constitute a majority of India's prison population, opened my eyes to the shocking infirmities in this system. Just as the story of Raju's journey to Tihar brought tears to my eyes, I felt proud of him for the quietly courageous way in which this honest and soft-spoken youth has rebuilt his life, educating himself enough to be entrusted with the job of managing the jail library.

The other fellow-prisoner, who became a dear friend, was Kobad Ghandy, a former ideologue of the Maoist movement. Widely respected for his gentleness and sensitivity, he is called 'Gandhiji' by both inmates and the jail staff. Meeting him, and knowing about his honest introspection into the reasons for the failure of the communist movements in India and worldwide, provided the happiest moments during my stay in jail. Tihar's 'Gandhi' not only read the manuscript of this book on Gandhi, but also wrote me a long letter giving comprehensively critical comments.

I eagerly look forward to the day when Kobad will be a free man.

I thank all my colleagues at ORF – especially Leena Wadia, Riddhi Chokhawala, Sharmeen Contractor, Varsha Raj, Shilpa Rao, Dhaval Desai, Anay Joglekar and others – for their assistance and helpful comments. Riddhi, who provided creative inputs, comes from a family that had a close association with the Mahatma. Special thanks to my ever-reliable secretary V. Kalyanaraman.

My dear friend and colleague, Radha Vishwanathan, read and re-read the many iterations of this book almost as often as I did, giving me valuable comments and suggestions all along the way and, indeed, making this project her own. She did all this even as she bravely, and successfully, battled a serious medical condition. Thank you, Radha.

My special thanks to five other dear friends. R.V. Pandit ('RV' to me) and Sadhvi Bhagwati, an American spiritual-seeker at Parmarth Niketan, Rishikesh, have both, in their own different ways, devotedly served the cause of inter-faith harmony, a seminal Gandhian ideal. (RV, now 81 and an accomplished publisher and editor himself, read every single line in the book and gave, besides numerous valuable suggestions, also encouragement in moments of writer's distress.) Bharatbala and his wife Kanika Myer have been serving the Gandhian cause through the medium of meaningful cinema. Their two inspiring creations deserve mention here – *Khadi: The Fabric of Freedom* and *Gurus of Peace* (interviews with Nobel Peace Prize winners on Mahatma Gandhi's message of nonviolence). Fujitasan, my

Japanese friend who quietly serves many a Gandhian cause (she is doing so now in Afghanistan), gave valuable feedback on the book.

My special and sincere thanks to my publisher, Sanjana Roy Choudhury; Supriya Saran, her creative designer; and all her colleagues at Amaryllis, especially Rashmi Menon and Tulika. Ever since I worked closely with Sanjana on an important project a few years ago, she and her husband Saibal have become my good friends. I admire her professionalism, but I admire even more her commitment to re-orienting the business of book publishing towards the noble goal of exploring and extracting the wisdom of India, both ancient and modern.

My earnest thanks to Saurabh Singh, a young, enthusiastic and truly gifted illustrator, who wanted to become a 'partner in this project'. Also to Sudhir Tailang, my friend and veteran cartoonist.

I have had the privilege of working closely with two great national leaders in my political life – Atal Bihari Vajpayee and L.K. Advani. The opportunity to work with Atal ji for six years (1998-2004) in the Prime Minister's Office was uniquely educative for me. It also became immensely fulfilling because of the high degree of trust he reposed in me. I dedicate this book to Atalji with humility and gratitude.

No less fulfilling has been my experience of working with Advaniji. I am overwhelmed whenever I think of his guile-less, tireless, selfless and *tapasvi*-like political life stretching back to pre-Independence years. It was with him that I first visited Gandhiji's birthplace in Porbandar, when I accompanied him on his sixty-eight-day all-India journey on road in 1997, called the 'Swarna Jayanti Rath Yatra'. Celebrating the golden jubilee of India's Independence, he visited almost all the important places in the country associated with the sacred memory of the martyrs and heroes of our Freedom Struggle. I later wrote a small book on the yatra, titled *A Patriotic Pilgrimage*. My long association with Advaniji, sustained by the deep trust he has had in me, is something that I greatly cherish.

It is my duty to thank one more person. Work on this book happened when I had temporarily distanced myself from my political activism with the BJP in mid-2009. That is when my association with ORF, a public policy think tank, began in Mumbai. During this period, I developed a valuable relationship with Mukesh Ambani. His generosity helped me concentrate on this project without having to bother about the means to support myself. A businessman's help is usually measured in monetary terms. In Mukesh*bhai* and his family, I found both understanding and the generosity of heart.

My family's contribution to this book is beyond words to express. Five solid pillars of strength, support, understanding and quiet encouragement all through my work on this project have been my wife Kamaxi, daughter Tapas, my mother, my father-in-law, and my sister-in-law Trupti. Kamaxi (Kamu), Tapas (Tapu) and my mother, in particular, bore the brunt of my intense involvement in this work, because it was all at the expense of the time I could, and should, have shared with them. Kamu and Tapu cared for the progress of the book in the spirit of it being our common mission. Kamu's contribution also came in another forceful way. 'It's not enough to write a book on Gandhi,' she often said to me. 'You should practice what you write.'

I also mention here my prodigiously talented nephew 'Minchu' (Chaitanya Shareef). He helped me write a part of this book at an idyllic Gandhi-inspired ashram, 'Sangam', in Dharwad (Karnataka), established by my brother Sanjeev and his wife Pratibha.

For any errors and lapses that may have crept into this book, I alone am responsible. If readers find anything of value and substance, the credit should go solely to what I have learnt at the feet of the saint and the teacher of humanity, Mahatma Gandhi.

Mumbai-Delhi: June 2012

LIST OF ABBREVIATIONS AND ACRONYMS

AI	Artificial Intelligence
AISA	All India Spinners' Association
AIVIA	All India Village Industries Association
ARPANet	Advanced Research Projects Agency Network
AYUSH	Ayurveda, Yoga & Naturopathy, Unani, Siddha and Homoeopathy
BAIF	Bharatiya Agro Industries Foundation
BJP	Bharatiya Janata Party
CAD	Computer-aided design
CBS	Columbian Broadcasting Service
CeNSE	Central Nervous System for the Earth
CERN	European Organisation for Nuclear Research
CII	Confederation of Indian Industries
CNC	Computerised numerical control
CSIR	Council of Scientific and Industrial Research
CWC	Congress Working Committee
DST	Department of Science and Technology
ERP	Enterprise Resource Planning
FAO	Food and Agriculture Organisation
FICCI	Federation of Indian Chambers of Commerce and Industry
FOSS	Free and open-source software

GDP	Gross domestic product
GEOSET	Global Educational Outreach for Science Engineering and Technology
GIST	Graphics and Indian Scripts Terminal
GM	Genetically modified
GNR	Genetics, nanotechnology and robotics
GNU	GNU's Not Unix
GRA	Global Research Alliance
HP	Hewlett Packard
HTML	Hypertext Markup Language
IAB	Internet Architecture Board
IANA	Internet Assigned Numbers Authority
IC	Integrated circuit
ICANN	*Internet Corporation for Assigned Names and Numbers*
ICBM	Inter-continental ballistic missiles
ICT	*information and communications technology*
IETF	Internet Engineering Task Force
IGNCA	Indira Gandhi National Centre for the Arts
IIM-A	Indian Institute of Management Ahemdabad
IISc	Indian institute of Science
IIT	Indian Institute of Technology
IMC	Indian Merchants Chamber
IMF	International Monetary Fund
INC	Indian National Congress
ISOC	The Internet Society
IT	Information Technology
ITER	International Thermonuclear Experimental Reactor
ITU	International Telecommunications Union
IUCN	International Union for Conservation of Nature
LDCs	Least developed countries
LHC	Large Hadron Collider
LIPS	Language Independent Programme Subtitles/Dubbing
LP	Long-playing records

MAD	Mutually Assured Destruction
MDG	Millennium Development Goals
MIT	Massachusetts Institute of Technology
MNREGS	Mahatma Gandhi National Rural Employment Guarantee Scheme
MRM	Electronic Manufacturers Recycling Management Company
MSMEs	Micro, Small and Medium Enterprises
NASSCOM	National Association of Software and Service Companies
NDDB	National Dairy Development Board
NGO	Non-governmental Organisation
NIF	National Innovation Foundation
NPT	Nuclear Non-Proliferation Treaty
NSF	National Science Foundation
OER	Open Educational Resources
ORF	Observer Research Foundation
OSDD	Open Source Drug Discovery
OSS	Open-source software
PC	Personal Computer
PLM	Product lifecycle management
PMO	Prime Minister's Office
R&D	Research and development
RFID	Radio frequency identification
RSS	Rashtriya Swayamsevak Sangh
RTE	Right to Education
RTI	Right to Information
S&T	Science and Technology
SEWA	Self employed Women's Association
SKA	Square Kilometre Array
TCP/IP	Transmission Control Protocol and Internet Protocol
TCS	Tata Consultancy Services

TED	Technology, Entertainment and Design
TEEB	The Economics of Ecosystems and Biodiversity
TPS	Toyota Production System
TQM	Total Quality Management
UIDAI	Unique Identification Authority of India
UN	United Nation
UNSC	UN Security Council
VLFM	Visionary Leaders for Manufacturing
WTO	World Trade Organisation
WWW	World Wide Web

INDEX